Fundamentals of
ATOMIC PHYSICS

Fundamentals of
ATOMIC PHYSICS

ATAM P. ARYA
West Virginia University

Allyn and Bacon, Inc.　　　　　Boston

In Memory of My Mother

Contents

Preface

This book was written for the students at junior and senior college levels, and for those first-year graduate students who have not taken a thorough course in modern physics or atomic physics. The level of sophistication is such that after going through this book, the reader is ready to take a course in nuclear physics, molecular physics, solid-state physics, or advance courses in atomic physics and theory of relativity. For students who are in the field of nuclear engineering and electrical engineering, and are involved in the study of semiconductors and solid-state devices, this book will serve well as a text for a prerequisite course. For a professional man who wants a basic understanding of atomic and modern physics, this book will not only acquaint him with basic laws and theories of physics, but will also expose him to unsolved interesting problems. In essence, the book attempts to present a clear and precise account for the reader who is starting in any field requiring a strong background in relativity, quantum mechanics, and atomic physics.

It is suggested that when the book is used as a text for an undergraduate one-semester, three-hour course, the first twelve chapters should be covered. If the students have already been exposed to introductory quantum mechanics, Chap. VI and most of Chap. IX may be omitted. When used for first-year graduate study, Chaps. VII through XV should be covered in a one-semester, three-hour course. Most of the experimental details are easily understood.

The book attempts to cover a number of topics in detail, with a balanced presentation between theory and experiment. The book is comprehensive and can be read with a minimum of outside help. The text can be conveniently divided into three parts. The first part, Chaps. II through VI, contains a detailed exposition to the theory of relativity, with basic discussions leading to the development of quantum theory. The second part, Chaps. VII through XII, deals with atomic physics, with the basic principles developed in the first part being extensively utilized. The third part, Chaps. XIII, XIV, and XV, dealing with hyperfine structure, molecular physics and solid-state physics, are the extension and applications of atomic physics and quantum physics.

An important feature of the book is the introduction of certain topics in separate chapters; for example: Chap. IV introduces black-body radiation; Chap. IX, quantum theory of the hydrogen atom; and Chap. XII, hyperfine structure. In order to make the readers fully aware of the scope of the theory of relativity, Chaps. II and III, have been devoted to this important subject. Many latest developments, such as the Mössbauer effect and lasers are discussed at length. Many other topics, which are not given full attention in undergraduate texts, such as the general theory of relativity, Doppler effect in relativity, twin paradox, graphical representation, Sommerfeld model, anamolous Zeeman effect, Paschen-Back effect, Landé's interval rule, LCAO (*Linear Combination of Atomic Orbitals*) method for molecular structure, band theory of solids, etc., are discussed to some extent. Another important and unique feature is the inclusion of Dirac's equation for deducing electron spin angular momentum. This topic is discussed in Chap. X.

Also, each chapter contains a generous sampling of problems and a complete bibliography with reference to the original work. For the student seeking supplementary reading a short list of suggestions for further reading is provided.

The author is indebted to colleagues, friends, and students for their help in preparing this publication. Thanks go to Professors J. L. Rodda, A. S. Pavlovic, M. S. Seehra, and W. E. Vehse of West Virginia University for their critical examination of the manuscript; to Professor S. Farr for some of the photographs; to students, N. Blaskovich and Dr. J. R. Champion for reading portions of the manuscript, and to D. L. Fox, H. M. Hartley, and R. J. Koshut for proofreading the manuscript. A special thanks is given to S. Summers for solving many of the problems.

The author is especially grateful to his wife, Pauline, for her frequent critical review and constructive suggestions, and to his father, whose encouragement has been a great aid throughout this writing project.

ATAM P. ARYA

Morgantown, West Virginia
April, 1971

Fundamentals of
ATOMIC PHYSICS

I

Introduction

1. GROWTH OF PHYSICS

The process of investigation in physics may be called a two-step process. This process can be described as (1) the development of generalizations that rise from repeated observations of physical phenomena, and (2) the explanation of these generalizations using logical reasoning. Investigation thus eventually leads to the formulation of hypotheses, theories, and laws.

The study of classical physics, which includes mechanics, thermodynamics, sound, optics, electricity, magnetism, and electromagnetic fields, was undertaken by many scientists in the sixteenth through nineteenth centuries. Some of the notable investigators in this period include: Galileo (1562–1642), Newton (1642–1727), Huygens (1629–1695), Faraday (1791–1864), Cavendish (1731–1810), Coulomb (1736–1806), Dalton (1766–1844), Young (1773–1829), Fresnel (1788–1827), Fraunhofer (1787–1826), Ampere (1775–1836), Ohm (1787–1844), Doppler (1803–1853), Maxwell (1831–1879), Hertz (1857–1894), Stefan (1835–1893), Rydberg (1854–1919), Fitzgerald (1851–1901), Roentgen (1845–1923), Becquerel (1852–1908), J. J. Thomson (1856–1940), and many others.

By 1890, the laws of classical physics in the present form were well formulated, and it was believed by many that all the laws and theories of physics were known. The only task remaining for the physicist was to improve upon the accuracy of experimentally measured quantities. Although it was

1

in 1808 that Dalton's atomic theory was put forth, according to which an atom was assumed to be the smallest indivisible unit of matter, nobody questioned this hypothesis until the close of the nineteenth century. It was assumed that the atom had no structure and hence the study of the atom, or atomic physics, did not mean much at that time.

By the close of the nineteenth century and the beginning of the twentieth many new experimental observations revealed that previous investigators had completely ignored two important aspects of the study of matter in classical physics. First, it was found that even though the laws of classical physics adequately explained macroscopic systems, (those of particles that are visible to naked eye), the laws were inadequate in explaining microscopic systems (those of particles whose size was on the order of that of atoms or smaller, i.e., $\lesssim 10^{-8}$ cm). This shortcoming, as we shall see later, led to the eventual development of quantum mechanics in 1925 by Schröedinger and others. Second, the classical theory also had to be modified if it were to apply to fast moving particles. This modification led to the development of Einstein's theory of relativity, in 1905, for particles moving with speeds approaching the speed of light, 3×10^{10} cm/sec. Some of the ideas and experiments that led to such drastic changes in the theories of physics are the following:

1. Discovery of x-rays by Roentgen   1895
2. Discovery of radioactivity by Becquerel   1896
3. Discovery of electrons by Thomson   1897
4. Black-body radiation and formulation of the basic postulate of quantum theory by Planck   1900
5. Formulation of the basic postulates of relativity by Einstein   1905
6. Photoelectric effect   1905
7. Optical line-spectra   1913
8. Compton effect (or Compton scattering)   1923
9. de Broglie hypothesis   1924

It is remarkable to note that the amount of knowledge that has been added to the field of physics in the present century far exceeds the amount of knowledge that had been accumulated up to the close of the previous century. However, the physicists of today are much less confident that the basic truths are known than were the physicists of 1890.

Physics may be divided into the following parts:

(a) *The Classical Physics.* This is the study of macroscopic subjects moving with speeds much smaller than that of the speed of light; the laws of which were understood before the start of the present century.

(b) *The Basic Concepts of Modern Physics.* This is essentially the developments of ideas and the study of experiments during the period 1895 to 1925, some of which have been mentioned earlier. These ideas led to the eventual development of new mathematical structures and physical theories.

(c) *The Theory of Relativity.* This is the study of objects, irrespective of size, that move with speeds approaching that of light, for which study one must modify the classical laws. The theory of relativity can be divided into two parts: (i) the special theory of relativity, dealing with uniform relative velocities, and (ii) the general theory of relativity, dealing with nonuniform or accelerated systems.

(d) *The Quantum Theory, or Wave Mechanics.* This is the mathematical structure that predicts and describes the behavior of particles of microscopic size, usually taken to be in the range of $\sim 10^{-8}$ cm and $\sim 10^{-12}$ cm. The quantum theory supplements the classical theory, which is valid only for large-scale phenomena.

(e) *The Relativistic Quantum Theory.* This is a combination of (c) and (d), i.e., it is the mathematical structure that predicts and describes the behavior of microscopic particles moving with speeds approaching that of light.

(f) *The Physical Theory of the Future.* As we shall see in Chapter II, the maximum speed with which an object can move is equal to the speed of light, but no lower limit to the size of the particles has been predicted. It is expected that completely new theories and mathematical structures will be needed to predict and describe the behavior of extremely small particles, say submicroscopic particles, moving with the speed of light.

Our plan of study in this book is the following: Chapters II and III are devoted to the theory of relativity. Chapters IV and V are devoted to the basic concepts mentioned in (b) above. Chapter VI briefly describes different aspects of quantum mechanics. Chapters VII through XIII will describe the investigations of atomic structure and atomic spectra in some detail. Chapters XIV and XV, dealing with molecular and solid-state physics, provide extension of the application of quantum theory and atomic physics.

2. THEORIES OF LIGHT AND THE RANGE OF ELECTROMAGNETIC WAVES

By the beginning of the seventeenth century, many properties of visible light were very well known. Among these were the rectilinear propagation with the constant speed of $\sim 3 \times 10^{10}$ cm/sec, Snell's laws of reflection and refraction, and the dispersion into different components—into different colors —by a prism. In an effort to explain these properties, the corpuscular theory was put forth by Newton. This theory could easily explain the rectilinear propagation of light as well as certain other characteristics, but it could not satisfactorily account for others. At the same time, Newton's contemporary Dutch physicist Huygens came up with the wave theory of light. The wave theory could explain almost all the then-known properties except for the rectilinear propagation of light. Primarily because of Newton's great authority, the wave theory was abandoned in favor of the corpuscular theory for the next one hundred years.

The phenomena of diffraction was discovered originally by Grimaldi (1618–1663), but it was studied extensively during the years 1700–1800. A major step was taken in 1801–1804 when Thomas Young was able to produce an interference pattern between two beams and explain it with the help of wave theory. This was further confirmed by the work of Fresnel who used wave theory to explain diffraction patterns. Finally, by the middle of the nineteenth century it was established that light was a transverse wave motion, and at that point the corpuscular theory was abandoned.

At that time, the sound wave was also under investigation, and a medium was needed for its propagation. As any other wave motion, a medium was assumed to be a prerequisite for propagation of light waves from one point to another. In order for light to travel through a vacuum, the "ether" was postulated as filling the vacuum. The properties of ether were derived from the speed of light through the medium. The very concept of the existence of ether and its peculiar properties were hard to visualize. The final solution to these problems came through the theoretical investigations of Maxwell.

In 1864 Maxwell derived the famous "four maxwell equations," which correctly described the relations between electric and magnetic fields in the neighborhood of an electric current. These equations correctly predict the magnetic field associated with a changing electric field, and the electric field associated with a changing magnetic field; these equations also predict the existence of such fields where no charges or currents are present. Where these fields change with time at a particular point in space, the changes are conveyed to all other points in space at some other time. The changes in the electric and magnetic fields are propagated through space or vacuum. The propagation of such a change or disturbance is called an electromagnetic wave.

It was further shown that the velocity with which electromagnetic waves travel through vacuum is the same as the velocity of light ($c = 3 \times 10^{10}$ cm/sec). These and other experimental evidence led to the conclusion that light waves are electromagnetic waves. As a matter of fact, visible light forms a very small fraction of the known spectral range of the electromagnetic waves. Gamma rays, x-rays, light waves, heat waves, microwaves, and radio waves are all electromagnetic waves, varying in frequencies from 10^{24} cycles per sec to less than one cycle per sec, as shown in Fig. 5.8, Chapter V.

All electromagnetic waves, irrespective of their frequencies and wave lengths, travel with the same speed (3×10^{10} cm/sec) in a vacuum, and because all electromagnetic waves show the phenomenon of polarization, all electromagnetic waves must be transverse in nature. Such was the picture of the theory of light as the closing of the nineteenth century approached. Changes that were brought about later will be discussed in Chapters IV and V. It is by means of these changes that the foundation of modern physics was laid.

II

The Theory of Relativity I

1. INTRODUCTION

By the close of the nineteenth century, classical mechanics as formulated by Newton—also called Newtonian mechanics—and the electromagnetic theory as formulated by Maxwell had been well established. According to Newton's first law of motion a system will remain at rest or in uniform motion if there are no external forces acting on the system, and there is no difference mechanically between a body at rest and one in uniform motion. The systems, or the coordinate frames of reference, in which Newton's first law, the law of inertia, holds are called the *inertial systems*. According to Newton, an ideal inertial system is a frame of reference fixed in space with respect to the stars. From a practical point of view, if we may neglect the small effects of the earth's rotation and orbital motion, a set of axes drawn on the earth may be regarded as an inertial coordinate system. Any set of axes moving with uniform velocity with respect to the earth is also an inertial system. Systems that are accelerated are not inertial systems. The inertial system that contains in it the observer at rest is called the *proper system*. As we shall see, it is the relative motion of these inertial systems with which the theory of relativity is concerned.

Now we may ask ourselves the following questions:

(1) How do we transform the description of a system from one inertial coordinate system to another?

(2)   What happens to the equations that describe the system when such a transformation is made?

(3)   Do Newton's laws of motion describe the motion of the system at all speeds?

In the next section we shall discuss the Galilean transformations that answer the first two questions. But two difficulties are encountered in the Galilean transformations:

(i)   They do not correctly transform electromagnetic equations.

(ii) These transformations are not good even for Newton's mechanics when the systems are moving with very high velocities, i.e., the velocities approaching that of light, 3×10^{10} cm/sec. Thus the answer to (3) above is that the mechanics of a particle must be modified when the particle is moving with high speeds. For example, a particle (say a proton) of mass m moving with velocity v_i will have kinetic energy, E_i, according to classical mechanics: $E_i = \frac{1}{2}mv_i^2$. Suppose v_i is equal to $\frac{9}{10}c$. Now suppose the energy of the particle is increased to four times the initial energy, $E_f = 4E_i$. According to the formula $E_f = \frac{1}{2}mv_f^2$, v_f is equal to $2v_i$, or $v_f = 2v_i = 2(\frac{9}{10})c = 1.8c$. Experiments have shown[1] that such is not the case for particles as small as the proton, i.e., even if the energy is increased four fold, the velocity does not double. As a matter of fact, the experiments indicate[2] that nothing moves with a velocity greater than the velocity of light.

Because of these difficulties, the laws of mechanics for particles moving with high speeds were modified by Einstein[3–5] in 1905. The resulting new mathematical structure is known as the special theory of relativity, which deals with inertial frames moving with uniform velocities with respect to each other. In 1916 Einstein introduced[6,7] another mathematical structure known as the general theory of relativity, which deals with the accelerated, or noninertial, frames of reference. This chapter and the next chapter will be devoted primarily to the development and applications of the special theory of relativity. At the end a brief mention will be made of the general theory.

Instead of starting with the formal development of the theory of relativity, we shall first discuss the Galilean transformation as applied to classical mechanics and electromagnetic theory.

2. THE GALILEAN TRANSFORMATIONS AND NEWTONIAN MECHANICS

Consider two observers located in two different inertial systems S and S' called the unprimed and primed systems, respectively. Let XYZ and $X'Y'Z'$ be the coordinate axes located in the systems S and S', respectively. The inertial system S' is moving with a velocity v with respect to the system S to the right along the X axis, and by the same token, S is moving with a velocity $-v$ with respect to S', as shown in Fig. 2.1, the X and X' axes being collinear. In order to describe an event, a physical phenomenon in an inertial system, the observer must specify, in addition to three space coordinates, a fourth coordinate: time. Let the event at P be described by the two sets of coordinates (x, y, z, t) and (x', y', z', t') corresponding to the two observers in the S and S' systems, respectively. According to Newton's concept, this fourth coordinate time has the same value in all systems; time passes uniformly and does not refer to any external object. This implies that $t = t'$. (We shall see that this is not true, and it is through the relaxation of this condition that an altogether different theory results.)

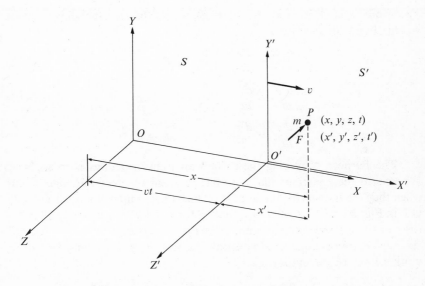

FIG. 2.1.   *Space and time coordinates of an event as measured by two observers, one in each of two inertial frames of reference, moving at a constant relative velocity v along the $X - X'$ axis.*

Observation of the event taking place at P as observed by the two observers are related by the equations:

$$
\begin{array}{ccc}
x' = x - vt & & x = x' + vt' \\
y' = y & & y = y' \\
z' = z & \text{or} & z = z' \\
t' = t & & t = t'
\end{array}
\qquad (2.1)
$$

These equations, which relate the space and time coordinates of these two coordinate systems moving with a uniform relative velocity, are called the *Galilean (or Newtonian) transformations.* The Newtonian theory of relativity is based upon these equations.

The Galilean velocity transformations may be obtained by differentiating Eqs. (2.1) and noting that because $t' = t$ the operators d/dt and d/dt' are identical.

$$\frac{dx'}{dt'} = \frac{dx}{dt} - v \qquad\qquad u'_x = u_x - v$$

$$\frac{dy'}{dt'} = \frac{dy}{dt} \qquad \text{or} \qquad u'_y = u_y \qquad\qquad (2.2)$$

$$\frac{dz'}{dt'} = \frac{dz}{dt} \qquad\qquad u'_z = u_z$$

And similarly by differentiating Eqs. (2.2), we get the corresponding Galilean acceleration transformations.

$$\frac{d^2x'}{dt'^2} = \frac{d^2x}{dt^2} \qquad\qquad a'_x = a_x$$

$$\frac{d^2y'}{dt'^2} = \frac{d^2y}{dt^2} \qquad \text{or} \qquad a'_y = a_y \qquad\qquad (2.3)$$

$$\frac{d^2z'}{dt'^2} = \frac{d^2z}{dt^2} \qquad\qquad a'_z = a_z$$

The purpose of writing these Galilean transformations is to see what happens to the equations that describe an event in one coordinate system when they are transformed to another. Thus, for example, if a point mass, m, at P in Fig. 2.1 is acted upon by a force $\mathbf{F}$ for which $\mathbf{F} = m\mathbf{a}$, what will be the form of force $\mathbf{F}$ when transformed to the primed system; will $\mathbf{F'} = m\mathbf{a'}$ still be true, i.e., remain unaltered in form? The answer is yes, as may be seen by writing $\mathbf{F}$ in component form,

$$F_x = m\frac{d^2x}{dt^2}, \qquad F_y = m\frac{d^2y}{dt^2}, \qquad F_z = m\frac{d^2z}{dt^2}, \qquad (2.4)$$

and by substituting for x, y, and z, from Eqs. (2.1) or directly substituting the results from Eqs. (2.3), we get:

$$F'_x = m\frac{d^2x'}{dt'^2}, \qquad F'_y = m\frac{d^2y'}{dt'^2}, \qquad F'_z = m\frac{d^2z'}{dt'^2} \qquad (2.5)$$

This implies that the form of the equation (in this case Newton's law) does not change under the Galilean transformation. This fact is stated as Newton's laws are invariant under the Galilean transformation. (Invariant in this context means the form of the laws or equations remains the same.) This statement has a very important implication. It says that in performing mechanical experiments it is impossible to distinguish between two frames of reference in order to find which one is at absolute rest and which one is moving with respect to the other, and it says that for all inertial systems the equations of motion have the same form. The statement is known as the *principle of Newtonian relativity*.

For another example to show the invariance of classical mechanics under Galilean transformation, let us consider the conservation of linear momentum in a collision between two particles of masses m and M as shown in Fig. 2.2.

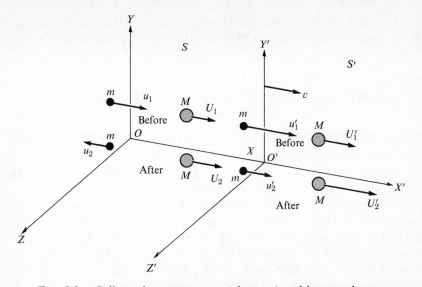

FIG. 2.2.   *Collision between two particles as viewed by two observers, one in each of two inertial frames of reference, moving at a constant relative velocity v. (Note that the collisions are along the X − X' axis only.)*

Let the velocities before and after the collision be u_1, U_1, and u_2, U_2, respectively, as observed from the unprimed system. According to the conservation of linear momentum:

$$mu_1 + MU_1 = mu_2 + MU_2 \qquad (2.6)$$

Using the velocity transformation Eqs. (2.2) in Eq. (2.6):

$$m(u_1' + v) + M(U_1' + v) = m(u_2' + v) + M(U_2' + v)$$

or

$$mu_1' + MU_1' = mu_2' + MU_2', \qquad (2.7)$$

which is the conservation of momentum in the primed system. Comparing Eqs. (2.6) and (2.7), we may conclude that the form of the conservation of linear momentum is unchanged. The equations show the invariance of conservation of linear momentum under Galilean transformation.

Mathematically, we can express the principle of Newtonian relativity— for all inertial systems the equations of motion have the same form—by saying that if a mechanical system is described in S by an equation of the form

$$f(x, y, z, t) = 0 \qquad (2.8)$$

then in the S' system it will have the form

$$f(x', y', z', t') = 0 \qquad (2.9)$$

Our next step will be to apply these transformations to electromagnetism; as we shall see, these Galilean transformations are inadequate for this purpose.

3. THE ELECTROMAGNETIC THEORY AND THE FAILURE OF THE GALILEAN TRANSFORMATIONS

By the close of the nineteenth century the electromagnetic theory as represented by Maxwell's equations was well established. In analogy with the mechanical vibrating systems where it is necessary to have a medium for the propagation of vibration, it was thought that there must be some sort of medium through which the electromagnetic waves are transmitted even though the Maxwell equations were developed without the need of any medium. The physicist of the nineteenth century assumed that Maxwell's equations were valid in any frame that was at rest with respect to the ether. Such a frame is called the *ether frame*. To be consistent with experimental facts, many strange properties were assigned to ether. For example, ether was assumed to be completely transparent and massless because electromagnetic waves can travel through a vacuum, but, on the other hand, it was assumed to have elastic properties in order to sustain the vibrations of wave motion. It was also assumed to transmit only transverse vibrations, which means it had almost infinite rigidity; yet all bodies, including planets, move through it freely. The ether was assumed to pervade vacuum as well as all transparent media.

The velocity of electromagnetic waves in the ether frame, which we may call the inertial frame S at rest, was found to be always the same and is given by[8]

$$c = \frac{1}{\sqrt{\epsilon_0 \mu_0}} = 2.997925 \times 10^{10} \text{ cm/sec} \qquad (2.10)$$

According to the Galilean transformations, the velocity of waves as measured in the inertial system S' and traveling parallel to X, X' axes will be $c - v$ or $c + v$ depending upon the direction of motion of S'. Thus we conclude that there is one frame of reference, the ether frame, that may be considered to be the *absolute frame*, or *rest frame*, in which the velocity of light is always c, while the velocities of the other inertial systems may be measured relative to this ether frame. Note that this is quite different from Newtonian mechanics where there is no absolute frame and the motions are only relative.

Before drawing any conclusions from the above discussion let us consider another aspect of the transformations. According to Newtonian mechanics, the equations of motion have the same form in all inertial systems, i.e., they are invariant as expressed by Eqs. (2.8) and (2.9). But if we try to transform Maxwell's equations with the Galilean transformations, we find that Maxwell's equations are not invariant. Thus, for example, by the use of

Maxwell's equations one finds that an electromagnetic spherical wave is propagated with a constant velocity c in free space (or ether frame). The equation of the spherical wave in the S system is

$$x^2 + y^2 + z^2 - c^2t^2 = 0 \qquad (2.11)$$

If this equation is invariant, its form in the S′ system should be

$$x'^2 + y'^2 + z'^2 - c^2t'^2 = 0 \qquad (2.12)$$

The direct substitution of the Galilean transformations given by Eqs. (2.1) yields

$$x^2 + y^2 + z^2 - c^2t^2 = (x' + vt)^2 + y'^2 + z'^2 - c^2t'^2$$

which implies that

$$x^2 + y^2 + z^2 - c^2t^2 \neq x'^2 + y'^2 + z'^2 - c^2t'^2 \qquad (2.13)$$

We may conclude that the Galilean transformations do not keep Maxwell's equations invariant. Thus we are confronted with a problem of bringing (a) Newton's law, (b) Maxwell's equations, and (c) the Galilean transformations together. Because the Galilean relativity principle applies to Newtonian mechanics but not to the Maxwell theory of electromagnetism, we must make a choice among the following three reasonable alternatives.

(1) A relativity principle is correct for mechanics but not for electrodynamics, which means that Maxwell's equations are not invariant, or they transform in some other way. One should be able to detect such deviations.
(2) In electrodynamics there is a preferred inertial frame, the ether frame. In this absolute inertial system the velocity of light is c, and it changes from c in other systems in such a way that Maxwell's equations may be transformed by the Galilean transformation.
(3) There exists another type of transformation (other than the Galilean) that will transform both mechanical and electromagnetic equations in an invariant form. This means that the Galilean transformations are not correct and hence Newtonian mechanics must be modified.

We shall see in the next section that the first two possibilities are completely ruled out by experimental observations. It is the third possibility that is correct and is the starting point for the formulation of the special theory of relativity.

4. THE EXPERIMENTS TO DETECT MOTION THROUGH ETHER

The ether hypothesis led to the following questions:

(i)   Is ether at rest with respect to the bodies moving through it? or
(ii) Is ether being dragged along with the bodies that move through it?

In attempting to answer these questions, different experiments were performed. The result was that neither one of the two alternatives were found to explain all these experimental observations. The purpose of this section is to discuss the following different experiments (A to D) in some detail:

A. Stellar Aberration
B. The Airy Experiment
C. The Fizeau Experiment
D. The Michelson-Morley Experiment
E. Attempts to Retain the Ether Hypothesis

A. Stellar Aberration

In 1727 the astronomer Bradley[9] reported the observation of an aberration of light; he noticed a variation of apparent direction of the stars at different times of the year. It is possible to explain this variation by assuming that the ether is at rest while the earth is moving with a velocity v through it. If the earth were at rest with respect to the ether, the light coming from a distant star located directly overhead would enter the telescope in the vertical position as shown in Fig. 2.3, and there would be no change in the position of the

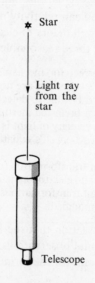

Fig. 2.3. *The star would be directly over the telescope if both the star and the earth were at rest with respect to the stationary ether.*

telescope at different times of the year. But this is not true. The actual observation shows that the telescope must be tilted at an angle α as shown in Fig. 2.4. Before we calculate the value of this angle we must explain that the aberration could not be observed if the earth moved in a straight line through the ether, because it is only the changes in the motion of the earth that are detected experimentally. This implies that a superposition of a uniform

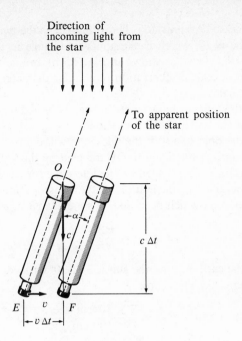

Direction of
incoming light from
the star

To apparent position
of the star

FIG. 2.4.   *The tilting required of the telescope to observe a star because
of the relative motion of earth with respect to the stationary ether.*

translational motion on earth's motion will have no effect on the aberration.
For this reason in the actual experiment of measuring α, the telescope on
earth is fixed at one position so as to view the star, and because after six
months the earth has moved in an opposite direction, as shown in Fig. 2.5(a)

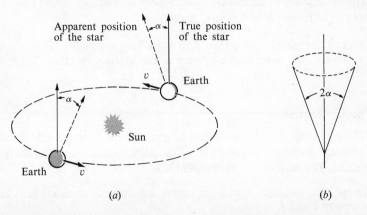

Apparent position
of the star

True position
of the star

Earth

Sun

Earth

(a)   (b)

FIG. 2.5.   (a) *Shows the change in the apparent direction of a star as
viewed from a telescope on earth.* (b) *A cone of aberration swept out in
one year by an earth-mounted telescope directed toward a star.*

the telescope has to be readjusted. The difference in the two angular positions of the telescope is 2α, which is the apparent change in the position of the star in six months. Thus, as shown in Fig. 2.5(b), in one year, the telescope axis sweeps out a cone of aberration of angular diameter 2α. We shall now calculate this angle.

Suppose the light coming from the star is in a direction perpendicular to the plane of the earth's orbit. As shown in Fig. 2.4, the light entering at the center of the objective 0 of the telescope will come out of the center of the eyepiece E only if the distance OF traveled by the light in time Δt is the same as the distance EF traveled by the telescope (or earth) in time Δt. This implies that the angle of inclination of the telescope must be given by the following relation, in which because α is small, $\tan \alpha \approx \alpha$:

$$\alpha \approx \tan \alpha = \frac{EF}{OF} = \frac{v\,\Delta t}{c\,\Delta t} = \frac{v}{c} \tag{2.14}$$

The speed of the earth around the sun is 3×10^6 cm/sec; the speed of light, c, is 3×10^{10} cm/sec. Therefore,

$$\tan \alpha = \frac{v}{c} = \frac{3 \times 10^6 \text{ cm/sec}}{3 \times 10^{10} \text{ cm/sec}} = 10^{-4}$$

or

$$\alpha \simeq 20.5'' \text{ of arc} \tag{2.15a}$$

and

$$2\alpha \simeq 41'' \text{ of arc} \tag{2.15b}$$

The observations made on different stars completely and accurately confirm the magnitude of the aberration. Thus in a course of one year, the period of earth around the sun, the stars appear to describe an eclipse of semimajor axis $20.5''$ as shown in Fig. 2.5(b).

The conclusion to be drawn from the observation of stellar aberration, in which light travels in a vacuum, is that:

The ether is stationary, while the earth is moving through it with a velocity of 3×10^6 cm per second with respect to the stationary ether. There is no ether drag.

B. The Airy Experiment

In 1871 Sir George Airy[10] attempted to measure the absolute velocity of the earth through the ether by making some modifications in the stellar aberration experiment. The plan of the experiment was:

(a) To measure the angle α with the normal telescope as discussed in A and as shown in Fig. 2.4,

(b) To fill the telescope with water so that the light passing through the water will be slowed down and the telescope will have to be tilted at a different angle in order to see the star in the eyepiece.

It was expected that the incident light making an angle α with the axis OE will be refracted along the line OG making an angle β with the axis OE as shown in Fig. 2.6. *The outcome of the experiment was completely negative.* Instead the light emerged along the line OF.

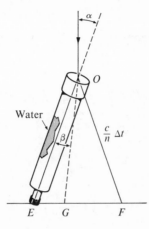

FIG. 2.6. *Airy's experimental setup to measure the velocity of earth through the ether by using a water-filled telescope in the observation of stellar aberration.*

One can explain the negative result of the Airy experiment by assuming that water partially dragged the light with it. Actually the dragging of light by a moving body was suggested by Fresnel[11] in 1818 in connection with observation of two stars through a prism. Let us see how the partial dragging explains the negative result of the Airy experiment.

Referring to Fig. 2.6, let v be the velocity of the earth through the stationary ether and let v' be its drag velocity. If the angles α and β are small and Δt is the time taken by the light to travel through the water-filled telescope, we can arrive at the following results.

$$EF = EG + GF$$

where

$$EF = v\,\Delta t$$

$$EG = OE\sin\beta = \frac{c}{n}\,\Delta t\sin\beta \simeq \frac{c}{n}\,\Delta t\,\beta$$

$$GF = v'\,\Delta t$$

where n is the index of refraction of water. Therefore,

$$v\,\Delta t = \frac{c}{n}\,\Delta t\,\beta + v'\,\Delta t$$

or

$$v' = v - \frac{c}{n}\beta \qquad (2.16)$$

Also from the laws of refraction

$$\sin \beta = \frac{1}{n}\sin \alpha, \qquad \text{or } \beta \simeq \frac{1}{n}\alpha \qquad (2.17)$$

And α from stellar aberration is

$$\alpha = \frac{v}{c} \qquad (2.18)$$

Combining Eqs. (2.17) and (2.18) with Eq. (2.16), we get:

$$v' = v\left(1 - \frac{1}{n^2}\right) \qquad (2.19)$$

or

$$v' = fv \qquad (2.20)$$

where

$$f = \left(1 - \frac{1}{n^2}\right) \qquad (2.21)$$

is called the *drag coefficient*. Because for water n (the index of refraction) is greater than 1, Eq. (2.20) implies that the water drags the light with a certain fraction, f, of its own velocity, v.

The conclusion from this experiment is the following:

If the earth is moving through a stationary ether-frame, by making observations of a light beam in a moving medium it should be possible to measure the absolute velocity of the earth through the ether, but the results were null. In order to explain the experimental results, it is necessary to assume that the ether is stationary while the water drags the light sideways.

Note the difference in this experiment and that of stellar aberration. With stellar aberration we are concerned with the motion of the medium relative to the observer, and the effect was positive. In Airy's experiment we are dealing with the motion of the medium and the observer with respect to the ether, and the result is null.

C. The Fizeau Experiment

The experiment performed by Fizeau[12] in 1851 serves to show two things:

(i)   It shows that the medium drags light waves as suggested by Fresnel and discussed above in explaining Airy's experiment.
(ii) The ether is assumed to be at rest, and there is no indication that it is being dragged, partially or totally, with the medium.

The arrangement of the Fizeau experiment is shown in Fig. 2.7. It, essentially, is based on the passage of light through flowing water. The water is

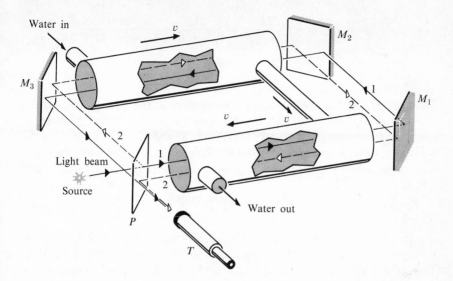

FIG. 2.7.   *The arrangement of the Fizeau experiment for observing ether drag imparted to light in a moving medium.*

made to flow with a velocity v through a system of tubes. The velocity v can be increased from 0 to v, and the direction of the flow of water may be reversed. A light beam coming from the source S is split into two beams by a half-mirrored plate P, which partially transmits and partially reflects. One beam always travels along the direction of the flow of water while the other always travels in the opposite direction, as shown by the dotted line for one and the continuous line for the other. Beam 1 reaches P after being reflected from the mirrors M_1, M_2, and M_3, while beam 2 reaches P after being reflected from M_3, M_2, and M_1. These two beams interfere and produce fringes as observed. The velocity of light in still water will be c/n. Let us assume that the ether is at rest; thus the velocity of light in a moving medium (water) with respect to the ether will be $c/n + fv$ along the flow of water, and $c/n - fv$ in the direction opposite to the flow of water. If the length of each water tube is L, the time t_1 taken by beam 1 in going through a complete cycle (in water) is:

$$t_1 = \frac{2L}{c/n - fv}$$

while time taken by beam 2 is

$$t_2 = \frac{2L}{c/n + fv}$$

Therefore, the time difference between the two beams when they reach P is (note that the times of transit outside the tubes are equal and hence cancel out)

$$\Delta t = t_1 - t_2 = \frac{2L}{c/n - fv} - \frac{2L}{c/n + fv} = \frac{4Lvf}{(c/n)^2 - (fv)^2}$$

or

$$\Delta t \approx \frac{4Lvfn^2}{c^2} \qquad (2.22)$$

Thus the path difference between the two beams at the time they reach P is $c \, \Delta t$. In terms of the fringe shift it will be equal to $c \, \Delta t / \lambda$. In an actual experiment, the fringe pattern is observed first with the water at rest. Then the water is made to flow in one direction, and the fringe shift is $c \, \Delta t / \lambda$ when the water reaches the velocity v. If the water direction is reversed, the total fringe shift, ΔN, is

$$\Delta N = 2 \frac{c \, \Delta t}{\lambda} = \frac{8Lvfn^2}{c^2} \qquad (2.23)$$

In Fizeau's experiment the following data was used: $v = 7$ m/sec, $L = 1.5$ m, $n = 1.33$, and $\lambda = 5.3 \times 10^{-7}$ m. The fringe shift observed was 0.23. This gave a value of f, from Eq. (2.23), of 0.47. This value compares well with the theoretical value given by

$$f = 1 - 1/n^2 = 0.44 \qquad (2.24)$$

These experiments were improved and repeated by Michelson and Morley in 1886, by Hock in 1868, and others, all giving the same results.

The conclusion to be drawn is the same as that in Airy's experiment:

The ether frame is stationary, while the introduction of the drag coefficient explains the results. But it is not possible to detect the absolute motion of the earth by observing the motion of both the medium and the observer with respect to the ether.

D. The Michelson-Morley Experiment

The purpose of this experiment was the same as those previously described, i.e., to find the absolute velocity of the earth with respect to the stationary ether. Thus the search for the preferred frame, which is the stationary ether-frame, was started again. The measurement of the speed of light in different inertial systems should result in some evidence as to the existence of a single unique system—the ether frame—in which the speed of light is c. Some attempts were made by F. T. Trouton and H. R. Noble[13], by A. A. Michelson[14] in 1881, and by A. A. Michelson and E. W. Morley[15] in 1887. The most representative of all these experiments is that of Michelson and Morley.

Previous experiments were attempts to measure the first-order effect, i.e., the ratio of the velocity of earth to the velocity of light:

$$\frac{v}{c} = \frac{3 \times 10^6 \,\text{cm/sec}}{3 \times 10^{10} \,\text{cm/sec}} \simeq 10^{-4}$$

which is one part in 10,000. While it was thought that the sure test of the ether hypothesis—either stationary or moving—would come from the measurements on the second-order effect, i.e., from $(v/c)^2 \approx 10^{-8}$, which is one part in 100 million. This was possible in the Michelson-Morley experiment as we shall see.

Michelson and Morley assumed that the ether is fixed with respect to the sun and that the earth (neglecting rotation and spinning) moves through the ether. The experiment was performed to test the following:

(1) Light waves travel with a velocity c ($= 3 \times 10^8$ m/sec) with respect to the ether itself, while the relative speed of light with respect to the moving object through the ether should differ from c.
(2) If this moving object is the earth, we should be able to derive the absolute velocity of the earth through the ether by making observations of light signals transmitted through the ether.

We shall discuss this experiment under three headings: (i) Michelson interferometer, (ii) the experiment, and (iii) the conclusion.

(i) *The Michelson Interferometer.*   The use of the Michelson interferometer provided the accuracy needed in this experiment. The schematic of the experimental arrangement is shown in Fig. 2.8. A beam of monochromatic

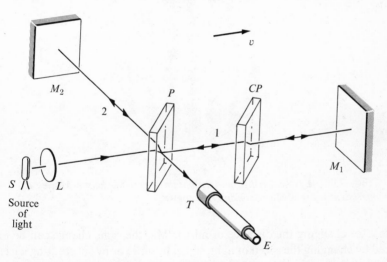

FIG. 2.8.   *The schematic of the Michelson-Morley experiment.*

light from source S after passing through a lens, L, falls on a half-mirrored plate P, that splits the beam into two coherent beams. A part of the beam (call it 1) is transmitted through the plate and travels toward mirror M_1, and a part is reflected (call it 2) and travels toward mirror M_2. Beam 1 after being reflected from mirror M_1 returns to the plate where it is partially reflected to the telescope, T. Beam 2 after being reflected from mirror M_2 returns to the plate where it is partially transmitted to the telescope, T. Beams 1 and 2 arriving in the telescope produce interference fringes that may be observed by the eye at E. The plate CP, called the compensating plate, of thickness equal to that of P is placed parallel to P in the path of beam 1. Beam 1 passes through P once, while beam 2 passes through three times. The introduction of CP removes the inequality in path lengths before the two beams reach the telescope. The whole apparatus is mounted on a large stone and floated in a tank of mercury in order to reduce air disturbances.

Plate P is placed at an angle of 45° to the incident beam while the mirrors, M_1 and M_2, are nearly perpendicular, but not quite, to each other and to beams 1 and 2, respectively. Under these conditions the type of interference pattern obtained is shown in Fig. 2.9. If the optical paths of beams 1 and 2 are equal, the beams will arrive in phase at E and will produce a bright line by constructive interference. If the path difference is changed by $\lambda/2$, by moving the mirror M_1 a distance $\lambda/4$, a dark fringe will be produced at E by destructive interference. By moving mirror M_1, the fringes may be made to move past a reference mark (cross-wires CC, C'C' in Fig. 2.9) and may be counted. But

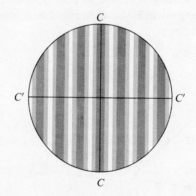

FIG. 2.9.   *A typical fringe pattern obtained in a Michelson-Morley experiment using a Michelson interferometer.*

instead of changing the distance of mirror M_1, the same change can be produced by changing the speed of light, say in beam 1; or by substituting a gas of density different from that of air, in the path of beam 1 (or beam 2 but not both).

(ii) *The Experiment.*   Let us suppose that the earth is moving to the right, as shown in Fig. 2.8, with a velocity v with respect to the stationary ether, and that the light travels with a speed c through the ether. The Michelson interferometer is arranged so that the two arms, PM_1 and PM_2, are of equal length l, and the arm PM is parallel to v, as shown in Fig. 2.8. The times taken by the beams of light to travel the distances PM_1P and PM_2P are unequal and may be calculated as follows:

The velocity of beam 1 traveling from P to M_1 is $c - v$ with respect to the apparatus. After reflection from M_1 the velocity of beam 1 on the return trip from M_1 to P is $c + v$. The time t_1 taken for this round trip PM_1P is

$$t_1 = \frac{l}{c - v} + \frac{l}{c + v} = \frac{2lc}{c^2 - v^2} \tag{2.25}$$

Because v is very small as compared to c, we may use the binomial theorem to expand the expression, retaining only up to and including the second order terms, and Eq. (2.25) takes the form

$$t_1 = \frac{2l/c}{1 - v^2/c^2} = \frac{2l}{c}(1 - v^2/c^2)^{-1}$$

$$= \frac{2l}{c}(1 + v^2/c^2 + \ldots)$$

or

$$t_1 \simeq \frac{2l}{c}(1 + v^2/c^2) \tag{2.26}$$

Beam 2 traveling toward mirror M_2 is reflected as shown along the dotted path in Fig. 2.10(a); this is due to the motion of the apparatus. Mirror M_2

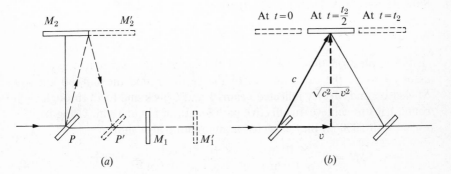

FIG. 2.10.   (a) *The path of beam 2 in the moving interferometer.* (b) *The velocity vector-diagram for beam 2.*

has moved to M_2', and plate P has moved to P'. The component of the velocity along the vertical direction (perpendicular to the direction of the motion of the interferometer) as shown in Fig. 2.10(b) is $\sqrt{c^2 - v^2}$. Thus the time taken by beam 2 for the round trip PM_2P is

$$t_2 = \frac{2l}{\sqrt{c^2 - v^2}} \tag{2.27}$$

Once again using the binomial theorem and keeping terms only up to and including the second order, we get

$$t_2 = \frac{2l}{c}\left(1 - \frac{v^2}{c^2}\right)^{-1/2}$$

$$= \frac{2l}{c}\left(1 + \frac{1}{2}\frac{v^2}{c^2} + \ldots\right)$$

or

$$t_2 \simeq \frac{2l}{c}\left(1 + \frac{1}{2}\frac{v^2}{c^2}\right) \tag{2.28}$$

The time difference of the two beams is obtained from Eqs. (2.26) and (2.28) to be

$$\Delta t = t_1 - t_2 = \frac{lv^2}{c^3} \tag{2.29}$$

If the interferometer is rotated through 90°, the two arms of the interferometer interchange their positions and hence paths 1 and 2 will interchange their roles. This results in a total retardation of 2 Δt. Under continuous rotation, there will be a retardation that will shift the interference fringes, and this shift can be measured with the help of the cross wires in the eyepiece of the telescope. The number of interference fringes shifted past the cross wires is given by

$$\Delta N = \frac{\text{path difference}}{\text{wavelength}} = \frac{c\,2\Delta t}{\lambda} \tag{2.30}$$

Substituting for Δt from Eq. (2.29) gives

$$\Delta N = \frac{2lv^2}{c^2\lambda} \tag{2.31}$$

In this expression the velocity, v, of the earth with respect to the ether is assumed to be the same as that of the earth around the sun, 30 km/sec. Michelson and Morley reflected beams 1 and 2 back and forth through eight round trips to achieve an effective path length of about 10 m. Using light of wavelength 5000 Å, they expected a minimum fringe shift of

$$\Delta N = \frac{2 \times 10 \text{ m} \times (3 \times 10^4 \text{ m/sec})^2}{(3 \times 10^8 \text{ m/sec})^2 \times 5.0 \times 10^{-7} \text{ m}} = 0.4 \text{ fringe}$$

Because a shift as small as 1/100 of a fringe can be detected, it should be easy to detect a shift of 0.4 fringe under a continuous rotation of the interferometer. No fringe shift was observed. The experiments were repeated day and night, during all seasons of the year, and at different locations in the United States and Europe. The conclusion from all these observations was that *there was no fringe shift at all.*

(iii) *The Conclusion.* The null result of the Michelson-Morley experiment was a big blow to the stationary-ether hypothesis. It seemed impossible to detect the absolute speed of the earth with respect to the ether. Many improved experiments were reported[16] over the next fifty years with the same null results. Once again we may draw the same conclusion that we drew from the Fizeau experiment:

It looks as if nature prevents us from observing the absolute motion of the earth if we make the observation of the medium and observer together with respect to the ether. On the contrary, the motion of the medium relative to the observer, as in the stellar-aberration experiment, produces a positive effect.

Another alternative would be to assume that the ether is not stationary and is being dragged with the earth. (This is contrary to the assumption made in the beginning of the discussion.) This would mean that there is no relative motion between the earth and the ether frame, and hence it would be impossible to measure the velocity of the earth with respect to the ether. But such an assumption of ether drag would not be able to explain the stellar-aberration experiment.

E. Attempts to Retain the Ether Hypothesis

The first attempt to retain the stationary-ether hypothesis and still explain the negative result of the Michelson-Morley experiment was made by Fitzgerald[17] in 1892 by introducing the Lorentz-Fitzgerald contraction hypothesis. (Originally this contraction hypothesis was introduced by Lorentz[18] in his electron theory of electromagnetism.) According to Fitzgerald, independent of Lorentz theory, the length of the arm of the interferometer that is moving in the direction of v is reduced, or contracted, by a factor $\sqrt{1 - \beta^2}$ where $\beta = v/c$. Thus the length PM in Fig. 2.8 is, therefore, no longer l but $l\sqrt{1 - \beta^2}$. Hence Eq. (2.25) takes the form

$$t_1 = \frac{l\sqrt{1 - \beta^2}}{c - v} + \frac{l\sqrt{1 - \beta^2}}{c + v} = \frac{2lc\sqrt{1 - \beta^2}}{c^2 - v^2} = \frac{2l}{c\sqrt{1 - \beta^2}} \qquad (2.32)$$

which is equal to t_2 as given by Eq. (2.27). Hence

$$\Delta t = t_1 - t_2 = 0 \qquad (2.33)$$

and there is no retardation and no fringe shift, thereby leading to the null result of the Michelson-Morley experiment.

But the success of the Lorentz-Fitzgerald contraction hypothesis fell through when Kennedy and Thorndike[19] repeated the Michelson-Morley experiment by using unequal arms, $PM_1 \neq PM_2$. It was expected that even when taking the contraction hypothesis into account, one could expect a fringe shift on rotation of the interferometer. No such shift, however, was observed.

The next attempt was to modify electrodynamical theory by saying that the velocity of light is the same in all inertial frames. This leads to the conclusion that the velocity of light is associated with the motion of the source and not with an ether frame, thereby explaining the Michelson-Morley experiment. The assumptions of this type about the source come under the category of emission theories[20-23]. All emission theories have been contradicted by experimental results[24-26], and it is found that the velocity of light is independent of the velocity of the source. This conclusion, *the velocity of the electromagnetic radiation is independent of the source*, is confirmed by using fast-moving terrestrial sources in more recent experiments[27,28].

We may now summarize our discussion in the following:

(1) The ether hypothesis seems to be unable to account for the results of all the relevant experiments.
(2) The laws of electromagnetics are correct and need no modification: the speed of light is the same in all inertial frames independent of the relative motion of the source and the observer.
(3) The Galilean transformations are correct for mechanics but not for electromagnetism.

5.   EINSTEIN'S POSTULATES OF SPECIAL RELATIVITY THEORY

All the experimental evidence presented thus far leads to the conclusion that there is no special frame of reference, and that all frames of references moving with uniform relative velocities are equivalent. The solution to this and many other problems in physics was provided by Einstein in 1905 in his paper[29] on the electrodynamics of moving bodies. Einstein not only accepted the above conclusions but also generalized them. The assumptions made by him can be stated in the form of two basic postulates.

POSTULATE 1:   THE PRINCIPLE OF EQUIVALENCE (OR RELATIVITY). The laws of physics, including those of mechanics and electromagnetism, are the same in all inertial frames of reference, even though these inertial frames may be in uniform translational motion with respect to each other. Thus all inertial frames are equivalent. (The preferred inertial frame such as the ether frame does not exist.)

POSTULATE 2:   THE PRINCIPLE OF THE CONSTANCY OF THE SPEED OF LIGHT. The speed of light in free space (vacuum) is always a constant, equal to c, independent of the inertial system and the relative motion of the source and the observer.

Postulate 1 is the generalization of the fact that all physical laws are invariant under all transformations, while postulate 2 states an experimental fact. These postulates have far-reaching consequences. They not only explain satisfactorily all the experimental results that had been performed up to the time but many more that were observed later. Essentially postulate 1 brings about the unity of laws of mechanics and electromagnetism.

Our next task is to find the equations of transformation for the inertial frames of reference moving with uniform velocities, which would keep the velocity of light constant; and the laws of physics should remain invariant under these transformations. These new transformation equations were derived by Einstein and are called the Lorentz transformation. The natural question to ask is: since Newton's Laws are invariant under Galilean transformation, will these and other laws of mechanics be invariant under new transformations? The answer is, as we shall see, that these laws are to be modified and generalized so as to obey the principle of relativity. And for low velocities these generalized laws will reduce to a form that will be approximately invariant under the Galilean transformation. The constancy of the velocity of light automatically insures that the laws of electromagnetism will be invariant under the Lorentz transformation.

Before deriving the Lorentz-transformation equations, it is essential to point out that it is through his altogether new concepts about the nature of time that Einstein was led to his revolutionary proposals of the special theory of relativity. In order to understand better the nature of time, we shall first discuss the meaning of simultaneity.

6. THE RELATIVE NATURE OF SIMULTANEITY[30,31]

In Newtonian mechanics time is assumed to be absolute; the same time scale applies to all inertial frames of reference moving with relative velocities. This assumption of universal time for all observers led to the fourth equation of the Galilean transformation,

$$t' = t$$

As pointed out earlier, it was this assumption with which Einstein did not agree. Closely connected to this concept of absolute time is the concept of absolute simultaneity. According to the universal, or absolute, time scale, when we say that events A and B occur at the same time, or that they are simultaneous, the statement is independent of any frame of reference. These statements are perfectly valid as far as Newtonian mechanics is concerned, and the reason for this is the hidden assumption that is made subconsciously that information is carried with infinite speed. Of course, in relativity (as we shall show in this chapter) nothing moves with a velocity greater than the velocity of light, and hence we must reinvestigate our concepts of time and simultaneity. In relativity there is no such thing as absolute simultaneity.

The concept of simultaneity taking place in a single frame of reference at a fixed point is simple. When we say, for example, that the train arrived at 7 o'clock, we really mean that the train arrived at a certain point, and the little hand of a nearby clock pointed to 7, *simultaneously*. But in order to construct a time scale, we must consider events happening at different locations, in which case the problems of determining simultaneity is not so easy. First of all we must have clocks distributed all through the frame of reference so that there is a nearby clock wherever an event takes place. All these clocks, of course, must be synchronized. For example, in the case of the train, the little hands of any two clocks, say at A and B, must point to 7 simultaneously. Let us see now how we define simultaneity in this case. The determination of simultaneity involves the transmission of signals between two physically sepa-

rated locations, A and B. The best type of signals are electromagnetic waves
with the following most important properties: the velocity c of waves is the
highest known velocity, and, as postulated already, the velocity of light c is
the same in all inertial frames independent of the relative motion of these
systems. The first is the most desirable feature while the second is more basic.
We are now in a position to see what we mean by simultaneity between two
events taking place at two physically separated locations A and B in Fig. 2.11.
According to Einstein's definition of simultaneity:

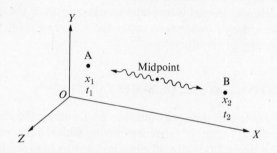

FIG. 2.11.   *The meaning of simultaneity according to Einstein.*

Two events taking place in a particular inertial reference frame at A and
B, at two instants of time, t_1 and t_2, and located at x_1 and x_2, respectively, are
simultaneous if light signals emitted simultaneously from the geometrical
midpoint between x_1 and x_2 arrive at x_1 at t_1 and at x_2 at t_2.

In other words we may say that events occurring at two different places
in an inertial system must be called simultaneous when the clocks at the two
respective places record the same time for the signals originating from the
midpoint of the two locations. (Actually this is the method of synchronizing
clocks. Place a light source at the exact midpoint of the straight line connecting A and B, and inform each observer to set his clock to $t = 0$ when a signal
from the midpoint reaches him. The light takes the same time to reach A as
it does to reach B.)

What we want to show now is that the two events that are simultaneous
in one reference frame are not necessarily simultaneous in other reference
frames that are in motion relative to the first. According to Einstein's theory,
the simultaneity does not have an absolute meaning, as it does in the classical
theory. We shall illustrate this by means of a simple hypothetical experiment:

Consider a train at rest at a railroad station. An observer at the platform
standing at point 0 places a can of paint and a flashing device at both A and
B; OA = OB (see Fig. 2.12). When a command is sent by means of a light
wave from O simultaneously to A and B, the paint splashes on the train leaving marks A′ and B′, while the flashing devices produce signals. To the observer at O the splashing of the paints and the flashing of lights at both A and

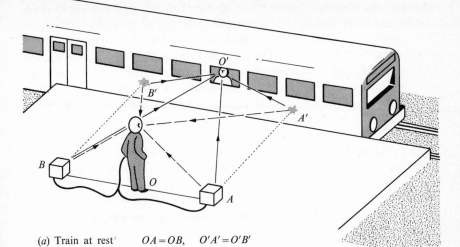

(a) Train at rest' $OA = OB$, $O'A' = O'B'$

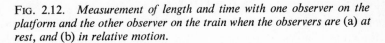

(b) Train moving $OA = OB$, $O'B' > O'A'$

FIG. 2.12. *Measurement of length and time with one observer on the platform and the other observer on the train when the observers are* (a) *at rest, and* (b) *in relative motion.*

B are simultaneous because the flashes reaching O from A and B take the same time, i.e., OA = OB. Also, to the observer O, OA′ = OB′. For an observer O′ on the stationary train whose position coincides with that of O, the events of splashing paint are simultaneous and O′A′ = O′B′.

Let us see what happens if the train were moving with velocity v from left to right. When the position of the observer O′ on the passing train coincides with the stationary observer O on the platform, the observer O sends a command to A and B, resulting in the splashing of paint and flashing of light signals. According to the observer at O the events at A and B are still simultaneous and OA = OB. But according to the moving observer O′, the flashing signal from A reaches him earlier than the signal from B, and hence the two events are *not* simultaneous. The distance B′O′ is larger than distance BO according to the observer at O′ (because $\Delta t_{B'O'} > \Delta t_{BO}$). According to the observer at O, the distance AB = A′B′. But according to the moving observer O′, A′B′ > AB because of his motion there is a difference in time taken by the signals to reach O′. Thus the events simultaneous in one inertial frame are not necessarily simultaneous in the other. One could find a way of making the events look simultaneous to the observer at O′, but then these would not be simultaneous to the observer at O; so which observer is correct? The answer to such questions will be discussed after we derive the Lorentz transformations.

7.   THE LORENTZ TRANSFORMATIONS

Einstein[29], making use of the two postulates of relativity stated in Section 5, derived new transformation equations, which were known as the Lorentz transformations because they were originated by H. A. Lorentz[18] in his electromagnetic theory of matter.

Consider two inertial systems S and S′. The coordinates of the two systems coincide at $t = t' = 0$. The S′ frame is moving with a velocity v along the common $X - X'$ axis as shown in Fig. 2.13. Let the coordinates of some point P in space where an event has taken place be (x, y, z, t) as measured from the S frame and (x', y', z', t') as measured from the S′ frame. Our aim is to find the relations between these two sets of coordinates; we are seeking functional relations of the form

$$
\begin{aligned}
x' &= x'(x, y, z, t) \\
y' &= y'(x, y, z, t) \\
z' &= z'(x, y, z, t) \\
t' &= t'(x, y, z, t)
\end{aligned}
\tag{2.34}
$$

Note that we have not taken time to be an absolute coordinate as is done in Newtonian mechanics. Equations (2.34) relate the space-time coordinates of an event as measured by two different observers. The restriction that the velocity is along the $X - X'$ axis does not produce any limitation because space is isotropic, i.e., what holds for one direction is good for any other. Because the space and time are homogeneous—all points in space and time are equivalent—the equations of transformation must be linear (they involve only the first power of the variable). This is required so as to have one-to-one correspondence between an event observed from S and the same event observed from S'. Thus Eqs. (2.34) take the most general form for the transformations as

$$x' = a_{11}x + a_{12}y + a_{13}z + a_{14}t$$
$$y' = a_{21}x + a_{22}y + a_{23}z + a_{24}t$$
$$z' = a_{31}x + a_{32}y + a_{33}z + a_{34}t$$
$$t' = a_{41}x + a_{42}y + a_{43}z + a_{44}t$$

(2.35)

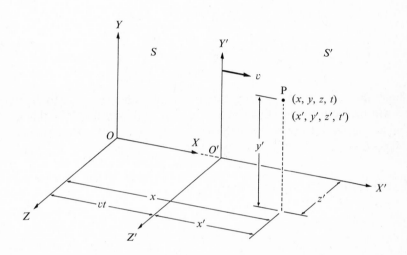

FIG. 2.13.   *The relation between the coordinates of a point P as measured from two frames of reference S and S' in relative motion.*

where $a_{11}, a_{12}, \ldots, a_{44}$ are constants. These constants can be determined by making use of Einstein's postulate 2. But before we do this, we can simplify these equations by making use of the fact that the relative velocity is along the $X - X'$ axis only. Because the directions perpendicular to the motion are always left unaffected by the transformations, and are effectively at rest, we would have

$$y' = y \quad \text{and} \quad z' = z \tag{2.36}$$

which implies that

$$a_{21} = a_{23} = a_{24} = 0$$
$$a_{31} = a_{32} = a_{34} = 0 \tag{2.37}$$

and

$$a_{22} = a_{33} = 1$$

That the transformation of x, t into x', t' (or vice versa) will not involve y and z (or y' and z') coordinates can be shown from a qualitative discussion.

There is no preferred single point in the YZ plane that may be designated as the origin. The shift of the origin in the YZ plane means the values of x' and t' cannot contain y and z. Therefore, it implies that

$$a_{12} = a_{13} = 0$$

and

$$a_{42} = a_{43} = 0 \tag{2.38}$$

(From symmetry it is easy to see that t' does not contain y and z.) Combining Eqs. (2.36), (2.37) and (2.38) with Eq. (2.35) we get

$$
\begin{aligned}
x' &= a_{11}x + a_{14}t \\
y' &= y \\
z' &= z \\
t' &= a_{41}x + a_{44}t
\end{aligned}
\tag{2.39}
$$

A point that has $x' = 0$ will appear to be moving with a velocity v to the right and will be given by the equation $x = vt$. The only way to derive this from $x' = a_{11}x + a_{14}t$ is to write this in the form $x' = a_{11}(x - vt)$ so that when $x' = 0$, $x = vt$, or

$$a_{14} = -va_{11}$$

Therefore, Eqs. (2.39) take the form

$$
\begin{aligned}
x' &= a_{11}(x - vt) \\
y' &= y \\
z' &= z \\
t' &= a_{41}x + a_{44}t
\end{aligned}
\tag{2.40}
$$

Now the three coefficients a_{11}, a_{41}, and a_{44} may be evaluated by making use of postulate 2, which is the constancy of the velocity of light. Let us assume that at $t = t' = 0$ (and the origins of S and S' coincide: $x = x' = 0$) a spherical electromagnetic wave leaves the origin. The propagating wave looks like a spherical bubble whose radius is expanding at a rate c. In the two inertial frames S and S', the spherical wave fronts may be expressed in the form

$$x^2 + y^2 + z^2 - c^2t^2 = 0 \tag{2.41}$$
$$x'^2 + y'^2 + z'^2 - c^2t'^2 = 0 \tag{2.42}$$

Note that the velocity of light is the same c in both coordinate frames. Equations (2.41) and (2.42) imply that the laws of electromagnetism are invariant under transformation. Substituting the values of x', y', z', and t' from Eqs. (2.40) into Eq. (2.42), and rearranging we get

$$(a_{11}^2 - c^2a_{41}^2)\,x^2 + y^2 + z^2 - 2(va_{11}^2 + c^2a_{41}a_{44})\,xt - (c^2a_{44}^2 - v^2a_{11}^2)t^2 = 0 \tag{2.43}$$

Comparing Eqs. (2.41) and (2.43),

$$a_{11}^2 - c^2 a_{41}^2 = 1$$
$$v a_{11}^2 + c^2 a_{41} a_{44} = 0 \qquad (2.44)$$
$$c^2 a_{44}^2 - v^2 a_{11}^2 = c^2$$

Solving these three equations for the three coefficients, we obtain

$$a_{11} = a_{44} = \frac{1}{\sqrt{1 - (v^2/c^2)}}$$

and

$$a_{41} = \frac{-v/c^2}{\sqrt{1 - (v^2/c^2)}} \qquad (2.45)$$

Substituting these values into Eq. (2.40), we get the required Lorentz transformation, i.e.,

$$x' = \frac{x - vt}{\sqrt{1 - (v^2/c^2)}}$$
$$y' = y$$
$$z' = z \qquad (2.46)$$
$$t' = \frac{t - (v/c^2)x}{\sqrt{1 - (v^2/c^2)}}$$

The reverse transformation from S′ to S may be obtained by replacing v by $-v$ and interchanging the primed and unprimed coordinates. The results of these transformations are shown in Table 2.1, where we have introduced

TABLE 2.1
THE LORENTZ TRANSFORMATION EQUATIONS

A. From S to S′	B. From S′ to S
$x' = \dfrac{x - vt}{\sqrt{1 - \beta^2}}$	$x = \dfrac{x' + vt'}{\sqrt{1 - \beta^2}}$
$y' = y$	$y = y'$
$z' = z$	$z = z'$
$t' = \dfrac{t - (v/c^2)x}{\sqrt{1 - \beta^2}}$	$t = \dfrac{t' + (v/c^2)x'}{\sqrt{1 - \beta^2}}$

$\beta = v/c$ for convenience. Note that the two times, t and t', are not the same and their relation to each other depends upon the position x, i.e., the place where the event is taking place.

Let us see what happens as $v \to 0$, i.e., $v/c \ll 1$, $v^2/c^2 \lll 1$, and $v/c^2 \lll 1$. Under these conditions Eqs. (2.46) reduce to, $x' = x - vt$, $y' = y$, $z' = z$, and $t' = t$ which are the Galilean transformations of Newtonian mechanics. Thus

$$\lim_{v \to 0} \text{(Lorentz transformations)} = \text{(Galilean transformations)} \quad \textbf{(2.47)}$$

or

$$\frac{v}{c} \ll 1$$

Note that v will be always less than c, otherwise $\sqrt{1 - (v^2/c^2)}$ would be an imaginary quantity, which is not possible physically. *Hence nothing can move with a velocity greater than the velocity of light in vacuum.*

8. THE LORENTZ VELOCITY TRANSFORMATIONS

Suppose a particle moving with respect to reference frame S has velocity **u** with components u_x, u_y, and u_z. The velocity of the same particle with respect to the S' frame is **u'**, with components u'_x, u'_y, and u'_z; while the velocity of S' with respect to S is v along the $X - X'$ axis, as shown in Fig. 2.14. By

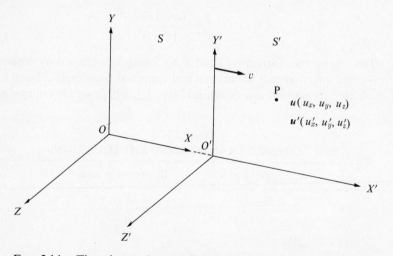

FIG. 2.14. *The velocity of a point P with respect to the observers in the inertial frames S and S' in relative motion.*

definition $u_x = dx/dt$, $u_y = dy/dt$, and $u_z = dz/dt$; and $u'_x = dx'/dt'$, $u'_y = dy'/dt'$, and $u'_z = dz'/dt'$. Using $\beta = v/c$ in Lorentz coordinate transformation Eq. (2.46) and differentiating, we get

$$dx' = \frac{dx - v\,dt}{\sqrt{1 - \beta^2}}$$

$$dy' = dy$$
$$dz' = dz$$
$$dt' = \frac{dt - v/c^2\, dx}{\sqrt{1 - \beta^2}}$$

(2.48)

Thus the velocity components are given by

$$u_x' = \frac{dx'}{dt'} = \frac{\dfrac{dx - v\, dt}{\sqrt{1 - \beta^2}}}{\dfrac{dt - v/c^2\, dx}{\sqrt{1 - \beta^2}}} = \frac{\dfrac{dx}{dt} - v}{1 - v/c^2\,\dfrac{dx}{dt}} = \frac{u_x - v}{1 - v/c^2 u_x}$$

$$u_y' = \frac{dy'}{dt'} = \frac{dy}{\dfrac{dt - \dfrac{v}{c^2}\,dx}{\sqrt{1 - \beta^2}}} = \frac{\dfrac{dy}{dt}}{1 - \dfrac{v}{c^2}\,\dfrac{dx}{dt}}\cdot\dfrac{1}{\sqrt{1 - \beta^2}} = \frac{u_y\sqrt{1 - \beta^2}}{1 - \dfrac{v}{c^2}\,u_x}$$

(2.49)

and

$$u_z' = \frac{dz'}{dt'} = \frac{dz}{\dfrac{dt - \dfrac{v}{c^2}\,dx}{\sqrt{1 - \beta^2}}} = \frac{\dfrac{dz}{dt}}{1 - \dfrac{v}{c^2}\,\dfrac{dx}{dt}}\cdot\dfrac{1}{\sqrt{1 - \beta^2}} = \frac{u_z\sqrt{1 - \beta^2}}{1 - \dfrac{v}{c^2}\,u_x}$$

which are the Lorentz velocity transformations. The inverse transformation may be obtained by replacing v by $-v$, and interchanging the primed and unprimed coordinates. The results of these transformations are shown in Table 2.2. It may be pointed out that unlike the space-coordinate transforma-

TABLE 2.2

THE LORENTZ VELOCITY TRANSFORMATION EQUATIONS

A. From S to S′	B. From S′ to S
$u_x' = \dfrac{u_x - v}{1 - \dfrac{u_x v}{c^2}}$	$u_x = \dfrac{u_x' + v}{1 + \dfrac{u_x' v}{c^2}}$
$u_y' = \dfrac{u_y\sqrt{1 - \beta^2}}{1 - \dfrac{u_x v}{c^2}}$	$u_y = \dfrac{u_y'\sqrt{1 - \beta^2}}{1 + \dfrac{u_x' v}{c^2}}$
$u_z' = \dfrac{u_z\sqrt{1 - \beta^2}}{1 - \dfrac{u_x v}{c^2}}$	$u_z = \dfrac{u_z'\sqrt{1 - \beta^2}}{1 + \dfrac{u_z v}{c^2}}$

tion, the velocity components u_y' and u_z' do depend upon the velocity u_x, and vice versa.

Using the above velocity transformations, we can show that (i) the velocity of light is always equal to c independent of the motion of the source or the observer, and (ii) nothing can move with a velocity greater than the velocity c with respect to any frame of reference.

Let us assume that a man in the S-frame of reference is flashing a light signal, while an observer at rest in S' is moving towards the light with a velocity $(3/4)c$ along the $X - X'$ axis (Fig. 2.15a). The velocity of light as meas-

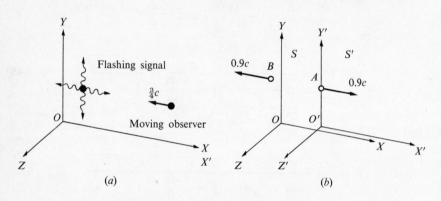

FIG. 2.15. (a) *An observer moving toward a flashing signal with a velocity (3/4)c. (b) Two electrons, A and B, moving in opposite directions each with a velocity 0.9c.*

ured by an observer in S is c. Let us calculate the velocity of the signal with respect to the observer in S'. Under these conditions $u_x = c$, $v = (-3/4)c$, and applying the first equation of Eq. (2.49), we get

$$u_x' = \frac{u_x - v}{1 - \frac{u_x v}{c^2}} = \frac{c - (-3/4c)}{1 - [c(-3/4c)/c^2]} = \frac{7/4c}{7/4} = c$$

Of course, this is what we expected because this is the basic assumption of relativity (postulate II) that we used initially to derive these transformations.

Let us consider two electrons, A and B, each moving with velocity $0.9c$ in exactly opposite directions as observed from an inertial system S. Let us calculate the velocity of one electron with respect to the other. Assume that electron A is traveling to the right along the $X - X'$ axis and is at rest in the S' system (Fig. 2.15b). Under these conditions $v = 0.9c$ and $u_x = -0.9c$. Therefore, the relative velocity of the electron B with respect to electron A is

$$u_x' = \frac{u_x - v}{1 - \frac{u_x v}{c^2}} = \frac{-0.9c - 0.9c}{1 - \frac{(-0.9c)(0.9c)}{c^2}} = -\frac{1.8}{1.81}c = -0.9945c$$

or

$$|u_x| < c$$

Thus electron B relative to electron A is moving in the $-X'$ direction with a velocity $0.9945c$. Note that according to Newtonian mechanics the relative velocity would be $-1.8c$, i.e., $|-1.8c| > c$. We may try all possible combinations, but we will always find that no relative velocity can be greater than c.

9. MEASUREMENT OF LENGTH AND TIME IN RELATIVITY

Because we have derived the formal Lorentz transformation-equations in relativity, we must now understand what we mean by length, time intervals, and simultaneity in different inertial systems that are in relative motion.

A. Length Contraction or Lorentz Contraction

According to classical physics, the length of an object, say a meter stick, is the same for all observers even though these observers may be in relative motion with respect to each other. But this is not so in relativity, and by making use of the Lorentz transformation-equations we shall show that the length of an object differs for different observers.

Consider two observers in inertial systems S and S' that are at rest at some time, say $t = t_0$. The observers agree that their meter sticks lying along the X and X' axis, respectively, are of length l_0. Now the inertial system S' (and hence the observer in this frame) starts moving with a velocity $\mathbf{v}$ along the $X - X'$ axis to the right. Thus for the observer in the S system, the length of his meter stick, according to him, is

$$l_0 = x_2 - x_1 \qquad \text{in S} \qquad (2.50)$$

where x_1 and x_2 are the coordinates of the end-points. Similarly, for the observer in the S' system, the length of his meter stick, according to him, is

$$l_0 = x_2' - x_1' \qquad \text{in S'} \qquad (2.51)$$

where x_1' and x_2' are the coordinates of the end-points, as shown in Fig. 2.16.

Our interest is to find the length of the S' observer's meter stick as measured by the observer in the S system. Using the Lorentz transformation-equations given by Eqs. (2.46) (or the left side equations in Table 2.1)

$$x_2' = \frac{x_2 - vt_2}{\sqrt{1 - \beta^2}}$$

$$x_1' = \frac{x_1 - vt_1}{\sqrt{1 - \beta^2}}$$

Subtracting

$$x_2' - x_1' = \frac{(x_2 - x_1) - v(t_2 - t_1)}{\sqrt{1 - \beta^2}} \qquad (2.52)$$

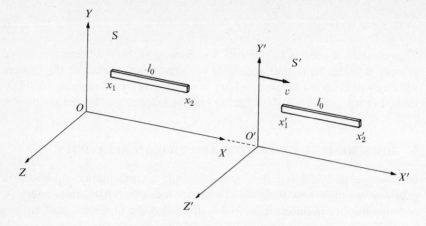

FIG. 2.16. *The coordinates of the end-points of a rod in two different inertial frames S and S' that are in relative motion.*

where $x_2' - x_1'$ is the length of the rod in S' as measured by the observer in S' and is equal to l_0 as given by Eq. (2.51); $x_2 - x_1$ is the length of this rod as measured by the observer in S and is denoted by l. Because the observer in S must measure the two ends of the rod simultaneously, i.e., $t_1 = t_2$; therefore, from Eq. (2.52)

$$x_2' - x_1' = \frac{x_2 - x_1}{\sqrt{1 - \beta^2}}$$

or

$$x_2 - x_1 = (x_2' - x_1')\sqrt{1 - \beta^2} \tag{2.53}$$

which means that

$$l = l_0\sqrt{1 - \beta^2} \tag{2.54}$$

The factor $\sqrt{1 - \beta^2}(= \sqrt{1 - (v^2/c^2)})$ is always less than unity, therefore l is always less than l_0, and the length of the meter stick is contracted as observed by the system S. Because $y' = y$ and $z' = z$, there is no observed change in the length in these directions. Hence we may conclude:

The measured length of an object is maximum when it is at rest relative to the observer. When the object moves with a velocity v relative to the observer its measured length is contracted in the direction of its motion by a factor $\sqrt{1 - \beta^2}$; but there are no change in dimensions in directions perpendicular to the direction of motion.

Thus the length is not absolute but depends upon the observer. The effect is reciprocal; if S' looks at S, the length of the rod in S will look contracted.

We may caution the reader to recognize that the contraction of length is not a physical process produced by cooling or by applying stress. In relativity, it is the definition of measuring the length of an object in relative motion with respect to the observer that results in the contraction of length.

B.   Time Dilation: The Slowing Down of Clocks

Like length, a time interval is also not absolute. The time interval elapsed between two events depends upon the relative motion of the observers. We can show this by making use of the Lorentz transformation-equations.

Consider an observer with a clock at x in inertial system S, and another observer with a clock at x' in the inertial system S'. To start with, both the inertial systems are at rest (and hence the observers are at rest); the observers synchronize their respective clocks. They both agree that the interval between two events as measured on their respective clocks is the same T_0; $T_0 = t_2 - t_1 = t_2' - t_1'$. Now the inertial system S' (and hence the observer in it) starts moving with a velocity v along the $X - X'$ axis. We want to find out how the time intervals between the two events that registered on clocks S and S' compare when both intervals are measured by S. Using the fourth equation on the right in Table 2.1,

$$t_2 = \frac{t_2' + \left(\dfrac{v}{c^2}\right) x_2'}{\sqrt{1 - \beta^2}}$$

and

$$t_1 = \frac{t_1' + \left(\dfrac{v}{c^2}\right) x_1'}{\sqrt{1 - \beta^2}}$$

subtracting

$$t_2 - t_1 = \frac{(t_2' - t_1') + \dfrac{v}{c^2}(x_2' - x_1')}{\sqrt{1 - \beta^2}} \qquad (2.55)$$

The use of this equation guarantees that it is the observer S who is looking at the clock of S' and then comparing it with his own. Because the clock of S' is fixed at one position in S' when S makes the observation, we must have $x_2' = x_1'$. Therefore

$$t_2 - t_1 = \frac{t_2' - t_1'}{\sqrt{1 - \beta^2}} \qquad (2.56)$$

or

$$T = \frac{T_0}{\sqrt{1 - \beta^2}} \qquad (2.57)$$

where $T_0 = t_2' - t_1'$ is the time interval recorded by S' between the two events, while $T = t_2 - t_1$ is the time interval recorded by S. Because $\sqrt{1 - \beta^2}$ is always less than unity, the time T_0 measured on the S'-clock is recorded as a *longer time*, T, on the S-clock. Equation (2.57) is the relation showing the phenomena of time dilation, or the slowing down of clocks. For example, if $v = 0.98c$, from Eq. (2.57) $T = 5T_0$. This means that according to S, the clock (say the hands of the clock) of S′ is moving much slower and takes a time interval five times greater for the same two events. The effect is reciprocal; when S′ looks at the clock of S, he thinks the clock of S is running slow. Thus we may conclude:

A clock appears to run at its fastest rate when it is at rest relative to the observer. When a clock moves with a velocity v with respect to the observer, its rate seems to be slowed down by a factor of $1/\sqrt{1 - \beta^2}$.

It may be pointed out that in the Lorentz transformation-equation

$$t = \frac{t' + \left(\dfrac{v}{c^2}\right) x'}{\sqrt{1 - \beta^2}}$$

the term $(v/c^2)x'$ is called the phase difference and results in the lack of synchronization of two clocks that are otherwise synchronized when at rest. Thus when $v = 0$, $t = t'$, the clocks are synchronized.

If an observer is at rest in a frame, this frame is called the *proper frame;* the time interval measured between events taking place in the same frame is called the *proper time*, the length of an object located and measured in this system is called the *proper length*. If the observer is moving with respect to the inertial frame in which the object is located and in which the events are taking place, the measured length and time interval are called *improper length* and *improper time*, respectively. There is no such thing as absolute-proper frame, time, or length.

C. Simultaneity

One of the fundamental differences between Newtonian mechanics and the relativistic mechanics is that in relativistic mechanics the space and time coordinates are so much interrelated that it is not possible to talk of one without the other, thus the definition of absolute simultaneity as in the classical sense is meaningless. For example,

(a) two events that are happening at x_1 and x_2 in the S frame and are simultaneous in S, $(t_1 = t_2)$, will not be simultaneous in S′, $(t_1' \neq t_2')$, and
(b) two events that are happening in S at the same position $(x_1 = x_2)$ but at different times will appear from S′ not happening only at different times but also happening at different locations as well $(x_1' \neq x_2'$ and $t_1' \neq t_2')$ as observed from S′. These results are mathematically obvious from the Lorentz transformation equations.

Examples confirming these concepts of length contraction and time dilation will be considered later[30,31].

One may think that because of the contraction, the object when viewed from improper frames will look distorted—a sphere may look like an ellipsoid. But this is not so, the objects are only rotated, and we may see some otherwise nonvisible portion of the moving objects[32,33]. (The apparent distortion of the moving object is not a relativistic effect.)

10. VARIATION OF MASS WITH VELOCITY

In classical mechanics the quantities length, time, and mass have absolute meaning. In the previous section we showed that length and time depend upon the relative velocity of the observers moving in different inertial systems. In this section, by considering collisions between two bodies, we shall show that the mass of a body appears to vary with its velocity. We shall apply the conservation of momentum, which we assume to be an unviolated principle in physics, together with the Lorentz transformations in order to arrive at the expression for the variation in mass with velocity.

Consider two observers, one at rest in the reference frame S and the other at rest in S', while S' is moving with a velocity v relative to S along the $X - X'$ axis. An observer in S has a perfectly elastic sphere, A, and the observer in S' has a perfectly elastic sphere, B. These two spheres are of equal masses, m_0, when compared at rest in the same inertial system. Let the two observers cause a perfectly elastic collision between the two spheres in the following fashion:

The observer in S throws sphere A vertically upward perpendicular to the X axis and along what he judges to be the $+ Y$ axis, with a velocity u_A. It travels a distance $y/2$, collides with B, and returns along the $- Y$ axis with the same velocity, u_A. The total time taken is T_0, and the velocity of sphere B as observed by the observer in S is u_B (u_B is the velocity component along Y-axis). To the observer in S the collision looks to be as shown in Fig. 2.17(a). *The situation is such that the behavior of sphere A is to the observer in S exactly the same as is the behavior of sphere B to the observer in S'.* This is shown in

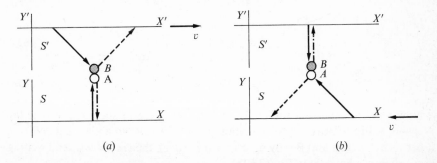

(a)   (b)

FIG. 2.17. *Perfectly elastic collision between two perfectly elastic spheres, A and B; (a) as viewed by an observer at rest in S system, (b) as viewed by an observer at rest in S' system.*

Fig. 2.17. Let us say the observer in S′ throws sphere B vertically upward, along the $-Y'$ axis with the velocity u_B'. It travels a distance $y'/2$, where $(y' = y)$, collides with A, and returns along the $+Y'$ axis with the same velocity u_B'. According to the observer in S′ the total time taken is T_0, and the velocity of A is u_A' (u_A' is the velocity component along Y'-axis). The situation is as shown in Fig. 2.17(b). The collision takes place midway between the X and X' axes. Thus

$$u_A = u_B' = \frac{y}{T_0} \tag{2.58}$$

and

$$u_B = \frac{y}{T} \tag{2.59}$$

where T is the time taken by sphere B in performing the collision as observed by the observer in the S system and is related to T_0 by the time dilation formula

$$T = \frac{T_0}{\sqrt{1 - (v^2/c^2)}} \tag{2.60}$$

Because the effect is reciprocal, according to the observer in S′,

$$u_A' = \frac{y}{T} \tag{2.61}$$

where again T is given by Eq. (2.60).

Let us now apply the conservation of momentum from the point of view of an observer in S, considering only the magnitudes, we may write

$$m_A u_A = m_B u_B \tag{2.62}$$

where m_A and m_B are the masses of the spheres, A and B, respectively, as measured by the observer in S. Substituting for u_A from Eq. (2.58) and for u_B from Eqs. (2.59) and (2.60), we obtain

$$m_A \frac{y}{T_0} = m_B \frac{y\sqrt{1 - (v^2/c^2)}}{T_0}$$

or

$$m_A = m_B \sqrt{1 - (v^2/c^2)} \tag{2.62a}$$

or

$$m_B = \frac{m_A}{\sqrt{1 - (v^2/c^2)}} \tag{2.62b}$$

Now if we assume that the collision is taking place in such a way that the sphere A in S is at rest, (this situation will correspond to a glancing collision between A at rest and B moving with a velocity v), then $m_A = m_0$, and writing $m_B = m$, we have from Eq. (2.62b),

$$m = \frac{m_0}{\sqrt{1 - (v^2/c^2)}} = \frac{m_0}{\sqrt{1 - \beta^2}} \tag{2.63}$$

This equation states that *if the mass of an object is m_0 when at rest, when it starts moving with a velocity v with respect to the observer, its mass appears to be increased to m, called the relativistic mass.* Note that the effect is reciprocal. We may also conclude that the mass m is no longer an invariant quantity as it is in classical mechanics. The quantity m_0 (and not m) is invariant in relativity physics.

In the nonrelativistic limits as $v \to 0$, from Eq. (2.63), $m \to m_0$, as it should. The mass m increases with increasing velocity v, and as $v \to c$, $m \to \infty$. This means that for a material particle to travel at the speed of light, the mass of the particle must be raised to infinity. This is another reason why c is a limiting velocity that is impossible to achieve by a material particle.

Even though the theory of relativity was given in 1905, the first experimental test of Eq. (2.63), the variation of mass with velocity, was performed by Bucherer[34] in 1909. The experiments performed on fast moving electrons discussed in detail in Sec. 4, Chapter III, showed that e/m is not constant, but e/m_0, is constant. The experiments have been repeated with much better accuracy by Zahn and others[35], and more recently by Bertozzi[36]. The results of the experiments are shown in Fig. 2.18, and it clearly demonstrates the functional dependence of mass on velocity as given by Eq. (2.63).

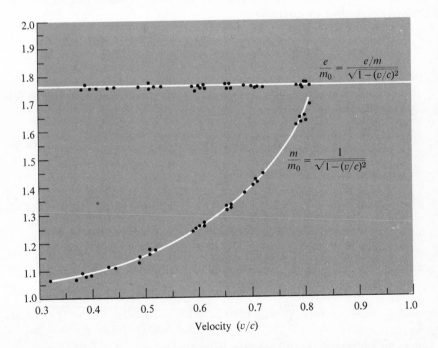

FIG. 2.18. *The variation of mass with velocity. The solid curve is a plot of m/m_0 versus v. The dots are experimental points obtained by Bucherer and by others.*

11. RELATIVISTIC MECHANICS

The laws of classical mechanics are invariant under Galilean transformations. Because we have shown that Galilean transformations must be replaced by Lorentz transformations for objects moving with high velocities, we must also investigate how to modify the classical laws so that these remain invariant under Lorentz transformations. (Note that we do not have to modify the laws of electromagnetism because the Lorentz transformations were derived while imposing the condition that the laws of electromagnetism remain invariant.) In this section we shall discuss the changes in classical mechanics brought about by the special theory of relativity under the following headings:

A. Newton's Second Law
B. Work and Kinetic Energy
C. The Relation Between Momentum and Energy
D. The Lorentz Force and Relativity (The Particle in a Magnetic Field)
E. The Acceleration of a Particle
F. Summary and Conclusion

A. Newton's Second Law

In the previous section we showed that the mass of an object varies with velocity according to Eq. (2.63):

$$m = \frac{m_0}{\sqrt{1 - (v^2/c^2)}}$$

Because the conservation of momentum is valid in all reference frames, the definition of momentum, $\mathbf{p} = m_0\mathbf{v}$, in classical physics is replaced by the following definition of momentum in relativity

$$\mathbf{p} = m\mathbf{v} = \frac{m_0\mathbf{v}}{\sqrt{1 - (v^2/c^2)}} \tag{2.64}$$

with the following three components

$$p_x = \frac{m_0 v_x}{\sqrt{1 - (v^2/c^2)}}, \qquad p_y = \frac{m_0 v_y}{\sqrt{1 - (v^2/c^2)}}, \qquad p_z = \frac{m_0 v_z}{\sqrt{1 - (v^2/c^2)}} \tag{2.65}$$

where $v^2 = v_x^2 + v_y^2 + v_z^2$.

Thus the force $\mathbf{F}$ acting on a body may now be defined as the time-rate of change of the relativistic momentum. Therefore, Newton's second law of motion takes the form

$$\mathbf{F} = \frac{d\mathbf{p}}{dt} = \frac{d}{dt}(m\mathbf{v}) = \frac{d}{dt}\left[\frac{m_0\mathbf{v}}{\sqrt{1 - (v^2/c^2)}}\right] \tag{2.66}$$

or as an alternative, Eq. (2.66) may be expressed as

$$\mathbf{F} = \frac{d\mathbf{p}}{dt} = m\frac{d\mathbf{v}}{dt} + \mathbf{v}\frac{dm}{dt} \tag{2.67}$$

Note that the definition of $\mathbf{F}$ is not equivalent to replacing m_0 by m in the classical definition of force, i.e., $\mathbf{F} \neq m\mathbf{a}$. In classical mechanics m is always constant, therefore, $\dfrac{dm}{dt} = 0$, and $\mathbf{F} = m\dfrac{d\mathbf{v}}{dt} = m\mathbf{a}$. But in relativistic mechanics this is not true, and the force is defined by Eq. (2.66) or Eq. (2.67).

B. Work and Kinetic Energy

Consider a particle of rest mass m_0 initially at rest but acted upon by a force of magnitude F which is applied in the X direction. Suppose the particle moves through a distance x, in time t, and attains the final velocity v. The kinetic energy K, which is defined as the work done on the particle in moving through a distance x is

$$K = \int_0^x F\,dx = \int_0^x \frac{d}{dt}(mv)\,dx = \int \frac{dx}{dt}\,d(mv) = \int_0^{mv} v\,d(mv) \quad (2.68)$$

substituting for $m = m_0/\sqrt{1 - (v^2/c^2)}$, and integrating:

$$K = \int_0^{mv} v\,d(mv) = \int_0^{mv} v\,d\left(\frac{m_0 v}{\sqrt{1 - (v^2/c^2)}}\right)$$

$$= m_0 \int_0^{mv} v\,d\left(\frac{v}{\sqrt{1 - (v^2/c^2)}}\right)$$

$$= m_0 \int_0^{v} \left[\frac{v}{\sqrt{1 - (v^2/c^2)}} + \frac{(v^3/c^2)}{(1 - v^2/c^2)^{3/2}}\right] dv$$

$$= m_0 \int_0^{v} \frac{v\,dv}{(1 - v^2/c^2)^{3/2}} = m_0 c^2 \left[\frac{1}{\sqrt{1 - (v^2/c^2)}}\right]_0^{v}$$

$$= m_0 c^2 \left(\frac{1}{\sqrt{1 - (v^2/c^2)}} - 1\right) = \frac{m_0 c^2}{\sqrt{1 - \beta^2}} - m_0 c^2$$

or,

$$K = mc^2 - m_0 c^2 = (m - m_0)c^2 \tag{2.69}$$

which is certainly different from the classical expression for the kinetic energy, $K = \frac{1}{2}m_0 v^2$. Before discussing the implications of Eq. (2.69), we shall show that this expression reduces to $\frac{1}{2}m_0 v^2$ for $v \ll c$. We expand Eq. (2.69) by the binomial theorem, keeping only the first two terms:

$$K = (m - m_0)c^2 = m_0 c^2 [(1 - v^2/c^2)^{-1/2} - 1]$$

$$= m_0 c^2 \left[1 + \frac{1}{2}\frac{v^2}{c^2} + \ldots - 1\right]$$

or

$$\underset{v/c \ll 1}{\text{Limit}}\ K \simeq m_0 c^2 + \frac{1}{2}\frac{v^2}{c^2}m_0 c^2 - m_0 c^2$$

$$\simeq \frac{1}{2}m_0 v^2$$

Once again we must note that the relativistic kinetic energy is not given by $\frac{1}{2}mv^2$ but by $K = mc^2 - m_0c^2$.

Going back to Eq. (2.69), we see that the increase in kinetic energy is due to the increase in mass; if

$$\Delta m = m - m_0$$

$$K = \Delta mc^2 \qquad (2.70)$$

This implies that all masses have energy associated with them. As a matter of fact we could interpret Eq. (2.69) in a slightly different way. Let E_0 be the *rest-mass energy* equal to m_0c^2, then from Eq. (2.69),

$$mc^2 = K + E_0 \qquad (2.71)$$

and to be consistent, we must identify mc^2 as the *total energy E*, i.e.,

$$E = K + E_0 \qquad (2.72)$$

where

$$E_0 = m_0c^2 \qquad (2.73)$$

and

$$E = mc^2 \qquad (2.74)$$

This equation represents the famous Einstein's mass-energy relations. According to these relations: *the rest-mass energy of a particle is equal to* c^2 *times its rest mass, while its total energy is equal to* c^2 *times its relativistic mass.*

If in addition to the kinetic energy, and rest-mass energy, the particle also has potential energy, then the total energy equation may be written as

$$mc^2 = K + V + m_0c^2 \qquad (2.75)$$

or

$$E = K + V + E_0 \qquad (2.76)$$

Thus we may conclude that *the theory of relativity ascribes energy to all mass* ($E = mc^2$) *and mass to all energy* ($m = E/c^2$). In general, we may say that if the mass of a body changes by Δm, the corresponding change in energy ΔE is

$$\Delta E = \Delta mc^2 \qquad (2.77)$$

It also becomes obvious that because mass and energy are equivalent and interchangeable, in relativity theory we must replace the separate classical laws of conservation of mass and conservation of energy by a single conservation law, the *conservation of mass-energy, or the law of conservation of total relativistic energy*, which states that *the total relativistic energy is invariant under a Lorentz transformation.* The total relativistic energy of an isolated system remains constant as observed from a given inertial system. Note that in relativistic mechanics, mass and energy are inseparably united, like space and time are in relativistic kinematics.

We shall now see how to convert from mass units to energy units and vice versa. A common unit for specifying energy (kinetic, rest, or total) in atomic and nuclear physics is the *electron volt* (eV), which is defined as the energy gained by a particle of charge e when accelerated by a potential differ-ence of one volt. This is also equal to 1.60×10^{-19} joule. The larger units of energy, defined in multiples of the electron volts are:

$$1 \text{ keV (one thousand electron volts)} = 10^3 \text{ eV}$$

$$1 \text{ MeV (one million electron volts)}\ \ = 10^6 \text{ eV}$$

$$1 \text{ BeV (one billion electron volts)}\ \ \ = 10^9 \text{ eV}$$

The masses of particles in atomic and nuclear physics are given in terms of atomic mass units, or amu, which is defined as

$$1 \text{ amu} = 1.660 \times 10^{-27} \text{ kg}$$

Thus the relation between the mass unit, amu, and the energy unit, MeV, may be found by making use of the relation $E = mc^2$.

$$E = mc^2 = 1 \text{ amu} \times c^2$$

$$= \frac{(1.66 \times 10^{-27} \text{ kg}) \times (3.0 \times 10^8 \text{ m/sec})^2}{(1.60 \times 10^{-19} \text{ joule/eV})(10^6 \text{ eV/MeV})}$$

$$= 931.478 \text{ MeV}$$

Therefore

$$1 \text{ amu} = 931.478 \text{ MeV}/c^2 \tag{2.78}$$

The rest mass of the proton is 1.00759 amu, while the rest mass of the electron is 1/1837 of the rest mass of the proton or 0.00055 amu, which in terms of energy units are

$$\text{proton rest mass}\ \ = 938.21 \text{ MeV}$$

$$\text{electron rest mass} = 0.51098 \text{ MeV}$$

We may also point out that a complete conversion of a small amount of mass produces a tremendous amount of energy. For example, if one gram of coal is completely converted into energy, then

$$E = 0.001 \text{ kgm } (3 \times 10^8 \text{ m/sec})^2$$

$$= 9 \times 10^{13} \text{ joules}$$

$$= 25,000 \text{ megawatt hours}$$

C. The Relation Between Momentum and Energy

We deal with momentum frequently, and hence it is useful to find a relation between momentum, p, and total energy, E. The expression

$$m = \frac{m_0}{\sqrt{1 - (v^2/c^2)}}$$

on squaring becomes

$$m^2(1 - v^2/c^2) = m_0^2$$

which on multiplying both sides by c^4 gives

$$m^2c^4 - m^2v^2c^2 = m_0^2c^4$$

substituting for $mv = p$, yields

$$m^2c^4 - p^2c^2 = m_0^2c^4$$

Because $E = mc^2$, we get

$$E^2 = p^2c^2 + m_0^2c^4 \qquad (2.79)$$

which is the required relation. Equation (2.79) may also be written as

$$E^2 = (pc)^2 + E_0^2 \qquad (2.80)$$

where $E = mc^2$ and $E_0 = m_0c^2$.

We shall now express the relation between m_0c^2, pc, K, and E in the form of a right-angle triangle as shown in Fig. 2.19. Note that

$$E = mc^2 = \frac{m_0}{\sqrt{1 - \beta^2}} c^2 = \gamma m_0 c^2 \qquad (2.81)$$

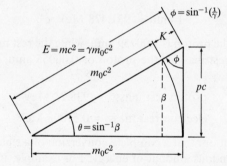

FIG. 2.19.   *A geometrical representation of the relations between m_0c^2, p, K, and E.*

where $\beta = v/c$ and $\gamma = 1/\sqrt{1 - \beta^2}$,

$$p = mv = \frac{m_0}{\sqrt{1 - \beta^2}} v = \gamma m_0 v \qquad (2.82)$$

$$K = mc^2 - m_0c^2 = m_0c^2 \left(\frac{1}{\sqrt{1 - \beta^2}} - 1 \right) = m_0c^2(\gamma - 1) \qquad (2.83)$$

Figure 2.19 also shows the relation

$$E = K + m_0c^2$$

Note that

$$\sin \theta = \beta \qquad (2.84a)$$

and

$$\sin \phi = \sqrt{1 - \beta^2} = \frac{1}{\gamma} \qquad \text{(2.84b)}$$

D. The Lorentz Force and Relativity

If a particle of rest mass m_0 and charge q is moving in electric and magnetic fields, the force (the Lorentz force) acting on the charged particle is given by

$$\mathbf{F} = q\mathbf{E} + q\mathbf{v}\mathbf{x}\mathbf{B} \qquad \text{(2.85)}$$

where $\mathbf{B}$ is the uniform magnetic flux density, and the motion of such a particle in relativity is described by the equation

$$q\mathbf{E} + q\mathbf{v}\mathbf{x}\mathbf{B} = \frac{d}{dt}\left(\frac{m_0\mathbf{v}}{\sqrt{1 - (v^2/c^2)}}\right) \qquad \text{(2.86)}$$

Let us consider the special case of a particle moving with a velocity $\mathbf{v}$ at right angles to the lines of uniform magnetic flux density, $\mathbf{B}$. Thus the magnetic force acting is

$$F_{\text{mag}} = qvB \qquad \text{(2.87)}$$

while the centripetal force, which keeps the particle moving in a circle, as shown in Fig. 2.20 is

$$F_{\text{cent}} = \frac{mv^2}{r} \qquad \text{(2.88)}$$

where r is the radius of the circle. Note that we used m and not m_0.

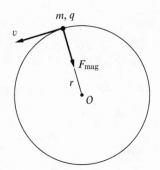

FIG. 2.20.   *Motion of a charged particle in a uniform transverse magnetic field.*

It is interesting to see that the motion of a charged particle in a magnetic field is such that the speed of the particle remains constant while its velocity changes (by changing directions). Thus in Eq. (2.67) for Newton's law

$$\mathbf{F} = \frac{d}{dt}(m\mathbf{v}) = m\frac{d\mathbf{v}}{dt} + \mathbf{v}\frac{dm}{dt}$$

$\dfrac{dm}{dt} = 0$, and hence $F = m\dfrac{dv}{dt} = ma$, where a is the centripetal acceleration, which according to Eq. (2.88) is v^2/r. Thus equating

$$F_{\text{mag}} = F_{\text{cent}}$$

$$qvB = \frac{mv^2}{r} \tag{2.89}$$

or

$$p = mv = q(Br) \tag{2.90}$$

The quantity Br is called the *magnetic rigidity* and may be defined as the momentum per unit charge, or

$$\left(\frac{p}{q}\right) = Br \tag{2.91}$$

Note that the expression for p in Eq. (2.90) is the same as the classical expression except that m is the relativistic mass.

E. The Acceleration of a Particle

Let us now derive an expression for the acceleration of a particle moving under the influence of a force. We know

$$\mathbf{F} = \frac{d\mathbf{p}}{dt} = \frac{d}{dt}(m\mathbf{v})$$

or

$$\mathbf{F} = m\frac{d\mathbf{v}}{dt} + \mathbf{v}\frac{dm}{dt} \tag{2.92}$$

Because $E = mc^2 = K + m_0 c^2$

$$\frac{dm}{dt} = \frac{1}{c^2}\frac{dE}{dt} = \frac{1}{c^2}\frac{dK}{dt}$$

But $\dfrac{dK}{dt}$ is nothing but the rate of doing work and is equal to $\mathbf{F} \cdot \mathbf{v}$. Therefore

$$\frac{dm}{dt} = \frac{1}{c^2}\mathbf{F} \cdot \mathbf{v}$$

Hence Eq. (2.92) takes the form

$$\mathbf{F} = m\frac{d\mathbf{v}}{dt} + \frac{\mathbf{v}}{c^2}\mathbf{F} \cdot \mathbf{v} \tag{2.93}$$

Therefore, the acceleration $\mathbf{a}$ of the particle from Eq. (2.93) is

$$\mathbf{a} = \frac{d\mathbf{v}}{dt} = \frac{\mathbf{F}}{m} - \frac{\mathbf{v}}{mc^2}(\mathbf{F} \cdot \mathbf{v}) \tag{2.94}$$

Note that the last term is in the direction of $\mathbf{v}$. Equation (2.94) tells us that, in general, the acceleration is not parallel to the force in relativity. However, there are two simple cases of Eq. (2.94) which we shall briefly describe.

Case I.   **a** is parallel to **F**, but **F** is perpendicular to **v**. This gives $\mathbf{F} \cdot \mathbf{v} = 0$, and hence $\mathbf{a} = \mathbf{F}/m$, or

$$\mathbf{F} = m\mathbf{a}$$

and when both **F** and **a** are perpendicular to **v**, as in the case of a charged particle moving in a magnetic field, we write

$$F_\perp = \frac{m_0}{\sqrt{1 - (v^2/c^2)}}\, a_\perp \qquad (2.95)$$

where the quantity $m_0/\sqrt{1 - (v^2/c^2)}$ is called the *transverse mass.*

Case II. F is parallel to **v** while **a** is parallel to both **v** and **F**. Thus the particle moves in a straight line as in the case of a charged particle starting from rest and moving in a uniform electric field. Because **a**, **F**, and **v** are parallel, we may write

$$F = m\frac{dv}{dt} + v\left(\frac{dm}{dt}\right)$$

substituting for $m = m_0/\sqrt{1 - (v^2/c^2)}$, we find, denoting F by $F_\|$ and a by $a_\|$

$$F_\| = \frac{m_0}{(1 - v^2/c^2)^{3/2}}\, a_\| \qquad (2.96)$$

where the quantity $m_0/(1 - v^2/c^2)^{3/2}$ is called the *longitudinal mass.*

F.   Summary and Conclusion

From Eqs. (2.63), (2.64), (2.69), (2.72) and (2.79) we have the following results

$$m = \frac{m_0}{\sqrt{1 - (v^2/c^2)}} \qquad (2.63)$$

$$p = mv = \frac{m_0 v}{\sqrt{1 - (v^2/c^2)}} \qquad (2.64)$$

$$K = mc^2 - m_0 c^2 = m_0 c^2 \left(\frac{1}{\sqrt{1 - (v^2/c^2)}} - 1\right) \qquad (2.69)$$

$$E = mc^2 = K + m_0 c^2$$
$$= K + E_0 \qquad (2.72)$$

and

$$E^2 = p^2 c^2 + m_0^2 c^4 \qquad (2.79)$$

We shall examine these relativistic equations under three conditions: (i) $v \ll c$, and (ii) $v \simeq c$, and (iii) $v = c$.

(i) $v \ll c$.   When the velocity of a particle is very small as compared to the velocity of light, the particle may be treated classically, and Newtonian mechanics is adequate to describe the motion. Under such conditions the relativistic equations reduce to the familiar classical expressions:

$$m \simeq m_0$$

$$p \simeq m_0 v \tag{2.97}$$

$$K \simeq \tfrac{1}{2} m_0 v^2$$

Also in this region

$$\frac{K}{E_0} = \frac{\tfrac{1}{2} m_0 v^2}{m_0 c^2} = \frac{1}{2} \left(\frac{v}{c} \right)^2 \ll 1$$

Therefore,

$$K \ll E_0 \quad \text{for} \quad v \ll c \tag{2.98}$$

(ii) $v \simeq c$. This is the more interesting case and results in many unfamiliar results, because $v \simeq c$ means that we are dealing with the extreme relativistic region. In this case the expressions for m, p, K, and E take the following form

$$m \gg m_0$$

$$p \simeq \frac{E}{c} \tag{2.99}$$

$$K \simeq E$$

$$E \gg E_0$$

In order to get some idea of when to use the two extremes, we quote the following example. If a particle is moving with a velocity such that $(v/c) < (1/10)$ or $(K/E_0) < (1/200)$, then using the expressions $K \simeq (1/2) m_0 v^2$ and $p = m_0 v$ does not result in an error greater than 1%. Similarly, considering the extreme relativistic case for $v/c > 0.99$, or $(K/E_0) > 6$, or $(E/E_0) > 7$, the use of the equation $E = pc$ does not result in an error greater than 1%.

(iii) $v = c$. This is the most interesting case. Let us first of all consider the equation

$$m = \frac{m_0}{\sqrt{1 - (v^2/c^2)}}$$

and if we substitute $v = c$, then $m = \infty$, which is not possible. But we can get around this dilemma by substituting $m_0 = 0$, in which case $m = 0/0$ is undeterminate and hence poses no difficulty. Under these conditions, Eqs. (2.63), (2.79), and (2.69) take the form

$$\left. \begin{array}{c} m_0 = 0 \\ E = pc \\ K = E \end{array} \right\} \quad \text{for} \quad v = c \tag{2.100}$$

According to this, a particle with $v = c$ has no rest mass but has energy and momentum. Such a particle makes no sense according to the classical theory but is quite possible according to relativity. One such particle is the photon which has the characteristics given by Eq. (2.100). The photon exists only for $v = c$.

PROBLEMS

1. Consider an elastic collision between two masses, and making use of the Galilean transformation equations, show that if kinetic energy is conserved in one inertial frame, it is conserved in all inertial frames.

2. If $\psi = E$ or H, show that the electromagnetic wave equation

$$\frac{\partial^2 \psi}{\partial x^2} + \frac{\partial^2 \psi}{\partial y^2} + \frac{\partial^2 \psi}{\partial z^2} - \frac{1}{c^2}\frac{\partial^2 \psi}{\partial t^2} = 0$$

is not invariant under the Galilean transformation, i.e., show that

$$\frac{\partial^2 \psi}{\partial x^2} + \frac{\partial^2 \psi}{\partial y^2} + \frac{\partial^2 \psi}{\partial z^2} - \frac{1}{c^2}\frac{\partial^2 \psi}{\partial t^2} \neq \frac{\partial^2 \psi}{\partial x'^2} + \frac{\partial^2 \psi}{\partial y'^2} + \frac{\partial^2 \psi}{\partial z'^2} - \frac{1}{c^2}\frac{\partial^2 \psi}{\partial t'^2}$$

[*Hint:* Start with $x = f(x', y', z', t')$]

3. Assuming the stationary-ether hypothesis in the Michelson-Morley experiment, what is the value of the expected fringe shift under the following conditions:
   (a) if the interferometer were rotated through 180° instead of 90°, and
   (b) if one arm of the interferometer made an angle θ ($\theta \neq 90°$) with the direction of motion, and the interferometer were rotated through 90°.

4. Would it be possible to perform a light aberration experiment to measure the speed of the earth through ether if the earth, instead of moving in a nearly circular orbit around the sun, were moving uniformly along a straight line?

5. Show that the electromagnetic wave equation is invariant under Lorentz transformation, i.e.,

$$\frac{\partial^2 \psi}{\partial x^2} + \frac{\partial^2 \psi}{\partial y^2} + \frac{\partial^2 \psi}{\partial z^2} - \frac{1}{c^2}\frac{\partial^2 \psi}{\partial t^2} = \frac{\partial^2 \psi}{\partial x'^2} + \frac{\partial^2 \psi}{\partial y'^2} + \frac{\partial^2 \psi}{\partial z'^2} - \frac{1}{c^2}\frac{\partial^2 \psi}{\partial t'^2}$$

where $\psi = E$ or H.

6. What are the Lorentz transformation equations for the case when the origins of two inertial systems in relative motion do not coincide, i.e., $x' \neq x$ when $t' = t = 0$?

7. A rod of length L makes an angle θ with the X axis and is at rest in the inertial system S. Find the length L' and the inclination angle θ' as measured by the observer in the inertial frame S' moving with velocity v along the $X - X'$ axis. If $L = 1.00$ meter, $\theta = 45°$, and $v = 3c/4$, find L' and θ'.

8. An observer on earth measures the length of a spaceship passing over the earth to be half the ship's proper length.
   (a) Find the speed of the spaceship relative to the observer.
   (b) If, according to the observer on earth, the spaceship was in sight for only 30 sec, how long was the earth in sight to the observer in the spaceship?

9. An inertial system S' moves relative to the inertial system S with a velocity $0.95c$ along the common $X - X'$ axis. An event occurs in S at $x = 200$ km, $y = 20$ km, and $z = 10$ km, at $t = 0$ sec. Calculate the coordinates x', y',

z', and t' of this event in the S' system. What will these coordinates be if $t = 2 \times 10^{-6}$ sec?

10. According to an observer, two guns are located along the X axis 100 miles apart and are fired simultaneously at 12 noon. Another observer (also moving along X axis), who had synchronized his clock with the first observer, is moving with a velocity $c/4$. According to the moving observer,
    (a) What is the distance by which these guns are separated?
    (b) What is the time at which these guns are fired?
    (c) If the two guns were located at the same position along the X axis, would they be heard simultaneously by the moving observer?

11. Two events occurring at (100, 10, 1, 0) and (1, 10, 100, 0) are simultaneous to S. If S' is moving with a velocity $v = 0.75c$, are these events simultaneous to S'? If not, what is the time interval between them? What happens if $v \to 0$?

12. Two superjets are approaching an airport from opposite directions with velocities of $0.9c$ and $0.8c$, respectively. What is the speed of one jet with respect to the other? What will be the relative velocity of one jet with respect to the other if the two jets were approaching at right angles to each other?

13. Two events occur at an interval of 2 sec and at a distance 1000 m apart along the X axis as observed by an observer in system S. How do these events appear to S', which is moving with a velocity $0.80c$ with respect to S along the $X - X'$ axis? Is there any frame of reference in which these events will appear simultaneously?

14. A pilot in a superjet moving at a speed of $c/2$ observed that it took him 8 sec according to the clock on earth to travel from planet A to planet B. How much time did it take to travel from A to B according to an observer on the earth?

15. In the S' inertial system, a particle is moving with a velocity of $0.9c$ along the Y' axis, while S' itself is moving with a velocity of $0.9c$ along the $X - X'$ axis with respect to the inertial system S. Calculate the components of the velocity of the particle with respect to the S system.

16. A particle of mass m is moving with a velocity $0.8c$ in the positive X direction with respect to a stationary observer. Another particle of mass M is moving with a velocity $0.8c$ in the negative X direction.
    (a) Calculate the relative velocity and mass of m as observed by M.
    (b) Calculate the relative velocity and mass of M as observed by m.

17. A particle is moving with a speed u in a direction making an angle θ with the X axis in the frame of reference S. Find the speed and the direction of this particle with respect to another frame of reference S' moving with a relative velocity v. Repeat the calculations for $u = c$.

18. A particle of mass 1 gm is moving in the S' frame of reference. The velocity of this particle as observed from the S frame of reference is $3/4c$. The velocity of S' with respect to S is $0.5c$ along the $X - X'$ axis. Calculate
    (a) the mass of the particle in the S frame, and
    (b) the velocity of the particle with respect to the S' frame.

19. An electron and a proton are accelerated from rest through a potential difference of 1 billion electron volts. Calculate (a) their speeds, and (b) the percentage increase in the masses.

20. How much energy is required to accelerate an electron and a proton from (a) $0.5c$ to $0.9c$, and (b) $0.9c$ to $0.98c$.

21. Calculate the speeds for which (a) an electron, and (b) a proton, will have their kinetic energies equal to their rest masses.

22. Calculate the radius of curvature of 10 MeV, 100 MeV, and 1000 MeV protons in a 10^4-gauss field. Calculate the percentage error in all three cases if a nonrelativistic expression is used.

23. An electron falls through a potential difference of 10^7 volts. Find the (a) mass, (b) speed, (c) kinetic energy, and (d) total energy. If the electron after being accelerated enters a uniform magnetic field of 2.0 webers/m², what is the radius of curvature? How does this radius compare with the classical value?

24. Repeat Problem #23 for the case of a charged π-meson that has a rest mass 273 times the rest mass of an electron.

25. The lifetime of a μ-meson is 2.3×10^{-6} sec while the laboratory measurement yields a value of 6.9×10^{-6} sec. The rest mass of a μ-meson is 207 times the rest mass of electron. Calculate the following:
    (a) the moving mass,
    (b) its kinetic energy, and
    (c) its momentum.

26. Consider a cube with each side equal to L_0 placed at the origin of the inertial system S. The rest mass of the cube is m_0 and its density is $\rho_0 = m_0/L_0^3$. Calculate the mass, volume, and density as viewed by an observer in an inertial frame S' that has a velocity v along the $X - X'$ axis.

27. Consider a collision between two identical particles, one at rest and the other moving with velocity v_L in the LAB coordinate system. If v_{cm} is the velocity in the CMCS, prove the following relation

$$\beta_{cm} = \frac{\beta_L \gamma_L^2}{1 + \gamma_L^2}$$

where

$$\beta_{cm} = \frac{v_{cm}}{c}, \qquad \beta_L = \frac{v_L}{c}, \qquad \text{and} \qquad \gamma_L = \frac{1}{\sqrt{1 - \beta_L^2}}$$

28. The sun is radiating energy at the rate of 10^{26} calories per sec. Calculate the decrease in the mass of the sun per sec. If the mass of the sun is 2×10^{33} gms, how long will the sun live? (This is one way of calculating the lifetime of the earth before it freezes completely.)

29. When a neutron and a proton are combined, a deuteron is formed. The energy released when the deuteron is formed is 2.22 MeV and comes from the decrease in the mass. If the masses of the neutron and the proton are 1.008665 and 1.007277 amu, respectively, what is the mass of the deuteron?

30. How much energy will be released if two neutrons, two protons, and two electrons combine to form a helium atom? The mass of the helium atom is 4.0026 amu.

31. For a particle of rest mass m_0 moving with velocity v, calculate the percentage error if one uses the expression $m_0 v^2/2$ for the kinetic energy instead of the relativistic expression. Make a plot of this error versus v for $v = 0.1c$, $0.2c$, $0.3c, \ldots, 0.9c, c$.

32. For what value of v will the use of the Galilean transformation-equations instead of the Lorentz transformation-equations not introduce an error of more than (a) 0.1%, (b) 1.0%, and (c) 10%?

33. In an experiment with colliding beams, two separate proton beams each with protons whose energy is 10 BeV are directed against each other in a headon collision.

   (a) What are the velocities of the protons as seen by an observer in the LAB coordinate system?

   (b) What is the relative velocity of one proton with respect to the other?

   (c) In the extreme relativistic case, the velocity v of the protons is very nearly equal to c. Let us define $\delta = c - v$. Show that the energy E of the proton is approximately equal to

   $$E = \frac{E_0}{\sqrt{\dfrac{2\delta}{c}}}$$

   where $E_0 = m_0 c^2$ is the rest mass energy (or self energy).

34. What is the minimum speed for a particle so that its total energy E can be identified as pc without causing an error of more than 1%. Calculate the kinetic energy of an electron and a proton at this speed.

35. (a) Show that the momentum of a particle may be written as

   $$p = \frac{1}{c}(K^2 + 2E_0 K)^{1/2}$$

   (b) When a particle of charge q moves at right angles to a uniform magnetic field of flux density B, it travels in a circle of radius

   $$r = (K^2 + 2E_0 K)^{1/2}/qcB$$

   where K is the kinetic energy and E_0 is the rest mass energy. Prove the relationship.

36. For a free particle, prove the following relation

   $$pc^2 = v\beta \quad \text{or} \quad \beta = \frac{pc}{E}$$

37. Suppose a frame of reference S' is moving with a velocity v_1 along the $X - X'$ axis and S'' is moving with a velocity v_2 relative to S along the $X' - X''$ axis. Show that the velocity v_3 of S'' relative to S is given by the Einstein addition law for velocities, i.e.,

   $$v_3 = \frac{v_1 + v_2}{1 + \dfrac{v_1 v_2}{c^2}} \quad \text{or} \quad \beta_3 = \frac{\beta_1 + \beta_2}{1 + \beta_1 \beta_2}$$

   Show that if $v_1 < c$, $v_2 < c$, then $v_3 < c$. Also if $v_1 = v_2 = c$, then $v_3 = c$.

38. A π-meson of mass m_π comes to rest and disintegrates into a μ-meson of rest mass m_μ and a neutrino of rest mass zero. Show that the kinetic energy K_μ of the μ-meson is

   $$K_\mu = \frac{(m_\pi - m_\mu)^2}{2m_\pi} c^2$$

39. The rest masses of an electron, μ-meson, and proton are 0.51 MeV, 103.5 MeV, and 931 MeV, respectively. If each of these particles has a momentum of 200 MeV/c, calculate β, K, and E for each.

40. Make a plot of E versus β and a plot of E versus p for an electron, μ-meson, and proton if their rest masses are 0.51 MeV, 103.5 MeV, and 931 MeV, respectively.

REFERENCES

1. Bertozzi, W., *Am. J. Phys.*, **32**, 551, (1964).
2. Sadeh, D., *Phys. Rev. Letters*, **10**, 271 (1963).
3. Einstein, A., *Ann. Physik*, **17**, 132, (1905).
4. Einstein, A., *Ann. Physik*, **17**, 549, (1905).
5. Einstein, A., *Ann. Physik*, **17**, 891, (1905).
6. Einstein, A., *Ann. Physik*, **49**, 749, (1916).
7. Einstein, A., *Principle of Relativity*, New York: Dover Publications, 1923.
8. Cohen, E. R., and J. W. M. DuMond, *Rev. Mod. Phys.*, **37**, 537, (1965).
9. Stewart, Albert, "The Discovery of Stellar Aberration," *Sci. Am.*, (March 1964).
10. Rosser, W. G. V., *An Introduction to the Theory of Relativity*, London: Butterworth, 1964.
11. Fresnel, A. J., *Ann. Chim. et Phys.*, **9**, 57, (1818).
12. Fizeau, H. L., *Compt. Rend.*, **33**, 349, (1851).
13. Trouton, F. T., and H. R. Noble, *Phil. Trans. Roy. Soc.*, **A202**, 165, (1903); *Proc. Roy. Soc.*, **72**, 132, (1903).
14. Michelson, A. A., *Am. J. Sci.*, **122**, 120, (1881).
15. Michelson, A. A., and E. W. Morley, *Am. J. Sci.*, **134**, 333, (1887).
16. Shankland, R. S., McCuskey, Leone, and Kuerti, *Rev. Mod. Phys.*, **27**, 167, (1955).
17. Lodge, O., *Nature*, **46**, 165, (1892).
18. Lorentz, H. A., *Amst. Verh. Akad. von Wetenschappen*, **1**, 74, (1892).
19. Kennedy, R. J., and E. M. Thorndike, *Phys. Rev.*, **42**, 400, (1932).
20. Ritz, W., *Ann. Chim. et Phys.*, **13**, 145, (1908).
21. Thomson, J. J., *Phil. Mag.*, **19**, 301, (1910).
22. Thomson, J. J., and A. Stewart, *Phys. Rev.*, **32**, 418, (1911).
23. Tolman, R. C., *Phys. Rev.*, **31**, 26, (1910).
24. DeSitter, W., *Proc. Amsterdam Acad.*, **15**, 1297, (1913), and **16**, 395, (1913).
25. Tomaschek, R., *Ann. Physik*, **73**, 105, (1924).
26. Miller, D. C., *Proc. Nat. Acad. Sci.*, **2**, 311, (1925).
27. Sadeh, D., *Phys. Rev. Letters*, **10**, 271, (1963).
28. Alväger, T., F. J. M. Farley, J. Kjellman, and I. Wallin, *Phys. Rev. Letters*, **12**, 260, (1964).
29. Einstein, A., *Ann. Physik*, **17**, 891, (1905).
30. Shankland, R. S., *Am. J. Phys.*, **31**, 47, (1963).
31. Erlichson, H., *Am. J. Phys.*, **35**, 89, (1967).

32. Scott, G. D., and M. R. Viner, *Am. J. Phys.*, **33**, 534, (1965).

33. Veisskopf, V. T., *Physics Today*, **13(9)**, (Sept. 1960).

34. Bucherer, A. H., *Ann. Physik*, **28**, 513, (1909).

35. Fargo, P. S., and L. Janossy, *Nuovo Cimento*, **V**, No. 6, 1411, (1957).

36. Bertozzi, W., *Am. J. Phys.*, **32**, 551, (1964).

SUGGESTIONS FOR FURTHER READING

1. Ney, E. P., *Electromagnetism and Relativity*, New York: Harper and Row, 1962.

2. Resnick, Robert, *Introduction to Special Relativity*, New York: John Wiley & Sons, 1968.

3. French, A. P., *Principles of Modern Physics*, Chap. 6, New York: John Wiley & Sons, 1958.

4. Bergmann, P. G., *Introduction to the Theory of Relativity*, Englewood Cliffs, N. J.: Prentice-Hall, 1942.

5. Helliwell, T. M., *Introduction to Special Relativity*, Boston: Allyn and Bacon, Inc., 1966.

6. Kacser, Claude, *Introduction to the Special Theory of Relativity*, Englewood Cliffs, N. J.: Prentice-Hall, 1967.

7. Yilmaz, H., *Theory of Relativity and the Principles of Modern Physics*, New York: Blaisdell Publishing, 1965.

8. Anderson, J. L., *Principles of Relativity*, New York: Academic Press, 1967.

9. French, A. P., *Special Relativity*, New York: W. W. Norton and Co., Inc., 1966.

10. Katz, R., *An Introduction to the Special Theory of Relativity*, Princeton, N. J.: D. Van Nostrand Co., Inc., 1964.

11. Schwartz, H. M., *Introduction to Special Relativity*, New York: McGraw-Hill, 1968.

12. Einstein, A., *The Meaning of Relativity*, Princeton, N. J.: Princeton Univ. Press, 1946.

III

The Theory of Relativity II

1. TRANSFORMATIONS OF MOMENTUM, ENERGY, MASS, AND FORCE

In many situations, especially in collision problems in nuclear physics, it is more useful to know the transformation equations of momentum and total relativistic energy from one reference frame to another, e.g., from center-of-mass coordinate system to LAB-coordinate system, and vice versa. We shall develop these transformation equations in this section.

Let us consider a particle of rest mass m_0 moving with velocity u along the $+X$ axis of reference frame S. In this inertial system the three components of momentum p_x, p_y, p_z, and the total relativistic energy E are given by

$$p_x = \frac{m_0 u}{\sqrt{1 - (u^2/c^2)}}, \qquad p_y = 0, \qquad p_z = 0$$

and

$$E = \frac{m_0 c^2}{\sqrt{1 - (u^2/c^2)}} \tag{3.1}$$

According to the observer in S', where S' is moving with velocity v along the $X - X'$ axis with respect to S, the components of momentum and total energy take the form

$$p'_x = \frac{m_0 u'}{\sqrt{1 - (u'^2/c^2)}}, \qquad p'_y = 0, \qquad p'_z = 0$$

and

$$E = \frac{m_0 c^2}{\sqrt{1 - (u'^2/c^2)}} \qquad (3.2)$$

where u' is the velocity of the particle with respect to the observer in S'.

Using the velocity addition theorem, $u' = (u - v)/[1 - (uv/c^2)]$, we can find a relation between p_x and p'_x. This results in the following transformation equations

$$p'_x = \frac{p_x - \dfrac{vE}{c^2}}{\sqrt{1 - (v^2/c^2)}}$$

$$p'_y = p_y \qquad (3.3)$$

$$p'_z = p_z$$

$$E' = \frac{E - p_x v}{\sqrt{1 - (v^2/c^2)}}$$

The inverse transformation may be obtained by substituting $-v$ for v and interchanging the primed and unprimed variables. The results are given in Table 3.1. Note the similarity of transformations between these equations

TABLE 3.1

THE RELATIVISTIC TRANSFORMATIONS
FOR MOMENTUM AND ENERGY

A. From S to S'	B. From S' to S
$p'_x = \dfrac{p_x - \dfrac{vE}{c^2}}{\sqrt{1 - \beta^2}}$	$p_x = \dfrac{p'_x + \dfrac{vE}{c^2}}{\sqrt{1 - \beta^2}}$
$p'_y = p_y$	$p_y = p'_y$
$p'_z = p_z$	$p_z = p'_z$
$E' = \dfrac{E - p_x v}{\sqrt{1 - \beta^2}}$	$E = \dfrac{E' + p'_x v}{\sqrt{1 - \beta^2}}$

and the space-time transformation equations given in Table 2.1. It looks as if p_x, p_y, p_z take the place of x, y, z; and E takes the place of ct. The most important conclusion that results from such an analogy is that if the energy and momentum are conserved in an interaction in a given inertial system, then they are conserved as viewed from any inertial system.

Using the energy transformation equations in $E = mc^2$, where $m = m_0/\sqrt{1 - (v^2/c^2)}$, one finds the mass transformation equations to be

$$m' = \frac{m(1 - u_x v/c^2)}{\sqrt{1 - (v^2/c^2)}} \qquad (3.4)$$

and its inverse

$$m = \frac{m'(1 + u_x' v/c^2)}{\sqrt{1 - (v^2/c^2)}} \qquad (3.5)$$

Similarly, one can obtain the relations between the components F_x, F_y, F_z of **F**, and F_x', F_y', F_z' of **F'**, where in frame S

$$F_x = \frac{d}{dt}(mu_x), \qquad F_y = \frac{d}{dt}(mu_y), \qquad F_z = \frac{d}{dt}(mu_z) \qquad (3.6a)$$

and in frame S'

$$F_x' = \frac{d}{dt'}(m'u_x'), \qquad F_y' = \frac{d}{dt'}(m'u_y'), \qquad F_z' = \frac{d}{dt'}(m'u_z') \qquad (3.6b)$$

The calculations and transformation equations are given in detail by Rosser[1].

2. INVARIANT QUANTITIES IN RELATIVITY

The implication of the experimental fact of the speed of light being constant irrespective of the motion of the source and the observer led to the formulation of the Lorentz transformation-equations, as we have already seen. We say that the speed of light is a scalar invariant quantity. Besides this, there are two other scalar quantities that are invariant. These quantities are: (a) the magnitude of the space-time four-vector, and (b) the magnitude of the momentum-energy four-vector.

A. Space-Time Four-Vector

In Newtonian mechanics the distance of a point (x, y, z) from the origin in an inertial system S is given by:

$$r^2 = x^2 + y^2 + z^2$$

The length of this vector remains invariant when it is observed from any other inertial system S' that is moving with a uniform velocity v with respect to S, provided $v \ll c$, i.e.,

$$r'^2 = x'^2 + y'^2 + z'^2$$

where

$$r'^2 = r^2 \qquad \text{if} \qquad v \ll c \qquad (3.7)$$

Equation (3.7) may be extended further to say that the distance between any two points is invariant in three-dimensional space irrespective of the relative velocity of the observer provided v is small compared to c, or

$$\text{space invariant: } \Delta r^2 = \Delta r'^2 \qquad (3.8)$$

Of course the assumption is that the two ends of the vector are measured simultaneously or the interval between the two events of locating the two ends of a vector is the same in all inertial systems.

Another consequence of Newtonian mechanics resulting from the Galilean transformations is that the time interval between any two events is invariant, or

$$\text{time invariant: } \Delta t = \Delta t' \tag{3.9}$$

Thus according to Eqs. (3.8) and (3.9) space and time are separately invariant quantities in Newtonian physics, while the speed of light is not an invariant quantity.

If we now impose the condition that the speed of light is constant, we are required to use the Lorentz transformations, which use four-dimensional space with three space-coordinates x, y, z and the fourth coordinate ict, (where $i = \sqrt{-1}$). In this space, the position of a point, or *the kinetic state* of a particle, is expressed by a four-vector S whose components are x, y, z, ict, and whose length is given by

$$S^2 = x^2 + y^2 + z^2 + (ict)^2$$

and this length is invariant when observed from any other frame of reference S′ moving with a velocity v with respect to the S frame, i.e.,

$$\text{space-time invariance:}$$
$$S'^2 = x'^2 + y'^2 + z'^2 + (ict')^2 \tag{3.10}$$
$$= x^2 + y^2 + z^2 + (ict)^2 = S^2$$

Thus we may say that the separate space and time invariants of Newtonian mechanics are replaced in relativity by a single space-time interval between any two events in four-dimensional space, or

$$\text{space-time invariance: } \Delta S^2 = \Delta S'^2 \tag{3.11}$$

where

$$\Delta S^2 = (x_2 - x_1)^2 + (y_2 - y_1)^2 + (z_2 - z_1)^2 + (ict_2 - ict_1)^2 \tag{3.12a}$$
$$\Delta S'^2 = (x_2' - x_1')^2 + (y_2' - y_1')^2 + (z_2' - z_1')^2 + (ict_2' - ict_1')^2 \tag{3.12b}$$

As a matter of fact by using Lorentz transformations in Eq. (3.12b) one can show that $\Delta S'^2 = \Delta S^2$.

We may point out that the four-dimensional vector space with three real and one imaginary component cannot be visualized in the manner of three-dimensional real space, but all the formal properties of three dimensional space may be extended to four-dimensional space.

B. Momentum-Energy Four-Vector

Another consequence of the constancy of speed of light is the invariance of the momentum-energy of a particle. The *dynamical state* of a particle is described by a single four-vector whose components are p_x, p_y, p_z, and iE/c. If a particle has momentum p, rest energy E_0, and total energy E, from relativity

$$E^2 = p^2 c^2 + E_0^2$$

where $p^2 = p_x^2 + p_y^2 + p_z^2$. Rewriting the above equation, we get

$$(E/c)^2 = p^2 + (E_0/c)^2$$

$$-(E_0/c)^2 = p^2 - (E/c)^2$$

or

$$(iE_0/c)^2 = p_x^2 + p_y^2 + p_z^2 + (iE/c)^2 \tag{3.13}$$

Because m_0 is constant, so is E_0. Thus iE_0/c, called the "length" in momentum units, is constant. Hence, from Eq. (3.13), the magnitude of the momentum-energy four-vector of a particle is invariant. We may state this in a slightly different way by saying that the rest energy, E_0, of a particle is invariant irrespective of the inertial frame of reference in which its momentum and energy are measured. Just as three space and one time component yield a four vector, similarly three components of momentum, p_x, p_y, p_z, and one component of energy, iE/c, form a momentum-energy four-vector. The assumption of relativistic dynamics is that the momentum-energy four-vector in any inertial system results in the same invariant quantity. Thus if the momentum and energy of a particle are measured in two different inertial systems, we may state the following:

momentum-energy invariance:

$$(iE_0/c)^2 = p_x^2 + p_y^2 + p_z^2 + (iE/c)^2$$

$$= p_{x'}^2 + p_{y'}^2 + p_{z'}^2 + (iE'/c)^2 \tag{3.14}$$

There is quite a resemblance between the space-time four-vector and the momentum-energy four-vector. One can write down the momentum-energy transformations given by Eq. (3.3) by making the following replacements in the Lorentz transformations

$$x, y, z \quad \text{by} \quad p_x, p_y, p_z, \quad \text{respectively,}$$

and

$$ict \quad \text{by} \quad iE/c \tag{3.15}$$

and vice versa.

3. OPTICAL EFFECTS IN RELATIVITY THEORY

We are now in a position to see some of the most interesting applications of the special theory of relativity to optical effects such as (a) aberration of light, and (b) doppler effect. Before considering the special cases, let us first derive some general relations concerning the propagation of electromagnetic waves as observed from different frames of reference.

Consider an inertial system S′ moving with a velocity v with respect to an inertial system S along the $X - X'$ axis. Let a source of light that is emitting plane monochromatic waves of unit amplitude and frequency be located at the origin 0′. The rays are emitted along the direction r' in the $X' - Y'$ plane, making an angle θ' as shown in Fig. 3.1. The propagation of the waveform in frame S′ may be described by the equation

$$\psi' = \cos 2\pi \nu' \left(\frac{r'}{c} - t' \right) \tag{3.16}$$

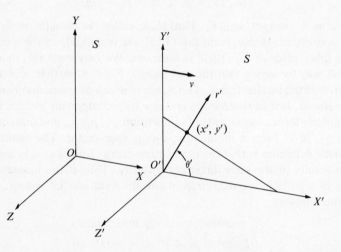

FIG. 3.1. *The direction of propagation r' of a plane monochromatic light-wave emitted from O' makes an angle θ' with the X' axis in the S' frame.*

where ψ' is the wave amplitude, which is a function of time t' and distance r' given by

$$r' = x' \cos \theta' + y \sin \theta'$$

Combining this with Eq. (3.16), we may write

$$\psi' = \cos 2\pi \left[\frac{x' \cos \theta' + y' \sin \theta'}{\lambda'} - \nu' t' \right] \tag{3.17}$$

where $\lambda' \nu' = c$. This equation reduces to the familiar expression for propagation along the $+X'$ axis and the $+Y'$ axis for $\theta' = 0°$ and 90°, respectively.

These waves will still be plane waves when viewed from the S frame because the Lorentz transformation is linear and a plane wave will transform into a plane wave except that the frequency and wavelength ν and λ are different but related to ν' and λ' by the relation $\nu\lambda = c = \nu'\lambda'$. If the wave as observed in the S frame makes an angle θ with the X axis, the expression for the propagation in S may be written as

$$\psi = \cos 2\pi \left[\frac{x \cos \theta + y \sin \theta}{\lambda} - \nu t \right] \tag{3.18}$$

We are interested in finding relations between λ, ν, and θ; and λ', ν', and θ'. This is achieved by substituting from the Lorentz transformations for x' and t' into Eq. (3.17) and comparing terms with Eq. (3.18). Thus from Eq. (2.46)

$$x' = \frac{x - \nu t}{\sqrt{1 - \beta^2}} \quad \text{and} \quad t' = \frac{t - (v/c^2)x}{\sqrt{1 - \beta^2}}$$

which is substituted into Eq. (3.17), and after rearranging, we get

$$\psi = \cos 2\pi \left[\frac{\cos \theta' + \beta}{\lambda'\sqrt{1 - \beta^2}} x + \frac{\sin \theta'}{\lambda'} y - \frac{(\beta \cos \theta' + 1)\nu'}{\sqrt{1 - \beta^2}} t \right] \tag{3.19}$$

Comparing the quantities in the square brackets in Eqs. (3.18) and (3.19), we obtain

$$\frac{\cos \theta}{\lambda} = \frac{\cos \theta' + \beta}{\lambda'\sqrt{1 - \beta^2}} \tag{3.20}$$

$$\frac{\sin \theta}{\lambda} = \frac{\sin \theta'}{\lambda'} \tag{3.21}$$

$$\nu = \frac{\nu'(1 + \beta \cos \theta')}{\sqrt{1 - \beta^2}} \tag{3.22}$$

which with the additional relation

$$\nu\lambda = \nu'\lambda' = c \tag{3.23}$$

are the four general relations. These relations are possible because any particular displacement in one frame is observed as such by other observers moving with different speeds, which means that the quantity $(r/\lambda) - \nu t$ is an invariant quantity, or

$$\frac{r}{\lambda} - \nu t = \frac{r'}{\lambda'} - \nu't'$$

$$\frac{x \cos \theta + y \sin \theta}{\lambda} - \nu t = \frac{x' \cos \theta' + y' \sin \theta'}{\lambda'} - \nu't' \tag{3.24}$$

We shall now discuss some applications of Eqs. (3.20) through (3.23) in the following.

A. Aberration of Light

The aberration was discussed in Chapter II, Sec. 4. The relativistic equation for the aberration of light is easily derived by dividing Eq. (3.21) by Eq. (3.20). We obtain

$$\tan \theta = \frac{\sin \theta'\sqrt{1 - \beta^2}}{\cos \theta' + \beta} \tag{3.25}$$

which relates the directions of propagation θ and θ' as observed by two different inertial frames. The inverse transformation may be obtained by replacing β by $-\beta$ and interchanging the primed and unprimed quantities:

$$\tan \theta' = \frac{\sin \theta \sqrt{1 - \beta^2}}{\cos \theta - \beta} \tag{3.26}$$

Of course this result does not seem to be familiar to us. We can show that the observed first-order aberration effect may be derived from Eq. (3.26) as a special case, resulting in the familiar classical expression. Consider a star directly overhead in the S frame. The light wave will propagate along the $-Y$ axis resulting in $\theta = 3\pi/2$. The corresponding value of θ' from Eq. (3.26) is

$$\tan \theta' = \frac{\sin (3\pi/2)\sqrt{1 - \beta^2}}{\cos (3\pi/2) - \beta} = -\frac{\sqrt{1 - \beta^2}}{-\beta}$$

or

$$\tan \theta' = \frac{\sqrt{1 - \beta^2}}{\beta} \tag{3.27}$$

This is an exact expression. But if $v \ll c$, β^2 is very small and may be neglected. Thus

$$\tan \theta' \simeq \frac{1}{\beta} = \frac{c}{v} \tag{3.28a}$$

Because $\alpha = (3\pi/2) - \theta'$, we get

$$\tan \alpha \simeq \frac{v}{c} \tag{3.28b}$$

which is in perfect agreement with the classical result, i.e., the observed first-order aberration effect as given by Eq. (2.14).

B. Relativistic Doppler Effect

Before discussing the relativistic Doppler effect, we shall briefly mention the properties of the Doppler effect in sound. If v_0 is the velocity of sound and v the velocity of an observer of the source that is less than v_0, the expressions for the Doppler effect are

$$\nu' = \nu \left(1 \pm \frac{v}{v_0} \right) \qquad \text{when the observer is in motion and the source is at rest} \tag{3.29a}$$

and

$$\nu' = \frac{\nu}{\left(1 \mp \frac{v}{v_0} \right)} \qquad \text{when the source is in motion and the observer is at rest} \tag{3.29b}$$

where $+$ corresponds to approaching and $-$ to receding of the source or observer.

In the case of light waves, because they do not require a medium for propagation, the Doppler effect is symmetrical in source and observer motion, which means that it depends upon the relative motion of the source and the observer (and doesn't matter which one is at rest). Unlike the classical case where there is only a longitudinal Doppler effect, for which the Doppler effect occurs only when the source and the observer move along the same line, in relativity both the longitudinal (source and observer moving along the same line) as well as the transverse (source and the observer moving perpendicular to each other) Doppler effects are observed, as we shall discuss below.

According to Eq. (3.22) the relativistic expression for the Doppler effect is

$$\nu = \frac{\nu'(1 + \beta \cos \theta')}{\sqrt{1 - \beta^2}} \qquad (3.30)$$

while the inverse case is

$$\nu' = \frac{\nu(1 - \beta \cos \theta)}{\sqrt{1 - \beta^2}} \qquad (3.31)$$

Before discussing the two cases mentioned above, we shall see how to reduce Eq. (3.31) to the first-order approximation, thereby resulting in classical Doppler effect. Thus if $v \ll c$, $\beta^2 \ll 1$, and hence β^2 may be neglected as compared to 1. Thus from Eq. (3.31),

$$\nu = \frac{\nu'\sqrt{1 - \beta^2}}{1 - \beta \cos \theta} = \nu'\left(1 - \frac{1}{2}\beta^2 + \ldots\right)(1 - \beta \cos \theta)^{-1}$$

or

$$\nu \cong \nu'(1 + \beta \cos \theta) \qquad (3.32)$$

Equation (3.32) is classical Doppler effect, which becomes clear if we substitute $\theta = 0$, corresponding to the source moving towards the observer or the observer moving towards the source.

$$\nu = \nu'(1 + \beta) = \nu'\left(1 + \frac{v}{c}\right) \qquad (3.33a)$$

Similarly, if $\theta = 180°$, corresponding to the source and observer moving away from each other, from Eq. (3.32) we get

$$\nu = \nu'(1 - \beta) = \nu'\left(1 - \frac{v}{c}\right) \qquad (3.33b)$$

Combining the two equations we get

$$\nu = \nu'\left(1 \pm \frac{v}{c}\right) \qquad (3.34)$$

which is the result predicted classically. Also if we substitute $\theta = 90°$ in Eq. (3.32), we get $\nu' = \nu$, as expected classically; thus there is no Doppler effect for perpendicular motion.

(i) *The Longitudinal Doppler Effect in Relativity.*   First consider the case when the source and the observer are moving towards each other, where $\theta = 0$, and Eq. (3.31) reduces to

$$\nu\sqrt{1 - \beta} = \nu'\sqrt{1 + \beta} \qquad \text{approaching} \tag{3.35}$$

Similarly, if $\theta = 180°$

$$\nu\sqrt{1 + \beta} = \nu'\sqrt{1 - \beta} \qquad \text{receding} \tag{3.36}$$

As an example consider a galaxy, reported by R. Minkowski, that is receding from earth with a velocity $\beta = \frac{1}{2}$. We would like to know the characteristic properties of its light. Assume that the frequency of the light from the atoms in the galaxy is ν'. The frequency ν as observed by us will be

$$\nu = \nu' \frac{\sqrt{1 - \beta}}{\sqrt{1 + \beta}} = \nu' \left(\frac{\frac{1}{2}}{\frac{3}{2}}\right)^{1/2} = \frac{\nu'}{\sqrt{3}}$$

or, using the relation $\nu\lambda = \nu'\lambda' = c$,

$$\lambda = \sqrt{3}\lambda' = 1.7\,\lambda'$$

Hence the wavelength λ that we observe is much longer (or redder) than the natural wavelength λ'; there is a shift towards the red, and hence it is called the *red shift*. Because the universe is expanding, all galaxies recede from each other, thereby, leading to red shifts for the wavelengths of their light waves.

(ii) *The Transverse Doppler Effect in Relativity.*   Again considering Eq. (3.31), and after rewriting,

$$\nu = \frac{\nu'\sqrt{1 - \beta^2}}{1 - \beta\cos\theta}$$

and substituting $\theta = 90°$, we get

$$\nu = \nu'\sqrt{1 - \beta^2} \tag{3.37}$$

or to a second-order approximation

$$\nu \simeq \nu'\left(1 - \frac{1}{2}\beta^2\right) \tag{3.38}$$

Once again from Eq. (3.37) or (3.38), we find the observed frequency ν to be smaller than the natural frequency ν'; the observed wavelength is longer than the natural wavelength. Hence there is a red shift as in the longitudinal Doppler effect. Note that transverse Doppler effect is a second order effect. Thus

$$\lambda = (\nu'/\nu)\lambda' = \frac{\lambda'}{\sqrt{1 - \beta^2}} \simeq \lambda'\left(1 + \frac{1}{2}\beta^2\right)$$

and for $\beta = \frac{1}{2}$

$$\lambda = 1.125\,\lambda' \quad \text{for transverse effect}$$

and

$$\lambda = 1.7\,\lambda' \quad \text{for longitudinal effect}$$

(iii) *Experimental Verification.* The relativistic Doppler effects have been experimentally verified both in first order and second order, originally in 1938 by Ives and Stilwell[2,3], and later on by Mandelberg and Witten[4], Otting[5], Kundig[6], and others. The experiments led to the verification of the theory of relativity.

According to the classical experiment of Ives and Stilwell, light emitted from excited hydrogen atoms (with precise velocity and well-defined direction) is observed while propagating towards a detector. By placing a mirror behind the beam, they were able to photograph simultaneously the light emitted in the forward and backward directions. This results in the shift of the center-of-gravity of the wavelengths in the forward and backward emitted light. The shift is that of second-order Doppler effect. Ives and Stilwell measured both the first- and second-order Doppler effects at different velocities of the atoms. The agreement between the predicted and the observed values is obvious, as shown in Fig. 3.2.

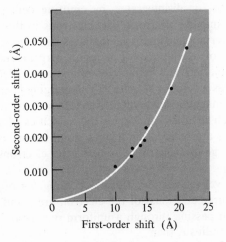

Fig. 3.2. *Comparison of experimental values (measured by Ives and Stilwell) of both first- and second-order Doppler effects as measured at different velocities with theoretically predicted values. Note the smallness of the second-order effect, which nonrelativistically is zero.*

4. EXPERIMENTAL VERIFICATION OF THE SPECIAL THEORY OF RELATIVITY

The results of the special theory of relativity are so well accepted that they are used without reservation in many calculations by physicists, especially those in nuclear and high-energy work. In addition to many indirect experimental verifications of the theory, there are some direct and well-established proofs. Because the readers at this stage may not be familiar with those parts of physics in which these experiments are conducted, it would be impossible to do full justification to the discussion of such experiments. For our purpose, we shall briefly outline several experiments, which verify the special theory of relativity, under the following headings:

A.   Variation of Mass with Velocity
B.   Length Contraction and Time Dilation (Meson Decay)
C.   The Relativistic Mass-Energy Relation
D.   The Addition of Velocities
E.   The Relativistic Doppler-Effect

A.   Variation of Mass with Velocity

The first experiment to verify the special theory by measuring the variation of mass with velocity, or, $m = m_0/\sqrt{1 - (v^2/c^2)}$, was done by Bucherer[7] in 1909 as outlined here. A beam of electrons is obtained from a radioactive source that decays, or disintegrates, by emitting beta particles. The beta particles are fast moving electrons. The electrons in this beam have speeds between 0 and a certain maximum value that is less than c. In order to obtain an electron beam of definite speed, or monoenergetic energy, the beta particles are first subjected to a suitable combination of electric and magnetic fields that works as a velocity selector. This emerging beam of electrons then enters a uniform magnetic field where the electrons are deflected along arcs, the radii of which are determined by the velocities of the electrons. The deflected electrons are received on a photographic film. From the traces on the film, the charge-to-mass ratio, e/m, of the electrons can be obtained easily.

Suppose the velocity of the electrons coming out of a velocity selector is v, while the charge and mass of the electron are e and m, respectively. If these electrons, in passing through a uniform magnetic field B, move in an arc of a circle of radius r, then

$$\frac{mv^2}{r} = Bev$$

or

$$\frac{e}{m} = \frac{v}{rB} \qquad (3.39)$$

If we substitute $m = m_0/\sqrt{1 - (v/c)^2}$, we get

$$\frac{e}{m_0} = \frac{e}{m\sqrt{1 - (v/c)^2}} = \frac{v}{rB\sqrt{1 - (v/c)^2}} \qquad (3.40)$$

Classically the radius of the electron circular path is

$$r = \frac{mv}{eB} \qquad (3.41)$$

while relativistically, r is given by

$$r = \frac{m_0 v}{eB\sqrt{1 - (v/c)^2}} \qquad (3.42)$$

The results of Bucherer's experiment are given in Table 3.2, which shows

TABLE 3.2
EXPERIMENTAL RESULTS OBTAINED BY BUCHERER
IN ORDER TO VERIFY $m = m_0/\sqrt{1 - (v^2/c^2)}$

Measured value of v/c	Measured value of e/m $(= v/rB)$ in units of coul/kg	Computed value of e/m_0 $(= e/m\sqrt{1 - (v^2/c^2)})$ in units of coul/kg
0.3173	1.661×10^{11}	1.752×10^{11}
0.3787	1.630×10^{11}	1.761×10^{11}
0.4281	1.590×10^{11}	1.760×10^{11}
0.5154	1.511×10^{11}	1.763×10^{11}
0.6870	1.283×10^{11}	1.767×10^{11}

that the e/m ratio is not constant, but e/m_0 is constant, thereby verifying the relation $m = m_0/\sqrt{1 - (v/c)^2}$.

Since the first experiment, many more experiments have been made using a wide range of velocities and for different particles. Some of these results are shown in Fig. 2.18. The mass-variation formula has been tested with an accuracy of better than 0.1%. The latest experiments have been done by Bertozzi[8], using high-energy accelerators in order to obtain very precisely defined velocities. The results firmly confirm the mass-variation formula.

A comparison of Eqs. (3.40) and (3.42) may tempt us to think that if we assume that the charge e, instead of mass m, varies with velocity as $e = e_0\sqrt{1 - (v/c)^2}$, we can still explain the results given in Table 3.2. But the direct consequence of relativistic electrodynamics is that the charge of a particle does not change with velocity. If this were not true, the charge neutrality of an atom, or any other system of particles, will be a function of the motion of the particles. The assumption that the charge is an invariant quantity, has been verified experimentally by Fleishmann and Kollath[9], and by Kollath and Menzel[10].

B. Length Contraction and Time Dilation (Meson Decay)

One of the most interesting experiments that establishes both the Lorentz length-contraction and time-dilation is concerned with the decay of meson particles. The masses of mesons are between the rest masses of electrons and protons, while the charge they carry may be positive, negative, or neutral. Mesons are not stable particles, and different mesons decay with different characteristic half-lives. The half-life, $T_{1/2}$, is defined as the time interval in which half of the particles decay away. In our discussion we shall limit ourselves to the charged pi mesons, or pions, (π^+ or π^- mesons) that have a mass of 279 times the mass of the electron rest-mass, and their half-life is $T_{1/2} = 1.77 \times 10^{-8}$ sec, which means that if we have 100 π mesons at rest at $t = 0$, then at $t_1 = 1 \times T_{1/2} = 1.77 \times 10^{-8}$ sec there will be only 50, while at $t_2 = 2 \times T_{1/2} = 2 \times 1.77 \times 10^{-8}$ sec there will be only 25 left, and so on.

High energy π mesons are produced in the laboratory by bombarding a target of light material such as Be or B with a beam of very-high-energy protons obtained from an accelerator. A typical well-collimated beam of π mesons leaves the accelerator with a speed of $0.99c$ or 2.97×10^8 m/sec. It has been observed that the intensity of the beam reduces to one-half its original value at a distance of 39 m from the target. According to the definition of half-life, which for π mesons is 1.77×10^{-8} sec, the distance x from the origin at which the intensity becomes one-half is $x = vt = 2.97 \times 10^8$ m/sec $\times 1.77 \times 10^{-8}$ sec $= 5.25$ m which is not in agreement with the measured value of 39 m. The apparent discrepancy can be removed either by using length contraction or time dilation—if we use proper frame of reference for our calculations as we show below.

(i) *Length Contraction (using π meson reference-frame).* When the π meson is at rest, or when it is in its own reference frame, its half-life is 1.77×10^{-8} sec. Now the π meson starts moving with a velocity $v = 0.99c$ with respect to the laboratory frame. It is the same thing to say that the π meson is still at rest while the laboratory is moving with a relative velocity of $0.99c$. Even though the distance traveled by the π meson in the laboratory frame is 39 m, when the π meson measures this distance in his own frame of reference, it is not 39 m but it seems to be contracted,

$$\Delta x' = \Delta x \sqrt{1 - (v^2/c^2)}$$
$$= 39\sqrt{1 - (0.99)^2} \text{ m} = 5.3\text{m}$$

and this corresponds to a time $\Delta t'$ (or half-life in this case)

$$T_{1/2} = \frac{\Delta x'}{v} = \frac{39\sqrt{1 - (0.99)^2} \text{ m}}{2.97 \times 10^8 \text{ m/sec}}$$
$$= 1.77 \times 10^{-8} \text{ sec}$$

which is exactly the value of the half-life of the π meson in its own reference frame. Hence the length contraction hypothesis has removed the discrepancy.

An alternative is to approach the problem from the viewpoint of the laboratory frame as we shall show now.

(ii) *Time Dilation (using laboratory reference-frame).* The distance of 39 m is measured in the laboratory reference-frame, while the half-life $T_{1/2} = 1.77 \times 10^{-8}$ sec is that of the meson in its own frame of reference, i.e., this is the proper time Δt. The time $\Delta t'$ as observed in laboratory frame is

$$\Delta t' = \frac{\Delta t}{\sqrt{1 - (v^2/c^2)}}$$

$$= \frac{1.77 \times 10^{-8} \text{ sec}}{\sqrt{1 - (0.99)^2}}$$

$$= 1.3 \times 10^{-7} \text{ sec}$$

Thus if the mesons are traveling at a speed of $v = 0.99c = 2.97 \times 10^8$ m/sec, the time to be used for calculation of distance traveled in the laboratory, should be the improper time $\Delta t' = 1.3 \times 10^{-7}$ sec. Thus

$$x = 2.97 \times 10^8 \text{ m/sec} \times 1.3 \times 10^{-7} \text{ sec} = 39 \text{ m}$$

agreeing with the actual measured value.

We may point out that the original calculations were made for the μ mesons produced in cosmic radiation traveling from the outer atmosphere towards the earth. Such calculations are given in detail by Frisch and Smith[11].

C. The Relativistic Mass-Energy Relation

The mass-energy relation $E = mc^2$ is well-established and experimentally confirmed to at least one part in 10^5. Every nuclear reaction utilizes this relation, and the results agree with measured values as, for example, in the calculations of energy release in nuclear fission and nuclear fusion.

D. The Addition of Velocities

The two observations, (i) the aberration of light, and (ii) the Fresnel drag coefficient, make use of the velocity-addition theorem for making calculation, and the results agree with the experimental values.

E. The Relativistic Doppler Effect

We have discussed this in Sec. 3, and it is shown there (see Fig. 3.2) how the relativistic calculations agree with the observed values.

Of course, according to special theory it is impossible for particles to travel faster than light because it would take an infinite amount of energy to get the particle speeding at the speed of light. However, this has not deterred scientists from making serious suggestions that particles can indeed travel faster than light. Such particles have been called *tachyons*, (from the Greek word *tachus* meaning *swift*). According to scientists, there is no reason why a particle cannot exist which travels faster than light. Such a particle is a tachyon. The tachyons have imaginary rest mass, while real momentum and energy. An outstanding characteristic of a tachyon is that as it loses energy it speeds up until it is travelling infinitely fast. At this speed, it has no energy at all.

Attempts have been made to create tachyons by surrounding a gamma ray source (source of electromagnetic waves of very high frequencies) such as cesium-134 with a lead shield. It was expected that photons will interact producing a pair of tachyons, T_+ and T_-. The pair carry equal and opposite charges. There has been no success as yet in detecting charged or neutral tachyons. There is some possibility that Einstein's Special Theory of Relativity may break down in certain regions of outer space, such as inside a quasar, where the matter is in a highly compressed state. There is some evidence for the existence of tachyons in the interior of quasars.

If the existence of tachyons is ever firmly established, it will lead to over all modifications of the present day theories of physics.

5. THE GRAPHICAL REPRESENTATION OF SPACE-TIME

The graphical representation of the transformation of events from one inertial system to another according to classical physics is quite simple. The simplicity arises from the fact that time is an invariant quantity, $t' = t$; the time coordinate t' does not depend upon the space coordinates x, y, z, and the time coordinate t does not depend upon the space coordinates x', y', z'. In relativistic physics, as we have already seen, time is a space-dependent coordinate, and the graphical representation will involve all four coordinates, x, y, z, and t, instead of only three space coordinates x, y, and z. The graphical representation of the Lorentz transformation was first shown by H. Minkowski[12], and we shall describe it briefly in the following.

A. Scaling the Axes

One of the basic properties of the Lorentz transformation is that the *relativistic line element*, G, also called the *ground invariant*, (equal to the square of magnitude of space-time 4-vector), defined below, is invariant, i.e.,

$$G = x^2 + y^2 + z^2 - c^2t^2 = x'^2 + y'^2 + z'^2 - c^2t'^2 \qquad (3.43)$$

For simplicity, we shall consider only one space coordinate on the X axis, while ignoring the Y and Z axes. In this case G takes the form

$$G = x^2 - c^2t^2 = x'^2 - c^2t'^2 \qquad (3.44)$$

Any construction that displays the points in space-time, called *world points*, will have to keep G invariant. In relativity, the coordinates of any event are (x, t). In order to have the same dimensions for both the coordinates, we use $\omega = ct$ instead of t, where c is the universal constant, the velocity of light. Thus the coordinates of any event or world point, WP, are given by (x, ω) in the coordinate system in which the X and ω axes of the inertial frame S are perpendicular, or orthogonal, as shown in Fig. 3.3. The loci of the world points is a *world line* of a moving particle in world space as shown.

The slope of the world line at any point is given by the tangent at that point: $1/\text{slope} = \tan\theta = dx/d\omega = dx/d(ct) = (1/c)(dx/dt) = v/c$. Because for any material particle v is less than c, therefore $\tan\theta < 1$, and hence the world line is always inclined at an angle of less than 45° to the time axis, ω. The world line for a light wave, for which $\tan\theta = c/c = 1$, is a straight line making an angle of 45° with the axes as shown in Fig. 3.3.

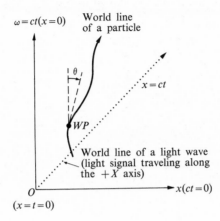

FIG. 3.3.   *World line of a particle in space-time (x, ω) representation.*

Let us consider the primed inertial frame S' moving with a relative velocity v with respect to frame S along the $X - X'$ axis. What we want to do now is to plot the space-time axes for both the inertial frames so that we can transform events from one frame to the other by reading these axes. Let (x, ω) be the coordinates of an event in S, and (x', ω') be the coordinates of the same event in S'. According to the Lorentz transformation-equations (noting that $\omega = ct$ and $\omega' = ct'$):

$$x' = \frac{x - \beta\omega}{\sqrt{1 - \beta^2}} \qquad x = \frac{x' + \beta\omega'}{\sqrt{1 - \beta^2}}$$

$$\omega' = \frac{\omega - \beta x}{\sqrt{1 - \beta^2}} \qquad \omega = \frac{\omega' + \beta x'}{\sqrt{1 - \beta^2}} \tag{3.45}$$

For the axis ω, $x = 0$, which means the ω axis is the world line of the clock at the origin of the S system. Similarly, for $x' = 0$, the ω' axis is the world line of the clock at the origin of the S' system, while $x = x' = 0$ and $\omega = \omega' = 0$ (or $t = t' = 0$) represents the origin where the clocks coincide as well as the origins of where S and S' coincide. In order to locate the axes of S', first substitute $x' = 0$ in Eq. (3.45), i.e.,

$$x' = 0 = \frac{x - \beta\omega}{\sqrt{1 - \beta^2}} \tag{3.46}$$

or

$$x = \beta\omega$$

and

$$\tan\theta_1 = \frac{dx}{d\omega} = \frac{x}{\omega} = \beta \tag{3.47}$$

Thus ω' is an axis for which $x' = 0$ and $x = \beta\omega$, and it is inclined at an angle $\theta_1 = \tan^{-1}\beta$ to the ω axis, as shown in Fig. 3.4. Note that the inclina-

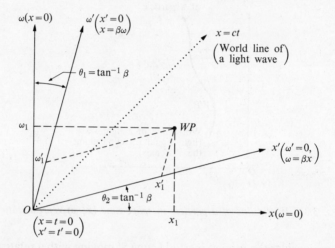

FIG. 3.4. *Geometrical representation of the space-time axes for transformation from S to S', and vice versa.*

tion is a function of the relative velocity v. Similarly, to obtain the x' axis, we substitute $\omega' = 0$ in Eq. (3.45), i.e.,

$$\omega' = 0 = \frac{\omega - \beta x}{\sqrt{1 - \beta^2}}$$

or

$$\omega = \beta x \tag{3.48}$$

and

$$\tan\theta_2 = \frac{d\omega}{dx} = \frac{\omega}{x} = \beta \tag{3.49}$$

Thus x' is an axis for which $\omega' = 0$, $\omega = \beta x$, and it is inclined at an angle $\theta_2 = \tan^{-1}\beta$ to the x axis as shown in Fig. 3.4. Note that the angle between the space axes of S and S' is the same as the angle between the time axes. Also even though x and ω axes are orthogonal, the x' and ω' axes produced by the Lorentz transformation are not orthogonal. According to Fig. 3.4, the coordinates of a world point, WP, are (x_1, ω_1) in S frame and (x_1', ω_1') in S' frame.

In order to complete the Minkowski diagram, we need the setting of scales on these axes. To do this we make use of the principle that G is invariant. Accordingly the unit distance on the scales will be given by $G = \pm 1$, i.e.,

$$G = \pm 1 = x^2 - \omega^2 = x'^2 - \omega'^2 \tag{3.50}$$

which is called the scale-normalization equation and fixes the so-called *metric* for the construction. Equation (3.50) can be directly plotted, and the result is a simple equilateral hyperbola as shown in Fig. 3.5. The alternative is as follows: Eq. (3.50) may be written as

$$(x + ct)(x - ct) = (x' + ct')(x' - ct') = G = \pm 1 \tag{3.51}$$

or

$$\eta\xi = \eta'\xi' = G = \pm 1 \tag{3.52}$$

where the new axes are defined by

$$x + ct = \eta \, (\xi = 0), \qquad x - ct = \xi \, (\eta = 0)$$
$$x' + ct' = \eta' \, (\xi' = 0), \qquad x' - ct' = \xi' \, (\eta' = 0) \tag{3.53}$$

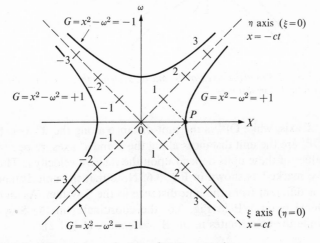

FIG. 3.5. *Plot of the scale-normalization equation.*

and are shown in Fig. 3.5. Note that the path of light is shown by dotted lines and is unique. This means η and η' are the same, and ξ and ξ' are also the same. Also shown in the figure are the plots of the metric given by Eq. (3.52), which is a simple equilateral hyperbola. These hyperbolas are called the calibration curves. Projection of the point P on the dotted line (path of the light waves) gives a unit distance from the origin as shown. Once we have obtained this unit length, we can mark both the dotted lines with this scale as shown in Fig. 3.5.

Our problem is slightly different. We are interested in scaling the axes of S and S' systems that are connected by the Lorentz transformations. This may be achieved very simply as shown in Fig. 3.6. The points where the axes cross the hyperbolas give us the unit distances from the origin on the corresponding axes as shown in Fig. 3.6. Thus the distance OP_1 is the unit distance

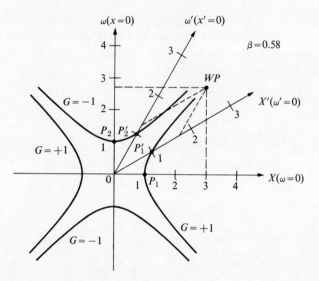

FIG. 3.6. *Scaling the axes of S and S' systems that are connected by Lorentz transformations.*

along the X axis, while OP_1' is the unit distance along the X' axis. Similarly OP_2 and OP_2' are the unit distances along the ω and ω' axes, respectively. The relative values of these units depend upon the relative velocity v. Thus all the axes can be marked as shown in Fig. 3.6. Note that the unit distance in the S' system is different from the unit distance in the S system. As an example, for the world point WP in Fig. 3.6, the coordinates in the S system are (3, 2.7), while the coordinates in the S' system are (1.8, 1.2).

B. Contraction and Dilation

Consider a meter stick at rest in S frame as shown in Fig. 3.7. Initially the meter stick is at rest with its ends at $x = 3$ and $x = 4$. With the passing of the time the length of the meter stick in the S frame remains the same because the world lines of both the ends of the stick trace out vertical lines parallel to the ω axis. The length of this stick is one meter whenever its ends are measured simultaneously in the S frame, say at any time ω_0. In order to find the length of this stick in the S' frame, which is in relative motion, we will have to measure simultaneously the points where the two world lines intersect the X' axis. This is as shown in Fig. 3.7, and, as is obvious, the length of

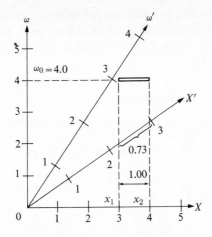

FIG. 3.7. *Geometrical illustration of contraction of length.*

the stick in the S′ frame is less than its length in the S frame. (It is 0.73 m in S′ and 1 m in S for a certain value of relative velocity.) Of course the effect is reciprocal (see Problem 3.10).

In order to demonstrate the time-dilation geometrically let us consider Fig. 3.8. Suppose a clock is at rest at x_0 in the frame S. The black dots on the

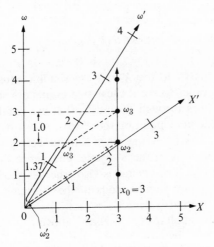

FIG. 3.8. *Geometrical illustration of dilation in time.*

vertical line at x_0 indicate the passing of a unit interval of time on the clock (say the ringing of a bell at each unit interval). Let us consider a particular interval marked between ω_2 and ω_3 in the S frame. In order to see the magnitude of this interval in the S′ frame we may draw lines at ω_2 and ω_3 that are parallel to the X' axis and find its intercept on the ω' axis as shown in Fig. 3.8. As is obvious the time interval as observed in the S' frame is longer than 1 unit ($= 1.37$ for some arbitrary relative velocity). Again the effect is reciprocal (see Problem 3.11).

C. Simultaneity and Past, Present, and Future

The geometrical representation of simultaneity is simple and interesting. The two events will be simultaneous if they have the same time coordinate in a given inertial system. Thus as shown in Fig. 3.9, the two events E_1 and E_2

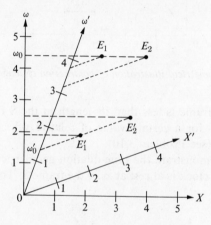

FIG. 3.9. *Geometrical illustration of simultaneity.*

that lie on a line parallel to the X axis are simultaneous at time ω_0 in the inertial S frame. In order to see if these two events are simultaneous in the S' frame, we draw lines through E_1 and E_2 that are parallel to X' and find out if they meet at the same point on the ω' axis. As is obvious from Fig. 3.9, these two events E_1 and E_2 taking place simultaneously in the S frame are observed at different times in the S' frame, and hence these are not simultaneous in the S' frame. The reverse is also true. As shown in Fig. 3.9, the events E_1' and E_2' that are simultaneous in the S' frame are obviously not simultaneous in the inertial system S.

The concepts of simultaneity discussed above can be extended further to explain what we mean by past, present, and future. In Fig. 3.10 the shaded area is bounded by the world lines of light waves. As discussed earlier all possible time axes will always lie inside the shaded cones, while all the space axes will lie outside the shaded cones. Let us consider an event taking place at P_1. If we join P_1 with the origin, the resulting line is the ω' axis. Thus the points 0 and P_1 are both located at the same space point ($x' = 0$) but are separated by a time interval equivalent to OP_1. Event P_1 always follows event at O in time, i.e., if something happens at O, it always happens at a later time at P_1. This is always true for any point lying in the upper shaded region. Thus the upper shaded region is referred to as *absolute future*.

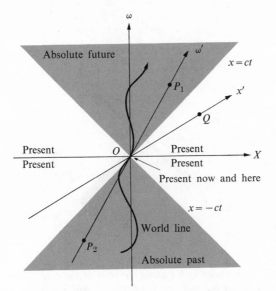

FIG. 3.10.   *Geometrical illustration of past, present, and future.*

The reverse is the case if we consider the lower shaded area in Fig. 3.10. If any event takes place at any point in this cone, say at P_2, this event will be observed at a later time at O, the origin. For both P_2 and O, $x' = 0$, but they are separated by time only. The lower shaded cone is referred to as *absolute past*, because anything happening in this cone is observed at a later time at the origin O, i.e., as far as the origin O is concerned anything that happened in the lower cone is of the past.

Thus it is possible to find events either in the upper shaded cone or lower shaded cone that are connected by time interval only and have no definite space order or separation. Such events are called *time-like* events.

Let us now consider the unshaded areas. Any point, say Q, connected to O will result in an axis for which $\omega' = 0$ and thus events occurring at O and Q will always be simultaneous, i.e., they are separated by space but are without time separation. This is the reason for calling the unshaded regions present. The events separated in these regions are called *space-like* events.

Thus, to summarize, the *world intervals* such as OQ in the present region are space-like because $\Delta S^2 = \Delta x^2 - c^2 \Delta t^2 = \Delta x^2 - 0$, which means that $\Delta S^2 > 0$; while world intervals like OP_1 or OP_2 in past and future regions are time-like because $\Delta S^2 = \Delta x^2 - c^2 \Delta t^2 = 0 - c^2 \Delta t^2$, which means that $\Delta S^2 < 0$. If we extend the above discussion to two-dimension space and one-dimension time, the regions and the light-cones are as shown in Fig. 3.11.

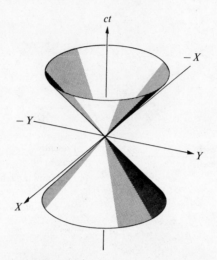

FIG. 3.11. *Light cones with t along the axis of the cones. The t axis is perpendicular to the mutually perpendicular X and Y axes.*

6. THE TWIN PARADOX[13–17]

The twin paradox, or the clock paradox, in relativity may be stated as follows. Suppose we have two clocks that are initially synchronized. One clock remains at rest while the second clock starts moving with a uniform speed, and after making a round trip is brought back to the initial position. According to the special theory of relativity, the second clock will have lost time as compared to the first, i.e., the moving clock has been running slower as compared to the first. Another way of stating this paradox is to consider twins R and M born at a given place on earth. The twin R remains on earth while twin M goes in outer space, moving with a speed close to the speed of light and returns to the initial place on earth after a certain length of time. The moving twin M aged, say, 10 years, as compared to the twin R who was at rest all the time who aged, say, 40 years. *The moving twin aged much slower and hence remained younger.* The paradox arises from the fact that according to the special theory of relativity the motion is relative and it is not possible to say who is at rest. The aging effect should be reciprocal and according to R, M should age less; while according to M, R should age less. Still the fact remains that M ages less. Our aim in this section is to give an explanation to resolve this paradox by showing that the two situations are not symmetrical and hence no reciprocal effect should be expected.

What we intend to demonstrate in the following is to show that the time elapsed according to different clocks moving in world space depends upon the actual paths. Let us consider two clocks R and M, initially synchronized, and located at O as shown in Fig. 3.12. The clock R remains at rest at O

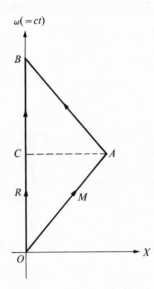

FIG. 3.12. *The paths of two clocks, one at rest and other moving, in world space.*

while the clock M starts moving with a uniform speed, say, $v = 0.8c$, to make a round trip. M then comes back to R after a certain time interval. In the world-space diagram, Fig. 3.12, R simply moves from O to B. The path of R is a world line along the time axis for which $x = 0$, while M moves out from O to A and eventually returns to B. This diagram insures that R moves only along the time axis while staying at the same spot as far as the space coordinate is concerned, while M after traveling in both space and time, returns to the initial space coordinate. Let us now calculate the time intervals elapsed on the two clocks. The relationship between the proper time interval $d\tau$ and the observed time interval dt is

$$d\tau = dt\sqrt{1 - (v^2/c^2)} = dt^2 - \sqrt{(dx^2/c^2)} \tag{3.54}$$

where $v\,dt = dx$ for the case of one dimension. Thus the time interval $\Delta\tau$ between any two events is given by

$$\Delta\tau = \int_1^2 d\tau = \int_1^2 \sqrt{dt^2 - \left(\frac{dx^2}{c^2}\right)} \tag{3.55}$$

For the straight line path from O to B in Fig. 3.12, $dx = 0$ and hence the time interval $\Delta\tau_1$ is

$$\Delta\tau_1 = \int_0^B dt = T_B - T_O = T \tag{3.56}$$

For the path OAB, the time interval $\Delta\tau_2$ is

$$\Delta\tau_2 = \int_0^A d\tau + \int_A^B d\tau = 2\int_0^A d\tau = 2\int_1^2 \sqrt{dt^2 - \left(\frac{dx^2}{c^2}\right)}$$

Because for the path OA, $dx = v\,dt$, we get

$$\Delta\tau_2 = 2\sqrt{1 - \frac{v^2}{c^2}}\int_0^A dt = 2\sqrt{1 - \frac{v^2}{c^2}}\left(\frac{T}{2}\right)$$

or

$$\Delta\tau_2 = \sqrt{1 - \frac{v^2}{c^2}}\,T \tag{3.57}$$

Comparing Eqs. (3.56) and (3.57) we find $\Delta\tau_2$ is always less than $\Delta\tau_1$:

$$\Delta\tau_2 < \Delta\tau_1 \tag{3.58}$$

Thus when the two clocks are brought together, the time intervals elapsed on the two clocks will be always different; the clock in the moving inertial frame will always have run slower.

The same results can be achieved by making a geometrical representation of the above events in the world space as shown in Fig. 3.13. At the

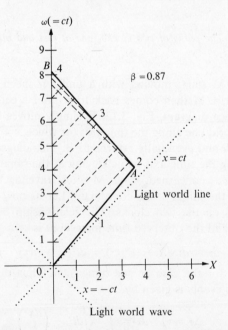

FIG. 3.13. *Geometrical illustration of the twin paradox in world space.*

start, the twins are at O. One starts moving along OB. The second starts from O along OA, reaching A he turns around, and then stops at B to be with his other twin. As is obvious from the marking on the paths, the second twin takes only four units of time as compared to eight units of the first. Note that both the twins are traveling in the region of absolute future in which the events are time-like.

The question that still remains unanswered is: Why are the two events not symmetrical so that the effect of "aging," or passing of time intervals, will be reciprocal? We may remind ourselves that the effects are reciprocal only if the two events taking place are in two inertial frames that are in relative uniform motion, so that it is hard to tell which one is moving and which one is at rest. But this is not the situation either in Fig. 3.12 or Fig. 3.13. In Fig. 3.13, one twin whose motion is described by the world line OB is always at rest and in the same inertial frame. For the other twin to start out along OA, he must accelerate before achieving uniform motion. When he reaches A, he must change his velocity to reverse his direction for the round trip. Finally, he must decelerate when he wants to stop to join the first twin at B. As a matter of fact if the second twin carried an accelerometer with him, he could tell that he was not always moving with a uniform velocity. All this implies that the second twin has been changing inertial frames, while the first twin was always in the same inertial frame. Thus the situations for the twins are not symmetrical and the asymmetry is introduced because of a changing velocity in one that does not exist in the other. It is this asymmetrical nature of the situations that exists in the case of clocks as well, and one can tell which one will run slower, or, in the case of the twins, who will age less.

We could elaborate the above effect by making numerical calculations using the Doppler effect. Suppose each twin is transmitting f pulses per unit time. Each receives the other's signal at a reduced frequency f' given by

$$\frac{f'}{f} = \left[\frac{(1 - \beta)}{(1 + \beta)}\right]^{1/2} \tag{3.59}$$

Thus as in Fig. 3.13 for the journey from O to A,

$$\frac{f'}{f} = \left[\frac{(1 - 0.87)}{(1 + 0.87)}\right]^{1/2} = \left[\frac{0.13}{1.87}\right]^{1/2} = \frac{1}{3.8}$$

which means that for every signal of the second twin, the first twin receives 3.8 signals of his own, or for every 1 year for the second twin, 3.8 years will pass for the first twin. This is as shown in Fig. 3.13. Similarly for the portion AB, we use

$$\frac{f'}{f} = \left[\frac{(1 + \beta)}{(1 - \beta)}\right]^{1/2} \tag{3.60}$$

which gives $f'/f = \dfrac{3.8}{1}$; again, for every 3.8 years for the second twin, 1 year passes for the first. Combining the two results, from O to A and from A to B, we find that for every 4 years for the second twin, about 8 years ($=$ 8.13 years) pass for the first twin, as demonstrated in Fig. 3.13.

Finally, before closing the argument we shall talk about the experimental test of the above paradox. Do the twins really differ in age after one has been traveling? The answer is yes. There is no difference between physical and biological clocks. We could have easily substituted heart beat or pulse rate as our clock. This would have meant a slowing down of the heart beat or pulse rate, and hence the process of aging would have slowed down while in motion. In order to test this experimentally, we shall have to send spacemen traveling at speeds nearing the speed of light. Such high speeds for space-craft have not been achieved. But there is an alternative experiment[15-17] that does not have this difficulty. We take a radioactive sample, say, iron-57, that at rest is emitting gamma rays at a certain rate. The emission of gamma rays may be thought of as the ticking of a clock. The source of gamma rays may be mounted on a rotor. The decay rate of this source may be measured as a function of the angular frequency of the rotor. The comparison of this emission rate with the emission rate of a source of gamma rays at rest shows that the emission rate is a function of velocity.

Of course it has been argued that the twin paradox should be treated by the general relativity theory because of the accelerations involved. We shall not go into detail but will conclude by saying that even if we use general relativity nothing new is achieved.

7. SPECIAL RELATIVITY AND ELECTROMAGNETISM[18-21]

The greatest impact of the special theory of relativity on electromagnetism is that by starting with Coulomb's law and special relativity, we can derive all the laws of electromagnetism provided we assume the experimentally verified fact that the charge of a moving particle is the same as when the particle is at rest, or the *charge is invariant* with respect to the motion or under Lorentz transformation. Thus

$$\text{electromagnetism} = \text{coulomb's law} + \text{special relativity}$$

The approach to be derived in this section can be used to show that the appearance or nonappearance of the magnetic force between two moving charged particles depends upon the reference frame of the observer and hence is a relativistic effect. For example, suppose two charges q_0 and q are moving with velocities v and u, respectively, parallel to the X axis in the inertial frame S. The charge q will feel a magnetic force $\mathbf{F_m} = q(\mathbf{u} \times \mathbf{B})$ where $\mathbf{B}$ is the field produced by q_0. Let us observe the situation from another frame, S'. If S' has a velocity u, the velocity of the charge q will be zero and hence $F'_m = 0$. If S' has a velocity v, the charge q_0 will be at rest in S' and will not produce $\mathbf{B}$, and, again, $F'_m = 0$.

From the above example, we may conclude that electric fields and magnetic fields do not exist as separate identities, but are combined into a single concept of electromagnetism. Whether an electromagnetic field will show up as a pure electric field, a pure magnetic field, or both will depend upon the reference frame. Thus it automatically leads to the conclusion that we must have relations to transform different quantities from one reference frame to another that are in relative motion. Thus we are concerned with

A.   The Transformation of Charge and Current Densities
B.   The Transformation Equations for the Fields

Just to illustrate our point we shall discuss A in some detail.

The Transformation of Charge and Current Densities

Consider a wire of cross-sectional area A_0 and length l_0 containing N electrons and lying parallel to the X' axis in the frame S'. The charge density, ρ_0, is Ne/l_0A_0, and the current density, j_0, is $\rho_0 u' = 0$, because the charges are at rest in S'. Let us observe this wire from the frame of reference S in which it is moving with a velocity u as shown in Fig. 3.14. Thus in the S frame the

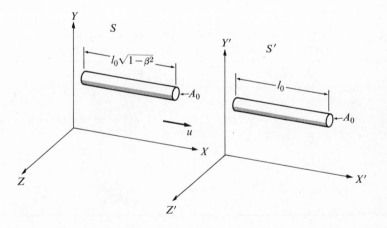

FIG. 3.14.   *A rod containing N electrons as viewed from two reference frames in relative motion.*

length of the wire will be $l_0\sqrt{1 - (u^2/c^2)}$, while the cross-sectional area A_0 will be unchanged. The charge density in S will be $\rho = Ne/(A_0l_0\sqrt{1 - (u^2/c^2)})$, and the current density, $j = \rho u$. Replacing Ne/l_0A_0 by ρ_0, we get

$$\rho = \frac{\rho_0}{\sqrt{1 - (u^2/c^2)}} \tag{3.61}$$

and

$$j = \frac{\rho_0 u}{\sqrt{1 - (u^2/c^2)}} \tag{3.62}$$

If we were dealing with the current-density vector $\mathbf{j}$ with components j_x, j_y and j_z, we would have obtained the following results.

$$j_x = \frac{\rho_0 u_x}{\sqrt{1 - (u^2/c^2)}}, \qquad j_y = \frac{\rho_0 u_y}{\sqrt{1 - (u^2/c^2)}}, \qquad j_z = \frac{\rho_0 u_z}{\sqrt{1 - (u^2/c^2)}}$$

and

$$\rho = \frac{\rho_0}{\sqrt{1 - (u^2/c^2)}} \tag{3.63}$$

There is an important significance in Eq. (3.63). Just as $c^2 t^2 - (x^2 + y^2 + z^2)$ is equal to an invariant quantity $c^2 \tau^2$, and $m^2 c^2 - (p_x^2 + p_y^2 + p_z^2)$ is equal to an invariant quantity $m_0^2 c^2$; similarly, we can treat $\rho^2 c^2 - (j_x^2 + j_y^2 + j_z^2)$ as an invariant quantity equal to $\rho_0^2 c^2$. This means that $\mathbf{j}$ and ρ transform exactly like $\mathbf{p}$ and m, and hence if in a general case, S' is moving with a velocity v along the $X - X'$ axis, the quantity (j_x, j_y, j_z, ρ) and $(j_x', j_y', j_z', \rho')$ are related by the transformation equations given in Table 3.3.

TABLE 3.3
THE RELATIVISTIC TRANSFORMATIONS FOR
CHARGE DENSITY AND CURRENT DENSITY

A. From S to S'	B. From S' to S
$j_x' = \dfrac{j_x - \rho v}{\sqrt{1 - (v^2/c^2)}}$	$j_x = \dfrac{j_x' + \rho' v}{\sqrt{1 - (v^2/c^2)}}$
$j_y' = j_y$	$j_y = j_y'$
$j_z' = j_z$	$j_z = j_z'$
$\rho' = \dfrac{\rho - v j_x/c^2}{\sqrt{1 - (v^2/c^2)}}$	$\rho = \dfrac{\rho' + v j_x'/c^2}{\sqrt{1 - (v^2/c^2)}}$

As an example of the application of the above transformation equations we consider a current-carrying wire at rest in the frame S. As shown in Fig. 3.15, the positive charges are at rest while the electrons are moving to the right with a velocity u. Thus the net charge density $\rho = \rho^+ + \rho^- = ne + (-ne) = 0$ where ne and $-ne$ are the positive and negative charge densities, respectively. The current density is $j = j^+ + j^- = \rho^+ \times 0 + \rho' u = \rho' u$. Because the charge density is zero (the wire is neutral) there is no electric field, while there is a magnetic field because the current density is not zero.

Let us view this wire from another reference frame, S', that is moving with a relative velocity v along the $X - X'$ axes. The total charge density in S' is given by

$$\rho' = \rho^{+\prime} + \rho^{-\prime} = \frac{\rho^+ - vj_x^+/c^2}{\sqrt{1 - (v^2/c^2)}} + \frac{\rho^- - vj_x^-/c^2}{\sqrt{1 - (v^2/c^2)}}$$

But $\rho^+ = +ne$, $\rho^- = -ne$, $j_x^+ = 0$, and $j_x^- = \rho^- u$, we thus obtain

$$\rho' = \frac{nevu/c^2}{\sqrt{1 - (v^2/c^2)}} \tag{3.64}$$

Thus the wire as observed in S' is not neutral but has a positive charge and thus will have an electric field in S'.

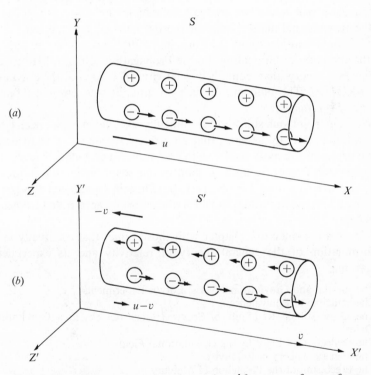

(a)

(b)

Fig. 3.15.   *A current-carrying wire as viewed from two reference frames in relative motion.*

The conclusion is that for an observer in S, the wire has $\mathbf{E} = 0$ but $\mathbf{B} \neq 0$, while for an observer in S' both $\mathbf{E} \neq 0$ and $\mathbf{B} \neq 0$.

8.   THE GENERAL THEORY OF RELATIVITY[22-26]

The development of the special theory of relativity and its eventual verification by application to different situations as seen in the previous sections should not lead us to think that there is no room for further improvements or extension. A slight reflection on classical mechanics reveals that not all problems can be tackled by the special theory of relativity. The first such problem that comes to mind is Newton's theory of gravitation, according to which the force F between two masses m_g and M is given by $F = Gm_gM/r^2$, where r is the distance between the two masses and G is the gravitational constant. The assumption in this expression is that the force between the two masses is conveyed instantly; it is a sort of action-at-a-distance that means that the force is conveyed with an infinite speed. This, of course, contradicts the special theory of relativity, according to which nothing moves with a velocity greater than the velocity of light. Also according to the law of inertia, $F = m_ia$, and it had always been assumed in Newtonian mechanics that the gravitational mass m_g and the inertial mass m_i are identical.

The above considerations led Einstein, in 1911, to publish the paper[22] "On the Influence of Gravitation on the Propagation of Light." He tried to formulate a theory that combined relativity ($F = m_ia$) with gravitation ($F = m_gGM/r^2$). The outcome of such an attempt was Einstein's famous *principle of equivalence*.

We may point out still another difficulty associated with special relativity. Special relativity assumes that all reference frames are equivalent if moving with uniform motion relative to each other. It excludes all accelerated (or noninertial) frames from its domain. In this sense the inertial frames are unique—a contradiction! Finally, in 1916, Einstein formulated the general theory of relativity, according to which all uniformly accelerated frames are equivalent.

We shall conclude this chapter with those topics that eventually led to the formulation of the general theory of relativity and its experimental verification.

A. The Inertial and Gravitational Mass, Eötvös Experiments
B. The Principle of Equivalence
C. The Gravitational Red-Shift of Spectral Lines (Clocks in a Gravitational Field)
D. The Deflection of Light by the Gravitational Field
E. The General Theory of Relativity
F. The Precession of the Perihelion of Mercury

A. **The Inertial and Gravitational Mass, Eötvös Experiment**[26-29]

The developments of most theories are based on some fundamental experiments. For example, the special theory of relativity is built on the Michelson-Morley experiments. Similarly, the equivalence principle of general relativity is based on the results of the Eötvös experiment[26], the purpose of which was to show the equivalence between the inertial mass m_i (used in the formula $F = m_ia$) and the gravitational mass m_g (used in the expression $F = m_gGM/r^2$). Thus when gravitation acts on a body, it acts on the gravitational mass, while a force produces an acceleration on the inertial mass. Suppose two bodies falling under gravitation have accelerations a_1, and a_2, then

$$F_1 = m_{i1}a_1 = m_{g1}\frac{GM}{r_e} \simeq m_{g1}g \qquad (3.65)$$

$$F_2 = m_{i2}a_2 = m_{g2}\frac{GM}{r_e} \simeq m_{g2}g \qquad (3.66)$$

where g is the acceleration due to gravity and r_e and M are the radius and mass, respectively, of the earth. Dividing the two equations and rearranging, we get,

$$\frac{m_{i1}}{m_{g1}}\left(\frac{a_1}{a_2}\right) = \frac{m_{i2}}{m_{g2}} \qquad (3.67)$$

Thus if we could show that $a_1 = a_2$, we would have proved the equivalence between the inertial mass and the gravitational mass. The accuracy of this equivalence depends upon the accurate measurements of the ratio a_1/a_2.

In 1700, when Newton stated his laws of motion, he assumed the equivalence of inertial and gravitational mass. Later by making measurements of a_1/a_2, Newton showed that if there were a difference between m_i and m_g of an object, it was less than one part in 1,000.

A different type of experiment to prove the equivalence was performed by Bessel. If we assume that m_i is different from m_g, the time period T of a pendulum should be

$$T = 2\pi \sqrt{\frac{l}{g}\frac{m_i}{m_g}}$$

where l is the length of the pendulum. By measuring periods of pendulums made of different materials, Bessel concluded that if there were any difference between m_i and m_g, it was less than 1 part in 6×10^4.

Finally, the results of more sensitive and precise experiments were reported by R. V. Eötvös[26] in 1922. Suppose a pendulum is hanging on the surface of the earth, as shown in Fig. 3.16, at a latitude of 45°. There are two forces acting upon it, $m_i\omega^2 r_e$ (the centrifugal force) and $m_g g$ (the gravitational force). The pendulum does not point towards the center of the earth but in the direction of the resultant of these two forces. The angle θ between the direction of the pendulum and the direction of the center of the earth is a function of (m_i/m_g). Experiments made with eight different materials and at different places on the surface of the earth indicated that if there is any difference between m_i and m_g, it is less than one part in 2×10^8. Eötvös' experiments have been redone by Dicke[27,28] using modern techniques, and the results indicate that the difference is less than one part in 10^{10}.

B. The Principle of Equivalence

The principle of equivalence states: *The effects produced by the gravitational field are identical to that produced by the acceleration, and there is no way of distinguishing one from the other; each is fully equivalent to the other.*

We shall illustrate this statement with a few simple examples. Suppose we have two reference frames. In one frame there is a uniform gravitational field and no acceleration; it is an inertial frame. In the other frame there is

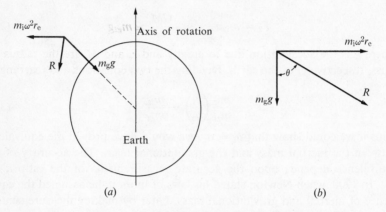

(a) (b)

FIG. 3.16. *As illustrated, the angle* θ *between the pendulum (along the resultant R) and the direction of the center of earth is a function of* (m_i/m_g).

no gravitational field but it is accelerated with respect to the first; it is not an inertial frame. The two reference frames are identical, or physically equivalent, in the sense that the experiments performed under similar conditions in these two frames yield identical results. To be more specific, suppose an astronaut is sitting in his spaceship on earth. Due to gravitation he feels a force $F = mg$, where m is his mass. Now the astronaut leaves the earth and moves into outer space where the rocket is moving with an acceleration $\mathbf{a} = -\mathbf{g}$. The astronaut still feels the same force and obtains the same results for any experiment that he performs while at rest on earth or in accelerated motion in outer space.

As another example, suppose we are standing in an elevator and we weigh two masses with spring balances. Let these weights be m_{1g} and m_{2g} while the elevator is at rest. Let us repeat the experiment when the elevator is accelerated downward with an acceleration $a = g/2$. We find that the two masses weigh $m_1 g/2$ and $m_2 g/2$. According to the principle of equivalence, if instead of accelerating the elevator, (i) we took these masses to outer space in a rocket that is moving with an acceleration $a = g/2$ or (ii) we took the masses to another planet where the acceleration due to gravity was one-half of that on the earth; the masses would weigh the same, $m_1 g/2 = m_2 g/2$.

Thus accelerated reference frames and reference frames in a gravitational field are completely equivalent. According to Einstein, it follows from the principle of equivalence that *there is no absolute accelerated frame of refer-*

ence, as in special relativity there is no absolute velocity frame. The motion of any accelerated frame is relative.

We may ask still another interesting question at this stage. If it is not possible to distinguish between gravitation and acceleration, is it possible to transform away all gravitation by going into a proper accelerated reference frame? The answer to this question, in general, is no. It is possible to achieve this in a limited region of space but not everywhere. An example of this is that of a satellite going around the earth in a circular (or elliptic) orbit. Let M be the mass of the earth and m of the satellite. If the angular velocity ω of the satellite system is such that

$$F = ma = m\omega^2 r = m\,\frac{GM}{r}$$

or

$$a = \omega^2 r = \frac{GM}{r^2} \tag{3.68}$$

where r is the distance from the center of the earth to the satellite. Thus inside the satellite there is no gravitation, and the objects released inside will not fall but will just appear to float in space. The astronaut inside such an orbiting object experiences weightlessness.

There are many situations that can be analyzed by combining the principle of equivalence with special relativity without going into general relativity as we shall show now.

C. The Gravitational Red-Shift of Spectral Lines (Clocks in a Gravitational Field)

Consider two observers E and R positioned a distance d apart in a frame S_g that is placed in a uniform gravitational field g, as shown in Fig. 3.17(a). The situation shown in Fig. 3.17(b) has no gravitational field g, but the reference frame S_i is moving with a uniform acceleration $\mathbf{a} = \mathbf{g}$ in the direction shown. From the equivalence principle, the reference frames S_g and S_i are identical.

Suppose there takes place an atomic transition at E, and light of frequency ν_0 is emitted in the gravitational field g. We would like to know the frequency of this light when it is received at R. Because Fig. 3.17(b) is equivalent to the part (a), we shall be using the (b) part to analyze this situation. Let us assume that both observers start from rest when the light signal is emitted at E. The time t taken by the signal to travel from E to R is $t = d/c$. In this time interval, due to the acceleration, both the observers acquire a velocity $v = v_0 + at = 0 + gd/c = gd/c$. When the observer R receives the signal he will be moving away from the source with a velocity $v = gd/c$, and he will see a red shift—the wavelength will be shifted toward the red. Accord-

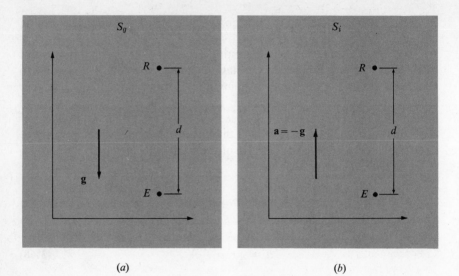

(a)   (b)

FIG. 3.17.   *The reference frame S_g in the gravitational field* **g** *is equiva-*
lent to the reference frame S_i that is moving with an acceleration **a** $= -$**g**.

ing to the Doppler principle, Eq. (3.36), the frequency ν of the light received
by R is given by

$$\nu = \nu_0 \sqrt{\frac{1 - \beta}{1 + \beta}} \tag{3.69}$$

Expanding the expressions under the radical sign, we get

$$\nu = \nu_0(1 - \beta + 3/4\beta^2 + \ldots) \tag{3.70}$$

Neglecting the higher order terms and noting that $\beta = v/c = gd/c^2$, we have

$$\nu \cong \nu_0\left(1 - \frac{gd}{c^2}\right) \tag{3.71}$$

$\nu < \nu_0$ or $\lambda > \lambda_0$, and hence the shift is toward the red. Thus we conclude
from Eq. (3.71) that a light signal in passing up through the gravitational
field has become redder. (Note that if the light signal were falling through
the gravitational field it would gain energy, its frequency would become
higher and hence the shift would be toward the blue.)

Pound and Rebka[29], in 1960, confirmed the above predictions by using
a very sensitive apparatus because the frequency change $\Delta\nu = \nu - \nu_0$ is very
small. (The Mössbauer effect discussed in Chapter XIII enables us to make
such sensitive measurements.) They used the 74-feet-high Jefferson tower at
Harvard in order for the light to travel in a uniform gravitational field. The
change expected as calculated is

$$\frac{\Delta\nu}{\nu_0} = \frac{gd}{c^2} = \frac{(980 \text{ cm/sec}^2)(2256 \text{ cm})}{(3 \times 10^{10} \text{ cm/sec})^2} \simeq 2.5 \times 10^{-15}$$

while the comparison with the experiment yielded

$$\frac{(\Delta\nu) \text{ expt.}}{(\Delta\nu) \text{ cal.}} = 1.05 \pm 0.10$$

In 1965, Pound and Snider[30] refined the above experiment and found the following comparison

$$\frac{(\Delta\nu) \text{ expt.}}{(\Delta\nu) \text{ cal.}} = 0.9990 \pm 0.0076$$

The above type of shift (not to be confused with the Doppler effect due to receding or approaching stars) is produced in the spectra of light received from a certain type of stars known as white dwarfs. The densities of these stars are about 10,000 times as high as ordinary matter. Light escaping from these stars has to go through the gravitational field, and hence the wavelengths are shifted when this light is received on earth as compared with the spectra emitted from the same kinds of atoms of these stars. This change in frequency can be calculated by making use of the expression for the gravitational potential energy $V = -(GM_s m/r_s)$, where M_s and r_s are the mass and the radius of the star, respectively; and m is the mass of the light signal equal to E_s/c^2 where E_s is the energy of the signal. Note that a change in V leads to a change in E and hence a change in ν_0. Thus for light leaving a star, we find

$$\nu = \nu_0\left(1 - \frac{GM_s}{c^2 r_s}\right) \qquad (3.72)$$

There is some evidence as to the gravitational red shift of light from these stars.

If the rate of emission (the frequency or the time period) is used as a clock, the above discussion will imply a slowing down of clocks. For example, because $T = 1/\nu$ and $T_0 = 1/\nu_0$, Eq. (3.71) may be written as

$$T \cong T_0(1 + gd/c^2) \qquad (3.73)$$

D. The Deflection of Light by the Gravitational Field

Let us regard each wave (or quantum; see Chapter V) in a signal of light as having a mass m. (It looks surprising to assign mass to a light signal, but we shall show in Chapter V that $m = h\nu/c^2$ where ν is the frequency, h is a constant, and c is the velocity of light.) Our aim is to calculate the deflection of this mass from its original path as it passes through the gravitational field of a planet. To be more specific we shall limit ourselves to the deflection by the sun of a light beam coming from a star. Classically, according to Soldner, we can calculate the deflection in the following manner.

Consider a light signal of mass m at point P that grazes the surface of the sun as shown in Fig. 3.18. At any instant let the distance of m from the center of the sun be r and the radius of the sun be R_s. Thus the force F acting on m at any instant is

$$F = \frac{GM_s m}{(R_s \sec \theta)^2} \tag{3.74}$$

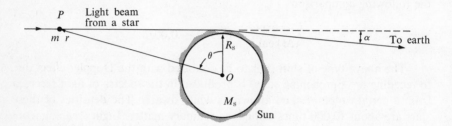

FIG. 3.18. *Deflection of a light beam from a star by the gravitational field of the sun.*

while the component of F perpendicular to the direction of motion, the transverse component, is given by

$$F_t = F \cos \theta = \frac{GM_s m}{(R_s \sec \theta)^2}$$

Using the expression $dP_t = F_t\, dt$, where P_t is the change in transverse momentum, dt is the time interval given by $dt = d(x/c)$, and $x = R_s \tan \theta$, we obtain the total change in the transverse momentum to be

$$P_t = \int dP_t = \int F \cos \theta\, dt = \frac{GM_s m}{cR_s} \int_{\theta = -\frac{\pi}{2}}^{\frac{\pi}{2}} \cos \theta\, d\theta = \frac{2GM_s m}{cR_s} \tag{3.75}$$

But the longitudinal $P = mc$ (= mass × velocity). Hence the angle α is given by

$$\alpha = \frac{P_t}{P} = \frac{\dfrac{2GM_s m}{cR_s}}{mc} = \frac{2GM_s}{c^2 R_s} \text{ radians} \tag{3.76}$$

The above classical calculations by Soldner yield a value of $\alpha = 0.87$ seconds of arc. This deflection was also calculated by Einstein as soon as he developed his general theory of relativity, and the value of α so obtained agreed with the classical value. Later, with further developments, it was found that the general theory yields a value of $\alpha = 1.75$ seconds of arc, or twice as large as the classical value. The experiment to measure the value of α is a difficult one, which we shall briefly outline here.

The experimental procedure consists in photographing a star field with the sun in the center, and then some time later ($\approx$ 6 months) photographing the same star field again without the sun. By comparing the two photographs, the displacement of the apparent position of a star can be measured. In order to photograph the star field with the sun present, we must have a total eclipse so that the stars are visible. But eclipses take place only once in several years and last only up to six or seven minutes, and the photographs must be taken within this limited time. The photographs taken during the eclipse must be compared with the same field at night in the absence of the sun. The second photograph must be taken with the same equipment six months later at night so that the star is at the same place. Because of the very small value of the displacement to be measured, the magnification of the instrument must remain constant during this interval. In order to measure within 0.1 seconds of arc, the magnification must be constant to about one part in 10^4.

In the interval between 1919 and 1969, the experiment has been performed 12 times and the measured values of α have been found to vary between 1.5 and 2.71 seconds of arc, with most of them clustering between 1.7 and 1.8. One cannot say with certainty that this is the final confirmation of the general theory.

E. The General Theory of Relativity

Starting with the equivalence principle as stated by Einstein, we have calculated the gravitational red shift of spectral lines and deflection of light by the gravitational field. Furthermore, it is quite obvious that the special theory of relativity is applicable only in the absence of a gravitational field. Thus there is a need for a theory that is applicable to both inertial (uniform motion) systems and noninertial (accelerated motion) systems equally well. Such a theory, the general theory of relativity was postulated by Einstein[31,32] in 1916. The general theory not only takes into account the equivalence principle, but also extends it to nonuniform (inhomogeneous) gravitational fields. Because the mathematical formulation of general relativity is complex and outside the limits of this book, we shall only briefly mention some features of it.

A nonuniform gravitational field may be transformed into an equivalent accelerated system by replacing each field point in the nonuniform gravitational field by a different accelerated frame at that point. These different accelerated frames are the local frames. In each of these local frames the special theory of relativity is applicable, and the ground invariant G or the geometrical line element S^2 is given by

$$G = S^2 = x^2 + y^2 + z^2 - c^2t^2 \qquad (3.77)$$

is invariant under Lorentz transformation. In order to describe a line element S^2 in general relativity (i.e., a line element in curved space) one makes use of Gaussian coordinates, and the relativistic line element in four-space is given by (Pythagorean theorem for 4-dimensional world)

$$G = S^2 = g_{11}x^2 + g_{22}y^2 + g_{33}z^2 + g_{44}t^2 + 2g_{12}xy + 2g_{13}xz$$
$$+ 2g_{14}xt + 2g_{23}yz + 2g_{24}yt + 2g_{34}zt \qquad (3.78)$$

The factors g_{11}, g_{22}, . . . , g_{34} are called the *factors of measure determination*. The values of the *gs* depend on the nature of the distribution of matter that results in the nonuniform gravitational field, i.e., the *gs* determine the *metric*, or *the gravitational field*. For example, in a gravitational-field free-space,

$$g_{11} = g_{22} = g_{33} = 1, \qquad g_{44} = -c^2$$
$$g_{12} = g_{13} = \ldots = g_{34} = 0 \tag{3.79}$$

and Eq. (3.78) reduces to Eq. (3.77) of the special theory of relativity. On the other hand, if all the *g*'s have nonzero values, the invariant is in the general theory. Hence the task of the general theory of relativity is to determine these factors for different situations. The purpose of this mathematical formalism is two-fold. First, the transformations are such that all observers are equivalent and hence the laws of physics are invariant. Second, it leads to the formalization of gravitation theory in which the gravitational effects propagate with the speed of light.

Besides Einstein's theory, there are other theories of gravitation that have developed in recent years[33]. All these theories are not easy to test experimentally. Of these Einstein's general theory is the simplest and has been tested experimentally with a reasonable accuracy. The tests of the general theory lie in the predicted effects in (a) the gravitational red shift, (b) the deflection of light in a gravitational field, and (c) the precession of the perihelion of Mercury.

The effects (a) and (b) have already been discussed, while (c) will be discussed in the following part. We may point out that all three effects may be calculated mathematically from general relativity[33] but we shall not go into such details.

F. The Precession of the Perihelion of Mercury

We are familiar with the application of Newton's laws to the solar system. If Einstein's general theory is applied, the result is that we get the same orbits but with higher accuracy. The test lies in calculating the deviations from Newton's laws and comparing with the experimentally measured values. Figure 3.19 shows a planet moving in a precessing orbit about a fixed center of force. Because of the presence of other planets, the perihelion (or the point of closest approach) shifts by an angle θ after each revolution as shown. In the case of the planet Mercury orbiting the sun, the perturbing effect of the planet Venus produces the precession of the Mercury orbit. The use of Newtonian mechanics results in a predicted precession of 5557.2 seconds of arc per century. The experimentally measured value is 5599.7 ± seconds of arc per century. This results in an anomalous precession of $\sim$43 seconds of arc per century.

Einstein, by making use of his general theory of relativity, showed that there is an added precession of 43 seconds of arc per century. G. M.

Clemence[23] has concluded that the measured value of the anomalous precession is 42.56 ± 0.94, while the general theory of relativity predicts a value of 43.03 ± 0.03 seconds of arc per century.

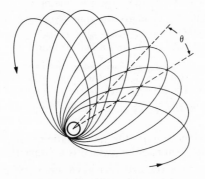

FIG. 3.19. *The precession of the perihelion of the orbit of a body about a fixed center of force. The shift in the perihelion is measured by the angle θ.*

PROBLEMS

1. Total momentum of a system of particles in an inertial frame is $\Sigma\mathbf{p}$, while the total relativistic energy is ΣE. Show that the velocity of the center-of-mass is $c^2\Sigma\mathbf{p}/\Sigma E$.

2. Proton-antiproton $(p - \bar{p})$ pairs were produced at the Berkeley Bevatron by bombarding proton target with high energy protons by the following equation (called nuclear reaction)

$$p + p + K \rightarrow p + p + (p + \bar{p})$$

   where K is the kinetic energy of the bombarding proton. If the rest mass energies of the proton and antiproton are each $M_0c^2 (= 938$ MeV), what is the value of K for proton-antiproton pair production?

3. The rest mass energy and mean life of Σ^+ (sigma plus) particle in its own reference frame are 1,190 MeV and 0.80×10^{-10} sec, respectively. Calculate the kinetic energy of this particle from the Laboratory frame of reference in which it seems to travel 1.1 mm before disintegrating.

4. Calculate the longitudinal and transverse Doppler shifts for **(a)** $\beta = 1/4$, **(b)** $\beta = 1/2$, and **(c)** $\beta = 3/4$.

5. A light in a spaceship that is receding from the earth at a speed of $0.25c$ appears yellow to the astronaut. What is the color of the light as seen from the earth? If the light source were fixed on earth and its color were yellow, what would be the color as seen from the spaceship?

6. Calculate the wavelength shift in the relativistic Doppler effect for the sodium D lines (5890 Å) emitted from a star receding from the earth with a relative velocity of $1/10c$. How does this compare with the classical result?

7. Calculate the Doppler shift for motion (a) in the forward direction, and (b) in the backward direction. Show that the average of these two results in the second-order Doppler shift.

8. Calculate the first- and second-order Doppler shifts for atoms having an energy of 5000 eV and emitting a spectral line of wavelength 6000 Å.

9. According to Euclidean geometry the shortest distance between two points is a straight line. In Minkowski space what is the relation between a straight world line between two events and a curved world line connecting the same two events?

10. If a meter rod is at rest in S' frame, show by geometrical construction that it looks contracted to the observer in S frame.

11. Demonstrate geometrically the time dilation reciprocal to the one shown in Fig. 3.8.

12. Is there any relation between the time dilation (which is symmetrical and reciprocal) and the twin-paradox (which is asymmetric and nonreciprocal)?

13. Twins A and B are born on earth. A stays at home while B travels to a planet 150 light years away at a speed of $0.9c$ and then returns to earth. What are the ages of the two after B's return?

14. Twins A and B are born on earth. Immediately after the birth, A travels with a velocity $0.8c$ to a planet X which is 100 light years away, while B travels with a velocity $0.9c$ to a planet Y which is 150 light years away. After arriving at their respective planets, they reverse their direction and travel towards the earth. What are the ages of A and B when they arrive at the earth?

15. Show that the angle ϕ between the direction of the plumb bob and the direction to the center of the earth is given by

$$\phi = \frac{\omega^2 R \sin \lambda \cos \lambda}{g - \omega^2 R \cos^2 \lambda}$$

where λ is the latitude. Calculate ϕ for a latitude of $45°$.

16. "We conclude that a balance clock at the equator must go more slowly, by a very small amount, than a precisely similar clock situated at one of the poles under otherwise uniform conditions." From Einstein (1905). Calculate the difference in the clocks.

17. Calculate the fractional change in wavelength of a photon falling in the gravitational field of the earth through (a) 50 ft., (b) 100 ft., (c) 150 ft.

18. The gravitational red-shift from a particular star equals to the Doppler shift at 5×10^6 cm/sec. If the mass of this star is 2×10^{23} gm., what is its density?

19. Show that for light escaping from the gravitational field of a celestial body, the fractional change in wavelength is $\Delta\lambda/\lambda = GM/Rc^2$. If the surface of the celestial body has constant g, what should be the distance through which the light should rise in this uniform field so that it will suffer the same red-shift as produced by escape from the gravitational field?

20. In general relativity $\alpha \,(= GM/c^2)$ is called the gravitational radius of the mass. (a) Show that α has dimensions of length. (b) If the gravitational energy were equal to the rest energy, show that the radius will be given by a similar expression.

REFERENCES

1. Rosser, W. G. V., *Contemp. Physics*, 1, 453, (1960).
2. Ives, H. E., and G. R. Stilwell, *J. Opt. Soc. Am.*, 28, 215, (1938).
3. Ives, H. E., and G. R. Stilwell, *J. Opt. Soc. Am.*, 31, 369, (1941).
4. Mandelberg and Witten, *J. Opt. Soc. Am.*, 52, 529, (1962).
5. Otting, G., *Z. Phys.*, 40, 681, (1939).
6. Kündig, W., *Phys. Rev.*, 129, 2371, (1963).
7. Bucherer, A. H., *Ann. Physik*, 28, 513, (1909).
8. Bertozzi, W., *Am. J. Phys.*, 32, 551, (1964).
9. Fleischmann, R., and R. Kollath, *Zeit. fur Physik*, 134, 526, (1953).
10. Kollath, R., and D. Menzel, *Zeit. fur Physik*, 134, 530, (1953).
11. Frisch, D. H., and J. H. Smith, *Am. J. Phys.*, 31, 342, (1963).
12. Minkowski, H., "Space and Time" in *The Principle of Relativity*, New York: Dover Publications, 1923.
13. Frisch, O. R., *Contemp. Physics*, 3, 194, (1962).
14. Darwin, C. G., *Nature*, 180, 967, (1957).
15. Hay, J. J., J. P. Schiffer, T. E. Cranshaw, and P. A. Egelstaff, *Phys. Rev. Letters*, 4, 165, (1960).
16. Bronowski, J., "The Clock Paradox," *Sci. Am.*, (Feb. 1963).
17. Kündig, W., *Phys. Rev.*, 129, 2371, (1963).
18. Resnick, R., *Introduction to Special Relativity*, Chap. IV, New York: John Wiley & Sons, 1968.
19. French, A. P., *Special Relativity*, Chap. VIII (The M. I. T. Introductory Physics Series) Boston: 1968.
20. Blokhintsev, D. I., *Soviet Phys. Usp.*, 9 (3), 405, (1966).
21. Purcell, E. M., *Electricity and Magnetism*, New York: McGraw-Hill, 1965.
22. Einstein, A., *Ann. Phys.*, 49, 769, (1916); Einstein, A., *The Special and General Theory*, New York: Crown Publishers, 1961.
23. Clemence, G. M., *Revs. Mod. Phys.*, XIX, No. 4, 361, (1947).
24. Witten, L., ed., *Gravitation: An Introduction to Current Research*, New York: John Wiley & Sons, 1962.
25. Dicke, R. H., *The Theoretical Significance of Experimental Relativity*, New York: Gordon and Breach, 1964.
26. Eötvös, R. V., D. Pekar, and E. Fekete, *Ann. Physik*, LXVIII, 11, (1922).
27. Dicke, R. H., *Sci. Am.*, (Dec. 1961).
28. Dicke, R. H., *Am. J. Phys.*, 35, 559, (1967).
29. Pound, R. V., and G. A. Rebka, Jr., *Phys. Rev. Letters*, IV, 337, (1960).
30. Pound, R. V., and J. L. Snider, *Phys. Rev.*, 140, B-788, (1965).
31. Einstein, A., *Ann. Phys.*, 49, 769, (1916); also Einstein, A., and others, *The Principle of Relativity*, New York: Dover Publications, 1923.

32. Einstein, A., *The Special and General Theory*, New York: Crown Publishers, 1961.

33. Ney, E. P., *Electromagnetism and Relativity*, Chap. 4, New York: Harper and Row, 1962.

SUGGESTIONS FOR FURTHER READING

1. Ney, E. P., *Electromagnetism and Relativity*, New York: Harper and Row, 1962.

2. Resnick, R., *Introduction to Special Relativity*, New York: John Wiley & Sons, 1968.

3. Bergmann, P. G., *Introduction to the Theory of Relativity*, Englewood Cliffs, N. J.: Prentice Hall, 1942.

4. Anderson, J. L., *Principles of Relativity*, New York: Academic Press, 1967.

5. Schwartz, H. M., *Introduction to Special Relativity*, New York: McGraw-Hill, 1968.

6. Panofsky, W., and W. Phillips, *Classical Electricity and Magnetism*, Chaps. 14–17. Reading, Mass.: Addison-Wesley, 1955.

7. McVittie, G. C., *General Relativity and Cosmology*, New York: Wiley, 1956.

8. Lorentz, H. A., A. Einstein, H. Minkowski, and H. Weyl, *The Principle of Relativity*, London: Methaen, 1923, and Dover Publications (paperbound).

9. Einstein, A., *The Meaning of Relativity*, Princeton, N. J.: Princeton University Press, 1946.

10. Taylor, J. G., "Particles Faster than Light," *Sci. Am.*, **43**, (Sept. 1969).

IV

Black-Body Radiation

1. THERMAL RADIATION

There are many experimental observations that can be derived theoretically by making use of the laws and methods of thermodynamics. By the close of the nineteenth century there came into existence certain aspects of thermal radiation, e.g., black-body radiation, for which classical theory could not account. This led Planck in 1901 to introduce a new concept, the quantization of energy, and this initiated the investigation of quantum theory. It is the importance of quantum theory that justifies the discussion of thermal radiation to some length in this book. We shall try to outline the reasoning by which the idea of quantization was formulated.

All substances above absolute-zero temperature radiate electromagnetic waves. According to classical theory a body above absolute zero is in a state of thermal agitation, which results in the acceleration of the charges in the body. These accelerated charges emit radiation. When a block of metal, say copper or iron, is heated, we can always feel the heat radiation, and there is no noticeable change in the physical appearance of the object below 1000°K. The quality and quantity of radiation is independent of the nature of the substance and is a function of the temperature only. At about 1000°K the metal appears with a dull-red glow. As the temperature rises, the color slowly changes to orange (at ~1500°K), then to yellow (at ~2000°K), finally becoming white at about 3000°K. Any further rise in the temperature only increases the intensity of the radiation without causing any noticeable change in the color of the body.

The spectrum of white light emitted from a body at $\sim$3000°K can be viewed by means of an experimental arrangement shown in Fig. 4.1. The

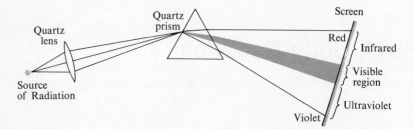

FIG. 4.1. *An experimental arrangement for observing the spectrum of radiation emitted from a body at a very high temperature* ($\sim$3000°K).

light from a heated source, such as a carbon-arc lamp, is caused to pass through a quartz lens and a prism, and the dispersed light is received on a screen. In addition to the visible light, the spectrum consists of ultraviolet and infrared radiations as shown in the figure. The ultraviolet radiation region may be detected by means of a fluorescent screen (ultraviolet light produces bright fluorescence) or by means of a photographic plate. The infrared radiation region may be detected by means of a group of thermo-couples (a thermopile). As the thermopile is moved across the spectrum, the reading of an ammeter will be a maximum in the middle of the infrared region.

Let dE_λ represent the amount of radiation energy of wavelengths between λ and $\lambda + d\lambda$ emitted per second. A plot of $dE_\lambda/d\lambda$ versus λ is said to represent the spectrum of the radiation. A typical spectrum of a heated body is shown in Fig. 4.2. The visible portion covers a very small region of wavelengths. The approximate extremes of the radiation are "very-hard" gamma rays with $\lambda \simeq 10^{-12}$ cm and long radio waves with $\lambda \simeq 10^{+6}$ cm. The visible region lies somewhere in the middle of the range on the logarithmic scale (λ from 4.5×10^{-5} cm to 7×10^{-5} cm). The spectrum of a heated solid covers from $\lambda \sim 8 \times 10^{-7}$ cm to $\lambda \sim 10^{-2}$ cm, as shown in Fig. 4.2, the intensity being very low for $\lambda > 10^{-3}$ cm.

We shall now proceed to state a few definitions and laws concerning thermal radiation, followed by the discussion of black-body radiation, which will show how classical theory failed to explain the black-body spectrum.

2. EMISSION AND ABSORPTION OF RADIATION

Several theories of heat radiation existed at different times, the most common one being the concept of cold and hot radiation. Eventually a generally acceptable explanation called the theory of exchanges was put forward by Prevost[1] in 1792. According to this theory, a body emits radiation energy at all temperatures, and the amount of radiation increases with temperature. The body while emitting radiation is also receiving radiation from other bodies. The net result is the difference between the amount emitted and the amount received. When a body remains at a fixed temperature, in thermal equilibrium, the body emits as much radiation energy as it receives from its surroundings.

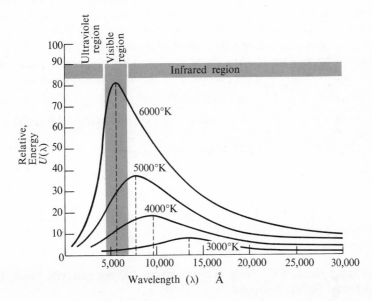

Fig. 4.2.   *A typical spectrum of a heated body at different temperatures. This spectrum is independent of the material of the body and depends only on the temperature.*

The rate at which a body emits or absorbs radiation energy at a given temperature depends upon the nature of the surface. For example, given two spheres of the same metal, one painted black and the other white, even though at the same temperature, the black sphere will emit more radiation than the white. We define the *emissivity*, *e*, (or emissive power) for a surface as the thermal radiant energy emitted from a unit area of the surface per second. The *absorptivity*, *a*, (or absorption coefficient) is defined as the ratio of the total thermal energy absorbed by the surface to the total thermal energy incident upon it. The emissivity and absorptivity of the bodies varies between 0 and 1. A body that has a fully absorbing surface, for which $a = 1$, is called a *black-body*. For all other surfaces *a* is less than 1.

It is a matter of common experience that objects that are good emitters of thermal radiation are also good absorbers of thermal radiation. This has been theoretically proved and is known as *Kirchoff's law of radiation*[2]; according to this law, for a given body

$$e = a \qquad (4.1)$$

Experiments had shown that the rate of cooling of a hot body is a function of the difference in the temperatures of the body and its surroundings. This is known as *Newton's law of cooling*[3]. After performing extensive experiments, Josef Stefan[4] in 1879 found a relation between the radiant heat energy E emitted by a black-body and its temperature. The same relation was later theoretically derived by Ludwig Boltzmann[5]. This theoretically and experimentally proven relation is known as the *Stefan-Boltzmann law* and may be stated as follows: If a black-body at absolute temperature T is surrounded by another black-body at absolute-zero temperature, the energy lost per square centimeter per second E by the first body is given by

$$E = \sigma T^4 \qquad (4.2)$$

where σ is known as the *Stefan constant*, its experimentally determined value being[6]

$$\sigma = 5.670 \times 10^{-5} \text{ ergs/sec/cm}^2/^\circ\text{K}^4$$

$$\sigma = 1.36 \times 10^{-12} \text{ cals/sec/cm}^2/^\circ\text{K}^4$$

$$\sigma = 5.67 \times 10^{-8} \text{ joul/sec/m}^2/^\circ\text{K}^4$$

If the surrounding body is at a temperature T_0 degrees absolute, instead of being at absolute zero, then Eq. (4.2) takes the following form

$$E = \sigma(T^4 - T_0^4) \qquad (4.3)$$

On the other hand, if the body at temperature T is not perfectly black, then Eq. (4.2) and Eq. (4.3) become

$$E = e\sigma T^4 \qquad (4.4)$$

and

$$E = e\sigma(T^4 - T_0^4)$$

where e is the emissitivity of the body.

3. THE BLACK-BODY SPECTRUM

The black-body is defined as a body that absorbs all the radiation that is incident on it, or one for which $a = 1$. In practice, a surface painted with lampblack absorbs about 97% of the radiant heat falling on it and may be considered a black body. There is, however, another way of achieving a black body. Consider an object with a black-painted cavity that is connected to the outside of the object through a very small hole, as shown in Fig. 4.3. Any radiation incident on the hole from the exterior upon once entering the cavity will be reflected back and forth from the interior walls of the cavity with practically no chance of getting outside; in this case the radiation will be completely absorbed. Such a cavity is classed as a black body. Now, if we heat this cavity by heating the whole body to a certain temperature and observe the radiation coming out of the hole, this radiation will have all the characteristics of the radiation from a black body at the same temperature. The radiation from a black body may be analyzed by means of an arrangement shown in Fig. 4.1.

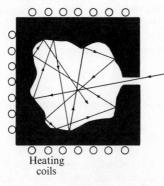

Heating
coils

FIG. 4.3. *An object with a black-painted cavity that has a narrow opening is almost a true black body.*

Detailed investigations of the spectrum of black-body radiation were made by Lummer and Pringsheim[7] (1899). The quantity $E_T(\lambda)$, defined as the energy of wavelength λ emitted per second from 1 square centimeter of surface at temperature T, was plotted against λ. Figure 4.4(a) shows the plots

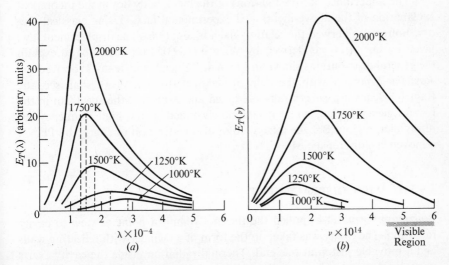

FIG. 4.4. (a) *Plots of $E_T(\lambda)$ versus λ for different values of T.* (b) *Plots of $E_T(\nu)$ versus ν for different values of T.*

of $E_T(\lambda)$ versus λ for different values of T. Figure 4.4(b) shows the plots of $E_T(\nu)$ versus ν for different values of T. We shall summarize below some of the outstanding features of these plots.

(a) The radiation spectrum of the black body is independent of type of material of which it is made.

(b) For a fixed temperature T, the radiant energy $E_T(\lambda)\, d\lambda$ emitted in the small wavelength range $d\lambda$ between λ and $\lambda + d\lambda$ first increases with decreasing wavelength (or increasing frequency), reaches a maximum, and then decreases with decreasing wavelength.

(c) At a particular wavelength or frequency, the value of $E_T(\lambda)\, d\lambda$ increases with temperature T, and hence the total energy (area under the curve in Fig. 4.4),

$$E_T = \int_0^\infty E_T(\lambda)\, d\lambda \tag{4.5}$$

increases with temperature T. This is in accord with the Stefan-Boltzmann law[8]:

$$E_T = \int_0^\infty E_T(\lambda)\, d\lambda = \sigma T^4 \tag{4.6}$$

(d) The maximum of the curve, which represents the wavelength that carries the maximum energy at a given temperature, shifts toward shorter wavelengths (or higher frequencies) as the temperature of the black body increases. This is obvious from the fact that when an object is heated, it changes its color from red (lower frequency) to blue (higher frequency) with increasing temperature, which implies that the wavelength λ_m corresponding to a maximum in the curve is inversely proportional to the temperature:

$$\lambda_m T = \text{constant} \tag{4.7}$$

This relation is called *Wien's displacement law*.

The importance of investigations of the black body lies in the theoretical explanation of the above-mentioned experimental facts. Using classical theory, Boltzmann derived the relation given by Eq. (4.6). The displacement law, given by Eq. (4.7) was derived by Wien[9] (1893). In an attempt to explain the general distributions shown in Fig. 4.4, Rayleigh and Jeans[10] derived the *Rayleigh-Jeans law* with the help of classical theory. As we shall see, the Rayleigh-Jeans law successfully predicted and explained the spectrum in the low-frequency region, while it completely failed in the high frequency, or ultraviolet, region. But the introduction of quantization of energy by Planck removed the discrepancies.

4. THE WIEN DISPLACEMENT LAW

Boltzmann[11] in 1884 applied the thermodynamical point of view to cavity radiation. The cavity was taken in the form of a cylinder with reflecting walls and a movable piston at one end. Thermal radiation inside the cavity exerts pressure. A relation between the work done and the pressure exerted by the thermal radiation can be derived by a series of expansions and compressions as in the case of a Carnot cycle. The energy density of the radiation, which is proportional to pressure, may thus be calculated.

Such considerations were further investigated in 1893 by Wien[9-12], who calculated the change in wavelength of the radiation due to the Doppler shift resulting from the reflection of the radiation from the moving piston. He concluded that the change in the wavelength is proportional to temperature:

$$\frac{d\lambda_1}{d\lambda_2} = \frac{T_1}{T_2} \tag{4.8}$$

Furthermore by the application of the Stefan-Boltzmann law and the equations of adiabatic processes, one obtains *Wien's formula* for the spectral distribution of black-body radiation:

$$U(\lambda) = \frac{A}{\lambda^5} f(\lambda T) \tag{4.9}$$

where $U(\lambda)$ is energy density per unit wavelength, A is a constant, and $f(\lambda T)$ is a quantity that is a function of λT.

From Eq. (4.9), at two different temperatures, T_1 and T_2, the corresponding energy densities are given by

$$U_1(\lambda) = \frac{A}{\lambda^5} f(\lambda T_1) \tag{4.10}$$

and

$$U_2(\lambda) = \frac{A}{\lambda^5} f(\lambda T_2) \tag{4.11}$$

Instead of λ, if we take $x = \lambda T$ as an independent variable, ($x_1 = \lambda T_1$ and $x_2 = \lambda T_2$), and introducing the quantity $y(x) = U(x)/T^5$, Eqs. (4.10) and (4.11) take the form

$$y_1(x_1) = \frac{A}{x_1^5} f(x_1) \tag{4.12}$$

and

$$y_2(x_2) = \frac{A}{x_2^5} f(x_2) \tag{4.13}$$

Without actually evaluating the function f, if we substitute

$$x_1 = x_2 \tag{4.14a}$$

we can say

$$y_1 = y_2 \tag{4.14b}$$

which means a plot of $y(= U(x)/T^5)$ versus $x(= \lambda T)$ is a single curve that represents the black-body spectrum at all temperatures. The plot of y versus x is shown in Fig. 4.5. The curve has a single maximum at $x = x_m$, which, according to the above discussion, should be the same at all different temperatures, or

$$x_m = \lambda_m T = \text{constant} \tag{4.15}$$

which is *Wien's displacement law*. The value of this constant is found to be

$$\lambda_m T \simeq 0.2898 \text{ cm} \times {}^\circ K \tag{4.16}$$

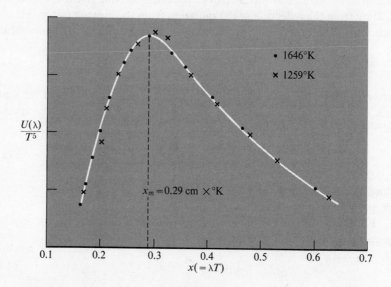

FIG. 4.5. *Experimental verification of Wien's displacement law. The continuous curve represents energy density versus wavelength for all temperatures. (The experimental points are those obtained by Lummer and Pringsheim in 1899.) [From Richtmyer, F. K., E. H. Kennard, and T. Lauritsen, Introduction to Modern Physics, 5th ed., New York: McGraw-Hill, 1955.]*

Also shown in Fig. 4.5 are the experimental points obtained from the black-body spectra measured by Lummer and Pringsheim[13] (1899) at temperatures 1646°K and 1259°K. The agreement between the theoretical curve and the experimental results is excellent.

5. THE RAYLEIGH-JEANS LAW

The relations discussed so far were derived from thermodynamical considerations for which it was not necessary to know the form of the distribution function $f(\lambda T)$. The true test of the applicability of the classical theory is to derive the form of this function for black-body radiation and to compare it with experimentally observed spectra. The distribution function $f(\lambda T)$ can be derived in two different ways using the classical theory.

(a) According to this method the accelerated electric charges in the walls of the cavity may be treated as a set of harmonic oscillators. According to classical theory each oscillator emits electromagnetic radiation of some particular frequency. All the oscillators are emitting and absorbing radiation in such a way that equilibrium is maintained at a fixed temperature.

(b) The second method, which we shall discuss in detail, was suggested by Rayleigh[14] in 1900 and by Jeans[15] in 1905 and led to the Rayleigh-Jeans Law. In this method, standing electromagnetic waves are assumed to be formed inside the cavity. By imposing suitable boundary conditions, we can calculate the possible modes of vibration, each of which is equivalent to a classical harmonic oscillator. By assigning an average energy of $\frac{1}{2}kT$ to each mode, as for a simple oscillator, one can find the energy density of the radiation as will be explained below.

Let us consider a metallic-walled cavity filled with electromagnetic radiation that is emitted by the walls of the cavity, which is maintained at a temperature T. For simplicity assume that the cavity is in the form of a perfect cube of edge length a; the results derived here, nevertheless, apply to a cavity of any shape. For a one-dimensional case, the equation representing the plane wave of the electromagnetic field is

$$\frac{\partial^2 \Psi}{\partial x^2} = \frac{1}{c^2} \frac{\partial^2 \Psi}{\partial t^2} \tag{4.17}$$

where Ψ is an electromagnetic field variable, $E(x, t)$ or $H(x, t)$, that is a function of x and t; and c is the velocity of light. For a wave of frequency ν, we may substitute

$$\Psi(x, t) = \psi(x)e^{i2\pi\nu t} \tag{4.18}$$

into Eq. (4.17) where $\psi(x)$ is a function of position only. After substituting $\nu/c = 1/\lambda = k_x$ (where k_x is the wave number), this results in the space-dependent equation of the form

$$\frac{d^2\psi}{dx^2} + 4\pi^2 k_x^2 = 0 \tag{4.19}$$

The solution of this equation representing the plane wave is

$$\psi(x) = A_x \sin (2\pi k_x x) \tag{4.20}$$

where A_x is a constant.

To extend our discussion to a three-dimensional problem, we must replace k_x by $\mathbf{k}$, the propagation vector, x by $\mathbf{r}$ and $\psi(x)$ by $\psi(x, y, z)$. Therefore,

$$\psi(x, y, z) = A_x A_y A_z \sin 2\pi(k_x x + k_y y + k_z z) \tag{4.21}$$

where k_x, k_y, and k_z are the component of k along X, Y, and Z axes, respectively. If α, β, and γ represent the angles between $\mathbf{k}$ and the X, Y, and Z axes, respectively, as shown in Fig. 4.6, Eq. (4.21) after substituting $A = A_x A_y A_z$ and $k_x = k \cos \alpha$, $k_y = k \cos \beta$, and $k_z = k \cos \gamma$, may be written as

$$\psi(x, y, z) = A \sin 2\pi(kx \cos \alpha + ky \cos \beta + kz \cos \gamma) \tag{4.22}$$

An incident wave traveling along a particular axis, say the X axis, is reflected from the wall of the cube. The incident and the reflected waves combine to form a standing wave. That the standing waves must have the nodes at the metallic walls of the cube can be easily understood. If there is a net electric vector **E** parallel to the wall (perpendicular to the direction of propagation),

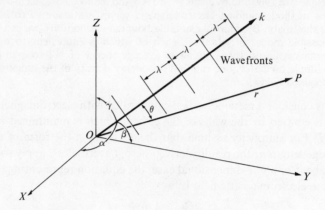

FIG. 4.6. α, β, and γ represent the angles between k and the X, Y, and Z axes, respectively, as shown.

currents will flow in the metallic conductor so as to neutralize the electric field. Thus the **E** vector must vanish at the boundaries so as to form nodes at the walls, or

$$\psi(x, y, z) = 0 \begin{cases} \text{at} \quad x = y = z = 0 \\ \qquad \text{and} \\ \text{at} \quad x = y = z = a \end{cases} \tag{4.23}$$

Imposing the boundary condition of Eq. (4.23) to Eq. (4.22), we get

$$2\pi k\, a \cos \alpha = n_x \pi$$
$$2\pi k\, a \cos \beta = n_y \pi \tag{4.24}$$
$$2\pi k\, a \cos \gamma = n_z \pi$$

where $n_x = 0, 1, 2, 3, \ldots$, $n_y = 0, 1, 2, 3, \ldots$, $n_z = 0, 1, 2, 3, \ldots$. Squaring and adding Eq. (4.24), we get

$$4k^2 a^2(\cos^2 \alpha + \cos^2 \beta + \cos^2 \gamma) = (n_x^2 + n_y^2 + n_z^2) \tag{4.25}$$

From the property of the angles α, β, and γ

$$\cos^2 \alpha + \cos^2 \beta + \cos^2 \gamma = 1$$

and noting that $k = 1/\lambda = \nu/c$, Eq. (4.25) reduces to

$$n_x^2 + n_y^2 + n_z^2 = \frac{4a^2\nu^2}{c^2} \tag{4.26}$$

Any possible set of numbers (n_x, n_y, n_z) denotes one possible mode of vibration of the waves in the cavity. From Eq. (4.26) the possible number of modes inside a given cavity are limited by the frequency ν. The possible number of modes can be calculated as follows: Draw a three-dimensional plot in which n_x, n_y, and n_z are used as three coordinates replacing x, y, and z, respectively (see Fig. 4.7). Then each point in this cubic lattice represents a possible mode

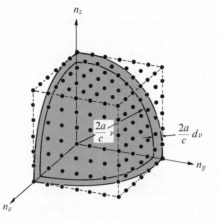

FIG. 4.7. *The possible number of modes in a positive octant of a sphere of radius $2a\nu/c$.*

of stationary vibration. According to Eq. (4.26) we may draw a sphere of radius $2a\nu/c$ and by counting the possible number of lattice points in the positive octant of this sphere, we get the possible number of modes of vibrations in the frequency range 0 to ν. For very large ν, the octant is almost a continuous function of ν, and we may assign one possible mode to each unit volume in this space. Thus the possible number of modes of vibration $N(\nu)$ between 0 and ν is equal to 1/8 the volume of the sphere of radius $2a\nu/c$ (only positive values of n_x, n_y, and n_z give a possible mode) (see Fig. 4.7), i.e.,

$$N(\nu) = \frac{1}{8} \frac{4\pi}{3} \left(\frac{2a\nu}{c}\right)^3 \qquad (4.27)$$

From Fig. 4.7 the possible number of modes $N(\nu) \, d\nu$ between the frequencies ν and $\nu + d\nu$ is equal to the volume of the shell:

$$N(\nu) \, d\nu = \frac{1}{8} 4\pi \left(\frac{2a\nu}{c}\right)^2 d\left(\frac{2a\nu}{c}\right)$$

or

$$N(\nu) \, d\nu = 4\pi \frac{\nu^2}{c^3} a^3 \, d\nu \qquad (4.28)$$

The number of modes (or number of waves) per unit volume of the cube between the frequencies ν and $\nu + d\nu$, that is $n(\nu) \, d\nu$, may be obtained by dividing both sides of Eq. (4.28) by a^3. Thus

$$n(\nu)\, d\nu = \frac{N(\nu)\, d\nu}{a^3}$$

or

$$n(\nu)\, d\nu = 4\pi \frac{\nu^2}{c^3}\, d\nu \qquad (4.29)$$

Because electromagnetic waves are transverse (unlike sound waves, which are longitudinal), we must specify the state of polarization. These waves are circularly polarized, either left-handed or right-handed and hence each mode has two degrees of freedom. Therefore, Eq. (4.29) must be multiplied by a factor of 2:

$$n(\nu)\, d\nu = 2\frac{4\pi\nu^2}{c^3}\, d\nu \qquad (4.30)$$

If the energy per mode at equilibrium is known, we can calculate the energy density. According to classical law of equipartition of energy the mean energy per mode is kT, where k is the Boltzmann constant. The simple oscillator has two degrees of freedom, each with mean energy $\tfrac{1}{2}kT$. Thus the energy density $U(\nu)$ within the range $d\nu$ is given by

$$U(\nu)\, d\nu = n(\nu)\, d\nu\, kT$$

or

$$U(\nu)\, d\nu = \frac{8\pi\nu^2}{c^3}\, kT\, d\nu \qquad (4.31)$$

which is the Rayleigh-Jeans law for the energy distribution of thermal radiation in a cavity or black body.

By using the relation $\nu = c/\lambda$

$$d\nu = -\frac{c}{\lambda^2}\, d\lambda \qquad (4.32)$$

and keeping in mind that

$$U(\nu)\, d\nu = -U(\lambda)\, d\lambda \qquad (4.33)$$

we may write Eq. (4.31) in the form

$$U(\lambda)\, d\lambda = \frac{8\pi kT\lambda}{\lambda^5}\, d\lambda \qquad (4.34)$$

This is another form of the Rayleigh-Jeans law. Comparison with Eq. (4.9) gives the form of the function $f(\lambda T)$ to be

$$f(\lambda T) = 8\pi kT\lambda \qquad (4.35)$$

Our next step should be to compare the results of this theory given by Eq. (4.31) or Eq. (4.34) with the experimental results of thermal radiation. Figure 4.8 shows such a comparison. As is obvious from this figure, there is some agreement between theory and experiment in the region of very small frequencies (or very large wavelengths), i.e., in the far-infrared region. At other frequencies there is a complete disagreement. The function $f(\lambda T)$ given by Eq. (4.35) does not give the experimentally observed shape of the spectrum. The comparison is especially bad at very high frequency (or small wavelengths), i.e., in the ultraviolet region where according to this theory $U(\nu) \to \infty$ as $\lambda \to 0$. This disagreement between the theory and the experiment is called the *ultraviolet catastrophe* because the disagreement comes in the ultraviolet frequency region. Also $\int_0^\infty U(\nu)\, d\nu$ goes to infinity at any temperature and that is not experimentally true.

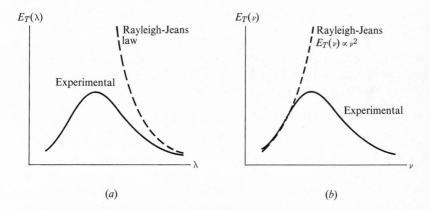

(a)   (b)

FIG. 4.8.   *Comparison of the theoretically calculated radiation spectrum of a black body (according to Rayleigh-Jeans) and an experimental spectrum. As is obvious the discrepancy occurs at high frequencies, thus the name ultraviolet catastrophe, (a) $E_T(\lambda)$ versus λ, and (b) $E_T(\nu)$ versus ν.*

Thus the ultraviolet catastrophe leads to the breakdown of classical theory. We must look for the true explanation elsewhere.

6.   THE PROBABILITY-DISTRIBUTION FUNCTION[16]

Before we can introduce the Planck energy-quantization hypothesis and show how it leads to the correct explanation of the black-body spectrum, it is necessary to investigate the following. According to kinetic theory, a system consisting of a number of particles (or molecules) always has a well-defined mean energy that is a function of the temperature T of the system. We would like to know, if the system has a total energy E, how this energy has to be distributed among N molecules so as to result in the well-defined mean energy $\bar{\epsilon} = E/N$. The nature of these temperature-dependent functions, which are known as the *probability-distribution functions*, is determined by the type of system. According to statistical mechanics, there are three different types of distribution functions used in different situations. The distribution function, or the statistics of interest in black-body radiation, is the Maxwell-Boltzmann distribution discussed below.

The Maxwell-Boltzmann statistics (or distribution function) is also called classical statistics and is used whenever a system consists of particles that are completely distinguishable. This usually happens when the particles are widely separated, as in the case of molecules in a gas. The classical distribution does not depend upon the angular momentum of the individual particles.

In the derivation of the Maxwell-Boltzmann distribution function, we start with a system consisting of a large number, N, of molecules; the possible energies these particles may take are $\epsilon_1, \epsilon_2, \epsilon_3, \ldots, \epsilon_i, \ldots$. Any one of the N particles may have energy ϵ_1, or there are N choices for this energy state. After the first energy state ϵ_1 has taken a molecule, the ϵ_2 energy state has $(N - 1)$ choices, and ϵ_3 has $(N - 2)$, and so on till the last energy state has only one choice. Because the molecules are individually distinguishable, the total number of possible permutations are

$$N(N - 1)(N - 2) \ldots 3 \cdot 2 \cdot 1 = N! \tag{4.36}$$

Let us further assume that there is no restriction on the number of molecules that can have the same energy, say N_1 molecules each have energy ϵ_1, N_2 molecules each have $\epsilon_2, \ldots, N_i$ molecules each have $\epsilon_i, \ldots$, and so on. Thus the number of possible distinct arrangements, remembering that the N_i particles in the ϵ_i energy group by permutation among themselves will not produce any distinct arrangement, will be given by

$$P = \frac{N!}{N_1! N_2! N_3! \ldots, N_i! \ldots} = \frac{N!}{\pi_i N_i} \tag{4.37}$$

where P is known as the thermodynamic probability. The conditions imposed on Eq. (4.37) are

$$\sum_i N_i = N \tag{4.38}$$

and

$$\sum_i \epsilon_i N_i = E \tag{4.39}$$

Our aim is to find the maximum value of P that will, therefore, give the most probable distribution. This can be done by causing a variation in P, equating it to zero, and imposing the conditions of Eqs. (4.38) and (4.39). Taking the logarithms of both sides of Eq. (4.37)

$$\log P = \log N! - \sum \log N_i! \tag{4.40}$$

If N is very large, then according to Stirling's approximation[17]

$$\log N! \simeq N \log N - N \tag{4.41}$$

and Eq. (4.40) takes the form

$$\log P = N \log N - N - \sum N_i \log N_i + \sum N_i \quad\quad (4.42)$$
$$= N \log N - \sum N_i \log N_i$$

because $N = \sum N_i$ according to Eq. (4.38). As the time goes on, the system will keep on changing and when it is in a state of maximum thermodynamic probability P_{max}, the variation of P_{max} in the N_i's is zero: from Eq. (4.42)

$$\delta \log P = 0$$

or,

$$-\sum N_i \delta \log N_i - \sum \log N_i \delta N_i = 0 \quad\quad (4.43)$$

But

$$\sum N_i \delta \log N_i = \sum N_i \frac{1}{N_i} \delta N_i = \sum \delta N_i = 0$$

Hence Eq. (4.43) reduces to

$$\sum \log N_i \delta N_i = 0 \quad\quad (4.44)$$

This results in the variations of N and E [from Eqs. (4.38) and (4.39)] becoming

$$\delta N = \sum \delta N_i = \delta N_1 + \delta N_2 + \ldots + \delta N_i = 0 \quad\quad (4.45)$$

and

$$\delta E = \sum \epsilon_i \delta N_i = \epsilon_1 \delta N_1 + \epsilon_2 \delta N_2 + \ldots + \epsilon_i \delta N_i = 0 \quad\quad (4.46)$$

Multiplying Eq. (4.45) by log A and Eq. (4.46) by β and combining these with Eq. (4.44), we get by using the method of Lagrange undetermined multipliers[18]

$$\sum (\log N_i - \log A + \beta \epsilon_i) \delta N_i = 0 \qu\quad (4.47)$$

where A and β are the unknown constants. Because the δN_i are independent, the coefficients are zero:

$$\log N_i - \log A + \beta \epsilon_i = 0 \qu\quad (4.48)$$

or

$$N_i = A e^{-\beta \epsilon_i} \qu\quad (4.49)$$

Equation (4.49) is the well-known Maxwell-Boltzmann distribution function. Such a distribution is shown in Fig. 4.9.

We can evaluate β from the classical consideration. According to classical theory any molecule can have energy between 0 and ∞. Thus the mean energy $\bar{\epsilon}$ of the molecules will be

$$\bar{\epsilon} = \frac{\int_0^\infty \epsilon A e^{-\beta \epsilon}\, d\epsilon}{\int_0^\infty A e^{-\beta \epsilon}\, d\epsilon} = \frac{1}{\beta} \qu\quad (4.50)$$

(Note that the subscript i has been dropped because of the continuous range of energies in classical theory.) If these molecules are collections of simple harmonic oscillators, then $\bar{\epsilon} = kT$ and hence $\beta = 1/kT$:

$$N_i = Ae^{-\epsilon/kT} \tag{4.51}$$

which is the Maxwell-Boltzmann probability distribution law applicable to a set of molecules with mean energy kT.

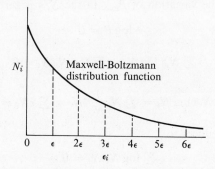

FIG. 4.9. *A graphical representation of the Maxwell-Boltzmann distribution function for continuous as well as discrete energies.*

7. PLANCK'S QUANTUM HYPOTHESIS AND RADIATION LAW

A. Planck's Hypothesis

We saw in Sec. 5 how classical theory failed to explain the black-body spectrum. In order to remove this discrepancy, Planck[19] introduced a new hypothesis that not only led to a satisfactory explanation of the black-body spectrum but also explained many new experimental facts that were yet to come. It lead to the eventual development of the quantum theory.

According to Planck's hypothesis, *any physical system executing a simple harmonic motion with frequency ν in one dimension can have only those energies that satisfy the condition*

$$\epsilon = nh\nu \qquad \text{where } n = 0, 1, 2, 3, \ldots \tag{4.52}$$

where h is a universal constant called Planck's constant.

Thus according to Eq. (4.52) the energy is quantized; the states having such quantized energies are the *quantum states* and n is the *quantum number*. The distinction between classical theory and Planck's hypothesis in the case of the simple harmonic oscillator is shown in Fig. 4.10.

B. Planck's Theory of Radiation

We shall now proceed with the derivation of the Planck radiation law, which will make use of the Boltzmann distribution function given by Eq. (4.51) and the quantization hypothesis given by Eq. (4.52). It is not necessary to assume the form of Eq. (4.52); it is enough to say that energy comes in multiples of ϵ_0, or $n\epsilon_0$ where $n = 0, 1, 2, 3, \ldots$. We shall show later that in order to explain the black-body spectrum, ϵ_0 must be $h\nu$. In the case of black-body radia-

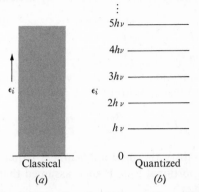

$$\vdots$$

$5h\nu$ ————

$4h\nu$ ————

$3h\nu$ ————

ϵ_i ϵ_i $2h\nu$ ————

$h\nu$ ————

0 ————

Classical   Quantized

(a)   (b)

FIG. 4.10. *Energy levels of a simple harmonic oscillator are:* (a) *continuous according to the classical theory, and* (b) *quantized according to Planck's hypothesis.*

tion, instead of assigning the energies $n\epsilon_0$ to the molecules, we assign these energies to the electromagnetic waves in a cavity. In order to find the energy density of the electromagnetic waves inside a cavity we still can use Eq. (4.31), except that instead of kT, we must calculate the mean energy $\bar{\epsilon}$ in the expression for the energy density,

$$U(\nu) \, d\nu = \frac{8\pi\nu^2}{c^3} \, d\nu \, \bar{\epsilon} \tag{4.53}$$

The number of electromagnetic waves or oscillators inside a cavity with energies permissible by the energy quantization hypothesis are given by Eq. (4.51) as

ϵ	0	ϵ_0	$2\epsilon_0$	$3\epsilon_0$	$\ldots$
$N_i(\epsilon)$	A	$Ae^{-\epsilon_0\beta}$	$Ae^{-2\epsilon_0\beta}$	$Ae^{-3\epsilon_0\beta}$	$\ldots$

Therefore, form Eqs. (4.38) and (4.39), the total number of oscillators and the total energy take the forms

$$N = \sum N_i(\epsilon) = A + Ae^{-\epsilon_0\beta} + Ae^{-2\epsilon_0\beta} + \ldots$$

or

$$N = \frac{A}{1 - e^{-\beta\epsilon_0}} \tag{4.54}$$

Similarly

$$E = \sum \epsilon N_i(\epsilon) = 0 \cdot A + \epsilon_0 \cdot Ae^{-\epsilon_0\beta} + \ldots$$

$$= \epsilon_0 Ae^{-\epsilon_0\beta}(1 + 2e^{-\beta\epsilon_0} + 3e^{-2\beta\epsilon_0} + \ldots)$$

or

$$E = \frac{\epsilon_0 A e^{-\epsilon_0 \beta}}{(1 - e^{-\beta \epsilon_0})^2} \tag{4.55}$$

Therefore, the mean energy $\bar{\epsilon}$ may be obtained by dividing E by N.

$$\bar{\epsilon} = \frac{E}{N} = \frac{\sum N_i(\epsilon)}{\sum \epsilon N_i(\epsilon)} = \frac{\epsilon_0 e^{-\epsilon_0 \beta}}{(1 - e^{-\beta \epsilon_0})} = \frac{\epsilon_0}{e^{\epsilon_0 \beta} - 1} \tag{4.56}$$

(Note that the integral has been replaced by the sum.)

Therefore, the expression for the energy density, after substituting $\beta = 1/kT$ as in Eq. (4.51), takes the form

$$U(\nu)\, d\nu = \frac{8\pi\nu^2}{c^3} \frac{\epsilon_0}{e^{\epsilon_0/kT} - 1}\, d\nu \tag{4.57}$$

This equation must satisfy the thermodynamical requirement according to which ϵ_0 must be proportional to ν. Planck assumed that $\epsilon_0 = h\nu$ where h is Planck's constant. Thus

$$U(\nu)\, d\nu = \frac{8\pi h\nu^3}{c^3} \frac{1}{e^{h\nu/kT} - 1}\, d\nu \tag{4.58}$$

or writing it in terms of wavelength for which $c = \nu\lambda$, and $d\lambda = -(c/\lambda^2)\, d\lambda$,

$$U(\lambda)\, d\lambda = \frac{8\pi hc}{\lambda^5} \frac{1}{e^{(hc/\lambda kT)} - 1}\, d\lambda \tag{4.59}$$

Equation (4.58) or Eq. (4.59) is the famous *Planck's radiation formula.* By choosing a proper value of h, one can get an excellent agreement between theory and experiment as shown in Fig. 4.11(a), while Fig. 4.11(b) shows the comparison with other laws as well. It was shown by Rubens and Michel[21] in 1919 that the Planck formula correctly predicts the radiation spectrum from $-160°C$ to $1800°C$. The latest accepted value of Planck's constant is[22]

$$h = 6.62559 \pm 0.00016 \times 10^{-34}\ \text{joule-sec} \tag{4.60}$$

C. Planck's Radiation Law and Classical Theories

If Planck's theory, or the quantum theory, is correct, then under proper conditions it must reduce to classical theory, i.e., we must be able to reduce Eq. (4.57) in the classical thermodynamical form to get (i) Rayleigh-Jeans law, (ii) Wien's displacement law, and (iii) Stefan-Boltzmann law.

(i) *Rayleigh-Jeans Law.*   If the expression of Eq. (4.59) is compared with

$$U(\lambda)\, d\lambda = \frac{A}{\lambda^5} f(\lambda T)\, d\lambda \tag{4.61}$$

we get

$$f(\lambda T) = \frac{8\pi hc}{e^{hc/\lambda kT} - 1} \tag{4.62}$$

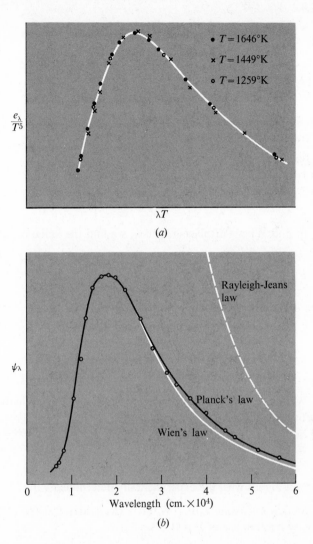

FIG. 4.11.   (a) *The agreement between the theoretical Planck's radiation-law (continuous curve) and the experimentally observed spectrum of a black body is good, as shown in the figure.* (b) *Three radiation laws compared with the experimental points. The ordinates are in arbitrary units.*

For very long wavelengths the exponent is very small, and hence keeping only the first two terms gives

$$e^{hc/\lambda kT} - 1 = 1 + \frac{hc}{\lambda kT} + \ldots - 1 = \frac{hc}{\lambda kT}$$

Therefore

$$f(\lambda T) = 8\pi hc \left(\frac{hc}{\lambda kT}\right)^{-1} = 8\pi\lambda kT \tag{4.63}$$

which is the same as Eq. (4.35) for $f(\lambda T)$ derived from the Rayleigh-Jeans law, i.e., Eq. (4.59) takes the form

$$U(\lambda)\, d\lambda = \frac{8\pi\lambda kT}{\lambda^5}\, d\lambda \tag{4.64}$$

which is the Rayleigh-Jeans law.

(ii) *Wien's Displacement Law.* We may rewrite Eq. (4.59) in the following form by making the substitution $x = hc/\lambda kT$:

$$U(\lambda) = \frac{8\pi k^5 T^5}{h^4 c^4} \frac{x^5}{e^x - 1} \tag{4.65}$$

In order to find Wien's displacement law, we find the value of x_m from Eq. (4.65) by equating $\frac{dU(\lambda)}{d\lambda} = 0$, i.e., for $x = x_m$, where $x_m = hc/\lambda_m kT$,

$$x_m = 5[1 - e^{-x_m}] \tag{4.66}$$

This equation, when solved numerically, gives $x_m = 4.965$, i.e.,

$$x_m = hc/\lambda_m kT = 4.965 \tag{4.67}$$

or

$$\lambda_m T = \frac{hc}{4.965\,k} = \text{constant} \tag{4.68}$$

which is Wien's displacement law. The constant may be evaluated by substituting for h, c, and k.

$$\lambda_m T = 2.898 \times 10^{-3}\ \text{m-}^\circ\text{K}$$
$$= 0.2898\ \text{cm-}^\circ\text{K} \tag{4.69}$$

This constant agrees with the experimentally determined value.

(iii) *Stefan-Boltzmann Law.* We may easily arrive at the Stefan-Boltzmann law by making use of Eq. (4.59), i.e.,

$$E_T = \int_0^\infty U(\lambda)\, d\lambda = \int_0^\infty \frac{8\pi hc}{\lambda^5} \frac{1}{e^{(hc/\lambda kT)} - 1}\, d\lambda \tag{4.70}$$

Substituting once again $hc/\lambda kT = x$

$$E_T = \frac{2\pi k^4}{h^3 c^2} T^4 \int_0^\infty \frac{x^3}{e^x - 1}\, dx$$

The integral is $\pi^4/15$, therefore

$$E_T = \frac{2\pi^5 k^4}{15 h^3 c^2} T^4 = \sigma T^4 \tag{4.71}$$

which is the Stefan-Boltzmann law, with the Stefan constant given by

$$\sigma = \frac{2\pi^5 k^4}{15 h^3 c^2} = 5.67 \times 10^{-8} \text{ joule sec}^{-1} \text{ m}^{-2} \text{ °K}^{-4}$$

$$= 5.67 \times 10^{-5} \text{ erg sec}^{-1} \text{ cm}^{-2} \text{ °K}^{-4}$$

(4.72)

8. COMMENTS ON ENERGY QUANTIZATION

The Planck energy quantization hypothesis for electromagnetic radiation revolutionized the thinking of scientists and had far-reaching consequences. As we shall see in the next chapter, subsequently many phenomena were successfully explained by assuming that emission of energy is discontinuous, contrary to the classical theory, and, according to Planck's hypothesis, an oscillator of frequency v will emit energies only in multiples of hv, where hv is the quantum of energy. Thus (a) the amount of energy absorbed from or emitted as an electromagnetic wave is in the amount of hv, and (b) all electromechanical systems can exist in certain definite energy states with only discrete energies, or energy levels. The units of the constant h are energy-sec, either erg-sec or joule-sec, which are the same as those of a well known quantity in mechanics called *action*. Action comes from the principle of least action, according to which a particle moves from point A to point B along a path for which the integral of the action along the path is a minimum. This analogy between the Planck constant h and action in mechanics leads to the eventual application of the quantum hypothesis to atomic systems.

One might very well ask is the energy quantized for all the known physical systems or only for the system of electromagnetic radiation? As we shall see later, the energies of all physical systems are quantized, i.e., the systems exist in discrete energy states; they can change from one discrete state to another but are not "capable" of a continuous range of energies. In our investigations we shall find that it is easy to verify these statements in the case of microscopic systems. In the case of macroscopic or large-scale systems, as in classical mechanics, it is not that the Planck hypothesis breaks down; it is because of the large energy of the system, the small changes that are of the order of hv are hard to detect. For example, in the case of a simple pendulum, the total energy is about 10 to 50 ergs, while hv is from 0.3×10^{-26} to 1.5×10^{-26} ergs, and it is practically difficult to detect such a small change.

PROBLEMS

1. A metallic sphere of 1 cm diameter and of emissive power 0.40 is suspended in a large evacuated chamber whose walls are at a room temperature, say 300°K. Calculate the power input needed to maintain the sphere at a temperature of 3000°K.

2. A perfect black body is maintained at a temperature of T_0. Calculate the percentage change in the total energy radiated per unit time if the temperature of the black body is changed to (a) $0.1T_0$, (b) $10T_0$, and (c) $100T_0$.

3. An object reflects 40% of the total energy that falls on it. What is the emittance of the object at a temperature of 800°K?

4. The thermal energy received by the earth from the sun is 1.4×10^6 ergs/cm² when the sun is directly overhead. If the sun behaves like a perfect black body, what is the temperature at the surface of the sun? The distance from the sun to the earth is $\sim 1.4 \times 10^{13}$ cm, and the diameter of the sun is $\sim 1.5 \times 10^{11}$ cm.

5. What will be the temperature of a black body that will radiate energy at the same rate as the earth receives from the sun? Assume that the energy received by the earth from the sun is ~ 0.323 calories/cm²/sec.

6. What is the surface temperature of the sun if the wavelength of the most intense radiation from it is approximately 5500 Å?

7. Calculate the wavelength corresponding to the maximum intensity of radiation from a black body at a temperature of (a) 500°K, (b) 1000°K, (c) 3000°K, and (d) 6000°K.

8. Calculate the radiation energy per unit volume between 4000 Å and 6000 Å emitted from a black body at 1200°K. Assume that E_ν is constant over this region.

9. Consider a black-body radiator cavity in the form of a cube of side 5 cm at a temperature of 1600°K.
   (a) Calculate the amount of the total radiant energy in the cavity in the visible wavelength band.
   (b) Calculate the number of modes of vibration per unit volume in the cavity in the visible wavelength band.

10. Consider photons in a cubic box of side 10 cm.
    (a) Calculate the momentum and energy of the photons for the following states: $(n_x, n_y, n_z) = (1, 0, 0), (1, 1, 0), (1, 1, 1), (2, 0, 0)$.
    (b) Find the energy differences between the states (1, 0, 0), (1, 1, 0) and (1, 0, 0), (2, 0, 0). How do these energy differences compare with the energy of the photon in state (1, 0, 0)?
    (c) What conclusions may one draw if the states were (100, 0, 0), (100, 1, 0), (100, 1, 1), and (101, 0, 0)?

11. Particles in a system may have energies E, $2E$, $3E$, and $4E$, where $E = 0.025$ eV. The system is in equilibrium at 300°K.
    (a) Calculate the ratio of the number of particles in each of the higher energy states to the number of particles in the lowest energy state.
    (b) What is the average energy of these particles when in equilibrium?

12. Show that the physical units of Planck's constant are the same as that of angular momentum.

13. How many visible quanta are emitted from a 100-watt electric light bulb if 0.7% of the total energy supplied is converted into visible light of wavelength 5600 Å?

14. The human eye is most sensitive to approximately 5500 Å receiving 5 quanta/cm²/sec. Calculate the energy equivalent to this sensitivity.

15. For an object to be clearly visible the eye must receive energy at the rate of 1.5×10^{-11} joule/m²/sec. Calculate the rate at which the photons must be

emitted to be visible to the eye that has a pupil of 0.8 cm^2 from a source of (a) red light, and (b) violet light.
Assume that the object is at a distance 30 cm.

REFERENCES

1. Planck, M., *Theory of Heat*, London: Macmillan & Co., Ltd., 1929. Planck, M., *Theory of Heat Radiation*, New York: Dover Publications, 1960.

2. French, A. P., *Principles of Modern Physics*, Chap. 4, New York: John Wiley & Sons, 1961.

3. Sears, F. W., and M. W. Zemansky, *University Physics*, 3rd ed., p. 397, Reading, Mass.: Addison-Wesley, 1963.

4. Stefan, J., *Fortsch. Physik*, 660, (1879).

5. Boltzmann, L., *Ann. Physik*, **22**, 31, 291, (1884).

6. See references given in E. R. Cohen and J. W. M. DuMond, *Revs. Mod. Phys.*, **37**, 537, (1965).

7. Lummer, O., and E. Pringsheim, *Transactions of the German Physical Society*, **2**, 163, (1900).

8. Stefan, J., *Wien. Ber.*, **79**, 391, (1879).

9. Wien, W., *Ann. Physik*, **58**, 662, (1896).

10. D. ter Haar, *The Old Quantum Theory*, Fair Lawn, N. J., Oxford University Press, 1966.

11. Boltzmann, L., *Ann. Physik*, **22**, 616, (1884).

12. Richtmyer, F. K., E. H. Kennard, and J. N. Cooper, *Introduction to Modern Physics*, 6th ed., Append. 5A, New York: McGraw-Hill, 1969.

13. Lummer, O., and E. Pringsheim, *Transactions of the German Physical Society*, **2**, 176, (1900).

14. Lord Rayleigh, *Phil. Mag.*, **49**, 539, (1900).

15. Jeans, J. H., *Phil. Mag.*, **10**, 91, (1905).

16. Maxwell, J. C., *Trans. Roy. Soc.*, **157**, 49, (1867); *Phil. Mag.*, **35**, 129, 185, (1868). L. Boltzmann, *Wien. Ber.*, **58**, 517, (1868).

17. Satterly, J., *Nature*, **111**, 220, (1923).

18. Boltzmann, L., *Vorlesungen uber Gastheorie*, 2 vols., Leipzig, (1896–1898); English translation: *Lectures on Gas Theory*, Berkeley, Calif., 1964.

19. Planck, M., *Ann. Phys.*, **4**, 553, (1901); *Verhandl. deut. Physik. Ges.*, **2**, 202, 237, (1900).

20. Planck, M., *Naturwiss.*, **31**, 153, (1943); also Einstein, A., *Zelt fur Physik.*, **18**, 121, (1917).

21. Rubens and Michel, *Phys. Zeitsch*, **XXII**, 569, (1921).

22. Cohen, E. R., and J. W. M. Dumond, *Revs. Mod. Phys.*, **37**, 537, (1965).

SUGGESTIONS FOR FURTHER READING

1. Planck, M., *Theory of Heat*, Parts 2 and 3, London: Macmillan & Co., 1929.

2. Simon, Ivan, *Infrared Radiation* (Momentum Book No. 12), Princeton, N. J.: D. Van Nostrand, 1966.

3. Richtmyer, F. K., E. H. Kennard, and T. Lauritsen, *Introduction to Modern Physics*, 6th ed., Chap. 4, New York: McGraw-Hill, 1955.

4. French, A. P., *Principles of Modern Physics*, Chap. 4, New York: John Wiley & Sons, 1961.

5. Stefan, J., "Temperature Radiation" in *A Source Book in Physics*. Ed. W. F. Magie. Cambridge, Mass.: Harvard Univ. Press, 1963.

V

Waves and Particles

1. DUAL NATURE OF LIGHT: PARTICLES AND WAVES

We shall start with the discussion of the theories of light and see how the controversies over these theories led to the assumption that light has a dual nature: waves and particles. According to Newton, light consists of tiny particles, called corpusculars, and this so-called corpuscular theory was remarkably successful in explaining the rectilinear propagation of light. Huygens, Newton's contemporary, suggested that light consists of not particles but waves. But because of Newton's authority and some apparent successes of the corpuscular theory, wave theory was discarded. It was not until the beginning of the nineteenth century that the wave theory was again revived. Young's experiments concerning the diffraction of light by single and double slits could be explained only if light was assumed to have wave properties. The development of Maxwell's field equations and the experiments of Hertz led to the conclusion that light waves were electromagnetic in nature. For a while, during the last two decades of the nineteenth century, it was thought that the final, correct theory of light had been established. But not long after, it was realized that certain significant experiments could not be explained by the wave nature of light. These experiments were

(a)   black-body radiation
(b)   the photoelectric effect
(c)   optical line-spectra

(d)   the Compton effect
(e)   x-ray spectra

We have seen in the last chapter that the spectra emitted from a black body was satisfactorily explained by Planck's quantization hypothesis, according to which radiation is emitted in bundles of size $h\nu$. Making assumptions that energy comes in the form of bundles leads one to suspect that light or all electromagnetic waves may be particles of some sort. As a matter of fact all of experiments, (a) to (e), mentioned above can be explained by this assumption—energy is quantized.

In the beginning of the twentieth century, interference, diffraction, and polarization experiments could be explained by assuming that light consisted of waves, but experiments (a) to (e), above, could be explained only if light consisted of some sort of particles. The only natural thing to conclude was that experimental conditions determine whether the phenomena observed would be explained by the wave theory or the particle theory. If there is any truth in this statement, one is automatically led to suspect that under some experimental conditions it should be possible to observe electrons, protons, neutrons, and other particles behaving as waves. This type of reasoning led in 1924 to de Broglie's hypothesis. The details of this will be investigated later; the basis of the hypothesis is that particles and waves are two manifestations of the same thing. In 1927 these ideas were confirmed when the diffraction of electrons was actually observed.

Once the dual nature of matter was established, it became a necessity to find a proper mathematical apparatus to handle these two apparently completely different aspects. This led to the development of *wave mechanics*, or *quantum mechanics*, by E. Schroedinger in 1926, and the development of *matrix mechanics* by M. Born, W. Heisenberg, and P. Jordon.

This chapter will describe and discuss some of the previously mentioned experiments, and establish once and for all the dual nature of matter.

2.   THE PHOTOELECTRIC EFFECT

Light, a certain range of electromagnetic radiation, falling on a metallic surface can under certain conditions eject electrons from the metallic surface. This phenomenon, the *photoelectric effect*, was first discovered by H. Hertz[1] in 1887. Hertz was carrying out experiments to confirm the existence of electromagnetic waves (and fields) produced by oscillating electric currents as was predicted by the Maxwell theory in 1864. Many characteristics were observed in connection with the photoelectric effect by Hallwasch[2] in 1888 and much more completely by R. A. Millikan[3]. We shall see that classical theory cannot explain all the experimentally observed facts about this phenomenon, and the correct explanation was given by Einstein[4] in 1905 using Planck's quantum hypothesis.

A. Experimental Arrangement and Results

An experimental arrangement for investigating different aspects of the photo-electric effect is shown in Fig. 5.1. It consists of a vacuum tube, T, in which is

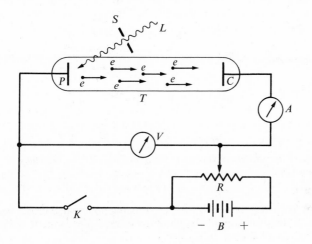

FIG. 5.1.   *An experimental arrangement for observing some character-istics of the photoelectric effect.*

placed a metallic plate, P, and a charge-collecting plate, C. When a beam of monochromatic light, L, after being collimated by the slit, S, falls on the elec-trode, P, electrons are ejected from this surface. The electrons ejected from P are collected by the plate, C, if C is at a positive potential with respect to P. The current read by the meter, A, indicates the charge collected by C, and we call this current the photocurrent, i_p. By increasing the voltage V, the cur-rent i_p increases until it reaches a saturation value. By applying a negative potential to C, the electrons will be repelled from C. The potential for which no electrons reach C is called the *stopping potential*. By varying the experi-mental conditions, i.e., changing the frequency (or wavelength) and intensity of incident light, and changing V and noting i_p, the following results are obtained.

(1)   Keeping the frequency of the incident light the same, *the photoelectric current*, i_p, *which is proportional to the number of photoelectrons emitted per second*, *increases with increasing intensity of the incident radiation.*

(2)   When the surface is illuminated with light, the photoelectron emission starts within less than 10^{-9} sec, i.e., *there is no observable time lag between the illumi-nation of the surface and the emission of photoelectrons,* no matter how small the intensity of the incident light.

(3)   The photoelectron emission from a given surface does not take place unless the frequency of the incident radiation is equal to or greater than a certain minimum frequency ν_0, the *threshold frequency*. The value of ν_0 is characteristic of the surface and is different for different surfaces.

(4) *The maximum kinetic energy,* K_{max}, *of the photoelectrons after emission is independent of the intensity of the incident radiation.* This is obvious from Fig. 5.2. If one uses incident radiation of different intensities ($I_1 > I_2 > I_3$) but of

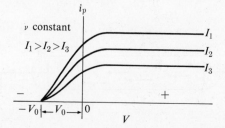

FIG. 5.2. *The maximum kinetic energy of the emitted electrons is independent of the intensity and is a function only of the frequency of the incident light.*

the same frequency, one finds that the stopping potential, which is equal to the maximum kinetic energy of the photoelectrons, is the same. If $-V_0$ is the retarding potential applied to C, then

$$eV_0 = \frac{1}{2} mv_{\max}^2 = K_{\max} \qquad (1.5)$$

i.e., if V is equal to or less than $-V_0$, no electrons reach the collector plate, as shown in Fig. 5.2.

(5) *The maximum kinetic energy,* K_{max}, *of the photoelectrons after emission from the surface is dependent upon the frequency of the incident radiation.* The maximum kinetic energy increases with increasing frequency. This is demonstrated in Fig. 5.3. One performs experiments with three different sources of light of

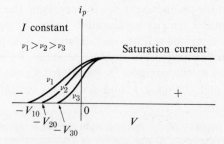

FIG. 5.3. *This figure shows that the maximum kinetic energy* K_{max} *of the electrons emitted depends upon the frequency of the incident light and increases with increasing frequency.*

frequencies ν_1, ν_2, and ν_3 such that $\nu_1 > \nu_2 > \nu_3$ and the intensities are the same in all the three cases. By applying the varying retarding potentials one finds the stopping potentials $-V_{10}$, $-V_{20}$, $-V_{30}$ for the three cases. As is obvious from

Fig. 5.3, $V_{10} > V_{20} > V_{30}$, i.e., the maximum kinetic energy, K_{max}, of the electrons increases with increasing frequency, ν.

(6) Finally, by repeating experiments of the type shown in Fig. 5.3 with different surfaces and incident radiations of varying frequencies, one finds that *there is a linear relation between K_{max} and ν for any given metal*. This relation is of the form

$$K_{max} = a\nu + b \tag{5.2}$$

where a and b are constants; a gives the slope of the straight line, and b is the intercept on the ordinate. Figure 5.4 shows such plots for cesium (Cs), potas-

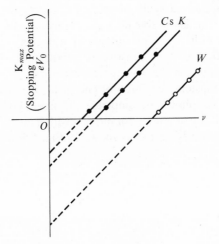

FIG. 5.4. *Variation of K_{max} with ν for different metals. Note that the slope is the same for all the metals.*

sium (K), and tungsten (W). It is clear from this figure that all three linear plots have the same slope but different intercepts for the ordinate, or the K_{max} axis.

B. Classical Theory and the Photoelectric Effect

Classical theory (or the electromagnetic-wave theory) can explain only point (1) of the previously described characteristics. According to (1), the photoelectron current i_p increases with increasing intensity, which is in agreement with classical theory. In contradiction to (2), however, classical theory predicts that the radiation of very weak intensity will take a much longer time (so as to accumulate enough energy) to extract photoelectrons from the surface. According to classical theory, there should be no minimum threshold frequency for photoelectron emission as found in point (3); if radiation impinges long enough, even if it has very low frequency, classical theory requires the emission of photoelectrons.

Similarly, classical theory contradicts points (4) and (5), and it does not predict the relation given in (6) by Eq. (5.2). Thus we may conclude that classical theory fails to predict and explain all the experimental facts observed in photoelectric effect phenomena.

C. The Quantum Theory and the Photoelectric Effect

The correct and satisfactory explanation of the photoelectric effect was given by A. Einstein[4] in 1905 by applying Planck's quantum hypothesis to electromagnetic radiation. According to quantum theory, electromagnetic radiation consists of photons, each carrying an amount of energy $h\nu$ ($= hc/\lambda$) where h is Planck's constant. This is the so-called photon hypothesis used by Planck to explain black-body radiation. This quantization of energy leads us to suspect that electromagnetic radiation consists of bundles, or packets, which suggests the particle nature of electromagnetic radiation.

According to Einstein, a photon of energy $h\nu$ interacts with an electron of an atom. Either the photon is completely absorbed, giving all its energy to the electron in the atom, or it does not interact with it at all. In case the photon disappears, the electron is ejected as shown in Fig. 5.5, which is a schematic

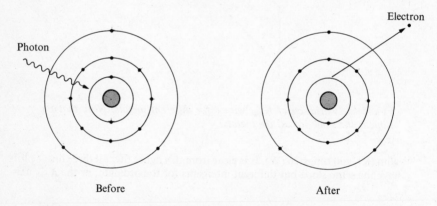

Fig. 5.5. *Schematic representation of the interaction between incident light and an electron in an atom, resulting in the emission of an electron, called the photoelectron.*

representation of the process in which the electrons are shown going around the nucleus in an atom. All the six points mentioned earlier can be explained now.

(1) As the intensity of the beam increases, the number of photons striking the surface also increases, resulting in an increase in photoelectron emission, i_p.

(2) Because the emission of each electron is due to the interaction of a single photon with a single electron, either an electron is emitted immediately or not at all; thus there is no time lag between illumination and emission.

(3) For photoelectron emission, the energy of each photon must be at least equal

to the energy required to pull the electron out of the atom. This energy is equal to the binding energy of the electron in the atom; this energy is also called the *work function*, ω_0. If ν_0 is the threshold frequency, then

$$\omega_0 = h\nu_0 \tag{5.3}$$

If ν is less than ν_0, no photoelectron emission takes place.

(4), (5), and (6)   If the frequency of the incident photon is $\nu\ (>\nu_0)$, it has energy $h\nu$. On being absorbed by the electron in the atom, part of this energy, equal to the work function, ω_0, is used up in pulling the electron out of the atom, while the rest of the energy $(h\nu - \omega_0)$ appears as the kinetic energy of the photoelectron emitted, i.e.,

$$K_{\max} = h\nu - \omega_0 \tag{5.4}$$

where $K_{\max} = \frac{1}{2}mv_{\max}^2$, $v_{\max}$ being the maximum velocity of the emitted photo electron. The relation of Eq. (5.4) is illustrated in Fig. 5.6. Equation (5.4) says that $K_{\max}$ is independent of the intensity of light but increases with increasing frequency ν, and agrees with the experimental observations (4) and (5).

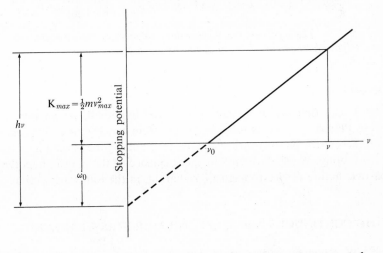

FIG. 5.6.   *Illustration of the relation between the incident energy $h\nu$, work function ω_0, threshold frequency ν_0, and maximum kinetic energy K_{max} of the photoelectron.*

Finally, comparing Eq. (5.4) with Eq. (5.2), we find h is identified with the slope a, and $-\omega_0$ with the intercept b. Because h is a constant, it is the same for all surfaces, while ω_0, the work function, is different for different metals. Thus the experimental results shown in Fig. 5.4 are explained by Eq. (5.4). Note that for an incident radiation of given frequency ν, not all the photoelectrons emitted have the maximum kinetic energy. In general

$$K_i = h\nu - \omega_i \tag{5.5}$$

where $K_i = \frac{1}{2}mv_i^2$, and $v_i < v_{\max}$. The relation between ω_0 and ω_i and Eq. (5.4) and Eq. (5.5) is illustrated in Fig. 5.7. This figure shows the surface of the metal under consideration and a schematic arrangement of electrons in different levels in the surface. Not all the electrons lie on the outermost layer of the surface for which the work function ω_0 is the least. For the electrons lying deeper in the surface, the work needed to pull them out, ω_i, is more than ω_0 which results in less available kinetic energy K_i for the photoelectron as given in Eq. (5.5) and illustrated in Fig. 5.7.

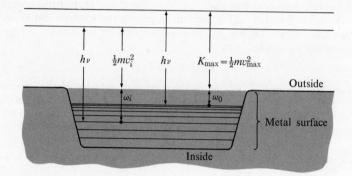

FIG. 5.7.   *The maximum kinetic energies of photoelectrons emitted from different layers of electrons inside a metal surface.*

D.   Conclusion

We have seen that the quantization-of-energy hypothesis, originally introduced by Planck, was successfully used by Einstein in explaining all the experimental facts of the photoelectric effect, thereby putting the photon hypothesis on firm footing. We shall discuss further evidence of the photon hypothesis, or particle nature of electromagnetic radiation, in the following section.

3.   THE CONTINUOUS X-RAY SPECTRUM (BREMSSTRAHLUNG)

In 1895 W. Roentgen[5] discovered that when fast moving electrons strike a metallic target, a highly penetrating radiation of unknown nature was produced; he named this radiation x-rays. Later polarization experiments performed on x-rays by Barkla[6,7] in 1906, and wavelength measurements in 1912, clearly demonstrated that x-rays are electromagnetic waves of very short wavelengths. According to modern classification, as shown in Fig. 5.8, the electromagnetic waves with wavelengths between 0.1 Å and 100 Å are called x-rays; thus the wavelength range of x-rays is below the ultraviolet region and above the region of gamma rays.

The most interesting and important aspect of x-ray production in the present context is that it is a process that is just the reverse of the photoelectric effect. Whenever fast moving electrons strike a target, the process of slowing down these electrons in the target results in the production of x-rays. The loss of kinetic energy of the electron appears as electromagnetic radiation, which, according to quantum hypothesis, should consist of photons. This fact we shall show in this section. Before we proceed with this discussion, however, it is appropriate to discuss the mechanism and the experimental arrangement for the production and observation of the characteristics of x-rays.

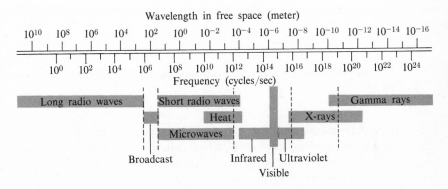

FIG. 5.8. *A complete range of electromagnetic waves. Note that the visible light forms a very small fraction of the whole range.*

According to classical electromagnetic theory, an accelerated charged particle radiates electromagnetic energy at a rate given by

$$dE/dt = 2e^2a^2/3c^3 \tag{5.6}$$

Whenever a charged particle, such as an electron or proton, moves in the field of the nucleus, it is accelerated and radiates electromagnetic waves; this radiation is called *Bremsstrahlung* (German for braking radiation or slowing-down radiation). As illustrated in Fig. 5.9, an electron with kinetic energy K_1 as it approaches the nucleus changes its path, which is equivalent to saying that the electron has been decelerated (or accelerated). The decrease in the kinetic energy of the electron appears as electromagnetic radiation. It is clear from Eq. (5.6) that the energy radiated is directly proportional to the square of the acceleration a. Therefore, the energy radiated is inversely proportional to the square of the mass because $a = F/m$, where F is the force and m is the mass of the charged particle. Because the force is proportional to the charge of the nucleus, we can say that the rate of energy loss by radiation is proportional to Z^2, where Z is the atomic number of the target material. Thus we may conclude that radiation loss is: (a) directly proportional to Z^2, (b) inversely proportional to m, the mass of the charged particle, and (c) increases linearly with increasing energy. Thus fast moving electrons incident on target nuclei of high Z form an efficient source for the production of electromagnetic radiation.

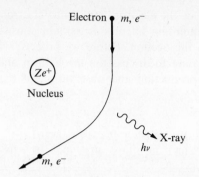

FIG. 5.9.   *Production of x-rays as electrons decelerate in the field of the nucleus.*

Figure 5.10 shows an x-ray tube used for the production of x-rays. Electrons are emitted from cathode *C*, which is heated indirectly by the heating filament *F* connected to the battery B. The electrons thus produced, after overcoming the binding energy, are said to be emitted by thermionic emission. The electrons are then accelerated in a vacuum by a high potential difference *V* (several thousand volts) applied between the anode *T* (the target) and the cathode *C*. The kinetic energy *K* of the electrons just before hitting the target *T* is given by

$$K = eV \tag{5.7}$$

Note that we have neglected (1) a small amount of kinetic energy that the electron has at the cathode before being accelerated, and (2) the small amount

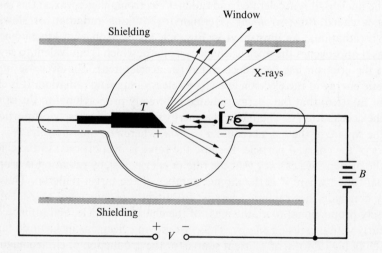

FIG. 5.10.   *Schematic of an x-ray tube for the production of x-rays.*

of energy, ω_0, which is the work function of an electron in the target T, that it gains as it enters the target.

As the electrons strike the target, they are decelerated, and after losing energy $K(= eV)$ are brought to rest. Most of this energy (about 98%) is lost in collisions that result in the production of heat in the target, which requires the cooling of the x-ray tube during operation. A small fraction of energy is used in producing electromagnetic radiation by the Bremsstrahlung process. Because x-rays are penetrating radiation, it is necessary to surround the x-ray tube with proper shielding. A well-collimated beam of x-rays for experimentation is obtained through a small window in the shielding, as shown.

A typical x-ray spectrum gives a plot of $N(\nu)$, the number of x-rays with frequency ν, versus ν, as shown in Fig. 5.11, while the plot of intensity $I(\nu)$

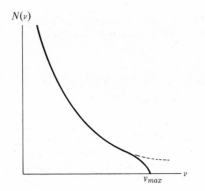

FIG. 5.11. *A typical x-ray spectrum showing the plot of $N(\nu)$ versus ν.*

versus ν is shown in Fig. 5.12. The spectra obtained in the case of tungsten (W) and molybdenum (Mo) for relative intensity versus ν and for relative

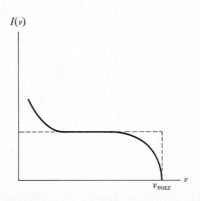

FIG. 5.12. *A typical x-ray spectrum showing the plot of radiation intensity $I(\nu)$ versus ν.*

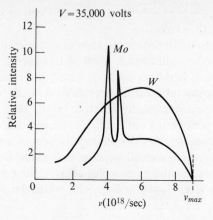

FIG. 5.13. *X-ray spectra of tungsten (W) and molybdenum (Mo), showing the plots of relative intensity I(ν) versus ν.*

intensity versus λ are shown in Fig. 5.13 and Fig. 5.14, respectively. The detailed investigations reveal the following:

(a) X-rays of all frequencies up to a certain maximum, ν_{max}, or to a certain minimum, λ_{min}, are produced. Hence a typical x-ray spectrum is continuous. The maximum frequency depends upon the value of the applied potential difference, V, and is independent of the target material, as shown in Fig. 5.13

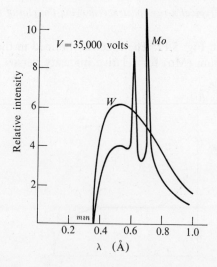

FIG. 5.14. *X-ray spectra of tungsten (W) and molybdenum (Mo), showing the plots of relative intensity I(λ) versus λ.*

and Fig. 5.14. The relation between ν_{max} and V is found to be independent of the target material and is given by

$$\frac{\nu_{max}}{V} = \text{constant} \tag{5.8}$$

(b) Superimposed on the continuous x-ray spectra are certain discrete lines as shown in the case of Mo in Fig. 5.13 and Fig. 5.14. The position of these discrete lines for a given target does not change with the change in the applied voltage, but these lines do appear at different positions for different target materials. These discrete frequency lines are called *characteristic x-rays*, and as the name indicates they depend upon the target material. The discussion of the characteristic x-ray spectrum will be postponed until Chapter XII.

Equation (5.8) states that for a certain voltage V, there exists a certain high-frequency limit ν_{max}. The limit ν_{max} is difficult to explain by means of classical electromagnetic theory, but it is easily understood if one assumes the photon hypothesis. Thus, for example, an incident electron with kinetic energy $K_1 = eV$ may lose its energy in producing any number of photons. But on the other hand, if it loses all its energy in producing a single photon of energy $h\nu_{max}$, then

$$h\nu_{max} = eV \tag{5.9}$$

Because e and h are universal constants,

$$\frac{\nu_{max}}{V} = \frac{e}{h} = \text{constant} \tag{5.10}$$

which is the experimentally observed relation given by Eq. (5.8). Equation (5.10) may also be written as

$$\frac{c}{\lambda_{min}} \frac{1}{V} = \frac{e}{h}$$

or

$$\lambda_{min} = \frac{hc}{eV} \tag{5.11}$$

which on substituting for h, c, and e yields

$$\lambda_{min} = \frac{1.24 \times 10^{-5}}{V} \text{ cm} \tag{5.12}$$

where V is in volts.

The value of the constant, e/h, determined from this method is in agreement with the values determined by other methods. Thus the photon hypothesis or the quantum theory of radiation has satisfactorily explained the production of x-rays. Also Eq. (5.9) is similar to Eq. (5.4) for the photoelectric effect if one takes into account the work function ω_0 in Eq. (5.9).

For very accurate work where this method is used for measuring the ratio of e/h, one must take into consideration the work functions while using

Eq. (5.10). As is obvious from Fig. 5.11, the spectrum of $N(v)$ versus v shows that

$$N(v) \propto \frac{1}{v} \qquad \text{for } v < v_{max}$$

$$= 0 \qquad \text{for } v = v_{max} \tag{5.13}$$

Therefore, the relative intensity $I(v)$ is given by

$$I(v) \propto hvN(v) \tag{5.14}$$

which when combined with Eq. (5.13) says that $I(v)$ is almost constant as shown in Fig. 5.12.

4. MASS, ENERGY, AND MOMENTUM OF THE PHOTON

In the last two sections we have shown that the photoelectric effect and the continuous x-ray spectra can be explained satisfactorily if we assume that electromagnetic radiation consists of discrete packets of energy called photons. Making such an assumption implies that the electromagnetic radiation consists of particles, the quanta of radiation, as opposed to the wave nature of electromagnetic radiation. If such an assumption is true, then let us find out what is the mass, energy, and momentum of such a photon.

According to the special theory of relativity, the mass m of a particle moving with velocity v is given by

$$m = \frac{m_0}{\sqrt{1 - \dfrac{v^2}{c^2}}} \tag{5.15}$$

where m_0 is the rest mass of the particle. A photon consists of a packet of electromagnetic energy moving with the speed of light c, thus $v = c$. According to Eq. (5.15), the moving mass m will be infinite unless rest mass m_0 is zero, in which case $m = 0/0$ and is an indeterminate quantity. That the rest mass of a photon is zero should not be surprising because photons are always found moving with the speed of light and are never at rest. The moving mass is found from the fact that each photon carries a bundle of energy E given by

$$E = hv \tag{5.16}$$

while according to the special theory of relativity

$$E = mc^2 \tag{5.17}$$

Combining Eqs. (5.16) and (5.17),

$$mc^2 = hv$$

gives the moving mass of the photon as

$$m = \frac{hv}{c^2} \tag{5.18}$$

According to the special theory of relativity, the equation

$$E^2 = p^2c^2 + m_0^2c^4$$

for $m_0 = 0$ in the case of photons reduces to

$$E = pc \qquad (5.19)$$

Combining this with Eq. (5.17) or Eq. (5.18) gives the momentum p of the photon to be

$$p = \frac{E}{c} = \frac{mc^2}{c} = mc \qquad (5.20)$$

(The definition, $p = mc$ (or $=mv$) is in accord with the definition of momentum.) Combining with Eq. (5.16)

$$p = \frac{E}{c} = \frac{h\nu}{c} \qquad (5.21)$$

Thus if the photon is to be treated as some sort of a particle, then it has zero rest mass, energy $h\nu$, moving mass $h\nu/c^2$, and its momentum is given by $h\nu/c$. The values of energy, moving mass, and momentum of a photon depend only on the frequency (or the wavelength).

5. THE COMPTON EFFECT: COMPTON SCATTERING

Of all the evidence of the particle nature (the photon hypothesis) of electromagnetic radiation the Compton effect is the most direct and clear-cut. The effect, named after the discoverer, American physicist A. H. Compton, is concerned with scattering of x-rays (or more generally, of electromagnetic radiation). In the photoelectric effect the photon of electromagnetic radiation is completely absorbed by the electron, and the energy of the photon appears as the binding energy and the kinetic energy of the electron. An alternative to this process is one in which the incident electromagnetic radiation interacts with the target particles resulting in the change of direction, or both in direction and wavelength of the incident radiation. The resulting radiation is called scattered radiation, and the process is *scattering*. The same definition of scattering applies for interaction between incident particles and the target particles.

According to classical electromagnetic theory, when the incident radiation of a certain frequency hits upon a free charged particle whose size is very small as compared to the wavelength of the incident radiation, the scattered radiation is given out in all directions with the same frequency (or wavelength) as the incident radiation. The process of scattering takes place in the following manner. The charged particle when acted upon by the periodically changing electric field of the incident radiation is forced to oscillate with the same frequency as that of the incident radiation. This oscillating charge will radiate electromagnetic waves in all directions. The intensity of the scattered radiation is maximum in the plane perpendicular to the direction of the oscillating charge and zero along the direction of oscillation. The charged particle is simply absorbing energy from the incident radiation and then reemitting all the energy in different directions. Such scattering in which no change in wavelength occurs is called *coherent scattering*. This classical theory of scattering agrees with experimentally observed scattering of visible light and of radiation with wavelengths longer than visible light. The scattering of very short wavelengths, say x-rays, brings a disagreement between the classical theoretical predictions and experimentally observed facts as we shall explain now.

By carefully measuring the wavelengths of scattered x-rays, Compton showed that when monochromatic x-rays are incident on a target, the scattered radiation at any angle consists of waves of two different wavelengths: one of the same wavelength as the incident radiation, the *unmodified wavelength*, and the other of the longer wavelength, the *modified wavelength*. The wavelength of the modified wave depends upon the angle of scattering. This type of scattering (as distinguished from the coherent scattering) is called the *compton effect*, or *compton scattering*. Classical theory offers no explanation for the Compton effect. A satisfactory explanation was given by A. H. Compton[8,9] in 1922 by making use of the photon hypothesis. He assumed that the incident electromagnetic radiation (x-rays in this case) consists of photons that are incident on free (or loosely-bound) electrons of the target material. Thus the collision between the photon and the electron at rest is equivalent to an elastic collision between two particles. By applying the laws of conservation of energy and momentum, Compton was able to calculate the change in wavelength.

A schematic of the experimental arrangement for observing the Compton effect is shown in Fig. 5.15. Monochromatic x-rays coming from the source

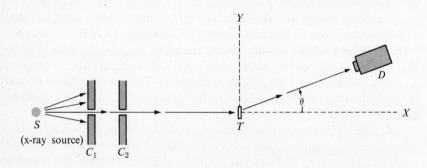

FIG. 5.15. *A schematic arrangement for observing the Compton effect.*

S are passed through collimators C_1 and C_2 in order to obtain a well-defined narrow beam of x-rays. These x-rays are incident on a target T, such as carbon, in which the loosely bound electrons are assumed to be free electrons.

The scattered radiation at any angle θ is detected by means of a detector. The detector D consists of a diffraction grating for measuring the wavelength of the scattered x-rays. (This method of measuring wavelengths of x-rays will be discussed in Sec. 7.)

The collision between the incident photon and the free electron is shown schematically in Fig. 5.16. According to the photon hypothesis, the radiation

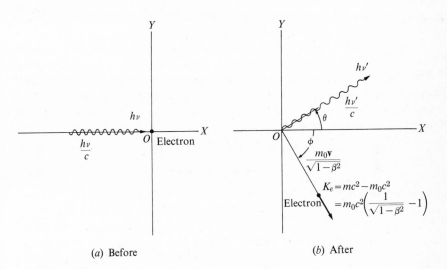

(a) Before   (b) After

FIG. 5.16.   *Schematic of a photon and a free electron* (a) *before collision and* (b) *after collision.*

consisting of photons of energy $h\nu$ and momentum $h\nu/c$ (with equivalent mass $h\nu/c^2$) is incident on an electron of rest mass m_0 (and rest mass energy m_0c^2) at rest as shown in Fig. 5.16(a) before the collision. After the elastic collision, as shown in Fig. 5.16(b), the scattered photon at an angle θ has energy $h\nu'$ (less than $h\nu$) and momentum $h\nu'/c$ (less than $h\nu/c$). Note that the scattered-photon frequency ν' is smaller than ν and hence its wavelength λ' is larger than λ of the incident photon. The decrease in the energy of the photon, $h\nu - h\nu'$, appears as the kinetic energy K_e of the recoil electron. If m is the moving mass of the electron, then

$$K_e = mc^2 - m_0c^2$$

$$= m_0c^2 \left(\frac{1}{\sqrt{1 - \beta^2}} - 1 \right) \qquad (5.22)$$

where $\beta = v/c$, v being the velocity of the recoil electron. The momentum p_e of the recoil electron is given by

$$p_e = mv = m\beta c = \frac{m_0\beta c}{\sqrt{1 - \beta^2}} \qquad (5.23)$$

Resolving different momenta into X and Y components and applying the conservation of linear momentum and energy to the situation shown in Fig. 5.16, we get

$$\frac{h\nu}{c} = \frac{h\nu'}{c} \cos \theta + \frac{m_0 \beta c}{\sqrt{1 - \beta^2}} \cos \phi \tag{5.24}$$

$$0 = \frac{h\nu'}{c} \sin \theta - \frac{m_0 \beta c}{\sqrt{1 - \beta^2}} \sin \phi \tag{5.25}$$

$$h\nu = h\nu' + K_e = h\nu' + m_0 c^2 \left(\frac{1}{\sqrt{1 - \beta^2}} - 1 \right) \tag{5.26}$$

These three equations contain four unknowns $h\nu'$, K_e, θ, and ϕ. But if one of these variable parameters, say ϕ, is fixed, then the values of the other three can be determined by solving these equations. Using Eq. (5.23) in Eqs. (5.24) and (5.25) and rewriting

$$p_e c \cos \phi = h\nu - h\nu' \cos \theta \tag{5.27}$$

$$p_e c \sin \phi = h\nu' \sin \theta \tag{5.28}$$

Squaring and adding those equations produces the following:

$$p_e^2 c^2 = (h\nu)^2 - 2(h\nu)(h\nu') \cos \theta + (h\nu')^2 \tag{5.29}$$

The total energy of the electron E_e may be written as

$$E_e = K_e + m_0 c^2 \tag{5.30}$$

and from relativity

$$E_e = \sqrt{p_e^2 c^2 + m_0^2 c^4} \tag{5.31}$$

Therefore, from these two equations

$$p_e^2 c^2 + m_0^2 c^4 = (K_e + m_0 c^2)^2$$

and substituting for $K_e = h\nu - h\nu'$ from Eq. (5.26) and rearranging, we get

$$p_e^2 c^2 = (h\nu - h\nu')^2 + 2(h\nu - h\nu')m_0 c^2 \tag{5.32}$$

Equating $p_e^2 c^2$ values from Eqs. (5.29) and (5.32), $h\nu'$ may be written:

$$h\nu' = \frac{h\nu}{1 + \alpha(1 - \cos \theta)} \tag{5.33}$$

where $\alpha = h\nu/m_0 c^2$; α, therefore, is the energy of the incident photon expressed in units of the rest mass energy of the electron.

Similarly, we can solve these equations for the kinetic energy of the electron K_e:

$$K_e = h\nu - h\nu' = h\nu \left(1 - \frac{1}{1 + \alpha(1 - \cos \theta)} \right) = h\nu \left[\frac{\alpha(1 - \cos \theta)}{1 + \alpha(1 - \cos \theta)} \right] \tag{5.34}$$

and

$$\cos \theta = 1 - \frac{2}{(1 + \alpha)^2 \tan^2 \phi + 1} \tag{5.35}$$

We can rewrite Eq. (5.33) in terms of wavelengths, $\lambda (= c/\nu)$ and $\lambda' (= c/\nu')$, of the incident and scattered photons, respectively. This results in the change in the wavelength, $\Delta\lambda = \lambda' - \lambda$, due to the Compton effect, given by

$$\lambda' - \lambda = \frac{h}{m_0 c}(1 - \cos \theta) \tag{5.36}$$

Note that the scattered-photon wavelength is longer than the incident-photon wavelength, and the change in the wavelength, $\lambda' - \lambda$, is independent of the incident photon's wavelength and depends only upon the scattering angle, θ, and the mass of the electron, m_0. The quantity $h/m_0 c$, which has the dimensions of length, is known as the *compton wavelength*. Substituting the values of m_0, h, and c, we get the Compton wavelength to be $h/m_0 c = 0.02426$ Å, or, from Eq. (5.36),

$$\Delta\lambda = 0.02426 \, (1 - \cos \theta) \text{ in Å} \tag{5.36a}$$

Thus at $\theta = 0°$, there is no change in the wavelength; at $\theta = 90°$, $\Delta\lambda(90°) = h/m_0 c = 0.02426$ Å; while at $\theta = 180°$, $\cos \theta = -1$, and the change in the wavelength is $\Delta\lambda(180°) = 2h/m_0 c = 0.04852$ Å. These changed wavelengths, λ', are the modified wavelengths. The intensities and the wavelengths λ and λ' as measured experimentally at different angles are shown in Fig. 5.17. As is obvious from this figure, the intensity and the wavelength λ' of the scattered photon both increase with increasing angle.

One can find the energy $h\nu$ of the incident photon by using Eq. (5.34) after measuring the recoil energy of the electron, which is maximum at $\theta = 180°$,

$$K_{e \text{ max}} = h\nu \left(\frac{2\alpha}{1 + 2\alpha} \right) = h\nu \left[\frac{2h\nu/m_0 c^2}{1 + 2h\nu/m_0 c^2} \right] \tag{5.34a}$$

Knowing $K_{e \text{ max}}$, $m_0 c^2$, one can calculate $h\nu$, the incident photon energy.

Even though classical theory can explain the existence of the unmodified line, i.e., coherent scattering, one would naturally like to see that coherent scattering is also accounted for by the quantum hypothesis. It is easy to explain this. Until now we assumed that the incident photons were scattered by the free electrons. Suppose the scattering takes place between the photon and one of the tightly bound inner electrons of the atom. In this case the whole atom takes part in the scattering, and in Eq. (5.36) m_0 should be replaced by M, the mass of the whole atom. Therefore, the Compton wavelength, h/Mc, is extremely small because M for the lightest atom (hydrogen) is about 1838 times the rest mass of the electron, i.e., $h/Mc = 0.0000133$ Å. Even at the extreme angle, $\theta = 180°$, h/Mc is negligible. Thus the scattering of

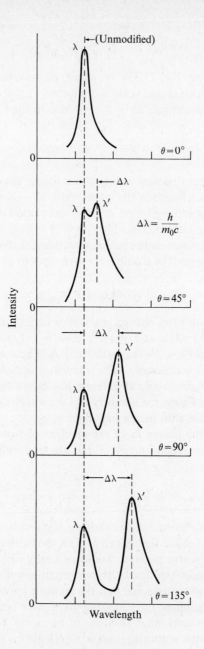

$$\lambda \; |\!\leftarrow\!\text{(Unmodified)}$$

$$\theta = 0°$$

$$\Delta\lambda$$

$$\lambda \qquad \lambda'$$

$$\Delta\lambda = \frac{h}{m_0 c}$$

$$\theta = 45°$$

$$\Delta\lambda$$

$$\lambda \qquad \lambda'$$

$$\theta = 90°$$

$$\Delta\lambda$$

$$\lambda \qquad \lambda'$$

$$\theta = 135°$$

Intensity

Wavelength

Fig. 5.17. *Relative intensities of the modified and unmodified wavelengths λ' and λ, respectively, at different angles.*

144

photons from the inner bound electron does not result in the change of wavelength. Once again from conservation of energy we can draw the same conclusion. In the collision the whole atom recoils and because of its large mass it takes away an almost negligible amount of kinetic, or recoil, energy, which implies that the photon is scattered without change in the energy.

From Eq. (5.36), we see that the change in the wavelength $\lambda' - \lambda$ will approach zero whenever either $h \to 0$ or $m_0 \to \infty$, i.e., coherent scattering is the classical limit of the quantum effect, or we may say that the quantum effect reduces to the classical effect under these conditions.

Thus we have demonstrated that the photon hypothesis (the quantum effect), can clearly explain the scattering of x-rays, while the classical theory fails.

6. THE de BROGLIE HYPOTHESIS

In the beginning of the present century interference and diffraction experiments were explained by assuming a wave nature of light; Maxwell's theory and Hertz's experiments by 1888 had completely established the electromagnetic-wave nature of light. The success of the wave theory was masked by its failure to explain two newly discovered phenomena, Planck's black-body radiation[10] and Einstein's photoelectric effect[4]. Because these and other phenomena could be explained only by assuming that light, thermal radiation, and x-rays consisted of photons and that energy was quantized and came in bundles of certain definite sizes, the period between 1905 and 1924 was a stalemate between the competing theories.

Instead of trying to seek an explanation for the apparent dual nature of radiation, French physicist Louis de Broglie[11] in 1924 postulated the dual nature of electromagnetic radiation as existing *throughout* the realm of physics. The following hypotheses, containing completely revolutionary ideas, were equally applicable to both radiation as well as matter.

(a) The motion of a particle of momentum p is guided by a wave whose wavelength λ is given by

$$\lambda = \frac{h}{p} \tag{5.37}$$

where h is Planck's constant.

(b) The square of the amplitude of the wave of wavelength, λ, is proportional to the probability of finding a particle of momentum p, where

$$p = \frac{h}{\lambda} \tag{5.38}$$

These hypotheses imply that a particle can be treated as a particle *or* a wave, and a wave can be treated as a wave *or* a particle. As a matter of fact we have already seen the dual nature of waves. In order to confirm de Broglie's hypotheses one would have to prove only that the particles behave like waves.

As we shall show in later sections, these suggestions were experimentally confirmed by C. S. Davisson and L. H. Germer[12] in 1927, and by G. P. Thomson[13] in 1928. They showed that a beam of electrons is diffracted and scattered just as are electromagnetic waves.

The ideas expressed by Eq. (5.37) and Eq. (5.38) were the results of very careful analysis by de Broglie who combined Planck's ideas with Einstein's theory of relativity in the following form. Consider a particle of rest mass m_0 moving along the X axis with velocity v with respect to a stationary frame of reference. According to de Broglie there is a characteristic frequency ν_0 associated with the particle, and hence the displacement ψ of the particle is given by

$$\psi = A \sin 2\pi\nu_0 t_0 \tag{5.39}$$

where A is the amplitude of the vibration. According to Planck, the particle has energy $h\nu_0$, while according to Einstein's special theory of relativity the particle has energy $m_0 c^2$. Hence

$$h\nu_0 = m_0 c^2 \tag{5.40}$$

Looking at this particle from a stationary frame of reference, using the transformation equations of the special theory of relativity,

$$t_0 = \frac{t - \left(\dfrac{vx}{c^2}\right)}{\sqrt{1 - \beta^2}} \tag{5.41}$$

and substituting this value of t_0 into Eq. (5.39), we get

$$\psi = A \sin 2\pi\nu_0 \frac{\left(t - \dfrac{vx}{c^2}\right)}{\sqrt{1 - \beta^2}} \tag{5.42}$$

or

$$\psi = A \sin 2\pi\nu \left(t - \frac{vx}{c^2}\right) \tag{5.43}$$

where

$$\nu = \frac{\nu_0}{\sqrt{1 - \beta^2}} \tag{5.44}$$

Comparing Eq. (5.43) with the equation of a wave of velocity ω, i.e.,

$$\psi = A \sin 2\pi\nu \left(t - \frac{x}{\omega}\right) \tag{5.45}$$

we get

$$\omega = \frac{c^2}{v} \tag{5.46}$$

Thus the de Broglie wavelength λ associated with the particle of mass m_0 and vibrational frequency ν_0 is given by

$$\lambda = \frac{\omega}{\nu} = \frac{c^2}{v} \cdot \frac{1}{\nu} \tag{5.47}$$

Substituting for ν from Eq. (5.44) and for ν_0 from Eq. (5.40), we get

$$\lambda = \frac{c^2}{v} \cdot \frac{\sqrt{1 - \beta^2}}{\nu_0} = \frac{h\sqrt{1 - \beta^2}}{m_0 v} = \frac{h}{mv}$$

or

$$\lambda = \frac{h}{mv} = \frac{h}{p} \tag{5.48}$$

where m is the relativistic mass and Eq. (5.48) is the relation given by Eq. (5.37).

Another important relation may be easily derived. Expressing $h\nu$ in terms of m

$$h\nu = \frac{h\nu_0}{\sqrt{1 - \beta^2}} = \frac{m_0 c^2}{\sqrt{1 - \beta^2}} = mc^2 = E \tag{5.49}$$

we get

$$\nu = E/h \tag{5.50}$$

Equations (5.48) and (5.50) have an important characteristic. The left sides of these two equations contain quantities λ and ν that are characteristic of waves, while the right sides contain p and E that are characteristic of particles (quantized momentum and quantized energy), and these different quantities are related through Planck's constant h.

The announcement and the subsequent confirmation of the de Broglie hypothesis led to the development of a new type of mathematical formulation called quantum mechanics, which is based on the premise of the dual nature of matter. The subject of quantum mechanics (or wave mechanics) will be developed in some detail in the next chapter. Before discussing the experimental confirmation of the de Broglie hypothesis (by showing diffraction of particles), we must clearly understand the diffraction of waves.

7. THE BRAGG LAW AND X-RAY DIFFRACTION

From the study of optics one is familiar with the phenomena of diffraction; one observes variations in intensity (maxima and minima) of light after it passes through a single or double slit. A surface containing many transparent and opaque lines, such as a glass surface on which several thousand lines per inch have been drawn, constitutes a diffraction grating, and a good diffraction grating is equivalent to several hundred thousand slits. Very fine gratings have been made by mechanically ruling as many as 30,000 lines per inch. The width of each slit in the grating (i.e., the width of a single transparent or opaque line) is the diffraction spacing and is usually denoted by d. The condition for observing diffraction patterns of visible light using a mechanical diffraction grating requires the spacing d to be of the order of the wavelength of the light being diffracted.

A. The Bragg Law

Light waves as well as x-rays are electromagnetic radiation, however, the wavelength of x-rays is much smaller than that of light waves. X-ray wavelength is of the order of about 1 Å. To cause diffraction of x-rays, therefore, one will need a diffraction grating with much narrower spacing than the mechanical gratings available. W. L. Bragg, in 1913, suggested the use of single crystals for x-ray diffraction gratings. The atoms in a crystal are not just randomly piled together; instead they are arranged in a regular manner in a lattice. Figure 5.18 shows a simple crystal lattice consisting of identical atoms separated by equal distances d; d is usually of the order of a few Å. An example of a simple crystal is the rock-salt single crystal, a portion of which is shown in Fig. 5.19. Na and Cl atoms in rock salt occupy alternate positions at the corners of cubes. The edge length of each small cube, or the separation between the adjoining atoms, is d. Different combinations of atoms may be considered to be defining families of planes, and three such planes are shown shaded in Fig. 5.19. These planes are called *Bragg planes*, and each family of Bragg planes is characterized by the separation distance, d, between its component planes. Figure 5.18 and Fig. 5.19 are examples of simple cubic lattices.

A beam of monochromatic x-rays incident on a crystal will strike a regular array of atoms lying in successive layers. Each atom is capable of scattering a small fraction of the beam energy in all directions as a spherical wave, and the phase is determined by the position of the scattering atom in the lattice. Because of the regular arrangement of the atoms, in certain directions interference between the scattered waves will lead to constructive interference with one another (coherent scattering), thus producing a diffraction pattern; while in all other directions there will be destructive interference (incoherent scattering). X-rays penetrate deep into the crystals, and hence one must consider the scattered waves not only from the atoms on the surface layer but also from a large number of successive layers of atoms lying deep in the crystal.

We shall now derive the condition for constructive interference between the scattered waves by using simple arguments first suggested by Sir William L. Bragg[14]. First of all we shall derive a condition for Bragg reflection and then will extend it further to the case of diffraction.

Consider a layer of atoms lying in a plane of a crystal as shown in Fig. 5 20. Two parallel rays AO_1 and BO_2 making an angle θ with the crystal plane are incident on two adjacent atoms O_1 and O_2, respectively. After scattering from these atoms, the scattered rays are O_1A_1 and O_2B_2 making an angle θ' with the plane. The points a and b lie on the same incident wavefront and thus are in phase. The path lengths aO_1a_1 and bO_2b_2 will be the same if the angle $\theta = \theta'$, and hence points a_1 and b_2 on the scattered wavefront will be in phase. The same argument can be extended to many other parallel rays scattered from adjacent atoms. Thus the points lying on the scattered

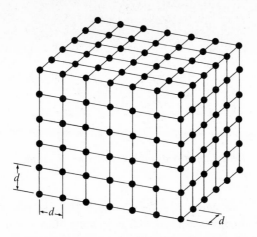

Fɪɢ. 5.18. *A schematic of a simple cubic crystal lattice consisting of identical atoms separated by equal distances d.*

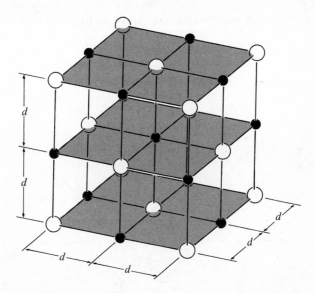

Fɪɢ. 5.19. *A schematic of a portion of a rock salt (sodium chloride, NaCl) single crystal. The shaded portions represent a family of planes, the Bragg planes.*

rays will form a wavefront that will be moving in the direction satisfied by the condition $\theta = \theta' = \theta'' = \ldots$. This process is *Bragg reflection* and is similar to a reflected beam of light from a plane mirror.

  In order to obtain a diffraction pattern of the scattered beam, the reflec-

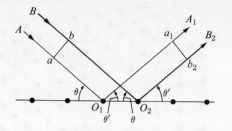

FIG. 5.20. *Reflection of two parallel rays from two adjacent atoms in a layer of atoms.*

tions from successive planes, as shown in Fig. 5.21, must take place in such a way that the scattered rays interfere constructively; otherwise destructive interference will lead to diffused scattering. Consider, for example, two rays AO_1 and BO_2 incident on atoms O_1 and O_2 as shown in Fig. 5.21, resulting in the scattered rays O_1A_1 and O_2B_2. The scattered rays will interfere constructively if they are in phase. This implies that the paths aO_1a_1 and bO_2b_2 differ by integral multiples of wavelength. As shown in Fig. 5.21, the path difference is

$$aO_1a_1 - bO_2b_2 = 2d \sin \theta$$

and the Bragg condition for constructive interference is

$$2d \sin \theta = n\lambda \qquad\qquad (5.51)$$

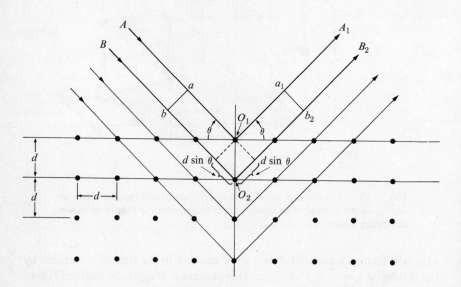

FIG. 5.21. *Parallel rays of light after being reflected from successive planes will result in constructive interference if after reflection these rays are in phase.*

where $n = 0, 1, 2, 3, 4, \ldots$, the order of reflection, d is the spacing, and λ is the wavelength of the x-rays. Equation (5.51) is referred to as the *Bragg law*. Notice that for constructive interference, the diffracted beam deviates from the incident path by an angle 2θ as shown in Fig. 5.21.

If one knows λ and measures θ, therefore, one can calculate the distance d, the spacing between planes; conversely, knowing d, one can calculate θ.

B. X-ray Diffraction

The study of x-ray diffraction is interesting and important from many points of view. If one knows the wavelength of incident x-rays, the diffraction patterns obtained can be used to measure interplanar dimensions between layers of atoms. As shown in Fig. 5.22, even in a simple cubic crystal, there are more

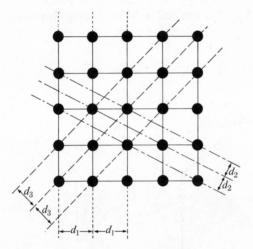

FIG. 5.22.   *Three sets of equidistant parallel successive planes with separation distances d_1, d_2, and d_3 in a simple cubic crystal are shown.*

than one set of equidistance parallel successive planes. Three different sets of such planes with spacings d_1, d_2, and d_3 are shown. By measuring these distances in a given crystal one can locate the positions of specific atoms in a given crystal, and hence one knows the structure of the crystal.

A schematic of a typical x-ray crystal spectrometer is shown in Fig. 5.23. A beam of x-rays, produced by an x-ray tube, after passing through lead window W is collimated by slit S and impinges on crystal C. The scattered beam is detected by means of a detector D, which may be an ionization chamber that measures the intensity of the radiation. Both the detector and the crystal may be rotated and the condition of maximum intensity is observed when Eq. (5.51) is satisfied. By rotating the crystal one can obtain the diffraction pattern from different planes of the form shown in Fig. 5.22.

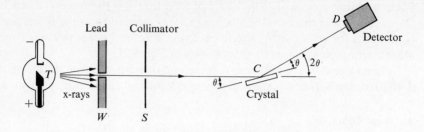

FIG. 5.23.   *A schematic of a typical x-ray spectrometer.*

We shall now discuss the form of diffraction patterns observed from a thin metallic foil instead of a single crystal. The experimental arrangement is shown in Fig. 5.24. The thin foil consists of many microcrystals oriented in a

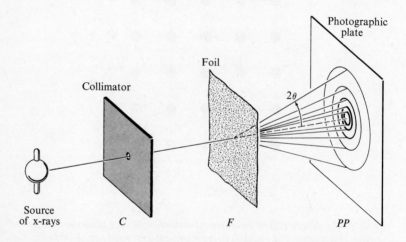

FIG. 5.24.   *An experimental arrangement for observing the diffraction pattern of x-rays from a metallic foil.*

completely random fashion. Of these only those microcrystals that satisfy the Bragg condition produce a strongly diffracted beam; the rest of the microcrystals do not diffract the incident beam to cause coherent scattering. Thus the beam emerging from the other side of the foil consists of two parts, one the strong unscattered beam and the other a scattered beam that is concentrated in a conical shell, making an angle 2θ with respect to the incident beam, as shown in Fig. 5.24. Because in a crystal of any given material there are many Bragg planes, many concentric circles of varying intensity are obtained. As an example, Fig. 5.25 shows a diffraction pattern observed from a sample of polycrystalline aluminum[15]. Similar studies were made by Debye and Scherrer[16], the patterns observed are called *powder patterns* and the rings are called *Debye-Scherrer rings*.

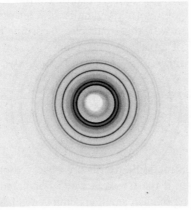

FIG. 5.25.   *X-ray diffraction pattern obtained from a sample of poly-crystalline aluminum. [Courtesy of Mrs. M. H. Read, Bell Telephone Laboratory, Murray Hill, N. J.]*

C.   Avogadro's Number from X-rays

Besides investigating the structure of crystals, x-ray diffraction has been utilized for accurate determination of Avogadro's number as we shall briefly explain now. Consider a simple cubic crystal, for example the rock salt shown in Fig. 5.19. The sodium and chlorine atoms (or actually Na^+ and Cl^- ions) are located at alternate corners of identical cubes, each at a distance d from each other. Thus there are $1/d$ atoms (half Na and half Cl) per cm along the edge of the cube, or there are $1/d^3$ atoms in a volume of one cubic centimeter. The number of atoms, the total of both sodium and chlorine, per gram is given by $2N_A/A$, where N_A is Avogadro's number and A is the molecular weight of sodium chloride (which in this case is $23.00 + 35.46 = 58.48$). If ρ is the density of sodium chloride, the number of atoms per unit volume is $2\rho N_A/A$. Thus we may say that

$$\frac{2\rho N_A}{A} = \frac{1}{d^3} \tag{5.52}$$

This expression may be used to determine N_A, Avogadro's number; ρ and A being known and d being measured by x-ray diffraction if the wavelength λ (determined by using a ruled diffraction grating at grazing incidence) of the incident radiation is known.

8. DIFFRACTION OF PARTICLES

If, according to the de Broglie hypothesis, particles like electrons, neutrons, protons, etc., can be treated as waves, then the beams of these particles when scattered from crystals and thin foils must exhibit the diffraction patterns as do x-rays. Before going into any details, first let us calculate the order of wavelengths associated with these particles according to de Broglie.

The wavelength of a particle whose mass is 1 gm and whose velocity is 10 cm per sec, according to Eq. (5.37) and using $m = m_0$, is

$$\lambda = \frac{h}{p} = \frac{h}{mv} = \frac{6.62 \times 10^{-34} \text{ joule-sec}}{(0.001 \text{ kgm})(0.1 \text{ m/sec})} = 6.62 \times 10^{-30} \text{ m} \qquad (5.53)$$

or

$$\lambda = 6.62 \times 10^{-20} \text{ Å}$$

Remembering that diffraction patterns are observed only if λ is of the order of the spacing, d, even if there were a wave associated with this particle, no ruled or crystal grating of such small spacing is available to cause diffraction of the wavelength of the order of $\sim 10^{-20}$ A. Hence let us abandon this example and consider another one of much smaller mass.

Consider an electron that has been accelerated through a certain potential drop V. The mass of the electron is $m = 9.108 \times 10^{-31}$ kgm. Therefore, from the relation $\frac{1}{2}mv^2 = eV$, (assuming the nonrelativistic case), the velocity of the electron is $v = \sqrt{2eV/m}$. Hence the wavelength associated with this electron is

$$\lambda = \frac{h}{p} = \frac{h}{mv} = \frac{h}{m\sqrt{\dfrac{2eV}{m}}} = \frac{h}{\sqrt{2meV}}$$

$$= \frac{6.62 \times 10^{-34} \text{ joule-sec}}{\sqrt{2 \times 9.108 \times 10^{-31} \text{ kgm} \times (1.6 \times 10^{-19} \text{ coul} \times V)}}$$

or

$$\lambda = \sqrt{\frac{150}{V}} \times 10^{-8} \text{ cm} \qquad (5.54)$$

$\lambda = 1.78$ Å for $V = 50$ volts, which is of the order of the wavelength of x-rays for this voltage. Thus it should be possible to cause the diffraction of a beam of electrons from a crystal grating in a manner similar to the diffraction of x-rays.

From this discussion we conclude that in order to observe diffraction of particles, we should consider only those particles for which the mass is so small that the resulting de Broglie waves associated with them are of the order a few Å.

We shall next discuss the following aspects of particle diffraction:

A. The Electron Diffraction Experiment of Davisson and Germer
B. The Diffraction Experiments of G. P. Thomson
C. The Diffraction of Neutrons
D. The Diffraction of Neutral Atoms

A. The Electron Diffraction Experiment of Davisson and Germer[17]

The first direct experimental confirmation of the de Broglie hypothesis that there are some sort of waves associated with particles came through the experiments of Davisson and Germer in 1927 in the United States. The two physicists at Bell Telephone Laboratories were investigating secondary electron emission using the experimental arrangement shown in Fig. 5.26. Sec-

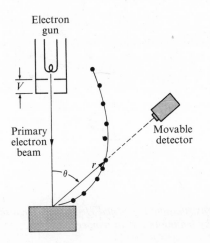

FIG. 5.26. *A typical experimental arrangement used for the investigation of secondary electron emission and the diffraction of electrons.*

ondary electrons are the electrons emitted from a solid when a beam of fast-moving electrons strikes it. In some cases the number of secondary electrons emitted is greater than the number of incident electrons.

The electrons obtained from the electron gun, as shown in Fig. 5.26, are accelerated in the range of a few electron-volts to a few hundred electron-volts. The particular solid under investigation by Davisson and Germer was polycrystalline nickel. The aim was to measure the intensity of the scattered electrons with the help of a movable detector as a function of the angle θ, which is the angle between the direction of emission and the direction of the incident electrons. According to classical theory, the distribution of the scattered electrons should be very much independent of the incident energy while the number of secondary electrons coming out at any angle should be proportional to cos θ. This was found to be the case as illustrated by the dotted line shown in Fig. 5.26, except for the minor variations. In this diagram the intensity is proportional to the radial distance r as shown and varies with θ.

As is usual in vacuum work, the system had some leaks. Air inside the apparatus oxidized the nickel. The nickel had to be baked in a high-temperature oven (in an inert gas atmosphere) to clean it. When the experiment was repeated with the heated sample, the results were quite different. There was a pronounced maximum at a particular angle for a given primary electron-energy, as shown in Fig. 5.27. The results of a particular set of experiments

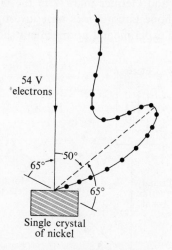

54 V
electrons

65°

50°

65°

Single crystal
of nickel

FIG. 5.27. *Distribution of emitted electrons after a nickel crystal had been cleaned by baking in a high-temperature oven.*

are illustrated in Fig. 5.28. In this latter case the detector was fixed at an angle of 50°, while the energy of electrons was varied in steps. It is quite clear that there is a maximum when the incident electron energy is 54 eV and the angle between the incident and the scattered electrons is 50°. Of course, there is

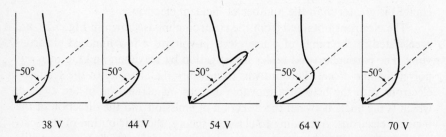

38 V   44 V   54 V   64 V   70 V

FIG. 5.28. *Distribution of electrons, at a fixed angle of 50°, for different accelerating voltages, i.e., for different incident electron energies.*

still secondary emission on which this maximum is superimposed. Putting the facts learned with the heated crystal together with the de Broglie hypothesis, as we shall explain below, it became clear that Davisson and Germer were observing the diffraction of electrons from crystals similar to the diffraction of x-rays from crystals.

An ordinary, polycrystalline, nickel sample consists of many small crystals, microcrystals, and these are oriented randomly in all directions. The beam of electrons striking such a sample will result in incoherent scattering of electrons. The effect of heating the nickel sample is to orient the microcrystals in the sample in such a way that the sample becomes one large single crystal so that all the atoms are aligned in a nearly perfect order, forming a regular lattice throughout the whole sample. The Bragg planes drawn through these atoms are illustrated by parallel lines in Fig. 5.27. For nickel the spacing between the Bragg planes as found from x-ray diffraction is $d = 0.91$ Å. From Fig. 5.27, the angle θ to be used in equation $2d \sin \theta = n\lambda$ is $(180° - 50°)/2 = 65°$. Thus according to Bragg's law given by Eq. (5.51), the wavelength resulting in such a diffraction is given by

$$n\lambda = 2d \sin \theta$$

or, for $n = 1$,

$$\lambda = 2d \sin \theta = 2 \times 0.91 \times \sin 65° = 1.65 \text{ Å} \tag{5.55}$$

If this is the wavelength associated with the incident electron, we should be able to arrive at the same result by using the de Broglie hypothesis, or $\lambda = h/p = h/mv$, where v is the velocity of the electron. In the present case, the electrons have an energy of 54 electron volts. Using Eq. (5.54), the de Broglie wavelength associated with these electrons is

$$\lambda = \left(\frac{h}{p}\right) = \frac{h}{\sqrt{2meV}} = \left(\frac{150}{V}\right)^{1/2} 10^{-8} \text{ cm}$$

$$= \left(\frac{150}{54}\right)^{1/2} 10^{-8} \text{ cm} = 1.67 \text{ Å} \tag{5.56}$$

which is in agreement with the wavelength given by Eq. (5.55). Hence it was confirmed that the electrons undergo diffraction as do x-rays, showing that there is some sort of wave associated with the electron and that the measured wavelength agrees with the wavelength predicted by the de Broglie hypothesis. (We may note that there will be corrections needed because of the change in energy as the electrons enter the crystal, and the presence of other Bragg planes complicate the problem further.)

It should be noted, as we shall discuss later, that whether a particle will behave like a particle or wave or whether a wave will behave like a wave or a particle depends upon the kind of experiment performed.

B. The Diffraction Experiments of G. P. Thomson[18]

Shortly after the confirmation of the de Broglie wave concept by Davisson and Germer, G. P. Thomson observed diffraction patterns by using much faster electrons, accelerated through many kilovolts that impinged on thin metallic foils. The experimental arrangement is shown in Fig. 5.29, which is

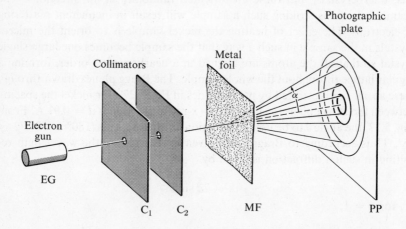

FIG. 5.29. *An experimental arrangement used for observing the diffraction of fast-moving electrons from a thin metallic foil.*

very similar to that shown in Fig. 5.24 used for observing diffraction of x-rays by thin foils. A beam of fast electrons is obtained from the electron gun and after being collimated by the collimators C_1 and C_2 it impinges on a thin foil. The foil is about 1000 Å thick, and it consists of a large number of micro-crystals oriented randomly. Because of the presence of all possible crystal orientations, the diffracted beam (in this case de Broglie waves of the diffracted electrons) will form a cone the axis of which lies along the direction of the incident beam. The angle α of this cone as shown in Fig. 5.29 is related to the θ shown in Fig. 5.24 by the relation $\alpha = 2\theta$ and $2d \sin \theta = n\lambda$, where λ is the wavelength of the electrons. For various Bragg planes there will be various cones making different angles. Thus if this diffracted beam is received on a photographic plate, many concentric circles will appear as shown in the photograph[19] of Fig. 5.30.

Even though the wavelength associated with these fast electrons is very small, by moving the photographic plate away from the scattering foil, a measurable size diffraction pattern is obtained. Thus, for example, for 50 keV electrons, λ from Eq. (5.54) is about 5.5×10^{-10} cm. For $d = 2.2 \times 10^{-8}$ cm, the expression

$$2d \sin \theta = n\lambda$$

becomes for $n = 1$, $\alpha = 2\theta$, and $\sin \theta \approx \theta$,

$$2d \sin \alpha/2 \simeq d\alpha = \lambda$$

or

$$\alpha \simeq \frac{5.5 \times 10^{-10}}{2.2 \times 10^{-8}} \text{ radians} = 1.6 \text{ degrees} \qquad \textbf{(5.57)}$$

Note that the diffraction pattern of Fig. 5.30 obtained by using an electron beam is very similar to the diffraction pattern of Fig. 5.25 using x-rays.

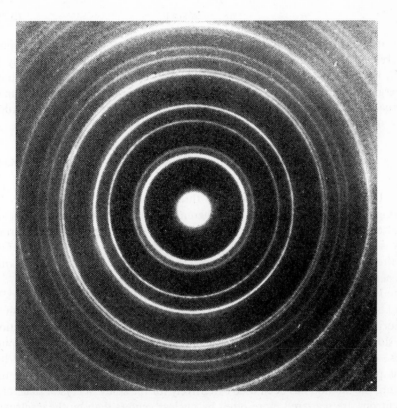

FIG. 5.30. *Photograph of a diffraction pattern of fast-moving electrons from a thin silver foil. [Courtesy, L. H. Germer, Bell Telephone Laboratories.]*

These two early experiments have established beyond doubt the de Broglie hypothesis, and lead to the conclusion that under different conditions matter can be made to be observed as particles or as waves. We shall now proceed with some further details concerning the diffraction of particles.

C. The Diffraction of Neutrons

W. Elsasser[20] and G. Wick[21] were the first to suggest that it might be possible to obtain diffraction patterns using slow neutrons. According to the de Broglie hypothesis, a neutron of mass m, velocity v, and energy E will have a wavelength λ given by

$$\lambda = h/mv = h/\sqrt{2mE} \qquad (5.58)$$

and as before, the Bragg condition is

$$n\lambda = 2d \sin \theta \qquad (5.59)$$

Because for diffraction to take place the spacing d must be of the order of the wavelength of the particle, this method, therefore, is limited exclusively to very low energy neutrons. It is possible to cause diffraction of neutrons whose energies are about 20 eV; and this limit is determined by the crystal planes. Usually the observation of neutron diffraction is limited to the first order, $n = 1$. For $n = 1$, combining Eqs. (5.58) and (5.59),

$$E = \frac{h^2}{8\,md^2 \sin^2 \theta} \qquad (5.60)$$

It may be noted that there are three different kinds of neutron scattering[22] that may take place: (a) coherent scattering, in which neutrons are scattered in phase; (b) incoherent, or diffused, scattering in which neutrons are scattered in random phase; and (c) inelastic scattering. It is coherent scattering that produces diffraction patterns by interference, and it is the kind of neutron scattering that we are interested in here.

Neutron diffraction was first observed by D. Mitchell and P. Powers[23] and by H. Halban and P. Preiswerk[24]. Crystals like calcium fluoride, lithium fluoride, and magnesium oxide can cause appreciable amounts of diffraction of slow neutron beams. Though originally this method was used for the purpose of obtaining a well-defined beam of neutrons, it is no longer used for this purpose. On the contrary, knowing the energy of the neutrons in the beam, the method has been used extensively for the study of crystal structure. Neutrons are scattered more often by nuclear centers than by the electrons; as a result the method has proved useful in identifying the positions of atoms in crystals. As x-rays are scattered more often by electrons, the study of x-ray and neutron scattering together is used for locating clusters of electrons and atoms in complicated crystals. With the availability of high-intensity beams of thermal neutrons from nuclear reactors, the investigation of crystal structure by this method has reached a high degree of perfection. The wavelength associated with thermal neutrons, i.e., neutrons that are in thermal equilibrium at room temperature, may be calculated as follows. From kinetic theory, the kinetic energy of a thermal neutron at room temperature $T(=27°\text{C}$ or $300°\text{K})$

$$K = \frac{1}{2}mv^2 = \frac{3}{2}kT \qquad (5.61)$$

where k is the Boltzmann constant, and m and v are the neutron mass and velocity, respectively. At $300°\text{K}$, K is of the order of $1/40$ eV. Thus

$$\tfrac{1}{2}mv^2 = \frac{p^2}{2m} = \frac{1}{2m}(h/\lambda)^2 = \frac{3}{2}kT$$

or

$$\lambda = \frac{h}{\sqrt{3mkT}} \qquad (5.62)$$

which for thermal neutrons gives $\lambda = 1.80$ Å.

Different arrangements have been used by W. Zinn[25], E. Wollan and C. Shull[26], and by others. A typical schematic of an experimental arrangement[27] is shown in Fig. 5.31, while the results obtained by Shull and Wolan[28] are shown in Fig. 5.32.

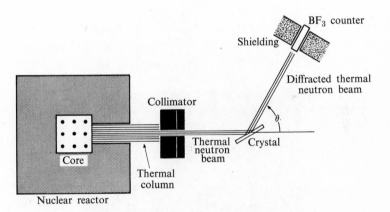

FIG. 5.31.   *A schematic diagram of neutron diffraction from a crystal. The angle of diffraction, θ, is determined by the Bragg's condition.* [*From: Arya, A. P.*, Fundamentals of Nuclear Physics, *p. 492, Boston: Allyn and Bacon, Inc., 1966.*]

D.   The Diffraction of Neutral Atoms

Estermann and Stern[29] in 1930 showed that even the neutral atoms show diffraction patterns. A lithium fluoride crystal was used as a diffraction grating, and a beam of helium atoms at $400°\text{K}$, which according to Eq. (5.62)

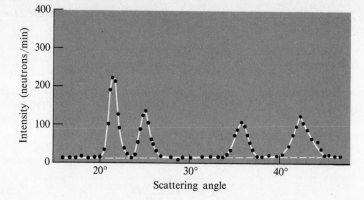

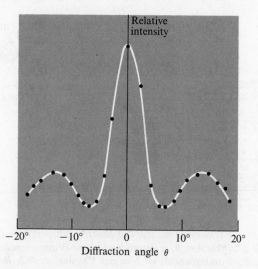

FIG. 5.32.   *The diffraction pattern of monoenergetic slow neutrons from powdered Pb.* [*From Shull, C. G., and E. W. Wollan*, Phys. Rev., *81, 527, (1951).*]

has a wavelength of 0.6 Å, was used as the incident beam. The scattered beam was detected by means of a very sensitive pressure gauge. The diffraction pattern (or distribution) obtained[30] is shown in Fig. 5.33.

FIG. 5.33.   *The diffraction distribution of neutral helium atoms using a lithium fluoride crystal as a grating.* [*From: Estermann and Stern*, Z. Physik, *61, 95, (1930).*]

PROBLEMS

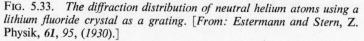

1.   A beam of light of wavelength 5500 Å strikes a metal surface for which the threshold wavelength is 7250 Å. Calculate (a) the work function in eV, (b) the

incident energy in eV, and (c) the maximum kinetic energy of the emitted electron. Find the stopping potential of the photoelectrons.

2. Will an ultraviolet light of wavelength 2000 Å falling on a tungsten surface, for which the work function is 4.53 eV, cause photoelectron emission? If so, what will be the kinetic energy of the emitted electron?

3. What should be the wavelength and frequency of the incident electromagnetic radiation so that photoelectrons emitted from sodium will have a maximum kinetic energy of 5 eV? The work function of sodium is 2.3 eV. What will be the wavelength of the threshold incident radiation?

4. A beam of light of wavelength 5000 Å is incident on a surface for which the work function is 1.8 eV. If the intensity of the beam is 4×10^{-11} watts/cm², calculate (a) the energy absorbed per cm² per sec, (b) the kinetic energy of the photoelectrons emitted, and (c) the number of electrons emitted per cm² per sec.

5. What should be the frequency of electromagnetic radiation incident on a potassium surface so that an emitted electron will have a velocity of (a) $0.1c$, and (b) $0.9c$? The work function of potassium is 2.20 eV.

6. A photon of wavelength 10 Å is incident on (a) a copper atom, and (b) a hydrogen atom. In the process the photons disappear and electrons are emitted. Calculate (i) the kinetic energies and velocities of the emitted electrons, and (ii) the kinetic energies and the velocities of the positive ions. The work functions for copper and hydrogen are 4.5 eV and 13.6 eV, respectively.

7. The binding energy of an inner electron in lead is 89.1 eV. When a lead radiator is bombarded with photons, the photoelectrons emitted from the lead enter a magnetic field of 10^{-2} weber/m² in which the electrons describe a circle of radius 0.25 m. Calculate (a) the energy of the incident photons, (b) the momentum of the photoelectrons, and (c) the relativistic kinetic energy of the photoelectrons.

8. Show that the photoelectric effect takes place only between photons and bound electrons, i.e., it is impossible for a photon to give up all its energy and momentum to a free electron.

9. Calculate the voltages applied across an x-ray tube in order to produce x-rays of wavelengths (a) 1 Å, (b) 0.5 Å, and (c) 0.1 Å.

10. An electron evaporated from a cathode is accelerated to an anode by a potential difference of 40 kV. (a) Calculate the final kinetic energy of the electrons before hitting the anode. (b) If the electron is suddenly brought to rest, what is the maximum frequency of the x-ray produced? (c) What changes will be observed in (a) and (b) and in the x-ray spectrum if the temperature of the cathode is changed?

11. A beam of electrons passing perpendicularly through a magnetic field of 0.005 weber/m² is bent into a circle of radius 25 cm. What will be the shortest wavelength (and maximum frequency) of the photons emitted when these electrons strike a metallic target?

12. (a) Calculate the wavelength associated with photons of energies 10 MeV, 20 MeV, and 100 MeV.
    (b) What are the wavelengths associated with photons of energies 3×10^{-19} joule and 4×10^{-13} joule?

13. What should be the energy, frequency, and wavelength of a photon for it to have the same momentum as (a) a 5 MeV electron, and (b) a 5 MeV proton?

14. If a photon and a proton have approximately the same momentum, what will be their energies?

15. For two monochromatic beams of equal intensities and of wavelengths λ_1 and λ_2, calculate the ratio of the number of photons of the two wavelengths crossing per unit area per sec.

16. A hydrogen atom at rest absorbs a photon of 10 keV. This results in the ejection of an electron in the same direction as the incident radiation. Calculate the momentum and energy of the electron and the proton (or H^+), neglecting the binding energy of 13.6 eV of the electron and the proton. Is the assumption true that the binding energy can be neglected?

17. X-rays of 500 keV are incident on a target of almost-free electrons. What is the energy and the angle of the scattered photons if the recoil energy of the electron is 350 keV?

18. Photons of 0.01 Å are scattered from free electrons. The wavelength of the photons scattered at an angle of 45° is 0.02 Å. Calculate the angle and energy of the recoil electron. What are the frequencies of the incident and the scattered photons?

19. A beam of monochromatic photons of wavelength 0.15 Å strikes a copper target. What two predominant wavelengths will be detected (a) at 60° and (b) at 90°. Calculate also the momentum and energy of the recoiling electron.

20. A beam of 500 keV electrons is brought to rest in a metallic target and produces x-ray photons. These photons are scattered by free electrons in a carbon target. Calculate the maximum kinetic energy, momentum, velocity, and direction of the recoil Compton electron. What is the direction, momentum, and energy of the corresponding scattered photon?

21. The recoil Compton electrons of maximum kinetic energy move in a circle of 5 cm radius when passing perpendicularly through a magnetic flux density of 0.30 weber/m^2. Calculate the energy of the incident photons.

22. Calculate the de Broglie wavelengths associated with the following particles moving with a velocity of 10^9 cm/sec: (a) electron, and (b) proton.

23. Calculate the de Broglie wavelength associated with (a) 50 keV electron, and (b) 50 keV proton. How do these wavelengths compare with the wavelength associated with 50 keV photons?

24. What is the kinetic energy of (a) an electron, and (b) a proton, whose de Broglie wavelength is equal to that of light of wavelength 6000 Å?

25. Show that the ratio of the de Broglie wavelength to the Compton wavelength of a particle of rest mass m_0 is $\sqrt{(c/v)^2 - 1}$.

26. For the case of a particle of mass m_0 and velocity v, make a plot of de Broglie wavelength λ versus v. Show that the slope $d\lambda/dv$ approaches minus infinity both at $v = 0$ and $v = c$. What do you conclude from this?

27. What are the angles at which the first three Bragg reflections will be observed if the spacing between the crystal planes is 0.5 Å and the x-rays of wavelengths 0.25 Å are used?

28. Estimate the spacing of crystal planes of a NaCl cubic crystal lattice with alternating Na and Cl atoms. The average atomic masses of Na and Cl are 22.9898U and 34.9681U, respectively.

29. Calculate the first and the second Bragg angles for the diffraction of x-rays of 0.5 Å wavelength from a calcite crystal for which the distance between adjacent planes is 3 Å.

30. The distance between the adjacent planes of a KCl crystal is 3.14 Å, while its density and molecular weight are 1.98×10^3 kgm/m^3 and 74.55, respectively. Calculate the value of Avogadro's number from this data.

31. A beam of monochromatic x-rays of wavelength 0.5 Å is incident on a sample of KCl powder, which consists of randomly oriented crystals. The lattice spacing of KCl is 3.14 Å. A flat photographic plate is placed perpendicular to the incident beam. Determine the first- and second-order Bragg radii.

32. Consider a diffraction of a beam of electrons of de Broglie wavelength 10^{-4} cm passing through a slit of 10^{-3} cm. Calculate the angular spread introduced because of diffraction.

33. Electrons after being accelerated through a potential difference of 75 volts strike a sodium chloride cubic crystal, which has a lattice spacing of 2.82 Å. Calculate the first two angles for which the Bragg condition is satisfied.

34. The reflecting planes in a crystal are 1 Å apart. What are the angles for first order reflection of neutrons with energies (a) 0.1 eV, (b) 1 eV, (c) 5 eV, and (d) 10 eV? If the minimum angle that may be measured is 25′, what is the maximum energy of the neutrons that may be diffracted?

35. At what maximum energy may neutrons be filtered through a grating with spacings of 2.1 Å between the reflecting planes?

36. A beam of thermal neutrons produced by a nuclear reactor is incident on a crystal of lattice spacing 1.6 Å. What angle should the Bragg planes make with the incident beam so that the neutrons of energy 0.025 eV are strongly diffracted at the first order? What is the angle between the incident and the diffracted beam?

REFERENCES

1. Hertz, H., *Ann. Physik*, **31**, 983, (1887).
2. Hallwachs, W., *Ann. Physik*, **33**, 301, (1888).
3. Millikan, R. A., *Phys. Rev.*, **7**, 355, (1916).
4. Einstein, A., *Ann. Physik*, **17**, 132, (1905).
5. Röntgen, W., *Sitz-ber. Phys.-med. Ges.*, Wurzburg, (1895); English translation: *Electrician*, Jan. 24, April 24, 1896.
6. Barkla, C. G., *Proc. Roy. Soc.*, **77**, 247, (1906).
7. Compton, A. H., and R. L. Doan, *Proc. Nat. Acad. Sci.*, **11**, 598, (1925).
8. Compton, A. H., *Phys. Rev.*, **21**, 715, (1923).
9. Compton, A. H., *Phys. Rev.*, **22**, 409, (1923).
10. Planck, M., *Ann. Physik*, **4**, 553, (1901).
11. de Broglie, L., *Ann. Physik*, **3**, 22, (1925).
12. Davisson, C. J., and L. J. Germer, *Phys. Rev.*, **30**, 705, (1927).
13. Thomson, G. P., *Nature*, **120**, 802, (1927).

14. Bragg, W. H., and W. L. Bragg, *X-Rays and Crystal Structure*, New York: Harcourt Brace & Co., 1924. Bragg, W. L., *Nature*, **90**, 410, (1912); Bragg, W. H., *Nature*, **91**, 477, (1913).

15. Read, M. H., Bell Telephone Laboratories, Murray Hill, N. J.

16. Debye, P., and P. Scherrer, *Zeit. fur Physik*, **17**, 277, (1916).

17. Davisson, C. J., and L. J. Germer, *Nature*, **119**, 558, (1927); *Phys. Rev.*, **30**, 705, (1927).

18. Thomson, G. P., *Nature*, **120**, 802, (1927), and **122**, 279, (1928); *Proc. Roy. Soc.*, A117, 600, (1928), and A119, 651, (1928).

19. Mark, H., and R. Wierl, *Zeit. fur Physik*, **60**, 743, (1930).

20. Elsasser, W. M., *Compt. Rend.*, **202**, 1029, (1936).

21. Wick, G. C., *Z. Physik*, **38**, 403, 689, (1937).

22. Fermi, E., and L. Marshall, *Phys. Rev.*, **72**, 193, (1947).

23. Mitchell, D. P., and P. N. Powers, *Phys. Rev.*, **50**, 486, (1936).

24. Halban, H., and P. Preiswerk, *Compt. Rend.*, **203**, 73, (1936).

25. Zinn, W. H., *Phys. Rev.*, **71**, 752, (1947).

26. Wollan, E. O., and C. G. Shull, *Nucleonics*, **3**, 8, (1948).

27. Arya, A. P., *Fundamentals of Nuclear Physics*, p. 492. Boston: Allyn and Bacon, Inc., 1966.

28. Shull, C. G., and E. O. Wollan, *Phys. Rev.*, **81**, 527, (1951).

29. Estermann, I., and O. Stern, *Z. Physik*, **61**, 95, (1930).

30. Estermann, I., and O. Stern, *Phys. Rev.*, **45**, 761, (1934).

SUGGESTIONS FOR FURTHER READING

1. Maurer, R. J., "Photoelectric Effect," in *Handbook of Physics*. Ed. E. U. Condon and H. Odishaw. New York: McGraw-Hill, 1959.

2. Arons, A. B., and M. B. Peppard, *Am. J. Phys.*, **33**, 367, (1965). [This is a translation of the *Ann. Physik* paper of 1905.]

3. Hughes, A. L., and L. A. DuBridge, *Photoelectric Phenomena*, New York: McGraw-Hill, 1932.

4. Compton, A. H., and S. K. Allison, *X-Rays in Theory and Experiment*, 2nd ed., Princeton, N. J.: D. Van Nostrand, 1935.

5. Compton, A., *Am. J. Phys.*, **29**, 817, (1961).

6. Shamos, M., ed., *Great Experiments in Physics*, Chap. 17, Appen. 2 and 5, New York: Holt, Rinehart and Winston, 1938.

7. de Broglie, L., *Physics and Microphysics* (Torchbooks), New York: Harper and Row, 1960.

8. Gamow, George, *Thirty Years That Shook Physics*, Garden City: Doubleday, 1966.

9. Meyer, Charles F., *The Diffraction of Light, X-Rays, and Material Particles*, Chicago: Univ. of Chicago Press, 1934.

10. Thomson, G., *Am. J. Phys.*, **29**, 821, (1961).

VI

Introduction to Quantum Mechanics

1. THE NEED FOR A NEW THEORY

In the previous chapter we have established beyond doubt that a particle may be observed as a particle or as a wave depending upon the experimental setup; similarly, a wave may be observed as a wave or a particle. Actually it is meaningless to assign positively either one or the other aspect to a wave or a particle. We showed that the de Broglie relation

$$p = \frac{h}{\lambda} \tag{6.1}$$

is true not only for electromagnetic waves but also for particles of matter. This assertion by de Broglie was not something completely new. A close similarity between the laws of geometrical optics and those of classical mechanics had been noticed as early as the first half of the nineteenth century by Hamilton[1]. In 1650 Fermat[2] stated the *principle of least time* according to which a ray of light of wavelength λ traveling in a heterogeneous (but isotropic) medium from point A to point B takes the path for which the time to travel is a minimum or a maximum. Mathematically, this variational principle is written as

$$\delta \int_A^B \frac{ds}{\lambda} = 0 \tag{6.2}$$

where ds is a small element of path length, and $\lambda = \lambda(x, y, z, \nu)$; ν is the frequency, which is constant. With the help of this principle it is possible to explain several phenomena in geometrical optics, such as reflection and refraction at plane boundaries, the focusing properties of concave mirrors, and others.

An analogous situation in classical mechanics is known as the *principle of least action*, which was given by Maupertuis[3] in 1740 and was mathematically formulated by Euler and Lagrange[4]. According to this principle, a particle of rest mass m_0 and total energy E, moving in a conservative field of potential $V = V(x, y, z)$ from point A to a point B takes that path for which

$$\delta \int_A^B \sqrt{2m_0(E - V)}\, ds = 0 \tag{6.3}$$

or because the momentum of the particle $p = \sqrt{2m_0(E - V)}$,

$$\delta \int p\, ds = 0 \tag{6.4}$$

where p is the classical momentum of the particle and $p = p(x, y, z, E)$, E being constant.

The two paths, the optical path given by Eq. (6.2) and the path of the particle according to classical mechanics given by Eq. (6.4), will be identical if one sets

$$p = \frac{K}{\lambda} \tag{6.5}$$

where K is a constant. Note that the unvaried ν in optics and unvaried E in mechanics play similar roles, and thus one would expect that in accordance with Eq. (6.5)

$$E = K'\nu \tag{6.6}$$

where K' is a constant. Comparing Eq. (6.5) with Eq. (6.1), one finds that the originality of de Broglie's contribution was in taking K to be Planck's constant h. Basing his argument on the relativistic invariance, de Broglie showed[5] that if $p = h/\lambda$ is true, then $E = h\nu$, and hence K' is also equal to Planck's constant h. Thus, we see that there is a formal similarity between the laws governing the path of a ray of light in a refractive medium and the laws governing the path of a particle in a potential field.

The introduction of the quantum of electromagnetic radiation by Planck and its application to different experimental observations, as investigated in the two previous chapters, clearly established the particle-like, or quantum, properties of electromagnetic radiation. Although we did establish that waves of some sort are associated with particles like electrons, protons, and neutrons, nothing was said about the characteristics of the waves. Thus the problem facing us at present is two-fold. First, what are the characteristics of the waves, the de Broglie waves, associated with these particles? Second, we must look for a new mathematical theory that will describe the dual nature equally well. The answer to the first question is given in the next section that describes the wave packets, or pilot waves, (so-called by de Broglie), associated with the particles. A solution to the second problem was given by Schrödinger[6] who developed a new mathematical formalism called quantum mechanics or wave mechanics, which will be formally developed in this chapter and applied to several experimental situations.

2. WAVE PACKETS TO DESCRIBE PARTICLES

We want to find out what type of waves are associated with particles. Of course, we can find a characteristic frequency ν associated with a particle of rest mass m_0 by making use of the Einstein relation

$$h\nu = m_0 c^2 \tag{6.7}$$

and the equation of the wave will be, denoting the displacement by ψ,

$$\psi = A \sin 2\pi\nu t \tag{6.8}$$

or in a more general form, setting wave number $k = 2\pi/\lambda$ and $\omega = 2\pi\nu$,

$$\Psi(x, t) = A \sin 2\pi\left(\frac{x}{\lambda} - \nu t\right)$$

or

$$\Psi(x, t) = A \sin\left(kx - \omega t\right) \tag{6.9}$$

The wave motion corresponding to Eq. (6.9) is shown in Fig. 6.1 and is a

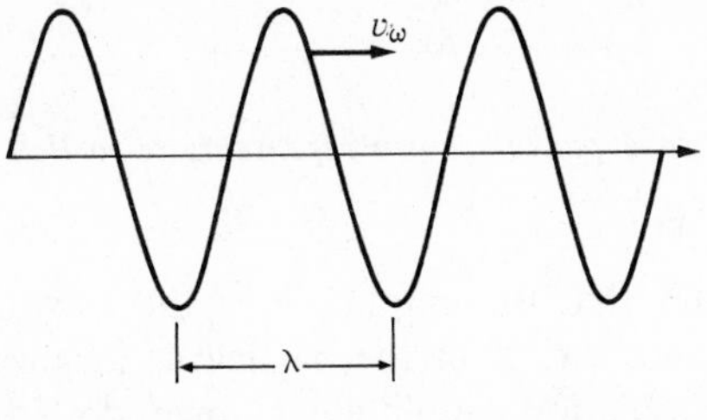

FIG. 6.1.   *A continuous harmonic wave as shown may be taken to represent an unlocalized particle.*

harmonic wave of constant amptitude. Using the de Broglie hypothesis and the relativistic relation, we can calculate the propagation velocity v_ω of the wave

$$v_\omega = \nu\lambda = \frac{E}{h}\frac{h}{p} = \frac{E}{p} \tag{6.10}$$

because $E^2 = p^2 c^2 + m_0^2 c^4$, we get

$$v_\omega = \frac{E}{p} = \frac{\sqrt{p^2c^2 + m_0^2c^4}}{p} = \sqrt{c^2 + \frac{m_0^2c^4}{p^2}}$$

$$= c\sqrt{1 + \left(\frac{m_0c}{p}\right)^2} \tag{6.11}$$

Equation (6.11) states that the wave velocity, v_ω, is greater than c, while the particle velocity, v_p, as we know is always less than c. Thus even though the particle and its associated wave may start together, eventually they will part, and thus Eq. (6.9) does not have much meaning. Besides, another difficulty is that any particle at any time is well localized in space, while the harmonic wave of Eq. (6.9) has no localization properties, and, on the contrary, is completely spread out.

A wave is characterized by its continuity. On the other hand, a particle is characterized by its localizability in space. Thus in order for a wave to represent a particle, the wave must have the following two properties: (a) its velocity must be the same as that of the particle, or $v_\omega = v_p$, and (b) the wave must have some localization properties in order to represent a particle. As an example, Fig. 6.2 represents a wave packet that has a localization

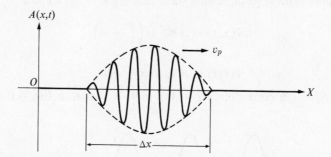

FIG. 6.2. *The wave packet shown represents a particle that is somewhere within Δx.*

property and indicates that the amplitude of the wave is zero everywhere except within a distance Δx. Thus the particle is localized to within a distance Δx. If the modulation amplitude (shown dotted) should have the velocity equal to the particle velocity, v_p, the above-mentioned conditions will be satisfied. The wave packets of the type shown in Fig. 6.2 can be constructed by the combination of waves of different frequencies, which in turn leads to the concept of group velocity, v_g, which is equal to the particle velocity, as we shall show below.

For the sake of mathematical simplicity, instead of considering a large number of waves of different frequencies, let us consider only two waves of slightly different frequencies and wave numbers but of equal amplitudes, i.e.,

$$\Psi_1(x, t) = A \sin (kx - \omega t) \tag{6.12}$$

and

$$\Psi_2(x, t) = A \sin [(k + \Delta k)x - (\omega + \Delta\omega)t] \qquad (6.13)$$

The sum of these two waves is a wave given by

$$\Psi(x, t) = \Psi_1(x, t) + \Psi_2(x, t) \qquad (6.14)$$

Substituting for Ψ_1 and Ψ_2 and using the result

$$\sin C + \sin D = 2 \cos \frac{C - D}{2} \sin \frac{C + D}{2}$$

we get

$$\Psi(x, t) = 2A \cos \left[\frac{\Delta k}{2} x - \frac{\Delta\omega}{2} t\right] \sin \left[\left(k + \frac{\Delta k}{2}\right)x - \left(\omega + \frac{\Delta\omega}{2}\right)t\right]$$

Neglecting $\Delta k/2$ as compared to k and $\Delta\nu/2$ as compared to ν, we get

$$\Psi(x, t) = 2A \cos \left(\frac{\Delta k}{2} x - \frac{\Delta\omega}{2} t\right) \sin (kx - \omega t) \qquad (6.15)$$

This represents a wave of original frequency ν, but with a modulated amplitude as shown in Fig. 6.3 where $\Psi(x, t)$ has been plotted versus x. The amplitude modulation factor A_m is

$$A_m = 2 \cos \left(\frac{\Delta k}{2} x - \frac{\Delta\omega}{2} t\right) \qquad (6.16)$$

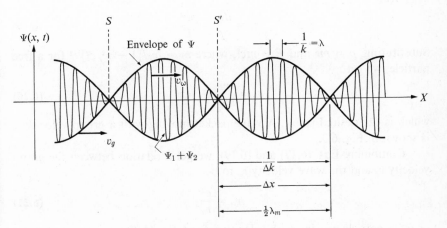

FIG. 6.3. *Illustration of the concept of superposition of waves and the relation between phase velocity and group velocity.*

The portion SS' represents a group of waves and moves with a certain velocity, the group velocity v_g, while the individual waves still move with the phase velocity v_ω. The phase velocity v_ω is calculated from the second term of Eq. (6.15) as

$$v_\omega = \frac{\omega}{k} \tag{6.17}$$

while the group velocity v_g is calculated from the first part of Eq. (6.15) or from Eq. (6.16), i.e.,

$$v_g = \frac{\Delta\omega/2}{\Delta k/2}$$

or in the limit $\Delta k \to 0$,

$$v_g = \frac{d\omega}{dk} \tag{6.18}$$

Thus according to Eq. (6.15) and Fig. 6.3, we have been able to construct wave packets, and we shall now show that the modulated amplitude that moves with velocity v_g is equal to the velocity v of the free particle. Because

$$\omega = \frac{E}{\hbar} \quad \text{and} \quad k = \frac{2\pi}{\lambda} = \frac{1}{\lambda} = \frac{p}{\hbar}$$

we get from Eq. (6.18)

$$v_g = \frac{d\omega}{dk} = \frac{dE/\hbar}{dp/\hbar} = \frac{dE}{dp}$$

but

$$E^2 = p^2c^2 + m_0^2c^4, \qquad \frac{dE}{dp} = \frac{pc^2}{E}$$

Therefore,

$$v_g = \frac{dE}{dp} = \frac{pc^2}{E} \tag{6.19}$$

Substituting, $p = mv$ and $E = mc^2$, where $m = m_0/[1 - v^2/c^2]^{1/2}$ for a free particle, we get

$$v_g = \frac{mv}{mc^2}c^2 = v \tag{6.20}$$

which is the desired result. A wave packet moving with a group velocity v_g is shown in Fig. 6.3.

Combining Eqs. (6.17) and (6.19), we get a relation between the group velocity v_g and the wave velocity v_ω to be

$$v_\omega = \frac{c^2}{v_g} \tag{6.21}$$

or for a particle moving with velocity v, from Eq. (6.20)

$$v_\omega = \frac{c^2}{v} \tag{6.22}$$

Because v is less than c, v_ω is larger than v_g, which means that in a particular group the individual waves are constantly moving from the rear to the front. We can also show (see Problem 6.4) that for a particle, or quantum, moving with velocity c, the group velocity is equal to the wave velocity.

In the above discussion we have taken a simplified example considering only two frequencies. But the problem is really much more complex. One must consider a very large number of frequencies and sum the waves according to the techniques of Fourier analysis[7,8]. Without going into the details, we state that the sum of these waves is given by

$$\Psi(x, t) = \frac{1}{\sqrt{2\pi}} \int_{-\infty}^{\infty} g(k)e^{i[kx - \omega(k)t]} \, dk \qquad (6.23)$$

where $g(k)$ is the amplitude modulation. From the argument of the exponent we see that the wave velocity is

$$\frac{x}{t} = \frac{dx}{dt} = \frac{\omega}{k} \qquad (6.24)$$

while the point of maximum of the amplitude-modulation factor moves with a velocity obtained by setting

$$\frac{\partial}{\partial k}(kx - \omega t) = 0$$

or

$$x - \frac{\partial \omega}{\partial k}t = 0$$

i.e.,

$$\frac{x}{t} = \frac{\partial \omega}{\partial k} = v_g \qquad (6.25)$$

as before.

From these considerations, it is possible to construct, by proper choice of $g(k)$, wave packets that will look like the one shown in Fig. 6.4. The weigh-

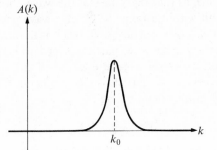

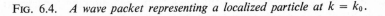

FIG. 6.4.   *A wave packet representing a localized particle at* $k = k_0$.

ing factor $g(k)$ is such that it is zero everywhere except in the vicinity of $k = k_0$. Thus we see that by proper combination of ν (or ω) and $g(k)$, we can construct wave packets looking more or less like a particle.

There are some other conditions that ought to be satisfied by $\Psi(x, t)$. We shall discuss these when we start with the mathematical formulation in Sections 3 and 4.

3. THE UNCERTAINTY PRINCIPLE

Much is gained by ascribing a dual nature to material particles and waves. But this gain is not without a sacrifice that comes in the form of a lower limit to the accuracy in the simultaneous determination of the following pairs of quantities.

(a) A simultaneous determination of position and linear momentum of a particle.
(b) A simultaneous determination of an angle and the angular momentum of a particle.
(c) A simultaneous determination of energy and life-time of a particle.

The limitation to the accuracy of these quantities comes from the fact that it is impossible to apply simultaneously the wave and particle description of a material particle or a photon. For example, if a moving particle is to be regarded as a de Broglie wave group instead of a localized entity, the result is that there is a fundamental limit to the accuracy with which we can measure its position and momentum simultaneously. The same is true of (b) and (c). We shall investigate the order of the magnitude of the limit of this accuracy in the following.

In the previous section we saw that in order to ascribe wave properties to a particle we were led to the construction of wave packets describing the position and momentum of the particle. This leads to the fact that the particle is no longer localized but is spread over a distance Δx as in Fig. 6.2 or in Fig. 6.3. This also means that the values of the wave numbers that make up this wave packet fall within a range Δk. If this wave packet is very narrow as in Fig. 6.4, it localizes the particle well, but it is hard to establish its wave length. On the contrary if the wave packet (or group) is very wide as shown in Fig. 6.3, one can easily get a good estimate of the wavelength but it is hard to find exactly where the particle is located. From Fig. 6.3, it is obvious that Δx is inversely proportional to Δk, i.e.,

$$\Delta x \, \Delta k \simeq 1 \qquad (6.26)$$

According to Eq. (6.23) and the Fourier analysis technique[9], $\Delta x \, \Delta k \simeq 2\pi$. We may arrive at a slightly different result from the following considerations. The width of each group from Fig. 6.3 is

$$\Delta x \approx \frac{1}{2} \lambda_m \qquad (6.27)$$

where λ_m is the wavelength of the modulation amplitude. From Fig. 6.3, the wave number of the modulation is

$$k_m = \frac{2\pi}{\lambda_m} = \frac{1}{2}\Delta k \tag{6.28}$$

Combining Eqs. (6.27) and (6.28), we get

$$\Delta x \approx \frac{1}{2}\lambda_m = \frac{1}{2}\frac{2\pi}{\Delta k/2}$$

or

$$\Delta x \, \Delta k \approx 2\pi \tag{6.29}$$

Now according to the de Broglie hypothesis $p = h/\lambda = hk/2\pi$, therefore,

$$\Delta k = \frac{2\pi}{h}\Delta p \tag{6.30}$$

substituting for Δk from Eq. (6.30) into Eq. (6.29),

$$\Delta x \, \Delta p \approx h$$

or more generally, because this is the lowest limit on the size of packet for locating the particle within Δx, we may write

$$\Delta x \, \Delta p \geqslant h \tag{6.31}$$

According to Eq. (6.31) if we say that a particle is completely localized at x so that its uncertainty $\Delta x = 0$, then $\Delta p \to \infty$, i.e., nothing is known about the momentum of the particle. We may say that the information about the localization of the particle is obtained at the expense of the knowledge about its momentum. Similarly, if the momentum of the particle is known precisely without any error or uncertainty, then $\Delta p = 0$, but $\Delta x \to \infty$, i.e., the particle is completely unlocalized and may be anywhere in space. The relation of Eq. (6.31) was given by Heisenberg[10] in 1927, and is known as *Heisenberg's uncertainty principle;* it is stated as: *It is impossible to know simultaneously and precisely both the position and the momentum of a particle.*

A more sophisticated and complete analysis[10] yields the following for the uncertainty principle (using the notation $h/2\pi = \hbar$, h bar)

$$\Delta x \, \Delta p \geqslant \hbar \tag{6.32}$$

For a particle moving in three dimensions, there are three independent uncertainty relations, one for each coordinate. If p_x, p_y, and p_z are the components of linear momentum corresponding to the rectangular coordinates x, y, and z, we may write the uncertainty relations as

$$\Delta x \, \Delta p_x \geqslant \hbar \tag{6.33a}$$

$$\Delta y \, \Delta p_y \geqslant \hbar \tag{6.33b}$$

$$\Delta z \, \Delta p_z \geqslant \hbar \tag{6.33c}$$

In case there is angular motion in some coordinate, say, L_θ, being the angular momentum corresponding to the angle θ, the uncertainty relation takes the form

$$\Delta\theta \, \Delta L_\theta \gtrsim \hbar \qquad (6.34)$$

We may point out that the uncertainty principle puts a lowest possible limit on the precision of the simultaneous measurement of certain quantities as in Eqs. (6.33) and (6.34) and has nothing to do with actual experimental accuracy. Actual errors are much more than the limit imposed by the uncertainty principle. No matter how precise the experimental apparatus may be, the uncertainty limit will still exist. As a matter of fact this uncertainty principle expresses a fundamental limitation on the accuracy with which a particle may be observed.

In order to understand that the limit imposed by the uncertainty principle is not due to any instrumental error but is an inherent nature of the observation process, we consider the following experiment. Suppose an electron is traveling along the Y axis as shown in Fig. 6.5. If the electron passes through

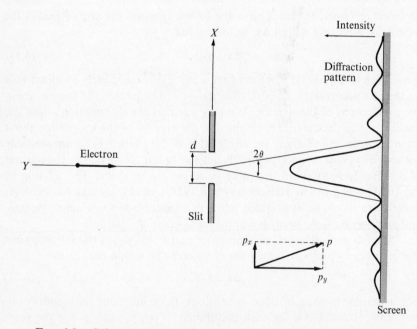

FIG. 6.5. *Schematic for measuring the position and momentum of a particle passing through a slit and leading to the uncertainty relation* $\Delta x \, \Delta p \sim \hbar$.

a slit then we can say that the position of the electron along the X axis is uncertain by an amount equal to the width of the slit, i.e., $\Delta x = d$, or

$$\Delta x \sim d \qquad (6.35)$$

We can make d smaller and hence the position of the electron will be determined with more accuracy. But when the electron passes through the slit its wave packet (or the field associated with the particle) is disturbed as is obvious because one obtains a diffraction pattern (instead of a spot) on the screen. The slit in a way produces uncertainty in the particle's momentum parallel to the x component. After the particle passes through the slit, the chances are that the particle is moving within the angle 2θ formed by the central maximum of the diffraction pattern, thus the uncertainty in momentum is determined by this angle. If the initial momentum is p, then the x component is $p \sin \theta$, i.e.,

$$\Delta p_x \sim p \sin \theta \tag{6.36}$$

But according to the theory of diffraction by a rectangular slit for the central maximum

$$d \sin \theta \doteq \lambda \tag{6.37}$$

which reduces Eq. (6.36) to, after substituting $p = h/\lambda$,

$$\Delta p_x \sim \left(\frac{h}{\lambda}\right)\frac{\lambda}{d} = \frac{h}{d} \tag{6.38}$$

Combining Eqs. (6.35) and (6.38), we get

$$\Delta x \, \Delta p_x \sim h > \hbar \tag{6.39}$$

which is in agreement with Eq. (6.33a). Note that in order to measure the position accurately we have to make the slit very narrow, but this increases the width of the central maximum, thereby increasing Δp according to Eq. (6.36). On the other hand, if one increases the size of the slit, it decreases θ, and hence Δp_x, but increases Δx. Thus there is a certain lower bound that limits the accuracy of simultaneous determination of x and p of the incident electron.

As another example, let us consider the location of an electron by a microscope as shown in Fig. 6.6. (This example was suggested by Bohr in 1930.) It is impossible to observe this electron without disturbing it. The electron is illuminated by light of some wavelength λ; the light scattered from this electron is received in the microscope, and hence the position of the electron located. The resolving power of the microscope determines the accuracy with which the particle may be located. The scattered photon of momentum $p_s = h/\lambda$, must travel within the cone of an angle α resulting in the uncertainty in the x component of the momentum to be

$$\Delta p \sim p_s \sin \alpha = \frac{h}{\lambda}\left(\frac{d}{2}\Big/ y\right) \tag{6.40}$$

where $\sin \alpha = (d/2y)$.

The uncertainty in the position of the electron is equal to the diameter of the central maximum of the diffraction pattern with $\sin \theta \sim \lambda/d$

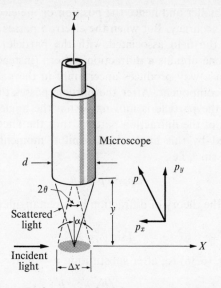

FIG. 6.6. *Schematic for measuring the position and momentum of a particle by using a microscope and light source of wavelength* λ.

$(= 1.22(\lambda/d)$ to be exact[11]). The diameter of the central maximum is $2y \sin \theta$, i.e.,

$$\Delta x \sim 2y \sin \theta = 2y \left(\frac{\lambda}{d}\right) \tag{6.41}$$

Combining Eqs. (6.40) and (6.41)

$$\Delta x \, \Delta p \sim 2y \left(\frac{\lambda}{d}\right) \frac{h}{\lambda} \left(\frac{d}{2y}\right)$$

or

$$\Delta x \, \Delta p \sim 2h \tag{6.42}$$

Thus once again we have demonstrated the truth in the uncertainty principle.

In classical mechanics we are always able to locate the particle with much more precision, the reason being that $\Delta p/p$ is a very small quantity because p is very large. On the contrary in microscale phenomena such as the electron, the fraction $(\Delta p/p)$ is a finite number and it is not possible to ignore. (See Problem 6.6.) Figure 6.7 illustrates the path of a particle in the phase space (in $x - p$ coordinates) according to classical mechanics and quantum mechanics. As is obvious from Fig. 6.7(b), one cannot find a well-defined path of a particle and, as we shall see, this leads to the concept of the *probability* of locating the particle instead of the concept of the definite location of the particle. In classical mechanics, of course, one works with the particle's definite location.

Before leaving the subject of the uncertainty principle, we shall talk about the uncertainty relation for time and energy. If simultaneous measurements are made of the energy, E, of a particle and the time, t, at which the particle has this energy, the relation between the uncertainty ΔE, of energy, and Δt, of time, is given by

$$\Delta t \, \Delta E \geqslant \hbar \qquad (6.43)$$

This relation can be again derived from the theory of Fourier analysis[8,9]. Suppose we observe a wave packet of a particle passing through a certain point within time Δt. The wave packet must be constructed from a range of frequencies, say $\Delta \nu$, centered around the frequency ν, and for this case Fourier analysis yields (noting $\omega = 2\pi\nu$)

$$\Delta t \, \Delta \omega \sim 1 \qquad (6.44)$$

But $E = h\nu = \hbar\omega$, therefore,

$$\Delta \omega = \frac{\Delta E}{\hbar} \qquad (6.45)$$

Combining Eqs. (6.44) and (6.45), we have

$$\Delta t \, \Delta E \sim \hbar \qquad (6.46)$$

i.e., according to Heisenberg, the measurement of the energy of a particle within a time Δt must be uncertain by an amount equal to ΔE, the relation between Δt and ΔE being given by Eq. (6.43).

We can arrive at Eq. (6.43) starting from Eq. (6.33), i.e., $\Delta x \, \Delta p \geqslant \hbar$. Let us measure the velocity of a wave packet by observing its position at two

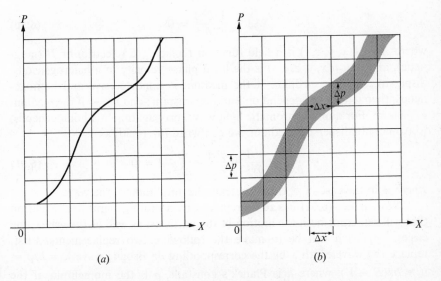

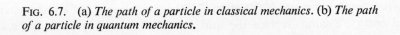

FIG. 6.7. (a) *The path of a particle in classical mechanics.* (b) *The path of a particle in quantum mechanics.*

different times. Let the width of the packet be Δx and its momentum uncertainty be Δp. Then the energy uncertainty is obtained (using a nonrelativistic expression) from

$$E = \frac{p^2}{2m}$$

i.e.,

$$\Delta E = \frac{p}{m} \Delta p = v \, \Delta p \qquad (6.47)$$

But uncertainty in time is

$$\Delta t = \frac{\Delta x}{v} \qquad (6.48)$$

combining Eqs. (6.47) and (6.48), i.e.,

$$\Delta E = \frac{\Delta x}{\Delta t} \Delta p \geqslant \frac{\hbar}{\Delta t}$$

or

$$\Delta t \, \Delta E \geqslant \hbar \qquad (6.49)$$

This relation is of great importance when we are talking about the excited states of the electrons in the atoms.

4. THE WAVE FUNCTION AND ITS INTERPRETATION

The most general form of the wave equation of physical optics, which is also applicable to the electromagnetic field, may be written as

$$\nabla^2 A - \frac{1}{u^2} \frac{\partial^2 A}{\partial t^2} = 0 \qquad (6.50)$$

where $A = A(x, y, z, t)$ is a field function replacing E (electric) or H (magnetic), and $u = u(x, y, z, t, \nu)$ is the local phase velocity in a heterogeneous, dispersive, moving medium. If the medium is nondispersive and homogeneous, then u does not depend on ν and is constant; and $u = c$ if the medium is vacuum. For a monochromatic light wave, propagating in a homogeneous, isotropic, nondispersive medium, we can write Eq. (6.50) as

$$\frac{\partial^2 A}{\partial x^2} + \frac{\partial^2 A}{\partial y^2} + \frac{\partial^2 A}{\partial z^2} + \frac{4\pi^2}{\lambda^2} A = 0 \qquad (6.51)$$

where A in the case of optics represents the amplitude of the wave.

Now, if Eq. (6.51) has to be replaced by a more general field equation that will represent both the motion of the particles, as well as the waves, the easiest approach will be to make the following two replacements. First, replace the wavelength λ by the corresponding de Broglie wave $\lambda = h/p = h/\sqrt{2m(E - V)}$, where h is Planck's constant, p is the momentum of the particle or of the quanta of radiation, E is the total energy, and V is the potential energy. Second, replace the field variable $A(x, y, z, t)$ by $\Psi(x, y, z, t)$, called the wave amplitude, or the *wave function*. With these changes, Eq. (6.51) takes the form

$$\frac{\partial^2 \Psi}{\partial x^2} + \frac{\partial^2 \Psi}{\partial y^2} + \frac{\partial^2 \Psi}{\partial z^2} + \frac{2m(E - V)}{\hbar^2} \Psi = 0 \qquad (6.52)$$

which is the famous time-dependent *Schrödinger wave equation*, or SWE. Of course, this is not the best way to arrive at the SWE, but we have done so with a certain purpose in mind. (An alternative and more general method of arriving at SWE is given in Sec. 6.) By making an analogy with the optical field variable, $A(x, y, z, t)$, we shall see what type of interpretation we can obtain for the wave function $\Psi(x, y, z, t)$.

In optics the field variable $A(x, y, z, t)$ has two important properties:

(a)   The field variable A must obey the principle of superposition, i.e., if A_1 and A_2 are each a solution of the Eq. (6.52) or (6.51), then the sum of the two solutions, $A_1 + A_2$, is also a solution. With this principle it is possible to explain the phenomena of interference and diffraction. For example, if the two solutions "add in phase" at a given point on the screen, the result is a bright fringe; on the contrary if they "add out of phase," the result is a dark fringe.

(b)   The intensity of illumination, I, is given by the square of the amplitude of A, i.e., by $|A|^2$. Suppose that the beam of light is assumed to consist of a large number of photons, then the intensity of illumination, I, will be proportional to the number, N, of photons falling on a unit area per unit time, i.e.,

$$I = |A|^2 \propto N \qquad (6.53)$$

In this respect $|A|^2$ may be interpreted as a measure of the statistical distribution of a large number of photons.

Our aim now is to extend the above two properties to the wave function $\Psi(x, y, z, t)$:

(i)   There is no difficulty in extending the first property. The principle of superposition always applies to the solutions of all linear differential equations and, of course, the SWE is linear. Thus if Ψ_1 and Ψ_2 are linearly independent solutions of the SWE, then $\Psi_1 + \Psi_2$ is also the solution of the SWE.

(ii)   The property (b) mentioned above cannot be directly extended to wave mechanics without some modification in its interpretation. The difficulty arises from the fact that the statistical interpretation given assumed a large number of photons (or particles), while at present we are trying to build the mechanics of a single particle. In order to understand this difficulty let us consider the following conceptual experiment pertaining to a single photon.

Figure 6.8 shows an interference experiment using Young's double slit arrangement. The interference pattern obtained on the screen can be explained satisfactorily by the wave theory of light, according to which the pattern is the result of the interference between the two beams from the slits A and B, respectively. Let us now assume that the source of light S emits a stream of photons instead of a continuous beam of light. The interference can still be explained if we assume that the photons passing through slit A interfere with the photons passing through slit B, which means that each photon passing through A must have a partner (or counterpart) passing through B with which it must interfere, and vice versa. But on the other hand, let us make the source of light very weak so that on the average only one photon is emitted at a time. Long film exposures reveal that one still obtains the

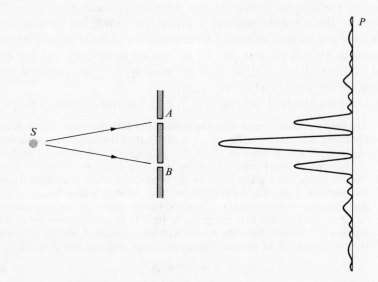

FIG. 6.8. *Schematic of Young's double slit experiment for observing the probability distribution of diffracted photons.*

same pattern, implying thereby that the pattern obtained cannot be explained by the statistical distribution of a large number of photons. Hence, contrary to the above assumption, it is necessary that a photon passing through a slit has to have a partner (or counterpart) passing through the other slit. The only possible way out of this dilemma is to *ascribe a statistical property to each individual particle.* We may point out that even though using a very weak source the interference patterns obtained are quite different when both slits are open or just one slit is open, thereby implying the following: Even though a single photon passes through only one slit, the pattern obtained on the screen is possible only if one assumes that the wave associated with the photon requires both slits open simultaneously, which allows the photon to pass through either slit according to some statistical property. Such considerations led Born[12] to the statistical interpretation of the wave function $\Psi(x, y, z, t)$, which is equivalent to the second property (b) above.

According to Born the product

$$|\Psi(x, y, z, t)|^2 \, dv \qquad (6.54a)$$

is a measure of the probability of finding the particle in a volume element $dv = dx \, dy \, dz$ *at the time* t. In case we are dealing with a stationary state, the wave function will be independent of time, and we may write the probability of finding the particle as

$$|\psi(x, y, z)|^2 \, dv$$

or

$$\psi^*(x, y, z)\psi(x, y, z) \, dv \tag{6.54b}$$

where ψ^* is complex conjugate of ψ.

Even though the above interpretation looks analogous to the one given to $|A|^2$ in optics, there is one fundamental distinction between A and Ψ. Whereas in optics A represents actual physical quantities like electric- or magnetic-field strengths, the wave function Ψ itself does not have any physical meaning in the sense of the classical physics; i.e., in optics both A and $|A|^2$ have meanings, while in wave mechanics only $|\Psi|^2$ has any physical meaning. Whenever the product $|\Psi|^2$ is large, the probability of finding the particle is large, and the probability of finding the particle is small whenever $|\Psi|^2$ is small.

In short, we may summarize that the wave function $\Psi(x, y, z, t)$ must be assigned the following three properties:

(a) Ψ can interfere with itself so that one can satisfactorily explain the results of diffraction experiments.
(b) Ψ must describe only the statistical behavior of a single particle or a photon.
(c) The square of the wave function is large in magnitude where the particle or photon is likely to be found and small everywhere else.

5. THE POSTULATES OF QUANTUM MECHANICS

The development of the mathematical structure by Schrödinger[6] in 1926 known as wave mechanics, or quantum mechanics, is based on certain fundamental postulates. The purpose was to start with the basic ideas of Planck's quantization rules and the de Broglie hypothesis, and to modify the laws of mechanics so as to include the particle nature and wave nature of various phenomena. Of course, the truth of these postulates is justified by their application to actual physical situations to see if theory agrees with experimental results. As mentioned earlier Schrödinger described the amplitude of a matter wave by the complex quantity $\Psi(x, y, z, t)$, the wave function, of the state of the system; the wave function describes the particular dynamical system under investigation. If the state of the system is stationary—the system does not change with time—the wave function will be independent of time and is denoted by $\psi(x, y, z)$. In describing the postulates we shall use the time-independent wave function $\psi(x, y, z)$ even though these are equally applicable to the time-dependent wave function $\Psi(x, y, z, t)$. We shall restrict ourselves to the discussion of a single particle because this will be the case most often encountered. The basic postulates of wave mechanics are the following:

I. The wave function, $\psi(x, y, z)$, that describes the state of a system must satisfy
    two conditions:
    A. The wave function, ψ, must be well-behaved, if it describes a physical
        system. It must, therefore, be single-valued and continuous. In other
        words the wave function ψ must satisfy the boundary conditions that ψ
        and its derivative, ψ', are continuous everywhere. (In addition, the wave
        function is zero at $\pm\infty$.)
    B. The quantity $\psi^*\psi$, where ψ^* is the complex conjugate of ψ, is always a real
        quantity. And according to Born, $\psi^*\psi\, dv = \psi^*\psi\, dx\, dy\, dz$ is interpreted
        as the probability of finding a particle in a volume element $dx\, dy\, dz$,
        which is finite. Thus ψ must satisfy the condition that the integral
        $\int \psi^*\psi\, dx\, dy\, dz$, taken over all space, has a finite constant value. If we
        set this arbitrary constant equal to unity, then

$$\int_{\text{all space}} \psi^*\psi\, dx\, dy\, dz = 1 \tag{6.55}$$

is called the normalization condition. Equation (6.55) implies that if ψ
represents the wave function of a single particle, then the probability of
finding the particle in all space must be unity. If there are N particles in
space, then Eq. (6.55) takes the form

$$\int_{\text{all space}} \psi^*\psi\, dx\, dy\, dz = N \tag{6.56}$$

where ψ is the unnormalized wave function while the normalized wave
function is $\psi/\sqrt{N}$.

II. To every observable physical quantity there corresponds an operator, the
     choice of which is arbitrary as long as the result of the operation of the
     operator on the wave function gives back the observable quantity and wave
     function. Table 6.1 gives the common classical dynamical quantities and

TABLE 6.1

THE QUANTUM MECHANICAL OPERATORS

Classical dynamical quantity	Quantum mechanical operator
x, y, z	x, y, z
$f(x, y, z)$	$f(x, y, z)$
p_x	$\dfrac{\hbar}{i}\dfrac{\partial}{\partial x} = -i\hbar\dfrac{\partial}{\partial x}$
p_y	$\dfrac{\hbar}{i}\dfrac{\partial}{\partial y} = -i\hbar\dfrac{\partial}{\partial y}$
p_z	$\dfrac{\hbar}{i}\dfrac{\partial}{\partial z} = -i\hbar\dfrac{\partial}{\partial z}$
p	$P = -i\hbar\nabla = -i\hbar\,\text{grad}$
E	$-\dfrac{\hbar}{i}\dfrac{\partial}{\partial t} = i\hbar\dfrac{\partial}{\partial t}$

the corresponding quantum-mechanical operator replacement. (Note that $i = \sqrt{-1}$.) Starting with these, many other operators can be derived. Thus we may associate with the vector momentum, the operator

$$\mathbf{P} \equiv -i\hbar\nabla \equiv -i\hbar\,\text{grad} \tag{6.57}$$

Then the equation

$$\mathbf{P}\psi = -i\hbar\nabla\psi = \mathbf{p}\psi \tag{6.58}$$

is called the eigenvalue equation, the equation that gives the proper values, and **p** is called the eigenvalue, the proper value. Then Eq. (6.58) has a solution

$$\psi = e^{i\mathbf{p}\cdot\mathbf{r}/\hbar} \tag{6.59}$$

where ψ is the eigenfunction. This leads to the conclusion that the only possible experimental values are the eigenvalues of its operator, operating on the well-behaved eigenfunction ψ.

III. If a physical system is in a state represented by the function $\psi(x, y, z)$, the average value of an observable o whose corresponding operator is O, is given by

$$\langle o \rangle = \frac{\displaystyle\int \psi^* O \psi \, dx \, dy \, dz}{\displaystyle\int \psi^* \psi \, dx \, dy \, dz} \tag{6.60}$$

The quantity $\langle o \rangle$ is also called the *expectation value* of the observable quantity. Thus if one knows the quantum mechanical operator corresponding to the dynamical variable, Eq. (6.60) will yield the expectation, or average values.

The meaning of these postulates will become clear as we apply them to different microscopic systems. After all, the only way to prove or disprove these postulates is to compare the results with experimentally measured values.

6. THE SCHRÖDINGER WAVE EQUATION

We are now in a position to write the Schrödinger wave equation of a particle. In actual practice, as we shall see in the following sections, solving a given problem means to solve the Schrödinger wave equation for the system with the help of the postulates given in the previous section.

Consider a particle of mass m moving in a coordinate system XYZ, having a velocity **v** and potential energy $V(x, y, z, t)$ at time t. The total energy E of the particle is given by

$$E = \frac{m}{2}(v_x^2 + v_y^2 + v_z^2) + V(x, y, z, t) \tag{6.61}$$

or

$$E = \frac{1}{2}mv^2 + V(x, y, z, t) \tag{6.62}$$

where v_x, v_y, and v_z are the components of **v**. If we represent the momentum of the particle by **p**, Eq. (6.62) takes the form

$$E = \frac{p^2}{2m} + V(x, y, z, t) \tag{6.63}$$

Let us replace the observables **p** and E by the corresponding operators given in Table 6.1:

$$\mathbf{p} \to \mathbf{P} \equiv -i\hbar\left(\mathbf{l}\,\frac{\partial}{\partial x} + \mathbf{m}\,\frac{\partial}{\partial y} + \mathbf{n}\,\frac{\partial}{\partial z}\right) \tag{6.64}$$

and

$$E \to i\hbar\,\frac{\partial}{\partial t} \tag{6.65}$$

where **l**, **m**, and **n** are the unit vectors along the X, Y, and Z axes, respectively. Similarly, we replace p^2 by the operator

$$p^2 = \mathbf{p} \cdot \mathbf{p} \equiv -\hbar^2\left(\frac{\partial^2}{\partial x^2} + \frac{\partial^2}{\partial y^2} + \frac{\partial^2}{\partial z^2}\right) \tag{6.66}$$

$$\equiv -\hbar^2 \nabla^2$$

If Ψ represents the eigenfunction of the state of the particle, then with the help of Eqs. (6.65) and (6.66), Eq. (6.63) is replaced by the following equation

$$-\frac{\hbar^2}{2m}\,\nabla^2\Psi + V(x, y, z, t)\Psi = i\hbar\,\frac{\partial\Psi}{\partial t} \tag{6.67}$$

or

$$H\Psi = E\Psi \tag{6.68}$$

where

$$H = -\frac{\hbar^2}{2m}\,\nabla^2 + V(x, y, z, t) \tag{6.69}$$

is the *Hamiltonian operator*. Equation (6.67), or Eq. (6.68), is the *time-dependent Schrödinger wave equation*. Equation (6.68) states that the Hamiltonian operator (or the energy operator) operating on the eigenfunction of the state yields the energy of the particle in that state and the wave function of the state.

In many situations, the system will not change with time, and, in addition, the potential energy $V(x, y, z, t)$ may be independent of time. In such cases, we can apply the method of separation of variables to Eq. (6.67) to get the time-independent Schrödinger wave equation (SWE) as shown below. Let

$$\Psi(x, y, z, t) = \psi(x, y, z)T(t) \tag{6.70}$$

Substituting for $\Psi = \psi T$ in Eq. (6.67) and dividing by ψT, we get

$$-\frac{\hbar^2}{2m}\,\frac{\nabla^2\psi}{\psi} + V(x, y, z) = i\hbar\,\frac{1}{T}\,\frac{\partial T}{\partial t} \tag{6.71}$$

The left side of this equation is a function of space coordinates only, and the right side is a function of time only, therefore, each must be equal to a constant. This constant turns out to be equal to E, the total energy, as we shall justify. Equating the left side of Eq. (6.71) with E,

$$-\frac{\hbar^2}{2m}\frac{\nabla^2\psi}{\psi} + V(x, y, z) = E$$

or

$$\nabla^2\psi + \frac{2m}{\hbar^2}[E - V(x, y, z)]\psi = 0 \qquad (6.72)$$

Equation (6.72) is the *time-independent Schrödinger wave equation*.
    Equating the right side of Eq. (6.71) equal to E, we get

$$i\hbar\frac{1}{T}\frac{\partial T}{\partial t} = E \qquad (6.73)$$

which on integration gives

$$T(t) = \exp\left[-i(E/\hbar)t\right] \qquad (6.74)$$

Because the exponent must be dimensionless, the constant E must be recognized as energy. Also because the energy is quantized, and because $E = \hbar\omega$, Eq. (6.74) takes the form

$$T(t) = \exp\left(-i\omega t\right) = \cos\omega t - i\sin\omega t \qquad (6.75)$$

i.e., $T(t)$ is a periodic function with angular frequency $\omega = E/\hbar$. According to Eq. (6.70) the time-dependent wave function is

$$\Psi(x, y, z, t) = \psi(x, y, z)e^{-i(E/\hbar)t}$$

Let us go back to Eq. (6.72), the time-independent Schrödinger wave equation, and consider some special cases. In the case of one-dimensional motion of a particle, the time-independent SWE takes the form

$$\frac{d^2\psi}{dx^2} + \frac{2m}{\hbar^2}(E - V)\psi = 0 \qquad (6.76)$$

(A) $E > V_0$, i.e., consider a particle with energy E moving in a constant potential field V_0 such that $E > V_0$. The solution of Eq. (6.76), the wave function of the particle, is given by

$$\psi(x) = Ae^{ikx} + Be^{-ikx} \qquad (6.77)$$

or

$$\psi(x) = A'\sin kx + B'\cos kx \qquad (6.78)$$

where

$$k = \frac{\sqrt{2m(E - V_0)}}{\hbar}$$

and A, B, A', and B' are constants.

(B) $E < V_0$, i.e., consider a particle with energy E moving in a constant potential field V_0 such that $E < V_0$. In this case Eq. (6.76) takes the form

$$\frac{d^2\psi}{dx^2} - \frac{2m}{\hbar^2}(V_0 - E)\psi = 0$$

or

$$\frac{d^2\psi}{dx^2} - k'^2\psi = 0 \tag{6.79}$$

where

$$k' = \frac{\sqrt{2m(V_0 - E)}}{\hbar}$$

and has the following solution

$$\psi(x) = Ce^{k'x} + De^{-k'x} \tag{6.80}$$

where C and D are constants.

(C) $V = 0$, i.e., consider a particle moving in a potential-free region. The SWE for the free particle becomes

$$\frac{d^2\psi}{dx^2} + \frac{2mE}{\hbar^2}\psi = 0 \tag{6.81}$$

which has the solution

$$\psi(x) = N \exp\left(\frac{\pm i\sqrt{2mE}}{\hbar}x\right) \tag{6.82}$$

where N is a constant.

We shall see later on that these cases (A), (B), and (C) will be helpful in discussing various problems of potential barriers and potential wells. Note that in all the above cases, k is defined as the wave number and is given by

$$k = \frac{\sqrt{2m(E - V_0)}}{\hbar} = \frac{p}{\hbar} = \frac{1}{\lambda} = \frac{2\pi}{\lambda}$$

where p is the momentum and λ is the de Broglie wave associated with the particle. Similarly

$$k' = \frac{\sqrt{2m(V_0 - E)}}{\hbar} = \frac{p'}{\hbar} = \frac{1}{\lambda'}$$

and for a free particle

$$k_0 = \frac{\sqrt{2mE}}{\hbar} = \frac{p_0}{\hbar} = \frac{1}{\lambda_0}$$

7. PROBABILITY CURRENT-DENSITY[18]

There will be many situations where we will be interested in discussing the motion of the particle, such as in scattering problems. In these circumstances it becomes necessary to talk in terms of the density of flow of the particles or the particle current, and hence we must find the suitable quantum mechanical operator, i.e., we must find the probability current-density.

The Schrödinger wave equation of a particle moving in a real potential V is

$$-\frac{\hbar^2}{2m} \nabla^2 \Psi + V\Psi = i\hbar \frac{\partial \Psi}{\partial t} \qquad (6.83)$$

The corresponding equation for the complex conjugate wave-function Ψ^* is, by taking the complex conjugate of Eq. (6.83),

$$-\frac{\hbar^2}{2m} \nabla^2 \Psi^* + V\Psi^* = -i\hbar \frac{\partial \Psi^*}{\partial t} \qquad (6.84)$$

To eliminate V, we multiply Eq. (6.83) by Ψ^* and Eq. (6.84) by Ψ, and subtract. The result, after rearranging, is

$$i\hbar\left(\Psi^* \frac{\partial \Psi}{\partial t} + \Psi \frac{\partial \Psi^*}{\partial t}\right) + \frac{\hbar^2}{2m}(\Psi^* \nabla^2\Psi - \Psi \nabla^2\Psi^*) = 0$$

which may be written as

$$\frac{\partial}{\partial t}(\Psi^*\Psi) + \frac{\hbar}{2im} \nabla \cdot (\Psi^* \nabla\Psi - \Psi \nabla\Psi^*) = 0 \qquad (6.85)$$

Equation (6.85) has the familiar form of the *equation of continuity*

$$\frac{\partial \rho}{\partial t} + \nabla \cdot \mathbf{S} = 0 \qquad (6.86)$$

Where ρ is the *probability density* and $\mathbf{S}$ is the *probability current-density*, or *particle current-density*, defined as

$$\rho = \Psi^*\Psi \qquad (6.87)$$

and

$$\mathbf{S} = \frac{\hbar}{2im}(\Psi^* \nabla\Psi - \Psi \nabla\Psi^*) \qquad (6.88)$$

Let $\psi^*\nabla\psi = Z$, an imaginary number $= x + iy$, then $\psi\nabla\psi^* = Z^* = x - iy$. Therefore $Z - Z^* = (x + iy) - (x - iy) = 2iy = 2iImZ$. Hence in Eq. (6.88) $\mathbf{S}$ may be written as

$$\mathbf{S} = \frac{\hbar}{m} Im(\Psi^* \nabla\Psi) \qquad (6.89)$$

where $Im(\ )$ stands for the imaginary part of $(\ )$.

With these interpretations of ρ and $\mathbf{S}$, Eq. (6.85) or Eq. (6.86) state the conservation of particle number by saying that the time derivative of the particle density, ρ, plus the divergence of the particle current-density, $\mathbf{S}$, must add up to zero. $\mathbf{S}$ is also sometimes thought of as a *flux vector*, and represents the average value of the particle current-density given by Eq. (6.88) or Eq. (6.89).

The equation of continuity is nothing new in quantum mechanics. Equation (6.86) is true in any theory in which the quantities like mass, charge, or heat energy are found to follow conservation laws of mass, charge, or heat energy, respectively. For example, in a compressible fluid of density ρ, the current of the fluid crossing per unit area per second is given by $\mathbf{S} = \rho\mathbf{v}$. In quantum mechanics because we deal with a single particle and its probability, we may give the following interpretation. The decrease of probability (say Ψ is changing with time) of finding a particle in a volume element dV is equal to the outward flow of probability current through the surface of dV.

As an example, consider free particles (i.e., $V = 0$) represented by the plane wave

$$\psi(x, y, z) = e^{\frac{i}{\hbar}[\mathbf{p}\cdot\mathbf{r}]} \tag{6.90}$$

Substituting this in Eq. (6.88) or (6.89) yields

$$\mathbf{S} = \frac{\hbar}{m} Im[\Psi^* \nabla\psi] = \frac{\hbar}{m} Im\left[e^{-\frac{i}{\hbar}\mathbf{p}\cdot\mathbf{r}} \cdot \frac{i}{\hbar}\mathbf{p}e^{\frac{i}{\hbar}\mathbf{p}\cdot\mathbf{r}} \right] \tag{6.91}$$

$$= \frac{\mathbf{p}}{m} = \mathbf{v} \,(= \mathbf{v}\psi^*\psi)$$

Equation (6.91) gives the current for a beam of particles moving with velocity $\mathbf{v}$, and the density of the beam $\psi^*\psi = 1$. (For time-dependent conditions see Problem 6.11.)

8. A PARTICLE IN AN INFINITELY DEEP ONE-DIMENSIONAL POTENTIAL WELL

One of the fundamental differences between classical mechanics and quantum mechanics is the continuous range of energies that a system in classical mechanics can almost assume. In quantum mechanics, however, systems can take only certain discrete values, because energy is quantized. As a simple example, we shall calculate the discrete energy levels of a particle in quantum mechanics.

Consider the one-dimensional motion of a single particle that is restricted by the reflecting walls of a one-dimensional potential well as shown in Fig. 6.9. For such a system,

$$V(x) = 0 \qquad \text{for } 0 < x < a$$
$$= \infty \qquad \text{for } x \leqslant 0, x \geqslant a \tag{6.92}$$

Because of the infinite walls of the potential well, a particle inside the well will remain inside, and the probability of finding it outside the well is zero, i.e.,

$$\psi(x) = 0 \quad \text{for } x < 0 \text{ and } x > a \tag{6.93}$$

while inside the well, the potential is zero, i.e., for $|x| < a$, $V(x) = 0$, and the Schrödinger wave equation for a particle inside the well takes the form

$$\frac{d^2\psi}{dx^2} + \frac{2mE}{\hbar^2}\psi = 0 \tag{6.94}$$

i.e.,

$$\frac{d^2\psi}{dx^2} + k^2\psi = 0 \tag{6.95}$$

where

$$k^2 = \frac{2mE}{\hbar^2} \tag{6.96}$$

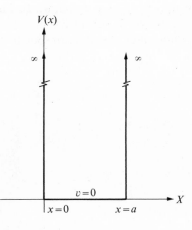

FIG. 6.9. *An infinitely deep one-dimensional potential well.*

Note that the particle inside the well is a free particle. The general solution of Eq. (6.95) is

$$\psi(x) = A \sin kx + B \cos kx \tag{6.97}$$

where A and B are arbitrary constants. In order to evaluate these constants we make use of the first boundary condition that $\psi(x)$ must be continuous everywhere. Also $\psi(x)$ must be zero at $x = 0$ and $x = a$. From Eq. (6.97) for $x = 0$

$$\psi(0) = 0, \qquad \text{only if } B = 0 \tag{6.98a}$$

if $B = 0$, then for $\psi(a) = 0$, we get

$$A \sin ka = 0 \tag{6.98b}$$

Equation (6.98b) is satisfied only if $A = 0$ or $\sin ka = 0$. If $A = 0$ and $B = 0$, it gives a trivial solution. Therefore, we must have

$$\sin ka = 0$$

i.e.,

$$ka = n\pi \qquad \text{where } n = 1, 2, 3, \ldots \tag{6.99a}$$

Thus the possible values of k are

$$k = \frac{n\pi}{a} \qquad \text{where } n = 1, 2, 3, \ldots \tag{6.99b}$$

Substituting this value of k into Eq. (6.96) and replacing E by E_n, we get

$$E_n = \frac{n^2\pi^2\hbar^2}{2ma^2} \quad \text{where } n = 1, 2, 3, \ldots \quad \textbf{(6.100)}$$

Equation (6.100) gives the possible discrete energy eigenvalues that a particle may take when inside the potential well. For $n = 1$, $E_1 = \pi^2\hbar^2/2ma^2$, while the higher energy states are $E_2 = 4E_1$ for $n = 2$; $E_3 = 9E_1$, for $n = 3$; $E_4 = 16E_1$ for $n = 4$; and $E_n = n^2E_1$ for $n = n$, as shown in Fig. 6.10. This is quite contrary to classical theory where the particle may take any energy value as shown in Fig. 6.11. (Note that $n = 0$, corresponding to $E = 0$, gives the

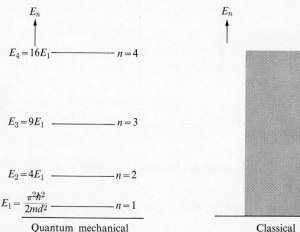

FIG. 6.10. *According to quantum mechanics a particle inside an infinitely deep potential well can take only the discrete energy values shown.*

FIG. 6.11. *According to classical theory a particle inside an infinitely deep potential well can take any of a continuous range of energies as shown.*

wave function of the particle at rest, and hence the lowest energy state is $n = 1$.) We may point out that the order of magnitude of the lowest, or ground, state energy level is in agreement with the uncertainty relation (see Problem 6.14).

Our next step is to find the eigenfunctions corresponding to different energy eigenvalues. Substituting for $B = 0$ and $k = n\pi/a$ in Eq. (6.97), we get

$$\psi_n(x) = A \sin\frac{n\pi x}{a} \quad \text{for } 0 < x < a \quad \textbf{(6.101)}$$

and $\psi_n(x) = 0$ everywhere else. The plots of these eigenfunctions for different n are shown in Fig. 6.12.

The normalization constant A may be calculated by making use of the normalization condition Eq. (6.55) and remembering that the particle is confined within the walls of the potential well; i.e.,

$$\int_{-\infty}^{\infty} \psi_n^* \psi_n \, dx = \int_0^a A^2 \sin^2 \frac{n\pi x}{a} \, dx = A^2 \int_0^a \sin^2 \frac{n\pi x}{a} \, dx = 1$$

or

$$A^2 \frac{a}{2} = 1 \quad \text{or} \quad A = \sqrt{\frac{2}{a}}$$

Hence the normalized eigenfunctions are

$$\psi_n = \sqrt{\frac{2}{a}} \sin \frac{n\pi x}{a} \quad \text{for } 0 < x < a \qquad \textbf{(6.102)}$$

Finally, we shall discuss the probability of finding the particle inside the well between $x = 0$ and $x = a$. According to classical theory, the particle has an equal chance of being found anywhere between $x = 0$ and $x = a$ for any energy value of the particle. But according to quantum mechanics the probability is given by $|\psi|^2 \, dx = \psi^* \psi \, dx$ and is definitely not constant as shown by the plots in Fig. 6.13. It varies very rapidly from point to point

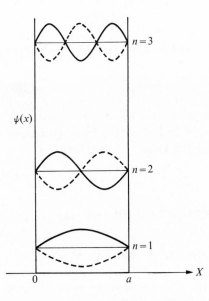

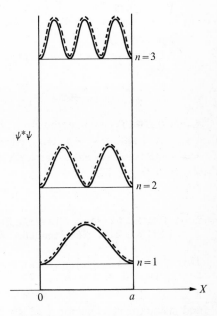

FIG. 6.12. *The plots of the first three eigenfunctions corresponding to the three lowest energy states of a particle in an infinitely deep potential well.*

FIG. 6.13. *The relative probabilities of finding a particle between 0 and a for the first three states (shown in Fig. 6.12) of the particle in an infinitely deep potential well.*

for low-energy eigenvalues. Of course, one will expect that for very high energy eigenvalues the results of quantum and classical mechanics should coincide. This is obvious from Fig. 6.14 where $\psi(x)$ and $\psi^*\psi$ are plotted for

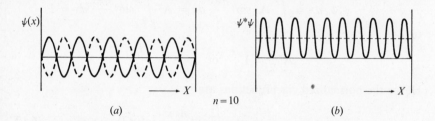

FIG. 6.14.   (a) *The wave function of a particle in an infinitely deep well for n = 10. (b) The rapid variations in the relative probability, $\psi^*\psi$, are for n = 10. The dotted line represents the relative probability calculated from classical theory. For large n, the average value of $\psi^*\psi$ agrees with the classical value.*

$n = 10$. In this case $\psi^*\psi$ changes rapidly back and forth, and hence the average value of $\psi^*\psi$ within a certain length dx is the same as the classical theory will yield. This means that for large values of n, quantum theory gives the same result as classical theory, which is an illustration of *the correspondence principle.*

A further interpretation of the wave function given by Eq. (6.101) results if we write it as

$$\psi_n(x) = \frac{A}{2i}\left[e^{n\pi ix/a} - e^{-n\pi ix/a}\right] \qquad (6.103)$$

Equation (6.103) is a superposition of two plane standing-wave solutions with $k = n\pi x/a$ and $k = -n\pi x/a$, respectively, corresponding to the picture of a particle being reflected elastically from the walls at $x = 0$ and $x = a$, as shown in Fig. 6.12.

9.   A PARTICLE IN A CLOSED, PERFECTLY RIGID, CUBICAL BOX (Box Normalization)

This is a simple extension from the one-dimensional infinitely deep potential well to the three-dimensional cube whose side is of length a as shown in Fig. 6.15. By perfectly rigid we mean that the potential at the walls is infinite and inside the box the potential is zero. Hence the particle simply is reflected from the walls and always stays inside the box. This condition, the particle being bound in the box, is similar to the electron in an atom, and a proton or a neutron in the nucleus.

Because the potential inside the box is zero, we may write the time-independent Schrödinger wave equation as

$$-\frac{\hbar^2}{2m} \nabla^2 \psi(x, y, z) = E\psi(x, y, z) \qquad (6.104)$$

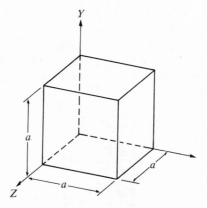

FIG. 6.15.   *A three-dimensional cubical box of length a with perfectly rigid walls.*

Once again we are dealing with the stationary system. Rearranging and substituting

$$k^2 = \frac{2mE}{\hbar^2} \qquad (6.105)$$

we get

$$\frac{\partial^2 \psi}{\partial x^2} + \frac{\partial^2 \psi}{\partial y^2} + \frac{\partial^2 \psi}{\partial z^2} = -k^2 \psi \qquad (6.106)$$

The corresponding boundary conditions are

$$\psi(0, y, z) = \psi(a, y, z) = 0 \qquad (6.107a)$$

and

$$\left.\frac{\partial \psi}{\partial x}\right|_{(0,y,z)} = \left.\frac{\partial \psi}{\partial x}\right|_{(a,y,z)} \qquad (6.107b)$$

with similar expressions of the boundary conditions for the y and z components.

We shall now use separation of variables to solve Eq. (6.106). We may write the wave function $\psi(x, y, z)$ in the factorable form as

$$\psi(x, y, z) = X(x)Y(y)Z(z) \qquad (6.108)$$

Substituting for $\psi = XYZ$ in Eq. (6.106)

$$YZ\frac{\partial^2 X}{\partial x^2} + XZ\frac{\partial^2 Y}{\partial y^2} + XY\frac{\partial^2 Z}{\partial z^2} = -k^2 XYZ$$

Dividing both sides by XYZ

$$\frac{1}{X}\frac{d^2 X}{dx^2} + \frac{1}{Y}\frac{d^2 Y}{dy^2} + \frac{1}{Z}\frac{d^2 Z}{dz^2} = -k^2 \qquad (6.109)$$

Each of the three terms on the left side is a function of a different independent coordinate, while the right side is equal to a constant. This is possible only if each of the three terms is equal to constant, say $-k_x^2$, $-k_y^2$, and $-k_z^2$, respectively. Therefore

$$\frac{1}{X}\frac{d^2 X}{dx^2} = -k_x^2 \qquad (6.110a)$$

$$\frac{1}{Y}\frac{d^2 Y}{dy^2} = -k_y^2 \qquad (6.110b)$$

$$\frac{1}{Z}\frac{d^2 Z}{dz^2} = -k_z^2 \qquad (6.110c)$$

or

$$\frac{d^2 X}{dx^2} + k_x^2 X = 0 \qquad (6.111a)$$

$$\frac{d^2 Y}{dy^2} + k_y^2 Y = 0 \qquad (6.111b)$$

$$\frac{d^2 Z}{dz^2} + k_z^2 Z = 0 \qquad (6.111c)$$

where

$$k_x^2 + k_y^2 + k_z^2 = k^2 \qquad (6.112)$$

Now the solution of Eq. (6.111a) with boundary conditions

$$X(0) = 0 \qquad \text{and} \qquad X(a) = 0 \qquad (6.113)$$

gives (from Sec. 8)

$$X(x) = A_x \sin k_x x \qquad (6.114)$$

where A_x is an arbitrary constant, and k_x has the values

$$k_x = \frac{n_x \pi}{a} \quad \text{where } n_x = 1, 2, 3, \ldots \qquad (6.115)$$

Similarly for y and z components, we get

$$Y(y) = A_y \sin k_y y \qquad (6.116)$$

and

$$Z(z) = A_z \sin k_z z \qquad (6.117)$$

where A_y and A_z are arbitrary constants, and k_y and k_z are given by

$$k_y = \frac{n_y \pi}{a} \quad \text{where } n_y = 1, 2, 3, \ldots \quad \textbf{(6.118)}$$

and

$$k_z = \frac{n_z \pi}{a} \quad \text{where } n_z = 1, 2, 3, \ldots \quad \textbf{(6.119)}$$

Note that $n_x = n_y = n_z = 0$, is excluded because this will mean $\psi = 0$, i.e., there is no particle in the box.

Combining Eqs. (6.114), (6.116), and (6.117) with Eq. (6.108), the complete wave function is given by

$$\psi(x, y, z) = A \sin k_x x \sin k_y y \sin k_z z \quad \textbf{(6.120)}$$

where $A = A_x A_y A_z$. Substituting for k_x, k_y, and k_z from Eqs. (6.115), (6.118), and (6.119), we get

$$\psi(x, y, z) = A \sin \frac{n_x \pi x}{a} \sin \frac{n_y \pi y}{a} \sin \frac{n_z \pi z}{a} \quad \textbf{(6.121)}$$

The constant A can be evaluated by making use of the normalization condition, i.e.,

$$\iiint_{\text{over space of interest}} \psi^*(x, y, z)\psi(x, y, z)\, dx\, dy\, dz = 1$$

or

$$A^2 \int_0^a \sin^2 \left(\frac{n_x \pi x}{a}\right) dx \int_0^a \sin^2 \left(\frac{n_y \pi y}{a}\right) dy \int_0^a \sin^2 \left(\frac{n_z \pi z}{a}\right) dz = 1 \quad \textbf{(6.122)}$$

or

$$A^2 \left(\frac{a}{2}\right)^3 = 1$$

Therefore

$$A = \left(\frac{2}{a}\right)^{3/2} \quad \textbf{(6.123)}$$

Hence, the complete normalized wave-function is

$$\psi(x, y, z) = \left(\frac{2}{a}\right)^{3/2} \sin \frac{n_x \pi x}{a} \sin \frac{n_y \pi y}{a} \sin \frac{n_z \pi z}{a} \quad \textbf{(6.124)}$$

Another way of arriving at this wave function is to assume that the cube is centered at the origin, and if the volume of the cube is $V = a^3$, we can arrive at the following short expression for the complete wave function (see Problem 6.15).

$$\psi = \frac{1}{\sqrt{V}} \exp\left(ik \cdot r\right) = \frac{1}{\sqrt{a}} \exp\left(ik_x x\right) \frac{1}{\sqrt{a}} \exp\left(ik_y y\right) \frac{1}{\sqrt{a}} \exp\left(ik_z z\right) \quad \textbf{(6.125)}$$

which is the same as Eq. (6.124) in its final results.

The different possible energy states in which the particle can exist inside the box are found by combining Eqs. (6.115), (6.118), and (6.119) with (6.112), i.e.,

$$k^2 = \frac{2mE}{\hbar^2} = k_x^2 + k_y^2 + k_z^2$$

$$= \left(\frac{n_x\pi}{a}\right)^2 + \left(\frac{n_y\pi}{a}\right)^2 + \left(\frac{n_z\pi}{a}\right)^2$$

or

$$E = (n_x^2 + n_y^2 + n_z^2)\frac{\pi^2\hbar^2}{2ma^2} \tag{6.126}$$

n_x, n_y, and n_z are the quantum numbers of a particle in the box, and different possible values of the energy levels corresponding to these quantum numbers are given in Table 6.2. The energy levels are shown in Fig. 6.16.

TABLE 6.2

DISCRETE ENERGY LEVELS OF A PARTICLE IN A BOX

Quantum numbers n_x n_y n_z			E in units of $\frac{\pi^2\hbar^2}{2ma^2} = n_x^2 + n_y^2 + n_z^2$	Degeneracy = number of possible energy levels having the same energies
1	1	1	3	1
2	1	1	6	3
2	2	1	9	3
3	1	1	11	3
2	2	2	12	1
3	2	1	14	6
3	2	2	17	3
3	3	1	19	3
3	3	2	22	3
3	3	3	27	1

Once again the introduction of boundary conditions has led to discrete energy levels and eigenfunctions as given by Eqs. (6.126) and (6.124), respectively. From the classical point of view the particle inside the box is bouncing around making perfectly elastic collisions with the walls. This implies that the particle inside the box is moving with constant speed, and classically the probability of locating the particle is $1/a^3$ everywhere. The quantum mechanical probability, $\psi^*\psi = |\psi|^2$, gives the same average value when n_x, n_y, and n_z become very large, i.e., $n_x, n_y, n_z \rightarrow \infty$. (See Problem 6.16.) This is another example of the correspondence principle where the classical and the quantum theories give the same results for large values of quantum numbers. Also if the box is very large, a^2 will be very large and hence, from Eq. (6.126), the spacing between various levels will be very narrow and the energy levels will form a continuum as in the classical theory.

Note that in Table 6.2 there are many levels that have the same energy for different quantum numbers. For example, corresponding to the values of (n_x, n_y, n_z) given by $(1, 1, 2)$, $(1, 2, 1)$, $(2, 1, 1)$, there are three levels, all of these have the same energy $= 6(\pi^2\hbar^2/2mL^2)$ but different wave functions. The levels that have the same energy but different wave functions are said to be degenerate. The same type of degeneracy occurs for other levels also.

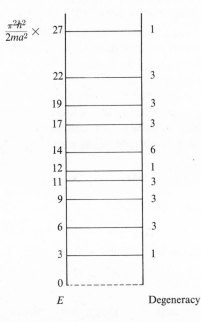

FIG. 6.16.   *The possible energy levels of a particle confined in a three-dimensional cubical box.*

There are many different situations where box normalization is used. Some of these are[14],[15]:

(a) The derivation of the Rayleigh-Jeans law
(b) Free electrons in an atom—conduction electrons
(c) The Thomas-Fermi statistical model of the atom, and
(d) The Fermi gas model of the nucleus.

As an example, let us calculate the energy of an electron in an atom. The mass of the electron is $m = 9.1 \times 10^{-28}$ gm, a ($=$ diameter of the atom) $= 10^{-8}$ cm, and $(n_x^2 + n_y^2 + n_z^2 = 1)$ therefore,

$$E_1 = \frac{\pi^2\hbar^2}{2mL^2} = \frac{(3.142)^2(1.054 \times 10^{-27})^2}{2 \times 9.1 \times 10^{-28} \times (10^{-8})^2} = 0.605 \times 10^{-10} \text{ ergs}$$

$$= 37 \text{ eV}$$

Similar calculations can be made for a proton or a neutron inside the nucleus (see Problem 6.9).

10. FINITE POTENTIAL STEPS AND BARRIERS

In the last two sections we found the discrete energy levels of a particle confined within the walls of infinite potential barriers. Here we shall be concerned with a different type of problem. First of all we shall be considering finite potentials. Secondly, we are interested in finding the probability that the particle will crossover the potential step, or barrier. If we deal with a single particle in these cases, we will have to use the time-dependent Schrödinger wave equation. On the other hand, if we use a continuous beam of particles incident on the type of potential under consideration, one can still make use of the time-independent Schrödinger wave equation. Many examples of these occur in atomic and nuclear scatterings, and in nuclear disintegrations. We shall investigate in some detail the following two cases:

A.   Finite Potential Step
B.   One-Dimensional Potential Barrier

A. Finite Potential Step

Consider a potential step of the form shown in Fig. 6.17 and given by

$$V(x) = 0 \qquad \text{for } x < 0 \qquad \text{region I}$$
$$\qquad = V_0 \qquad \text{for } x > 0 \qquad \text{region II} \qquad\qquad \textbf{(6.127)}$$

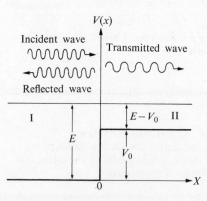

FIG. 6.17. *A particle of energy E is incident on a potential step, for which $V = V_0$ if $x > 0$, and $V = 0$ if $x < 0$.*

Let a beam of particles be incident from the left, with each particle having a definite energy E. Two cases are possible, either $E > V_0$, or $E < V_0$. We shall consider these two separately.

(i) $E > V_0$. In this case according to classical theory the particle will always cross the potential step but according to quantum mechanics there is a finite chance, or probability, that the particle will be reflected. Thus as shown in Fig. 6.17, in region I there are both incident and reflected waves, while in region II there are only transmitted waves. We shall show this mathematically. The Schrödinger wave equations for the two regions are the following:

For region I:

$$\frac{d^2\psi_I}{dx^2} + \frac{2mE}{\hbar^2}\psi_I = 0 \tag{6.128}$$

For region II:

$$\frac{d^2\psi_{II}}{dx^2} + \frac{2m}{\hbar^2}(E - V_0)\psi_{II} = 0 \tag{6.129}$$

The solutions of these two equations in the two regions are

$$\psi_I(x) = Ae^{ik_1x} + Be^{-ik_1x} \tag{6.130}$$

where

$$k_1 = \sqrt{2mE}/\hbar = p_1/\hbar \tag{6.131}$$

and

$$\psi_{II}(x) = Ce^{ik_2x} \tag{6.132}$$

where

$$k_2 = \sqrt{2m(E - V_0)}/\hbar = p_2/\hbar \tag{6.133}$$

We can define the *reflection coefficient*, R and the *transmission coefficient*, T, just as in optics, in the following way

$$\text{reflection coefficient} = \frac{\text{reflected intensity}}{\text{incident intensity}} = \frac{(\text{reflected amplitude})^2}{(\text{incident amplitude})^2}$$

i.e.,

$$R = \frac{|B|^2}{|A|^2} \tag{6.134}$$

Similarly

$$\text{transmission coefficient} = \frac{\text{transmitted intensity}}{\text{incident intensity}} = \frac{(\text{transmitted amplitude})^2}{(\text{incident amplitude})^2}$$

i.e.,

$$T = \frac{|C|^2}{|A|^2} \tag{6.135}$$

According to classical theory R should be equal to zero while T should be equal to 1; but we shall show that this is not so according to quantum mechanics. R and T may be calculated by applying the following boundary conditions

$$\psi_I(0) = \psi_{II}(0) \tag{6.136}$$

and

$$\frac{d\psi_I}{dx}\bigg|_{x=0} = \frac{d\psi_{II}}{dx}\bigg|_{x=0} \tag{6.137}$$

yielding

$$A + B = C$$

and

$$ik_1(A - B) = ik_2C$$

Solving these equations

$$\frac{B}{A} = \frac{k_1 - k_2}{k_1 + k_2} \tag{6.138a}$$

or

$$R = \frac{|B|^2}{|A|^2} = \left(\frac{k_1 - k_2}{k_1 + k_2}\right)^2 \tag{6.138b}$$

and

$$\frac{C}{A} = \frac{2k_1}{k_1 + k_2} \tag{6.139a}$$

or

$$T = \frac{|C|^2}{|A|^2} = \left(\frac{2k_1}{k_1 + k_2}\right)^2 \tag{6.139b}$$

As is obvious, neither is R zero nor is T unity. The particles coming from left have velocity $v_1 = k_1\hbar/m$, and as soon as these encounter the potential, they are slowed down to velocity $v_2 = k_2\hbar/m$. In addition there is a definite probability that a fraction of these will be reflected back even though each one of these particles has enough energy to cross the barrier.

In this steady state one might be misled into thinking that the sum of the reflected and transmitted intensities is equal to the incident intensity. However,

$$|A|^2 \neq |B|^2 + |C|^2 \tag{6.140}$$

as can be shown by substituting the values from Eqs. (6.138) and (6.139). On the other hand, if we use probability current-densities, we can show

$$S_{inc} = S_{ref} + S_{tran} \tag{6.141}$$

or in other words

$$S_I = S_{II} \tag{6.142}$$

where

$$S_I = \frac{\hbar}{m} Im\left(\psi_I^* \frac{d\psi_I}{dx}\right)$$

$$= \frac{\hbar}{m} Im[(A^*e^{-ik_1x} + B^*e^{ik_1x})ik_1(Ae^{ik_1x} - Be^{-ik_1x})] \tag{6.143}$$

$$= \frac{\hbar}{m} k_1[|A|^2 - |B|^2]$$

Similarly,

$$S_{II} = \frac{\hbar}{m} Im\left(\psi_{II} \frac{d\psi_{II}}{dx}\right)$$

$$= \frac{\hbar}{m} Im[C^* e^{-ik_2 x}(ik_2) C e^{ik_2 x}] \qquad (6.144)$$

$$= \frac{\hbar}{m} k_2 |C|^2$$

Combining Eqs. (6.143) and (6.144) with (6.141)

$$\frac{\hbar k_1}{m} [|A|^2 - |B|^2] = \frac{\hbar k_2}{m} |C|^2$$

or

$$k_1 |A|^2 = k_1 |B|^2 + k_2 |C|^2 \qquad (6.145)$$

i.e.,

$$v_1 |A|^2 = v_1 |B|^2 + v_2 |C|^2 \qquad (6.146)$$

i.e., not the intensities given by Eq. (6.140), but the total currents (ρv) given by Eq. (6.145) or (6.146) are conserved.

Let us consider particles of energy E that are incident from the right instead of the left. In this case the particles will be accelerated as soon as they enter the region where $x < 0$. According to quantum mechanics the particles will be still reflected, and, as a matter of fact, the reflection coefficient is the same as in the above case (Problem 6.27).

(ii) $E < V_0$. An interesting case occurs when E is less than V_0. The wave function of the particle in region I is still the same, with k_1 being real, i.e.,

$$\psi_I = Ae^{ik_1 x} + Be^{-ik_1 x} \qquad (6.147)$$

But in region II, the wave number k_2 is purely imaginary given by

$$k_2 = \frac{i\sqrt{2m(V_0 - E)}}{\hbar} = iK \qquad (6.148)$$

with the wave function given by

$$\psi_{II} = Ce^{-Kx} \qquad (6.149)$$

(The increasing exponential e^{Kx} is not bound and hence is not a solution.) Either by applying the boundary conditions at $x = 0$, or by directly substituting $k_2 = iK$, in the Eq. (6.138a) and Eq. (6.139a), we get

$$\frac{B}{A} = \left(\frac{k_1 - iK}{k_1 + iK}\right) \qquad (6.150)$$

and

$$\frac{C}{A} = \left(\frac{2k_1}{k_1 + iK}\right) \qquad (6.151)$$

From Eq. (6.150), it is obvious that $R = |B|^2/|A|^2 = 1$, i.e., the $S_{inc} = S_{ref}$, and $S_{tran} = 0$ (see Problem 6.24). This is in accord with classical theory which states that the particle will be totally reflected from the step. However, the wave function to the right is not zero because C is not zero as given by (6.151), i.e.,

$$\psi_{II} = \frac{2k_1}{k_1 + iK} Ae^{-Kx} \tag{6.152}$$

This means that the particle penetrates into the step barrier, and there is some probability ($\psi_{II}^* \psi_{II}$) of finding the particle in the region that is classically not accessible.

B. One-Dimensional Potential Barrier

Let a particle of rest mass m and kinetic energy E be incident upon a potential barrier of height V_0 such that $E < V_0$ and

$$V(x) = \begin{cases} 0 & \text{for } x < 0 \\ V_0 & \text{for } 0 \leqslant x \leqslant a \\ 0 & \text{for } x > a \end{cases} \tag{6.153}$$

as shown in Fig. 6.18. Because of the symmetrical nature of the problem, the particle may be incident either from the left or from the right. We assume, in this case, that it is incident from the left.

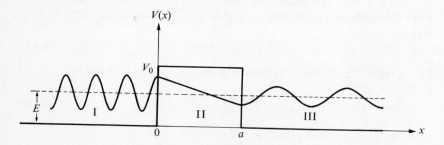

FIG. 6.18. *A particle of energy E is incident from the left on a square potential barrier for which V(x) = V₀ if 0 < x < a, and V(x) = 0 if x < 0 or x > a.*

Classically, a particle with kinetic energy $E < V_0$ can never penetrate the potential barrier. But quantum-mechanically we shall show that even though $E < V_0$, the particle has some probability of crossing the potential barrier. This probability of penetration of the barrier, or *transparency*, is defined, as before,

$$\text{transparency} = \frac{\text{transmitted intensity}}{\text{incident intensity}}$$

$$= \frac{(\text{transmitted amplitude})^2}{(\text{incident amplitude})^2}$$

(6.154)

For regions I and III, the time-independent Schrödinger wave equation is

$$\frac{d^2\psi}{dx^2} + \frac{2mE}{\hbar^2}\,\psi = 0 \qquad (6.155)$$

with the solution in the two regions being

$$\psi_{\text{I}} = Ie^{ik_0x} + Re^{-ik_0x} \qquad (6.156)$$

$$\psi_{\text{III}} = Te^{ik_0x} \qquad (6.157)$$

where $k_0 = \sqrt{2mE}/\hbar$, and I, R, and T are the incident, reflected, and transmitted amplitudes, respectively.

In region II, the time-independent Schrödinger wave equation is

$$\frac{d^2\psi}{dx^2} - \frac{2m}{\hbar^2}(V_0 - E)\psi = 0 \qquad (6.158)$$

The solution of this equation is

$$\psi_{\text{II}} = Ae^{Kx} + Be^{-Kx} \qquad (6.159)$$

where $K = \sqrt{2m(V_0 - E)}/\hbar$, and A and B are constants.

In order to calculate the transparency, we have to evaluate the constants, which can be done by making use of the fact that the wave function must be well-behaved. Thus, by applying the boundary conditions that ψ and $d\psi/dx$ (denoted by ψ') must be continuous at $x = 0$ and $x = a$, i.e., by using

$$\psi_{\text{I}}(0) = \psi_{\text{II}}(0)$$

$$\psi_{\text{I}}'(0) = \psi_{\text{II}}'(0)$$

$$\psi_{\text{II}}(a) = \psi_{\text{III}}(a)$$

$$\psi_{\text{II}}'(a) = \psi_{\text{III}}'(a)$$

(6.160)

we get the following set of equations

$$I + R = A + B$$

$$ik_0(I - R) = K(A - B)$$

$$Ae^{Ka} + Be^{-Ka} = Te^{ik_0a}$$

$$K(Ae^{Ka} - Be^{-Ka}) = ik_0Te^{ik_0a}$$

(6.161)

Eliminating A and B from these equations and solving for T/I we get[16] (see Problem 25.)

$$\text{transparency} = \frac{|T|^2}{|I|^2}$$

$$= \frac{(2k_0/K)^2}{(1 - k_0^2/K^2)^2 \sinh^2 Ka + (2k_0/K)^2 \cosh^2 Ka} \qquad \text{for } E < V_0 \quad (6.162)$$

which is definitely not zero. For $E = 0$, the transmission is zero, but it increases with increasing E as shown in Fig. 6.19.

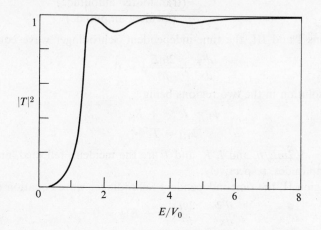

FIG. 6.19. *The plot of transparency of a square potential barrier as a function of the energy of the incident particle.*

For the case when the particle energy is $E > V_0$, we redefine the wave number in region II by replacing K by k, as $k = \sqrt{2m(E - V_0)}/\hbar = iK$, obtaining the following expression for the transparency

$$\text{transparency} = \frac{(2k/k_0)^2}{(1 + k^2/k_0^2)^2 \sin^2 ka + (2k/k_0)^2 \cos^2 ka}$$

$$\text{for } E > V_0 \qquad \textbf{(6.163)}$$

A plot of Eq. (6.162) together with Eq. (6.163) is shown in Fig. 6.19. Transparency increases with increasing E and becomes almost unity with small oscillatory variations for E large compared to V_0. Maximum transmission occurs whenever $ka = n\pi$, where n is an integer. This is a phenomena equivalent to total transmission of light through a thin refracting layer.

11. PARITY

Parity is a property of a wave function that describes its behavior under inversion of the coordinate system, i.e., the behavior of the eigenfunction when the signs of the coordinates are changed. Furthermore, if I is the parity operator, or *inversion operator*,

$$I\psi(x, y, z) = \psi(-x, -y, -z) \qquad \textbf{(6.164)}$$

and

$$I\psi(-x, -y, -z) = \psi(x, y, z) \qquad \textbf{(6.165)}$$

Let K be the eigenvalue of the operator I, then from Eqs. (6.164) and (6.165),

$$I^2\psi(x, y, z) = IK\psi(-x, -y, -z)$$
$$= KI\psi(-x, -y, -z)$$
$$= K^2\psi(x, y, z)$$

i.e.,

$$K^2 = 1 \quad \text{or} \quad K = \pm 1 \tag{6.166}$$

This leads to the definition of even and odd wave functions. If

$$\psi(-x, -y, -z) = +\psi(x, y, z) \tag{6.167}$$

the wave function is said to have *even parity*, and if

$$\psi(-x, -y, -z) = -\psi(x, y, z) \tag{6.168}$$

the wave function is said to have *odd parity*.

We shall now show that if the potential $V(r)$ is symmetrical about $r = 0$, the eigenfunctions satisfying the Schrödinger wave equation have definite parity. Changing the sign of r in the SWE

$$-\frac{\hbar^2}{2m} \nabla^2\psi(r) + V(r)\psi(r) = E\psi(r) \tag{6.169}$$

and because $V(-r) = V(r)$, we get

$$-\frac{\hbar^2}{2m} \nabla^2\psi(-r) + V(r)\psi(-r) = E\psi(-r) \tag{6.170}$$

Thus both $\psi(r)$ and $\psi(-r)$ satisfy the same wave equation, and they must be related by a constant, i.e.,

$$\psi(-r) = K\psi(r) \tag{6.171}$$

Changing the sign of r again

$$\psi(r) = K\psi(-r) \tag{6.172}$$

Substituting for $\psi(-r)$ from Eq. (6.171) into Eq. (6.172) gives $K^2 = 1$ or $K = \pm 1$, which is the result we obtained in Eq. (6.166). The wave functions, therefore, have either even ($K = +1$) or odd ($K = -1$) parity.

12. A POTENTIAL WELL OF FINITE DEPTH

Consider a particle of mass m and energy E inside a potential well of depth V_0 as shown in Fig. 6.20. According to classical theory, as long as the total energy E of the particle is less than V_0 it cannot come out of the potential well. But according to quantum mechanics we shall show that not only the particle inside the well has discrete-energy eigenvalues but also that there is some finite probability of finding the particle outside the well. According to Fig. 6.20

$$V(x) = +V_0 \quad \text{for } |x| > a$$
$$= 0 \quad \text{for } |x| < a \tag{6.173}$$

In this case for which $E < V_0$, the corresponding energy eigenvalues obtained are called the *bound states* of the system.

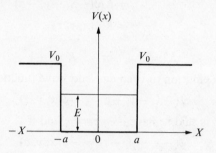

FIG. 6.20.   *A potential well of finite depth V_0. The energy E of the particle inside the well is less than V_0.*

Inside the well, $V(x) = 0$, and the SWE is

$$\frac{d^2\psi_i}{dx^2} + \frac{2mE}{\hbar^2}\psi_i = 0 \tag{6.174}$$

where ψ_i is the wave function inside the well and the solution of Eq. (6.174) is

$$\psi_i(x) = A\sin\alpha x + B\cos\alpha x \tag{6.175}$$

where

$$\alpha^2 = \frac{2mE}{\hbar^2} \tag{6.176}$$

and A and B are constants.

Outside the well, $V(x) = V_0$ and the SWE is

$$\frac{d^2\psi_o}{dx^2} - \frac{2m(V_0 - E)}{\hbar^2}\psi_o = 0 \tag{6.177}$$

ψ_o is the wave function outside the well. The solution of Eq. (6.177) is

$$\psi_o(x) = Ce^{-\beta x} + De^{\beta x} \tag{6.178}$$

where

$$\beta^2 = \frac{2m(V_0 - E)}{\hbar^2} \tag{6.179}$$

and C and D are constants. Note that because ψ_o must be zero as $x \to \pm\infty$, Eq. (6.178) yields

for $x > a$, $D = 0$ and $\psi_o(x) = Ce^{-\beta x}$ \qquad (6.180)

and

for $x < a$, $C = 0$ and $\psi_o(x) = De^{\beta x}$ \qquad (6.181)

Using Eqs. (6.175), (6.178), (6.180) and (6.181) and the following boundary conditions

$$\psi_o(-a) = \psi_i(-a)$$

$$\psi_i(a) = \psi_o(a)$$

$$\psi_o'(-a) = \psi_i'(-a)$$

$$\psi_i'(a) = \psi_o'(a)$$

(6.182)

we get, after rearranging

$$(-\sin \alpha a)A + (\cos \alpha a)B \quad + \quad\quad\quad + (-e^{-\beta a})D \; = 0 \qquad \textbf{(6.183)}$$

$$(\sin \alpha a)A \; + (\cos \alpha a)B \quad + (-e^{-\beta a})C \quad\quad\quad = 0 \qquad \textbf{(6.184)}$$

$$(\alpha \cos \alpha a)A + (\alpha \sin \alpha a)B \quad\quad\quad + (-\beta e^{-\beta a})D = 0 \qquad \textbf{(6.185)}$$

$$(\alpha \cos \alpha a)A + (-\alpha \sin \alpha a)B + (\beta e^{-\beta a})C \quad\quad\quad = 0 \qquad \textbf{(6.186)}$$

These equations form a set of four homogeneous equations in four unknowns, A, B, C, and D. To have nontrivial solutions, the determinant of the coefficients must vanish, or solving directly, we get two solutions. Either:

I. Even-parity solutions, i.e., the wave function is even

$$A = 0, \quad\quad C = D, \quad\quad \text{and} \quad\quad \alpha \tan \alpha a = \beta \qquad \textbf{(6.187)}$$

or

II. Odd-parity solutions, i.e., the wave function is odd

$$B = 0, \quad\quad C = -D, \quad\quad \text{and} \quad\quad \alpha \cot \alpha a = -\beta \qquad \textbf{(6.188)}$$

The energy levels according to the above two solutions can be found either numerically or graphically. We shall follow the graphical procedure.

A. Even-Parity Solutions

Substituting for $\alpha = (2mE/\hbar^2)^{1/2}$ and $\beta = [2m(V_0 - E)/\hbar^2]^{1/2}$, in Eq. (6.187) and $b = \sqrt{E/V_0}$, we get

$$\tan \sqrt{\frac{2ma^2V_0}{\hbar^2}}\, b = \frac{\sqrt{1 - b^2}}{b} \qquad \textbf{(6.189)}$$

The plots of the left-hand side and the right-hand side of Eq. (6.189) are shown in Fig. 6.21, both for a small value of V_0a^2 and a large value of V_0a^2. The intersections of the two plots are the possible solutions. It is quite obvious that no matter how shallow the well, there is always at least one solution, i.e., there is always at least one eigenfunction corresponding to the bound state. The number of bound states is in general a function of a and b, as shown in Fig. 6.21.

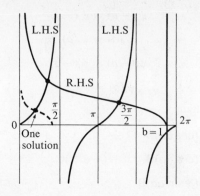

FIG. 6.21. *Graphical solution of the even-parity states of a particle inside a finite potential well. Dotted curve is for small value of $V_0\,a^2$.*

B. Odd-Parity Solutions

Once again substituting for α, β, and $b = \sqrt{E/V_0}$ in Eq. (6.188), yields

$$-\cot\sqrt{\frac{2ma^2V_0}{\hbar^2}}\,b = +\frac{\sqrt{1-b^2}}{b} \qquad (6.190)$$

The graphical solutions are given in Fig. 6.22. In this case it is possible to

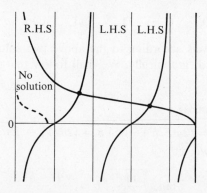

FIG. 6.22. *Graphical solution of the odd-parity states of a particle inside a finite potential well. Dotted curve is for small value of $V_0\,a^2$.*

make the well so narrow (i.e., a small) or so shallow (V_0 small) that there may be no odd-parity bound state.

In Fig. 6.23 we show the plots of the wave functions for the first three lowest states. It is apparent that the wave functions do not actually vanish at the boundaries of the well or even beyond, (i.e., leak out of the well) even

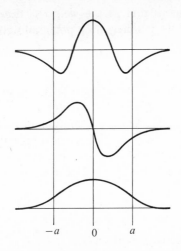

FIG. 6.23.   *Plots of the wave functions for the three lowest states of a particle in a finite potential well where $E < V_0$. Contrary to classical theory, the wave functions do leak out of the well even though they decay exponentially outside the well.*

though they decay exponentially outside the well. This is contrary to classical theory predictions.

The energy levels obtained both for even and odd solutions are shown in Fig. 6.24. For comparison, the energy levels for an infinitely deep well are

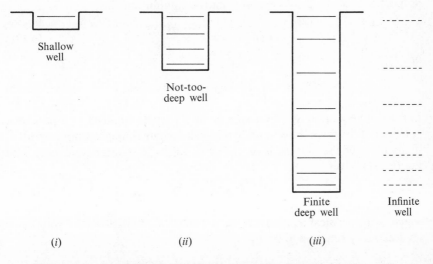

FIG. 6.24.   *Possible energy levels of a particle in* (i) *a very shallow well,* (ii) *a not-too-deep well, and* (iii) *a finite deep well. For comparison, the levels of a particle in an infinitely deep well are shown dotted.*

also shown. It is obvious that as the well gets deeper, the energy levels coincide with those of the infinitely deep potential well.

C. Unbound States $E > V_0$

We shall not go into the general solution of this problem which may be attempted in a manner similar to the case for $E < V_0$. The general results obtained are the following. We get a continuum of states. The states are unbound, and hence when $E > V_0$, we are dealing with scattering problems. Within the region from $x = -a$ to $x = +a$, the particle speeds up, while outside this region it has a lower speed. The wave functions are sinusoidal both inside and outside.

13. LINEAR HARMONIC OSCILLATOR

In the previous sections we have discussed different types of potential steps, barriers, and wells, which all involved constant potentials. As a final example we shall consider one of the most important situations involved both in classical theory as well as in quantum theory, the one-dimensional linear harmonic oscillator. The use of the harmonic oscillator lies not only in the basic problems of classical dynamics, it is used extensively in quantum mechanics in solving such problems as vibrations of atoms in molecules and crystals[17] and in the quantization of wave fields[18]. In a linear harmonic oscillator a particle is bound to an equilibrium position by a force that is proportional to the displacement from the equilibrium; i.e.,

$$F(x) = -kx = -\frac{dV(x)}{dx} \tag{6.191}$$

or

$$V(x) = -\int F(x)\,dx = \int kx\,dx = \frac{1}{2}kx^2 \tag{6.192}$$

which is an equation of a parabola. Thus a particle confined to a parabolic potential of the form shown in Fig. 6.25 will execute simple harmonic motion. If the mass of the particle is m, then $F = m(d^2x/dt^2)$, after combining with Eq. (6.191), gives

$$\frac{d^2x}{dt^2} + \frac{k}{m}x = 0 \tag{6.193}$$

which is the classical equation of motion of such a particle whose solution is an oscillatory function given by

$$x(t) = A\sin(\omega_c t + \phi) \tag{6.194}$$

where A is the amplitude of the oscillations, $\omega_c = 2\pi\nu_c$ is the classical angular

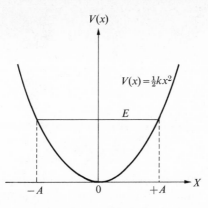

FIG. 6.25.   *A particle confined to a parabolic potential of the form shown here will execute simple harmonic motion.*

frequency, and ϕ the phase angle. The classical oscillatory frequency ω_c is given by

$$\omega_c = \sqrt{k/m} \qquad (6.195)$$

Substituting the value of k from Eq. (6.195) into Eq. (6.192), the potential $V(x)$ may be expressed in the form

$$V(x) = \frac{1}{2} m\omega_c^2 x^2 \qquad (6.196)$$

Before actually solving this problem from the quantum-mechanical point of view, we can make some predictions with the help of the experience gained in previous sections.

1. We expect to obtain discrete energy levels contrary to classical theory where the oscillator can assume a continuous range of energies.
2. The minimum energy is going to differ from zero.
3. The particle will penetrate the potential barrier and will be found beyond the classical limits of $+A$ and $-A$. Finally, at the end, we shall compare the results of quantum theory with the classical theory.

   Thus for a one-dimensional harmonic oscillator whose total energy is $(p^2/2m) + V(x)$, the corresponding Hamiltonian operator is

$$H = -\frac{\hbar^2}{2m}\frac{d^2}{dx^2} + \frac{1}{2} kx^2 \qquad (6.197)$$

while the Schrödinger wave equation to be solved is given by

$$\frac{d^2\psi}{dx^2} + \frac{2m}{\hbar^2}\left[E - \frac{1}{2} kx^2\right]\psi = 0 \qquad (6.198)$$

It is convenient to put this equation into a dimensionless form by introducing the following dimensionless independent variables:

Let

$$y = \sqrt{\frac{mk}{\hbar^2}}\, x = \alpha x \quad \text{where } \alpha = \sqrt{\frac{mk}{\hbar^2}} \qquad \textbf{(6.199)}$$

$$\lambda = \frac{2E}{\hbar}\sqrt{\frac{m}{k}} = \frac{2E}{\hbar\omega} \quad \text{where } \omega = \sqrt{k/m} \qquad \textbf{(6.200)}$$

Thus Eq. (6.198) takes the form

$$\frac{d^2\psi}{dy^2} + (\lambda - y^2)\psi = 0 \qquad \textbf{(6.201)}$$

In order to solve this equation, we first look for the asymptotic solution, i.e., the form that ψ must take as $y \to \pm\infty$. A physically bounded solution must satisfy the condition that $\int_{-\infty}^{\infty} \psi^*\psi \, dy$ is finite. For large values of $|y|$, $y^2 \gg \lambda$, and hence we may neglect λ as compared to y^2, and Eq. (6.201) becomes

$$\frac{d^2\psi}{dx^2} - y^2\psi \simeq 0$$

which has a solution

$$\psi(y) \simeq e^{-y^2/2} \qquad \textbf{(6.202)}$$

Because of the rapid decay of this function as y becomes large, the product of this function with another finite polynomial will still have the same asymptotic behavior. This suggests that it is possible to write the exact solution of Eq. (6.201) in the form

$$\psi(y) = H(y)e^{-y^2/2} \qquad \textbf{(6.203)}$$

where $H(y)$ is a finite polynomial in y. Substituting Eq. (6.203) into Eq. (6.201), we get

$$\frac{d^2H(y)}{dy^2} - 2y\frac{dH(y)}{dy} + (\lambda - 1)H(y) = 0 \qquad \textbf{(6.204)}$$

which is the differential equation obeyed by $H(y)$. To find a solution for $H(y)$, we assume $H(y)$ has the following form of a finite polynomial,

$$H(y) = a_0 + a_1 y + a_2 y^2 + a_3 y^3 + \ldots$$

$$= \sum_{k=0}^{\infty} a_k y^k \qquad \textbf{(6.205)}$$

From this equation

$$\frac{dH(y)}{dy} = \sum_{k=1}^{\infty} ka_k y^{n-1}; \qquad y\frac{dH(y)}{dy} = \sum_{k=0}^{\infty} ka_k y^k \qquad \textbf{(6.206)}$$

and

$$\frac{d^2H(y)}{dy^2} = 1\cdot 2a_2 + 2\cdot 3a_3 y + 3\cdot 4a_4 y^2 \ldots = \sum_{k=2}^{\infty} k(k-1)a_n y^{k-2}$$

Replacing k by $k + 2$, we get

$$\frac{d^2 H(y)}{dy^2} = \sum_{k=0}^{\infty} (k + 2)(k + 1)a_{k+2}y^k \qquad (6.207)$$

Substituting Eqs. (6.206) and (6.207) into Eq. (6.204), we obtain

$$\sum_{k=0}^{\infty} [(k + 2)(k + 1)a_{k+2} - (2k + 1 - \lambda)a_k]y^k = 0 \qquad (6.208)$$

This equation must hold for all values of y, and therefore the coefficient of each power of y must be zero separately. This leads to the following *recursion relation* connecting the coefficients a_{k+2} and a_k;

$$a_{k+2} = \frac{2k + 1 - \lambda}{(k + 2)(k + 1)} a_k \quad \text{where } k > 0 \qquad (6.209)$$

Because any second-order differential equation has two arbitrary constants to be determined from the boundary conditions, let us assume that a_0 and a_1 are the arbitrary constants. The other constants in the series expansion $H(y)$ of Eq. (6.205) may be expressed in terms of these two constants by making use of the above recursion relation, Eq. (6.209).

In order for the series to remain finite, there must be an upper cutoff to the coefficients. The condition to be satisfied, from Eq. (6.208) is obtained by replacing k by n, as

$$2n + 1 - \lambda = 0$$

or

$$\lambda = 2n + 1 \quad \text{where } n = 0, 1, 2, 3, \ldots \qquad (6.210)$$

Suppose n is even, then not only a_{n+2} is equal to zero but all the other even terms are also zero, because of the recursion relation. Similarly if a_{n+2} is odd, then all the odd terms in the series are zero. This leads to the assumption that the terms in the series are either all even or all odd, i.e., either

for n even, $a_1 = 0$ and hence $a_3 = a_5 = a_7 = \ldots = 0$ (6.211)

or

for n odd, $a_0 = 0$ and hence $a_2 = a_4 = a_6 = \ldots = 0$ (6.212)

This behavior is always expected whenever V is an even function, i.e., as in this case where $V = \frac{1}{2}kx^2$.

Substituting the value of λ from Eq. (6.200) into Eq. (6.210), we get the allowed energy levels of the one-dimensional linear oscillator to be

$$\frac{2E}{\hbar\omega} = 2n + 1$$

or

$$E_n = \left(n + \frac{1}{2}\right)\hbar\omega \quad \text{where } n = 0, 1, 2, 3, \ldots \qquad (6.213)$$

Thus, contrary to classical theory, the quantum-mechanical theory yields equally spaced energy levels as shown in Fig. 6.26. Also unlike classical

n	E_n
7 ————————	$E_7 = \frac{15}{2}\hbar\omega_0$
6 ————————	$E_6 = \frac{13}{2}\hbar\omega_0$
5 ————————	$E_5 = \frac{11}{2}\hbar\omega_0$
4 ————————	$E_4 = \frac{9}{2}\hbar\omega_0$
3 ————————	$E_3 = \frac{7}{2}\hbar\omega_0$
2 ————————	$E_2 = \frac{5}{2}\hbar\omega_0$
1 ————————	$E_1 = \frac{3}{2}\hbar\omega_0$
0 ————————	$E_0 = \frac{1}{2}\hbar\omega_0$

FIG. 6.26. *According to quantum mechanics the possible energy levels of a particle confined to a parabolic potential of the form shown in Fig. 6.25 are equally spaced, which means that the energy levels of a simple harmonic oscillator are discrete and equally spaced. Note that the minimum energy is not zero but $\frac{1}{2}\hbar\omega$.*

theory according to which the minimum energy of the oscillator is zero, the quantum theory establishes the minimum energy as $\frac{1}{2}\hbar\omega$ corresponding to $n = 0$. The ground state energy $\frac{1}{2}\hbar\omega$ is called the *zero-point energy* and is characteristic of quantum mechanics only. The zero-point energy is in accord with the uncertainty relation, i.e., the minimum energy should be $[(\Delta p)^2/2m] + \frac{1}{2}k(\Delta x)^2$, where Δp and Δx are the spread in the momentum and position, respectively. We may point out that Planck[19] in 1900 assumed that the energy of the oscillator is quantized and is given by $n\hbar\omega_c$. By this assumption he was able to explain the spectrum of black-body radiation. However; in his derivation, the assumption that the minimum energy is zero did not make any difference.

In order to completely determine the wave functions corresponding to different energy levels we must find the values $H_n(y)$ and substitute into Eq. (6.203). The polynomial $H(y)$ that is the solution of Eq. (6.204), i.e., for $\lambda = 2n + 1$,

$$\frac{d^2 H_n(y)}{dy^2} - 2y \frac{dH_n(y)}{dy} + 2nH_n(y) = 0 \qquad (6.214)$$

is called the *nth Hermite polynomial*, $H_n(y)$. Equation (6.214) itself is called the *Hermite equation*. These polynomials are well known in mathematics[20] and can be obtained with the help of the generating function. The alternative way of obtaining these functions is by the use of the recursion relation Eq. (6.209). Some of these functions are given in Table 6.3 with their corresponding quantum number, n, and their energies.

TABLE 6.3

HERMITE POLYNOMIALS CORRESPONDING TO DIFFERENT
ENERGY LEVELS OF AN HARMONIC OSCILLATOR

n	λ	E_n	$H_n(y)$
0	1	$\frac{1}{2}\hbar\omega$	1
1	3	$\frac{3}{2}\hbar\omega$	$2y$
2	5	$\frac{5}{2}\hbar\omega$	$4y^2$
3	7	$\frac{7}{2}\hbar\omega$	$8y^2 - 12$
4	9	$\frac{9}{2}\hbar\omega$	$16y^4 - 48y^2$
5	11	$\frac{11}{2}\hbar\omega$	$32y^5 - 160y^3 + 120y$

In general, these Hermite polynomials are given by[20]

$$H_n(y) = (-1)^n e^{y^2} \frac{d^n}{dy^n}(e^{-y^2}) \qquad (6.215)$$

Thus the complete wave functions according to Eq. (6.203) are

$$\psi_n(y) = N_n H_n(y)(\exp -y^2/2) \qquad (6.216)$$

where $H_n(y)$ is given by Eq. (6.215), and N_n are the normalization constants. Substituting the value of y we get

$$\psi_n(x) = N_n H_n(\alpha x) \exp(-a^2 x^2/2) \qquad (6.217)$$

The normalization constants N_n may be evaluated from

$$\int_{-\infty}^{\infty} \psi_n^* \psi_n \, dx = 1$$

which yield[22]

$$N_n = \frac{\alpha}{\sqrt{\pi}\, 2^n n!} \qquad (6.218)$$

Hence

$$\psi_n(x) = \left(\frac{\alpha}{\sqrt{\pi}} \frac{1}{2^n n!}\right)^{1/2} H_n(\alpha x) \exp\left(-\frac{\alpha^2 x^2}{2}\right) \qquad (6.219)$$

The plots of the wave functions $\psi_1, \psi_2, \ldots, \psi_5$ are shown in Fig. 6.27. As expected the wave functions do penetrate the barrier, and there is some probability of finding the particle outside the classical region.

In order to compare the quantum-mechanical oscillator with the classical oscillator we must consider the probability distribution in both the cases. The quantum-mechanical probability distribution is given by $\psi^*\psi$ while the classical probability distribution may be calculated in the following manner:

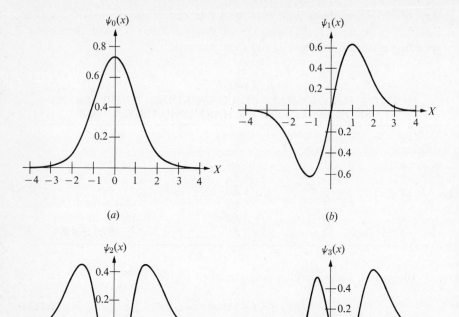

FIG. 6.27. *Plots of the first four lowest energy state eigenfunctions of a linear oscillator.* [*From J. B. Russell,* J. Math. Phys., *12, 291, (1933).*]

According to Eq. (6.194), the displacement $x(t)$ is given by

$$x(t) = A \sin(\omega_c t + \phi) \tag{6.220}$$

while the total energy, which is the sum of the kinetic and the potential energies, is given by

$$E = \frac{1}{2} m \left(\frac{dx}{dt}\right)^2 + \frac{1}{2} mx^2 = \frac{1}{2} mA^2 \omega_c^2 \cos^2(\omega_0 t + \phi) + \frac{1}{2} mA^2 \omega_c^2 \sin^2(\omega_c t + \phi)$$

i.e.,

$$E = \frac{1}{2} mA^2 \omega_c^2 \tag{6.221}$$

or the amplitude of the classical oscillator is given by

$$A = \sqrt{2E/m\omega_c^2} \tag{6.222a}$$

In order to compare this with the quantum mechanical oscillator, we must substitute $E = (n + \frac{1}{2})\hbar\omega_c$ so that we compare oscillators of the same energy, and we get

$$A = \sqrt{\frac{(2n + 1)\hbar}{m\omega_c}} = \frac{\sqrt{2n + 1}}{\alpha} \tag{6.222b}$$

where α is defined by Eq. (6.199). In one complete time period, T, if the particle travels a distance dx from x in time dt, the particle will spend time $2\,dt$ out of a complete period, T, at distance x between x and $x + dx$. Therefore, the probability $P(x)\,dx$, according to the classical oscillator, may be written as

$$P(x)\,dx = \frac{2\,dt}{T} \tag{6.223}$$

From Eq. (6.220), the velocity is given by

$$v(x) = \frac{dx}{dt} = \omega_c A \cos(\omega_c t + \phi) = \omega_c \sqrt{A^2 - x^2} \tag{6.224}$$

Therefore,

$$dt = \omega_c \frac{dx}{\sqrt{A^2 - x^2}} \tag{6.225}$$

Also

$$T = 2\pi/\omega_c \tag{6.226}$$

Substituting for dt and T from Eqs. (6.225) and (6.226) into Eq. (6.223), we get

$$P(x)\,dx = \frac{2\,dt}{T} = \frac{dx}{\pi\sqrt{A^2 - x^2}} \tag{6.227}$$

Substituting the value of A from Eq. (6.222) into Eq. (6.227), we get

$$P(x) = \frac{1}{\pi\sqrt{\dfrac{2n + 1}{\alpha} - x^2}} \tag{6.228}$$

The plots of the wave functions ψ_n given by Eq. (6.219), $\psi_n^*\psi_n$, and $P(x)$ given by Eq. (6.228) are shown[22,23] in Fig. 6.28. The following points may be observed in comparing the two oscillators.

1. The quantum-mechanical wave functions extend beyond the limits of the classical oscillator.
2. For the lowest energy state, i.e., for $n = 0$, the plot of $P(x)$ is shown by dotted line in Fig. 6.28 while $\psi_0^*\psi_0$ is shown by the solid line. Classically, the probability is maximum at the ends, while quantum mechanically it is maximum at the center.
3. For larger values of the energy say for $n = 11$, the plots of $P(x)$ and $\psi_{11}^*\psi_{11}$ show that the value of the probability given by $P(x)$ is approximately the same as the average value of $\psi_{11}^*\psi_{11}$ except according to the quantum-mechanical

probability distribution there are still points between the two extremes where the probability is very small (almost zero). Thus for large values of n, i.e., on the macroscopic scale, the result of the two theories are the same.

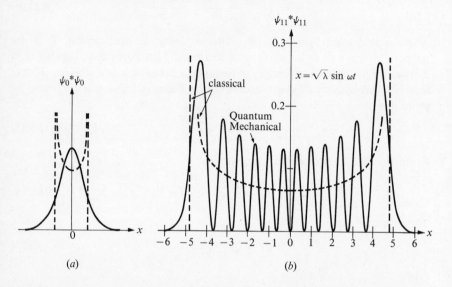

(a)

(b)

FIG. 6.28. *Quantum probability density (solid curve) and classical probability distribution (dotted curve) for the one-dimensional harmonic oscillator with energies* (a) $\frac{1}{2}\hbar\omega$ *and* (b) $\frac{23}{2}\hbar\omega$, *corresponding to wave functions* ψ_0 *and* ψ_{11}, *respectively.* [*From J. B. Russell,* J. Math. Phys., *12, 291, (1933); and E. R. Smith,* Am. Math. Monthly, *43, 354, (1936).*]

PROBLEMS

1. Show that in reflection and refraction across a plane boundary, the light path from a point A to a point B is the one for which the time taken is minimum.

2. Show that in the case of a concave mirror, the light path is one for which the time taken is maximum.

3. If we assume that the motion of a particle is described by $\psi = e^{i(kx - \omega t)}$, derive an expression for the group velocity.

4. Using de Broglie's hypothesis and quantum hypothesis, show that for a quantum or a particle moving with velocity c (the velocity of light) the group velocity is equal to the wave velocity.

5. A particle of mass 10 gm is moving with a velocity 10 cm/sec. If this particle may be located within 10^{-4} cm, what is the uncertainty in its momentum. What is the value of $[(\Delta p/p) \times 100]\%$?

6. A particle of mass 9×10^{-31} kgm is moving with a velocity of 10^6 m/sec. If this particle may be located within 10^{-4} cm, what is the uncertainty in its

momentum? What is the value of $[(\Delta p/p) \times 100]\%$, and how does this compare with the value obtained in Problem 5?

7. If we assume that an electron is confined inside an atom of radius 10^{-8} cm (i.e., $\Delta x = 2 \times 10^{-8}$ cm), what is the minimum kinetic energy of the electron?

8. If we assume that an electron is confined inside a nucleus of radius 10^{-12} cm (i.e., $\Delta x = 2 \times 10^{-12}$ cm), what is the minimum kinetic energy of this electron? Compare this with the observed values of ~ 5 MeV.

9. If a proton (or a neutron) were confined in a cubical box of length 10^{-12} cm what is the lowest proton energy in this case? How does this energy compare with that of an electron confined within an atom?

10. Consider two plane waves traveling in opposite directions so that the wave function is given by

$$\psi = A_1 e^{i\mathbf{p}\cdot\mathbf{r}/\hbar} + A_2 e^{-i\mathbf{p}\cdot\mathbf{r}/\hbar}$$

Show that for this case

$$\mathbf{S} = (|A_1|^2 - |A_2|^2)\frac{\mathbf{p}}{m}$$

What is the physical significance of this?

11. Consider a particle whose wave function is represented by

$$\Psi = A e^{i(\mathbf{p}\cdot\mathbf{r}-Et)/\hbar}$$

Calculate the value of $\mathbf{S}$ for this case and state any physical significance you may attach to this situation.

12. Calculate $\mathbf{S}$ if the wave function of a particle is given by Eq. (6.103).

13. Suppose a particle is confined between $x = 0$ and $x = a$. Using the uncertainty principle, calculate the particle's kinetic energy. How does this value compare with the ground-state energy of a particle in an infinite potential well?

14. Calculate the uncertainty in the energy of a particle confined to a one-dimensional box of length a. How does this compare with the lowest allowed energy?

15. Derive Eq. (6.125).

16. Show that in the case of a cubical box if n_x, n_y, and n_z become very large, the quantum mechanical probability $\psi^*\psi = |\psi|^2$ gives the same average value as the classical value.

17. Show that for very large n, the probability of finding a particle in a box between x and $(x + dx)$ is independent of x as expected from classical theory.

18. Consider a particle of mass m confined to a two-dimensional box of length a and width b. By solving the Schrödinger equation, show that the allowed energies and wave functions of the particle are

$$E = (\pi^2\hbar^2/2m)\left(\frac{n_x^2}{a^2} + \frac{n_y^2}{b^2}\right)$$

and

$$\psi = A \sin\left(\frac{n_x\pi x}{a}\right) \sin\left(\frac{n_y\pi y}{b}\right)$$

where n_x and n_y are positive integers. What happens, in terms of degeneracy, when $a = b$?

19. Consider an electron confined to a one-dimensional potential well of width 100 Å. Incident light is used to locate this electron with an accuracy of 1%, i.e., $\Delta x = 0.1$ Å. According to the uncertainty principle, what is the uncertainty in the momentum? How does this effect the zero-point energy of the electron? Show by calculations.

20. Show that for a particle confined in a box, the fractional energy difference $\Delta E/E$ is given by $(2n + 1)/n^2$.

21. Consider a particle confined to (i) a one-dimensional, (ii) two-dimensional, and (iii) a three-dimensional box, and calculate the following for each case:
    (a) The number of levels with momentum between p and $(p + dp)$.
    (b) The number of levels with energy E and $(E + dE)$.
    What is the effect of making the boxes very large or very small?

22. Derive Eqs. (6.138) and (6.139).

23. By directly applying the boundary conditions, derive Eqs. (6.150) and (6.151).

24. Using Eqs. (6.147)–(6.151), i.e., for $E < V_0$, show that $S_{\text{inc}} = S_{\text{ref}}$, while $S_{\text{tran}} = 0$. Also calculate the values of R and T in this case.

25. Derive Eq. (6.162).

26. Solving the SWE for the case $E > V_0$, derive Eq. (6.163).

27. In Fig. 6.17 the particles are incident from the right instead of left. Calculate the reflection coefficient and the transmission coefficient. How do these compare with the case where the particles are incident from the left? Also show that $S_{x>0} = S_{x<0}$.

28. Consider potential barriers of the form shown in Fig. P6.28. Write the Schrödinger wave equations for different regions, and draw approximately the wave function for a particle incident from the left with energy E such that (a) $E < V_{01}$, (b) $V_{01} < E < V_{02}$, and (c) $E > V_{02}$.

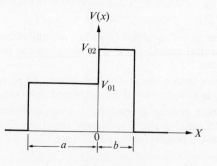

FIG. P 6.28

29. Consider potential barriers of the form shown in Fig. P 6.29. Write the Schrödinger wave equation and the wave functions in different regions for a particle of energy E such that (a) $E < V_0$ and (b) $E > V_0$. Also sketch an approximate wave function in these regions.

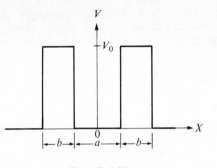

FIG. P 6.29

30. Consider a potential barrier of the form shown in Fig. P 6.30. Write the Schrödinger wave equations, and sketch the wave functions in different regions for a particle of energy E such that **(a)** $E < 0$, **(b)** $0 < E < V_0$, and **(c)** $E > V_0$. Consider two cases: Particles incident from the left and from the right.

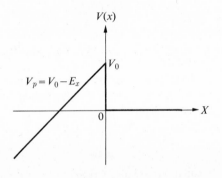

FIG. P 6.30

31. Repeat Problem 29 for a potential barrier of the form shown in Fig. P 6.31.

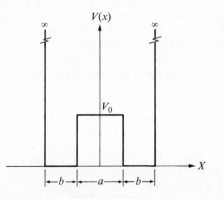

FIG. P 6.31

32. For a particle with $E > 0$, write the Schrödinger wave equation and wave function in different regions for the potentials shown in Fig. P 6.32. What is the minimum depth of V_0 so that a bound state will exist?

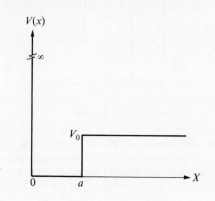

FIG. P 6.32

33. Find the average values of x, x^2, p, and p^2 for a particle in a one-dimensional potential well for the states $n = 1$ and $n = 2$.

34. Two operators $\mathbf{A}$ and $\mathbf{B}$ are said to commute if $(\mathbf{AB}\psi - \mathbf{BA}\psi) = (\mathbf{AB} - \mathbf{BA})\psi = 0$, otherwise they are noncommuting. Show that

$$(xp_x - p_x x)\psi = i\hbar\psi$$
$$(yp_x - p_x y)\psi = 0$$
$$(zp_x - p_x z)\psi = 0$$

The above three equations are also written as $[x, p_x] = i\hbar\psi$, $[y, p_x] = 0$, and $[z, p_x] = 0$.

35. How do you determine the parity of a wave function of a particle confined to a three-dimensional potential box?

36. What is the minimum energy (in eV) of a second pendulum? How do you show that the pendulum has quantized energy states but that the separation between these states is so small that these levels may be considered as continuous? Make any reasonable assumption.

37. If in a CO molecule the two atoms oscillate with a frequency 6.42×10^{11} cycles/sec, calculate the zero-point energy and the spacing between the energy levels.

38. Show by direct integration that the first three harmonic oscillator wavefunctions ψ_0, ψ_1, and ψ_2 are normalized. Also show that ψ_0 is orthogonal to ψ_1 and ψ_2, i.e.,

i.e.,
$$\int \psi_0\psi_1 \, dx = 0 \quad \text{and} \quad \int \psi_0\psi_2 \, dx = 0,$$
$$\int \psi_n\psi_{n'} \, dx = 0 \quad \text{for} \quad n \neq n'.$$

39. Show that the parity of a one-dimensional (or three-dimensional) harmonic oscillator wave function is even or odd depending upon whether n is even or odd. (*Hint:* Find the relation between $H_n(-y)$ and $H_n(y)$ for n even and odd.) Wave functions with even parity are called symmetric wave functions, while those with odd parity are called antisymmetric wave functions.

40. Find the average values or expectation values of x, x^2, p, and p^2 for the harmonic oscillator corresponding to the states $n = 0$ and $n = 1$.

REFERENCES

1. Goldstein, H., *Classical Mechanics*, pp. 225–238. Reading, Mass.: Addison-Wesley, 1950.

2. Magie, W. F., *A Source Book in Physics*, New York: McGraw-Hill, 1935.

3. Sommerfeld, A., *Mechanics*, New York: Academic Press, 1950.

4. Lindsay, R. B., and H. Margenau, *Foundations of Physics*, New York: John Wiley & Sons, 1936. [Reprinted by Dover (New York), 1957.]

5. de Broglie, Louis, *Phil. Mag.*, **47**, 446, (1924).

6. Schrödinger, E., *Ann. Physik*, **79**, 489, (1926), **80**, 437, (1926), and **81**, 109, (1926).

7. Churchill, R. V., *Fourier Series and Boundary Value Problems*, Chaps. 4 and 5, New York: McGraw-Hill, 1963.

8. Powell, J. L., and B. Crasemann, *Quantum Mechanics*, Secs. 2.5–2.7, 3.1, and 3.4, Reading, Mass.: Addison-Wesley, 1961.

9. Bohm, D., *Quantum Theory*, Chaps. 3 and 5, Englewood Cliffs, N. J.: Prentice-Hall, 1951.

10. Heisenberg, W., *Zeits. fur Physik*, **43**, 172, (1927).

11. Jenkins, F. A., and H. E. White, *Fundamentals of Optics*, 3rd ed., p. 304, New York: McGraw-Hill, 1957.

12. Born, M., *Zeit. fur Physik*, **37**, 863, (1926), and **38**, 803, (1926).

13. Bohm, D., *Quantum Theory*, pp. 83, 197, Englewood Cliffs, N. J.: Prentice-Hall, 1951.

14. Thomas, L. H., *Proc. Comb. Phil. Soc.*, **23**, 542, (1927).

15. Fermi, E., *Zeit. fur Physik*, **48**, 73, (1928).

16. Gamow, G., *Zeit. fur Physik*, **51**, 204, (1928); also Gurney, R. W., and E. U. Condon, *Nature*, **122**, 439, (1928).

17. Herzberg, G., *Spectra of Diatomic Molecules*, New York: Dover Publications, "Molecular Spectra and Molecular Structure," 1950.

18. Heisenberg, W., and W. Pauli, *Zeit. fur Physik*, **9**, 338, (1931); also Fermi, E., *Revs. Mod. Phys.*, **1**, 87, (1932).

19. Planck, M., *Ann. Physik*, **4**, 553, (1901).

20. Jahnke, E., and F. Ende, *Table of Functions*, New York: Dover Publications, 1945.

21. Powell, J. L., and B. Crasemann, *Quantum Mechanics*, p. 133, Reading, Mass.: Addison-Wesley, 1961.

22. Russell, J. B., *J. Math. Phys.*, **12**, 291, (1933).

23. Smith, E. R., *Am. Math. Monthly*, **43**, 354, (1936).

SUGGESTIONS FOR FURTHER READING

1. Gamow, G., "The Principle of Uncertainty," *Sci. Am.*, Jan. 1958.

2. Heisenberg, W., *The Physical Principles of the Quantum Theory*, New York: Dover Publications, 1930.

3. de Broglie, L., *Physics and Microphysics* (Torchbooks), New York: Harper and Row, 1960.

4. Condon, E., *Physics Today*, p. 37, Oct. 1962.

5. Hund, F., *Physics Today*, p. 23, Aug. 1966.

6. Powell, J. L., and B. Crasemann, *Quantum Mechanics*, Reading, Mass.: Addison-Wesley, 1961.

7. Schiff, L. I., *Quantum Mechanics*, 2nd ed., New York: McGraw-Hill, 1955.

8. Matthews, P. T., *Introduction to Quantum Mechanics*, 2nd ed., New York: McGraw-Hill, 1968.

9. Ziock, K., *Basic Quantum Mechanics*, New York: John Wiley & Sons, 1969.

10. Bohm, D., *Quantum Theory*, Englewood Cliffs, N. J.: Prentice-Hall, 1951.

11. Messiah, A., *Quantum Mechanics*, New York: John Wiley & Sons, 1961.

12. Landau, N. D., and E. M. Lifshitz, *Quantum Theory, Non-Relativistic Theory*, Reading, Mass.: Addison-Wesley, 1958.

13. Eisberg, R. M., *Fundamentals of Modern Physics*, Chaps. 6, 7, 8, and 9, New York: John Wiley & Sons, 1961.

14. Davydov, A. S., *Quantum Mechanics*, Reading, Mass.: Addison-Wesley, 1965.

VII

Nuclear Model of the Atom

1. EARLY MODELS OF ATOMIC STRUCTURE

One of the basic problems of physics is the determination of the structure of the atom. Investigations of the constituents of an atom establish new facts, which, in turn, generate new models for the structure of the atom. Many models have been rejected: Dalton's atomic theory, according to which the atom was a basic indivisible unit of all elements, was proved to be incorrect, as was Prout's, according to which the atoms of all elements are composed of atoms of hydrogen. It was not until the beginning of the twentieth century, when many more experimental facts became available, that more fruitful theories were advanced. The discovery of the electron by J. J. Thomson[1] in 1897 renewed interest in atomic models.

Because the cathode of a cathode-ray tube or photoelectric tube emits electrons, the implication was that atoms, of which the cathode consists, must contain electrons. Because all matter is electrically neutral, the atom must be built up of positively charged material together with the requisite number of electrons. The electron's mass being almost negligible, the positively charged material must provide most of the mass of the atom. Further evidence of the existence of electrons in atoms came from the scattering of x-rays by atoms from the experiments of Barkla and others[2] in 1910. From these experiments, it was found that the number of electrons, Z, in an atom was roughly equal to $A/2$, where A is the chemical atomic weight. It was also known that the radius of an electron was $\sim 10^{-13}$ cm, while the radius of an atom was $\sim 10^{-8}$ cm. Some of these considerations led Lenard[3] to suggest in 1903 a new model. According to him, most of the atom was empty space (because fast electrons penetrated appreciable thicknesses) in which positive charges and electrons paired up in the form of neutral doublets. This model did not provide any clue as to what characterized the atoms of various elements.

A more attractive model of the atom that was in accord with experimental observations was suggested by J. J. Thomson[4] and is known as the *plum-pudding model* of the atom. According to this model, the mass and the positive charge making up the atom are distributed uniformly over a sphere of radius $\sim 10^{-8}$ cm with electrons embedded in it, as shown in Fig. 7.1. The

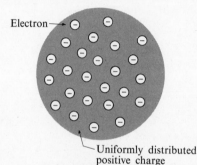

FIG. 7.1.   *The plum-pudding model of the atom as suggested by J. J. Thomson.*

electrons are uniformly distributed in shells, or rings. As according to Thomson, a shell of rotating electrons is stable until the number of electrons in the shell exceeds a certain limit, beyond which a second shell begins to form. This picture of the atom could account for the periodicity of chemical properties according to Mendeleev's periodic table. Many of the experimentally observed facts can be explained according to this model.

First of all, Thomson's model provides a hard, elastic model needed for the kinetic theory of gases. Second, because the loosely attached electrons are rather easily removed from the atom, this model explains the emission of electrons by thermal and photoelectric effects. Third, the model accounts for the addition or removal of an electron from an atom that leads to the formation of a negatively or positively charged ion. Fourth, it can explain in a simple way the emission of electromagnetic waves. According to this model, if an atom is in its lowest possible energy state, the electrons are fixed at their equilibrium position. If the atoms in a substance are heated, which leads to excited states of the atoms, the electrons would vibrate about their equilibrium position and emit radiation according to classical theory. This did explain the qualitative features of the radiation but not the quantitative aspects of it. Thus, for example, there was no quantitative agreement between the experimentally observed optical spectra and this model.

The crucial test of the model came with the observation of the scattering of alpha particles by Geiger and Marsden. The Thomson model of the atom could not explain the results of alpha scattering experiments; the model had to be abandoned in favor of Rutherford's model. Before we describe Geiger and Marsden experiments, we shall describe the discovery of natural radio-activity.

2. DISCOVERY OF RADIOACTIVITY AND IDENTIFICATION OF ALPHA PARTICLES

In the process of investigating fluorescent salts, which emit radiation on ex-posure to sunlight, Henri Becquerel[5] accidently discovered the phenomenon of radioactivity in 1896. He found that a uranium salt, well wrapped in thick paper when placed next to a photographic plate fully protected from light, caused the exposure of the plate. Becquerel concluded that radiation was coming out of the uranium salt. He called this radiation the Becquerel rays, which later became known as the radioactive ray. This phenomenon of emis-sion is now called *radioactivity*, and the elements that exhibit this are called radioactive elements. Since 1896 many more naturally occurring radioactive elements have been discovered, and hundreds of radioactive isotopes have been produced in the laboratories.

Following the discovery of radioactivity, many efforts were directed to the investigation of the properties of this radiation, especially (a) the pene-trating power in different materials, (b) the specific ionization in different gases, and (c) the influence of electric and magnetic fields. The radiations from radioactive substances were classified into three different components, depending upon their penetrating powers. One component, with a very weak penetrating power, is stopped by an ordinary sheet of paper, but caused intense ionization in air. These are alpha rays, or α-rays. A second type has less ionization power but is more penetrating than α-rays and could easily pass through metal foils a few mm thick. These are beta rays, or β-rays. The third type caused even less ionization but could penetrate many centimeters of different substances. These are gamma rays, or γ-rays. The existence of these three types of radiation can be demonstrated by a simple experiment devised by Mme. Curie[6].

A small amount of radioactive sample, say radium, is placed at the bottom of a long hole drilled in a lead block, as shown in Fig. 7.2. This produces a well-collimated beam of radiation. A strong magnetic field is applied at right angles to the plane of the figure (pointing out of the paper). A photographic plate, exposed to the radiation, will show points of exposure in various locations; α-particles produce an image at the right at only one spot, indicating that these are monoenergetic and positively charged;

β-particles produce images at varying locations to the left of the central portion because they are of nonuniform intensity with energies that vary from zero to a certain maximum value, and are negatively charged; and γ-rays appear at the center because they do not carry any charge. We shall briefly summarize the characteristics of these radiations.

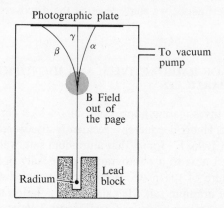

FIG. 7.2. *Experimental arrangement showing the deflection of α-, β-, and γ-rays by a magnetic field.*

A. Alpha Particles

Alpha particles cause fluorescence in some substances. If the fluorescence is examined closely with a magnifying glass, it is found to consist of a series of scintillations. The scintillations are produced by the impact of the particles on the fluorescent matter, which proves that alpha rays are discrete particles.

Alpha particles always ionize the gas through which they travel, and in the process of ionization, they lose energy and velocity. Finally, after reaching thermal velocities, when they can cause no further ionization, they capture electrons and become neutral atoms. Most of the alpha particles from radioactive elements are given out with velocities between 1.4×10^9 cm/sec and 2.2×10^9 cm/sec.

Measurements of the charge and charge-to-mass ratio for alpha particles, determined by the deflection in electric and magnetic fields, show that alpha particles are actually fast-moving doubly ionized helium atoms, He^{++}.

B. Beta Particles

Beta particles produce brilliant fluorescence, which on close observation appear as discrete scintillations, and hence are discrete masses and charges. They cause less ionization but are $\sim$100 times more penetrating than alpha particles. The measurement of e/m and e identifies beta particles to be ast-moving electrons.

C. Gamma Rays

Gamma rays also produce fluorescence, and they also cause ionization of a gas, but to a lesser degree than that caused by α-rays or β-rays. The penetrating power of γ-rays is $\sim$100 times greater than that of β-rays. Because they carry no charge, they are not deflected by electric or magnetic fields, and they exhibit all the characteristics of electromagnetic waves. In fact, γ-rays are x-rays of very short wavelength traveling at the speed of light, with wavelengths between 1.7×10^{-10} cm and 4.1×10^{-8} cm.

3. THE GEIGER-MARSDEN EXPERIMENT[7] (The Scattering of Alpha Particles)

Once the sources of natural radioactivity became available, many experiments were performed in the first decade of the present century in order to investigate the characteristics of alpha particles. The most important of these were the experiments on the scattering of alpha particles by thin foils of various substances performed by Sir Ernest Rutherford[8] and his collaborators H. Geiger and E. Marsden. As we shall see, alpha particles were actually used as probes to investigate the distribution of mass and charge in the atom.

A typical experimental arrangement used by Geiger and Marsden (1909) is shown in Fig. 7.3. A beam of alpha particles is given out from a radioactive source, R, positioned in a lead block. Radon was the source used, giving out 5.5 MeV alpha particles. The beam is well collimated by means of two slits, S_1 and S_2, before being incident on a thin metallic foil, F. Most of the alpha particles go straight through this foil as if the foil contained empty spaces, but some of the alpha particles collide with atoms of the foil and bounce off at different angles. This process in which the particle changes its direction is called scattering and in this case a special name, Rutherford scattering, is applied. The scattered particles within a small range of angle $\Delta\theta$ at an angle θ strike the fluorescent screen, S, consisting of a thin layer of the crystalline compound ZnS. Each alpha particle striking the screen produces a tiny flash of light, or scintillation, which is easily observed with a microscope, M, or even with a magnifying glass. The whole apparatus is placed in a vacuum chamber because alpha particles are easily stopped by a few-cm-thick layer of air.

Geiger and Marsden measured the number of alpha particles scattered at different angles. They found that most of the alpha particles are observed to pass through the foil with little—less than a few degrees—or no deviation. A few of the alpha particles, however, were observed to be deflected through large angles. It was found that some of them (1 out of ∼8,000) were scattered by angles greater than 90°, so that they emerge on the entrance side of the foil.

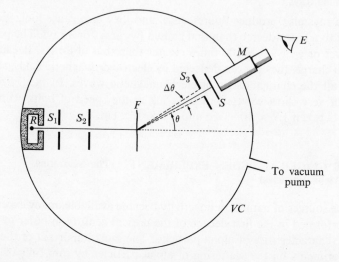

FIG. 7.3. *Experimental arrangement used by Geiger and Marsden for investigating scattering of alpha particles. R is radium, the radioactive α-source; S_1, S_2, S_3 are slits; F is the metallic foil; S is the ZnS screen; M is the microscope; E is the eye; and VC is the vacuum chamber.*

It was this large-angle scattering that gave a clue as to the distribution of mass and charge in the atom. As we shall show in the following section, the large-angle deflections cannot be explained by the Thomson model of the atom.

4. FAILURE OF THE THOMSON MODEL

Our aim in this section is to see if it is possible, on the basis of the Thomson model of the atom, to explain the scattering of alpha particles by thin metallic foils as observed by Geiger and Marsden.

Each atom of the scattering material contains both positive and negative charges, and the α-particle itself has a positive charge of two units. Thus there will be electrostatic forces between the α-particle and the atom. The magnitude and direction of these forces will depend upon how close the α-particle happens to approach the center of an atom. The path of a single α-particle passing through an atom may be represented as shown in Fig. 7.4(a). The net deflection is the sum of (i) the electrostatic repulsion between the α-particle and the positive charge of the atom, the positively charged sphere, and (ii) the electrostatic attraction between the α-particle and the electrons in the atom. The electrostatic repulsion from (i) is the one that contributes mostly to the deflection. Due to the electrostatic attraction the electrons will be simply pulled away from their respective positions producing vibrations about the equilibrium, or they will be completely detached from the atom. Thus such deflections, or the effect of electrostatic attraction, may be neglected.

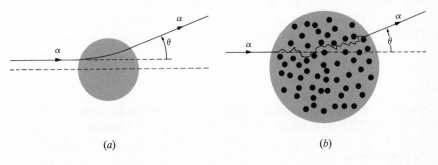

(a)   (b)

FIG. 7.4. *Trajectory of an alpha particle assuming Thomson's model of the atom.* (a) *The over-all net result of scattering, and* (b) *details of the collision process.*

We shall now proceed to calculate the magnitude of the following two deflections[9]:

(a) In a collision between the incoming alpha particle and the electron at rest, the maximum velocity that an electron can gain (from simple conservation of momentum and energy laws) is twice the incident particle velocity. Thus the maximum value of deflection, θ_{max}, ($\sim \Delta p_\alpha / p_\alpha$, where p_α is the momentum of the α-particle) is $\sim 10^{-4}$ radians. This also represents the maximum value of the deflection from a similar collision in traversing through an atom, because the probability of striking head-on with more than one or two electrons is negligible.

(b) The maximum force between the α-particle and the positively charged sphere is $F_{max} \sim 2Ze^2/R^2$ where R is the radius of the atom. Let $\Delta t = R/v$ be the transient time through the atom. Thus $\Delta p_\alpha = F_{max} \Delta t$. For a typical 5-MeV α-particle, $\theta_{max} \sim \Delta p_\alpha / p_\alpha \simeq 10^{-4}$ radians.

Thus we have shown that in crossing through an atom, the total deflection is $\sim 10^{-4}$ radians. In a foil that is of the order to 10^{-4} cm thick, the number of atoms that the α-particle may have to cross is, $n \simeq 10^{-4}$ cm$/10^{-8}$ cm $\simeq 10^4$ atoms. With such a large number of atoms, the problem may be treated completely from a statistical point of view. The net average-scattering angle, θ_{av}, from such statistical considerations is given by [10]

$$[(\theta^2)_{av}]^{1/2} = \sqrt{n}\, [(\theta_j^2)_{av}]^{1/2} \tag{7.1}$$

where $n \simeq 10^4$ atoms and $\theta_j \sim 10^{-4}$ radians. This gives $\theta_{av} \simeq 1°$, which is in agreement with the experimental values of Geiger and Marsden for small-angle scattering (because most of the particles are scattered through less than 3°). From statistical considerations, if N_0 is the total number of α-particles incident at $\theta = 0$ and θ_{av} is the average deflection of the beam, the number of particles, N, scattered through an angle greater than θ is given by[10]

$$N = N_0 \exp\left(-\theta^2/\theta_{av}^2\right) \qquad (7.2)$$

This equation agrees with the experimental values of θ provided θ is very small, $\sim 3°$. But for large-angle scattering, it does not give the right answer. Thus the fraction of α-particles scattered through an angle greater than 90°, according to Eq. (7.2), is

$$\frac{N}{N_0} = \exp\left[-(90°)^2/(1°)^2\right] \simeq 1/10^{3500}$$

which is very small as compared to the experimentally observed value of $N/N_0 \simeq 1/8000 \sim 1/10^4$, as measured by Geiger and Marsden. Also according to Eq. (7.1), θ is proportional to $\sqrt{n}$, while experimentally it is found to be proportional to n.

Thus we conclude that the Thomson model of the atom, because of multiple scattering, cannot explain the large-angle scattering of alpha particles, and we must seek the answer somewhere else.

5. THE RUTHERFORD NUCLEAR MODEL OF THE ATOM

In this section we shall discuss in detail the nuclear model suggested by Rutherford, develop the theory of alpha scattering, and, finally, compare the theoretical predictions with the experimental results.

A. Rutherford's Model[11]

Rutherford suggested a simple model of the structure of the atom that satisfactorily explains the experimental results of α-particle scattering. According to this model all the positive charge of the atom and hence almost all the mass of the atom is assumed to be concentrated in a small central region in the atom, called the nucleus.

The electrons in an atom are assumed to be distributed around the nucleus, similar to the planets around the sun in the universe, in such a way as to account for the radius of the atom being $\sim 10^{-8}$ cm. Because the electrons are almost point masses, most of the space around the nucleus in the atom is empty.

According to this model of the atom, alpha particles can come very close to a large amount of charge all at once and will experience a large deflecting force. Because the mass of the incident α-particle is much smaller than the mass of the target nucleus, backscattering is possible in a single collision between them.

The force of interaction between the α-particle and the nucleus is that of Coulomb repulsion, which is inversely proportional to the square of the distance, r, between them. The orbit is a conic section for any inverse-square law: an elliptical orbit, closed orbit, for an attractive force—like those of planets around the sun where gravitational force is attractive—and an hyperbolic orbit, an open orbit, for a repulsive force. Thus the orbit of an α-particle, because of the repulsive force, is a hyperbola with the nucleus at the outside focus as shown in Fig. 7.5. Thus the nucleus is located at 0 while the path of

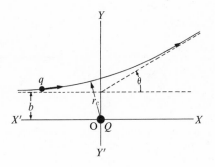

FIG. 7.5.   *The hyperbolic orbit of an alpha particle in the Coulomb field of the nucleus. Also shown are the impact parameter, b, the distance of closest approach, r_c, the scattering angle, θ, and the asymptotes, the dotted lines, to the orbit. Q being the charge of the nucleus.*

the α-particle is shown by a solid curve; the dotted lines are the asymptotes of the hyperbola. The distance by which the α-particle would have missed the nucleus if there were no repulsive force is called the *impact parameter*, *b*, as shown in Fig. 7.5. The angle θ between the two asymptotes, which is the angle between the initial and final directions of the α-particle, is the *angle of scattering*. The *distance of closest approach to the nucleus* is denoted by r_c.

B.   Rutherford Theory of Alpha Scattering

Starting with the Rutherford model we can formulate the theory of alpha scattering[12]. We shall make the following justifiable assumptions:

1.   The Coulomb repulsive force between the α-particle and the target nucleus is the only force affecting the path of the α-particle.
2.   Newton's second law is applicable in determining the deflection of the α-particles.
3.   The α-particle and the target nucleus may be assumed to be point charges and masses.

We may also neglect the recoil energy of the target nucleus because usually the target nucleus is much heavier than the incident bombarding particle.

The derivation given below is after Gordon[13] and is significant in the respect that it demonstrates the special nature of the inverse-square-law force in classical scattering theory. Figure 7.6 shows the scattering of an incoming

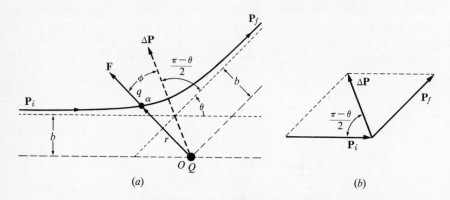

(a)   (b)

FIG. 7.6.   (a) *Scattering of an alpha particle by a repulsive conservative central-force of the stationary nucleus at 0.* (b) *Vector diagram of the change in momentum during scattering.*

particle by a nucleus at point 0, which is the center of the repulsive force. The incoming particle has a mass m, velocity v_o, and charge q. Its momenta long before and long after collision are $\mathbf{P}_i$ and $\mathbf{P}_f$, respectively, where $|\mathbf{P}_i| = |\mathbf{P}_f|$. This particle has an impact parameter b and is deflected through an angle θ in the process of scattering. The scattering center, the nucleus, has charge Q.

Consider a conservative central force, $\mathbf{F}(r)$, without assuming any special form to it. The application of the impulse-momentum theorem gives

$$\Delta \mathbf{P} = \int \mathbf{F}(r)\, dt \tag{7.3}$$

where $\Delta \mathbf{P} = \mathbf{P}_f - \mathbf{P}_i$ is the total change in the momentum vector, the integration extending from $-\infty$ to $+\infty$, and r being a function of t. If θ is the scattering angle, then from Fig. 7.6(b) one finds by applying the law of cosines

$$|\Delta \mathbf{P}| = 2mv_0 \sin (\theta/2) \tag{7.4}$$

In order for the angular momentum to be conserved, $\Delta \mathbf{P}$ must point directly towards or directly away from the center of force. The force, $\mathbf{F}(r)$, between the nucleus and the particle makes an angle ϕ with the direction of $\Delta \mathbf{P}$. Only those components of $\int \mathbf{F}(r)\, dt$ that are parallel to $\Delta \mathbf{P}$ add up to $\Delta \mathbf{P}$; all other perpendicular components add up to zero. Thus combining Eqs. (7.3) and (7.4), we get:

$$2mv_0 \sin(\theta/2) = \int_0^\infty |F(r)| \cos\phi \, dt \qquad (7.5)$$

and

$$0 = \int_0^\infty |F(r)| \sin\phi \, dt \qquad (7.6)$$

Because there is no external torque on the particle around the nucleus, the angular momentum must be conserved. The initial value of the angular momentum, long before the collision, is mv_0b, where b is the impact parameter; the angular momentum at any other time during scattering is $mr^2\omega$, where ω is the angular velocity given by $\omega = d\phi/dt$. These two must be equal, that is

$$mr^2\omega = mv_0b \qquad (7.7)$$

Rewriting Eq. (7.5) in the form

$$2mv_0 \sin(\theta/2) = \int_{-(\pi-\theta)/2}^{+(\pi-\theta)/2} |F(r)| \cos\phi \, \frac{dt}{d\phi} \, d\phi \qquad (7.8)$$

i.e., changing the variables from dt to $d\phi$ and the limits of integration to $-(\pi - \theta)/2$ and $+(\pi - \theta)/2$, and substituting for ω from Eq. (7.7),

$$2mv_0^2b \sin(\theta/2) = \int_{-(\pi-\theta)/2}^{+(\pi-\theta)/2} r^2|F(r)| \cos\phi \, d\phi \qquad (7.9)$$

In the above equation r is now a function of ϕ, and not of t. Making the substitution $\mu = \sin\phi$, $d\mu = \cos\phi \, d\phi$,

$$2mv_0^2b \sin(\theta/2) = \int_{-\cos(\theta/2)}^{+\cos(\theta/2)} r^2|F(r)| \, d\mu \qquad (7.10)$$

The limits of integration in Eq. (7.10) are the same for the attractive as well as the repulsive force law. Equation (7.10) applies to conservative central forces in general. In order to know $b = b(\theta)$, we must know the dependence of r on ϕ, i.e., $r = r(\phi)$. But for a special case of the inverse-square-law force, it is not necessary to know $r(\phi)$ because

$$r^2|F(r)| = C(\text{constant}) = kqQ \qquad (7.11)$$

where $k = 1/4\pi\epsilon_0$. Combining Eq. (7.10) with Eq. (7.11), we get

$$b = \left(\frac{kqQ}{mv_0^2}\right) \cot\frac{\theta}{2} \qquad (7.12)$$

or

$$\cot\frac{\theta}{2} = \left(\frac{mv_0^2}{kqQ}\right)b \qquad (7.13)$$

Equation (7.12) states that if a particle of charge q is directed with an impact parameter b towards a target of charge Q, it will be scattered through an angle θ. The meaning of Eq. (7.12) may be made more clear with the help of Fig. 7.7. Figure 7.7(a) shows the angle of scattering depending upon the value of the impact parameter from a fixed scattering center N. It is clear that the smaller the value of the impact parameter, the larger is the scattering angle. Figure 7.7(b) shows a more practical situation in which a large number of α-particles are incident on a thin metallic foil. The following points are to be noted.

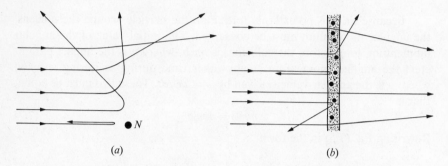

(a)   (b)

FIG. 7.7.   (a) *The scattering angle is shown to depend upon the impact parameter.* (b) *A more realistic situation shows a large number of alpha particles incident on a thin foil.*

(i)   The foil is so thin that no nucleus "hides" behind another nucleus, and hence there is no possibility of multiple scattering.

(ii) Depending upon the value of the impact parameters, different α-particles are scattered through different angles. Figure 7.8 shows that the particles that are

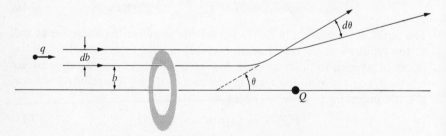

FIG. 7.8.   *Particles with impact parameters between b and $(b + db)$ will be scattered through an angle between θ and $(\theta - d\theta)$.*

directed toward the scattering center with the impact parameter between b and $(b + db)$ will be scattered through an angle between θ and $(\theta - d\theta)$. Also Eq. (7.13) implies that the particles with impact parameters less than b will be scattered through angles greater than θ. Thus the particles falling within the area πb^2 around the nucleus will be scattered through an angle θ or greater than θ, where according to Eq. (7.13), θ is given by

$$\theta = 2 \text{ arc cot} \left[\left(\frac{mv_0^2}{kqQ} \right) b \right] \tag{7.14}$$

The quantity πb^2 may be called *cross-section* for scattering through an angle $\geqslant \theta$.

In order to compare theory with experiment, Eq. (7.14) must be put in a different form because b is not the quantity that is measured experimentally. Once again consider Fig. 7.7(b). Let A be the area, t be the thickness of the foil, n be the number of nuclei per unit volume, and πb^2 the cross-sectional area surrounding each nucleus. If there are N_i particles incident on the foil, we would like to calculate how many particles will be scattered at an angle θ. There are nt nuclei per unit area. The area available for scattering in this unit area is $nt\pi b^2$, and we call this *sensitive area per unit area* of the foil. The sensitive area of the whole foil will be $nt\pi b^2 A$ for the total area of the foil A. The fraction f of the alpha particles that will be scattered through an angle $\geqslant \theta$ will be equal to the ratio of the sensitive area to the total area of the foil, i.e.,

$$f = \frac{nt\pi b^2 A}{A} = nt\pi b^2 \qquad (7.15)$$

Substituting for b from Eq. (7.12),

$$f = \pi b^2 nt = \pi nt \left(\frac{kqQ}{mv_0^2}\right)^2 \cot^2 \frac{\theta}{2} \qquad (7.16)$$

The fraction of alpha particles that are scattered into a cone between angles θ and $(\theta + d\theta)$ and is received into a zone of a sphere of radius r and width $r\,d\theta$ (the area shown shaded in Fig. 7.9) may be obtained by differentiating Eq. (7.16),

$$df = -\pi nt \left(\frac{kqQ}{mv_0^2}\right)^2 \cot \frac{\theta}{2} \csc^2 \frac{\theta}{2}\,d\theta \qquad (7.17)$$

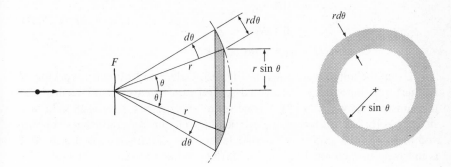

FIG. 7.9. *Particles scattered into a cone between the angles θ and $(\theta + d\theta)$ are received in a zone (shown shaded) of a sphere of radius r and width $r\,d\theta$.*

where the minus sign means that as θ increases f decreases. Thus $N_i|df|$ is the number of particles received into the shaded area. The number of particles

$N(\theta)$ received per unit area at angle θ and distance r from the foil is

$$N(\theta) = \frac{N_i|df|}{dA} \tag{7.18}$$

where dA is the shaded area in Fig. 7.9 and is given by

$$dA = 2\pi r \sin \theta \, r d\theta = 2\pi r^2 \sin \theta \, d\theta \tag{7.19}$$

Combining Eqs. (7.17), (7.18), and (7.19),

$$N(\theta) = \frac{N_i \pi n t \left(\frac{kqQ}{mv_0^2}\right)^2 \cot \frac{\theta}{2} \csc^2 \frac{\theta}{2} \, d\theta}{2\pi r^2 \sin \theta \, d\theta} \tag{7.20}$$

Rearranging and substituting $K_\alpha = \frac{1}{2}mv_0^2$ where K_α is the kinetic energy of the incident particle, $q = 2e$ and $Q = Ze$, we get

$$N(\theta) = \frac{N_i n t k^2 e^4 Z^2}{4r^2 K_\alpha^2 \sin^4 (\theta/2)} \tag{7.21}$$

Equation (7.21) gives the number of particles scattered into a unit area of the detector placed between θ and $(\theta + d\theta)$ at a distance r from the foil. Thus Eq. (7.21) is in the form that may be tested experimentally.

C. Experimental Verification of the Theory

In order to verify experimentally the results of the theory given by Eq. (7.21), one must show that the number of particles scattered into a unit area of a detector placed at angle θ and distance r from the center of the foil must change with t, Z, K_α, and θ in the following manner.

$$\begin{aligned} &\text{(i)} \quad N(\theta) \propto 1/\sin^4 (\theta/2) \\ &\text{(ii)} \quad N(\theta) \propto t \\ &\text{(iii)} \quad N(\theta) \propto Z^2 \\ &\text{(iv)} \quad N(\theta) \propto 1/K_\alpha^2 \end{aligned} \tag{7.22}$$

Using the apparatus shown in Fig. 7.3, Geiger and Marsden working in Rutherford's laboratory, performed several experiments[14] and verified the relations given by Eq. (7.22). In one set of experiments, they used gold and silver foils for the scattering of α-particles (given out from radioactive radon) and measured the number of α-particles scattered at different angles. If $N(\theta)$ is inversely proportional to $\sin^4 (\theta/2)$, the product $N(\theta) \sin^4 (\theta/2)$ should be constant at various angles. The results of their measurements for gold foil are shown in Table 7.1. The product in the last column is approximately constant and lies within the limits of statistical error.

In another experiment to test the dependence on thickness t, they used foils of (different Z) gold, silver, copper, and aluminum of varying thicknesses, while the scattering angle θ was fixed at 25°. The source of α-particles used was radium (B + C) (radioactive lead and bismuth). The results of the

TABLE 7.1
RESULTS OF GEIGER AND MARSDEN EXPERIMENTS:
SCATTERING OF ALPHA PARTICLES FROM GOLD FOIL

Angle of scattering θ	$\dfrac{1}{\sin^4 (\theta/2)}$	Number of scintillations per unit time $N(\theta)$	$N(\theta) \times \sin^4 (\theta/2)$
150°	1.15	33.1	28.8
135°	1.38	43.0	31.2
120°	1.79	51.9	29.0
105°	2.53	69.5	27.5
75°	7.25	211	29.1
60°	16.0	477	29.8
45°	46.6	1,435	30.8
30°	223	7,800	35.0
15°	3,445	132,000	38.4

experiments are shown in Fig. 7.10. Note that $N(\theta)$ is plotted as number of scintillations per minute; while instead of using the actual thickness of the foil, the air equivalent of the foils in cm is used. The graphs clearly show the variation of $N(\theta)$ with t and Z.

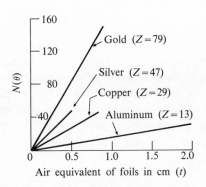

FIG. 7.10. *The number of scintillations per minute, $N(\theta)$ versus air equivalent thickness of the foil in cm, i.e., the variation of $N(\theta)$ with t for different Z. Note that scattering is directly proportional to t and Z. [From Henry Semat,* Introduction to Atomic and Nuclear Physics, *4th ed., New York: Holt, Rinehart and Winston, 1963.]*

Finally, if $N(\theta)$ is inversely proportional to K_α^2, the product of $N(\theta)K_\alpha^2$ or $N(\theta)v_0^4$ (because $K_\alpha = \frac{1}{2}mv_0^2$) should be constant. Geiger and Marsden, in order to change the velocity of the alpha particles, placed absorbing screens of mica between the α-particle source and the scattering foil. The results of their observations are given in Table 7.2. It is obvious from the last column that the product $N(\theta)v_0^4$ is constant.

TABLE 7.2

RESULTS OF GEIGER AND MARSDEN EXPERIMENTS:
SCATTERING OF α-PARTICLES OF DIFFERENT VELOCITIES

Relative velocity v_0	Relative values of $1/v_0^4$	Number of scintillations per unit time $N(\theta)$	$N(\theta)v_0^4$
1.0	1.0	24.7	25
0.955	1.20	29.0	24
0.904	1.50	33.4	22
0.851	1.91	44	23
0.770	2.84	81	28
0.694	4.32	101	23
0.574	9.22	255	28

Thus the Rutherford nuclear model of the atom, according to which the nucleus occupies a very small volume at the center of the atom while most of the space in the atom is practically empty, became firmly established as a workable model.

6. SIZE AND STRUCTURE OF THE NUCLEUS

In the last section we saw how the nuclear model of the atom was firmly established. There are two more questions that must yet be answered. First, how are the electrons in an atom distributed around the nucleus? Second, what is the size, charge, and structure of the nucleus itself? The answer to the first question will be given in the next few chapters where we shall investigate different aspects of extra-nuclear electrons. A brief answer to the second question will be given in this section, while the details are to be found in a book on nuclear physics[15,16], and in some more advanced experiments on α-scattering[17,18].

A. Size of the Nucleus

The scattering of α-particles from different nuclei can be used to obtain some idea about the size of the nucleus. In the extreme case of a head-on collision between an α-particle and a nucleus, backscattering, in which the angle of scattering is 180°, will take place. In such instances the α-particle will attain its distance of closest approach to the target nucleus. As the α-particle of kinetic energy K_α travels towards the target nucleus, the electrostatic repulsion increases. When the α-particle reaches the point of closest approach, its kinetic energy is equal to electrostatic repulsion; the α-particle momentarily comes to rest and then turns back. As shown in Fig. 7.11, the α-particle may be imagined to be climbing the electrostatic hill around the nucleus up to a distance r_c from the nucleus where its kinetic energy is entirely converted into potential energy, and then it starts sliding back down the hill regaining its kinetic energy. Thus we have

$$\frac{1}{2} m v_0^2 = \frac{kqQ}{r_c} \tag{7.23}$$

Because $q = 2e$ for an α-particle, and for the nucleus $Q = Ze$,

$$r_c = \frac{4kZe^2}{m v_0^2} \tag{7.24}$$

Rutherford, using very energetic α-particles from radium ($K_\alpha = 7.68$ MeV) and using gold, aluminum, and other materials was able to obtain values of r_c. For example, for gold, $r_c = 3.2 \times 10^{-12}$ cm; for Al, $r_c = 3 \times 10^{-12}$ cm. These values of r_c do not give the radius of the nucleus, but only the upper limit of the nuclear radius. Thus we may conclude that the radius of the nucleus is of the order of 10^{-12} cm, which as compared to the size of the atom ($\sim 10^{-8}$ cm) is $1/10,000$ times smaller.

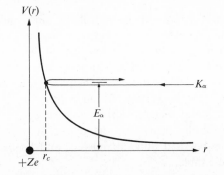

FIG. 7.11.   *Variation of Coulomb potential as a function of distance r from a nucleus of charge Ze. The distance of closest approach, r_c, corresponds to the turning point of the incident alpha particle.*

It may be pointed out that the above approach is correct only for $K_\alpha < 10$ MeV. For higher-energy α-particles, besides Coulomb scattering other processes such as absorption and inelastic scattering[19] also take place and the above approach must be modified. The detailed investigations[15] yield the following value for the nuclear radius R,

$$R = 1.35 \times 10^{-13} A^{1/3} \text{ cm} \tag{7.25}$$

where A is the mass number.

B. Structure of the Nucleus

We have not said much about the structure of the nucleus as yet except that most of the mass and the positive charge of the atom is located in the nucleus.

Until 1932, the nucleus was supposed to consist of A protons and $(A - Z)$ electrons, thus leaving a net $+Ze$ charge on the nucleus. ($A - Z$ protons with $A - Z$ electrons form neutral pairs.) This is the so called proton-electron model of the nucleus. In the 1930's many difficulties were encountered that did not allow the assumption that electrons exist inside the nucleus; and hence the proton-electron model was abandoned. In 1932, Chadwick[20] discovered a new particle, the neutron, which has approximately the same mass as the proton but no charge. A new model, the proton-neutron model[21], of the nucleus was suggested. According to this model there are Z protons and $(A - Z)$ neutrons inside the nucleus of radius $\sim 10^{-12}$ cm, giving a net $+Ze$ charge, and mass number A to the nucleus. Also there are Z electrons around the nucleus and inside the atom between the spheres of radii 10^{-12} cm and 10^{-8} cm. This picture of the atom and the proton-neutron model of the nucleus is the currently accepted model today.

7. ISOTOPES AND MASS SCALES

The discovery of radioactivity at the end of the nineteenth century and the investigation of the properties of radioactive elements gave sufficient experimental evidence to support the suggestion that all the atoms of one element need not be identical in mass. Further study of radioactive elements showed that there were many elements that were chemically identical but had different masses. For example, lead (Pb) is found in three different mass numbers, 206, 207, and 208. Soddy suggested the name *isotopes* (from *isos* meaning equal and *topos* meaning place) for elements that were identical in their chemical properties but had different masses, and hence occupy the same place in the periodic table.

After the existence of isotopes among radioactive elements had been established, the search for isotopes among the nonradioactive elements was initiated by J. J. Thomson in about 1910. By using electric and magnetic deflections of positive rays, or positive ions, the first element successfully investigated by him was neon, which was found to be a mixture of two isotopes of atomic masses 20 and 22 with the abundances 90% and 10%, respectively, i.e.,

$$\text{atomic mass of neon} = \frac{(9 \times 20) + (1 \times 22)}{(9 + 1)} = 20.20$$

The details of this method, called the parabola method of positive-ray analysis, and other methods have been developed for precise measurements of isotopic masses. All these measurements show that the atomic masses of all the different isotopes of different elements are very close to whole numbers.

The formal definition of an isotope is the following: Atoms with the same atomic number, Z but with different atomic masses are *isotopes* of the element Z.

For the purpose of measuring atomic masses, two different scales are commonly used: (1) the chemical, or atomic, scale, and (2) the physical scale. The chemical mass scale takes the mass of the natural isotopic mixture of oxygen as 16.000000 atomic mass units (amu). The natural isotopic mixture of oxygen is (99.76%) $_8O^{16}$, (0.04%) $_8O^{17}$, and (0.20%) $_8O^{18}$. The physical mass scale takes the mass of the most abundant isotope of oxygen, $_8O^{16}$, as 16.000000 amu. The ratio of the two mass scales is:

$$\frac{\text{physical mass scale}}{\text{chemical mass scale}} = 1.000275 \pm 0.000005$$

Masses measured on the chemical mass scale are also referred to as atomic weights of the elements, and those measured on the physical mass scale are referred to as isotopic weights, or, better, isotopic masses.

Recently another unit of atomic mass has been suggested. In 1960, the Tenth General Assembly of the International Union of Pure and Applied Physics recommended the exact number 12 as the mass of the carbon isotope C^{12}. The symbol suggested for this unit is U. The ratio of the two physical mass scales is:

$$\frac{O^{16} \text{ mass scale}}{C^{12} \text{ mass scale}} = 0.99968218$$

At present both physical mass scales are in use. We shall now find the relation between the atomic mass unit and the gram, a unit of mass used more commonly in everyday life. The mass number of carbon is 12, which means that 12 grams of carbon contains N_A carbon atoms, where N_A is Avogadro's number. Because carbon is 12 U, therefore,

$$1 \text{ U} = \frac{1}{12} \frac{12 \text{ grams}}{N_A}$$

or

$$1 \text{ U} = \frac{1 \text{ gram}}{N_A} \tag{7.26}$$

substituting for N_A

$$1 \text{ U} = \frac{1}{6.02252 \times 10^{23}} \text{ gram}$$

or

$$1 \text{ U} = 1.66043 \times 10^{-24} \text{ gm} = 1.66043 \times 10^{-27} \text{ kgm} \tag{7.27}$$

PROBLEMS

1. Suppose in an atom there are A positive charges, each with a radius of r_0, and there are A electrons each with a radius of 10^{-13} cm. If the actual radius of an atom is 10^{-8} cm, what should be the value of r_0 so as to completely fill the atom? How does this value of r_0 compare with the experimentally measured value of 1.35×10^{-13} cm? Can you conclude from this that most of the space inside of the atom is empty? Calculate the fraction of empty space.

2. A radioactive source emits α-particles of 5-MeV energy and β-particles with a maximum end-point energy of 1.5 MeV. Calculate the amount of deflection produced by a magnetic field of 2 webers/m². Make any appropriate assumptions.

3. Calculate the number of α-particles that must be slowed down to form helium atoms so that their spectroscopic analysis may be made. It is assumed that the helium gas formed must exert a pressure of 0.2 mm of Hg and the minimum volume should be 0.5 cm³.

4. Show that in a collision between an α-particle and an electron at rest the maximum deflection of the α-particle is $\sim 10^{-4}$ radian.

5. Show that in a single collision between a 5-MeV α-particle and a positively charged sphere of radius 10^{-8} cm the deflection of the α-particle is $\sim 10^{-4}$ radian.

6. Show that if a mass M moving with velocity v strikes a particle of mass m, $m \ll M$, the maximum velocity gained by m is $2v$.

7. (a) If an α-particle makes a head-on elastic collision with an electron at rest, what is the maximum energy it will lose?
   (b) How much is the energy loss if an α-particle makes a head-on collision with a gold nucleus at rest. Compare the results with (a).

8. Calculate the maximum amount of energy lost by a 5.5-MeV α-particle in a head-on collision with an electron at rest. Calculate the velocity of the electron after the collision and the change in velocity of the α-particle.

9. If α-particles of 7.5-MeV energy are scattered through an angle of 45° by a metal foil, what is the magnitude of the change in momentum, Δp.

10. Alpha particles emitted from $_{84}Po^{210}$ having kinetic energies of 5.3 MeV are incident on a gold foil of thickness 5×10^{-6} cm. Calculate the fraction of α-particles scattered through angles greater than (a) 30°, (b) 60°, and (c) 90°.

11. 3.7×10^{10} α-particles per second, of 5.5-MeV kinetic energy, are incident on a gold foil of thickness 10^{-5} cm and area 1 cm². Assume that the beam is spread over the whole area of the foil. Calculate the number of particles that will scatter into a detector of area 4 cm² at a distance of 50 cm from the foil and making an angle of 45° with the beam.

12. Alpha particles of 6.5-MeV energy are scattered by a gold foil of 10^{-5} cm thickness. For the α-particles that are scattered through 15°, what is the impact parameter? What fraction of the α-particles will be scattered through angles greater than 15°?

13. What is the thickness of the gold foil if one out of every 5000 α-particles of 5-MeV energy is scattered through an angle of 135° or more?

14. Using the equations of conservation of angular momentum and energy, show that the impact parameter b is given by

$$b = r_c \sqrt{\left(1 - \frac{qQ}{r_c K_\alpha}\right)}$$

where r_c is the distance of closest approach and K_α is the kinetic energy of the incident alpha particles.

15. An incident α-particle of mass M, charge ze, and kinetic energy K_α is scattered through an angle θ by a nucleus of charge Ze. Show that the distance of closest approach r_c as a function of θ is given by

$$r_c = \frac{kZze^2}{2K_\alpha} \left(1 + \frac{1}{\sin\frac{\theta}{2}}\right)$$

16. Alpha particles of 8.5-MeV kinetic energy are incident on a silver foil 10^{-5} cm thick. Calculate the number of particles that are scattered through an angle greater than 45°. What is the distance of closest approach in this case?

17. 8-MeV α-particles are incident on a thin gold foil. Calculate r_c for different values of θ. Make a plot of r_c versus θ for the following scatters: **(i)** gold, and **(ii)** aluminum.

18. Calculate the distance of closest approach of 8-MeV α-particles scattered from U^{238} at an angle of 135° in the LAB coordinate system.

19. **(a)** Calculate the distance of closest approach of 5-MeV α-particles from Po^{210} in a head-on collision with a $_{79}Au^{197}$ target. What estimate do you obtain for the maximum size of the nucleus?
(b) Repeat the calculations for 8.78-MeV α-particles given out by Po^{213} and compare the results with **(a)**.

20. If α-particles of 7-MeV energy are incident on a copper foil of thickness 5×10^{-5} cm, calculate the distance of closest approach in a head-on collision. What is the scattering angle if the impact parameter is 2×10^{-11} cm?

21. Calculate the ratio of the number of α-particles scattered by a foil between 60° and 90° to those scattered through angles of 90° or more.

22. Show that the error made in using a nonrelativistic treatment of α-particles with energies less than 10 MeV is negligible. What is the order of percentage error?

23. Calculate the height of potential barrier of Al $(Z = 13)$, Fe $(Z = 26)$, Mo $(Z = 42)$, Nd $(Z = 60)$, Au $(Z = 79)$, Pb $(Z = 82)$, and Pu $(Z = 94)$.

24. From the height of the potential barrier of Al $(Z = 13)$, Fe $(Z = 26)$, and Au $(Z = 79)$, calculate the value of r_0 from the equation $R = r_0 A^{1/3}$, where R may be assumed to be the distance of closest approach in a head-on collision. How do these values of r_0 compare with the value $r_0 = 1.414 \times 10^{-13}$ cm determined from α-scattering experiments using refined calculations.

REFERENCES

1. Thomson, J. J., *Phil. Mag.*, **44**, 293, (1897).

2. Barkla, C. G., *Proc. Roy. Soc.*, **77**, 247, (1906).

3. Thomson, J. J., *The Corpuscular Theory of Matter*, London: Constable & Co., 1907.

4. Thomson, J. J., *Proc. Cambridge Phil. Soc.*, **15**, 465, (1910).

5. Becquerel, H., *Compt. Rend.*, **122**, 420, (1896).

6. Curie, M., *Compt. Rend.*, **126**, 1101, (1898).

7. Geiger, H., and E. Marsden, *Proc. Roy. Soc.*, **A82**, 495, (1909).

8. Geiger, H., *Proc. Roy. Soc.*, **83**, 492, (1910).

9. Eisberg, R. M., *Fundamentals of Modern Physics*, Sec. 4-4, p. 92, New York: John Wiley & Sons, 1961.

10. Preston, R. D., *Kinetic Theory of Gases*, p. 66, New York: McGraw-Hill, 1958.
11. Rutherford, E., *Phil. Mag.*, **21**, 669, (1911).
12. Goldstein, H., *Classical Mechanics*, pp. 81–85, Cambridge: Addison-Wesley, 1951.
13. Gordon, M. M., *Am. J. Phys.*, **23**, 247, (1955).
14. Geiger, H., and E. Marsden, *Phil. Mag.*, **25**, 604, (1913); also Chadwick, J., *Phil. Mag.*, **40**, 734, (1920).
15. Arya, A. P., *Fundamentals of Nuclear Physics*, Chap. VI, Boston: Allyn and Bacon, Inc., 1966.
16. International Conference of Nuclear Sizes and Density Distributions, *Revs. Mod. Phys.*, **30**, 412, (1958).
17. Farwell, G. W., et al., *Phys. Rev.*, **95**, 1212, (1957).
18. Kerlee, D. D., et al., *Phys. Rev.*, **107**, 1343, (1957).
19. Chadwick, J., *Phil. Mag.*, **40**, 734, (1920); also Rutherford, E., and J. Chadwick, *Phil. Mag.*, **50**, 889, (1925).
20. Chadwick, J., *Proc. Roy. Soc.*, **A136**, 692, (1932).
21. Arya, A. P., *Fundamentals of Nuclear Physics*, Chap. I, Boston: Allyn and Bacon, Inc., 1966.

SUGGESTIONS FOR FURTHER READING

1. Gordon, M. M., *Am. J. Phys.*, **23**, 247, (1955).
2. Rutherford, E., J. Chadwick, and C. D. Ellis, *Radiations from Radioactive Substances*, Chaps. II and VIII, Cambridge, England: Cambridge Univ. Press, 1930.
3. Arya, A. P., *Fundamentals of Nuclear Physics*, Chaps. II, V, and VI, Boston: Allyn and Bacon, Inc., 1966.
4. Eisberg, R. M., *Fundamentals of Modern Physics*, Chap. 4, New York: John Wiley & Sons, 1961.
5. Melissinos, A. C., *Experiments in Modern Physics*, Chap. 6, New York: Academic Press, 1966.

VIII

Bohr and Sommerfeld Models
of the Hydrogen Atom

1. THE CLASSICAL MODEL OF THE ATOM

In the previous chapter we demonstrated that the concept of the nuclear atom suggested by Rutherford was in agreement with experimental observations. According to this model, an atom, with a radius of $\sim 10^{-8}$ cm, consists of a nucleus with a radius of $\sim 10^{-12}$ cm that carries the positive charge and most of the mass of the atom. The next question that arises is: What is the arrangement of the electrons in the atom?

We may start with the simplest classical planetary model of the atomic structure. According to this model electrons are constantly moving around the heavy stationary nucleus in circular or elliptical orbits in a manner similar to that of the planets moving around the sun. The gravitational force in the astronomical planetary system is replaced by the Coulomb electrostatic force in the atomic system. Gravitational attraction is also present between particles in the atom, but its magnitude as compared to electrostatic forces is smaller by a factor of $\sim 10^{38}$, and one may easily neglect this. (See Problem 8.4.)

Let us consider a hydrogen atom, and assume for simplicity that the electron is moving in a circular orbit around the hydrogen nucleus, a proton in this case; the nucleus is assumed to be at rest, as shown in Fig. 8.1. The centripetal force F_c holding the electron of mass m moving with velocity v in a circular orbit of radius r is given by

$$F_c = \frac{mv^2}{r} \tag{8.1}$$

This force is provided by the electrostatic attractive force F_e between the electron and the proton and is given by

$$F_e = k\frac{e^2}{r^2} \tag{8.2}$$

where k is a constant equal to $1/4\alpha\epsilon_0$ which is, 8.99×10^9 newton-m^2/coulomb^2 in the MKS system and unity in the CGS system; and e is the electronic charge. Equating Eqs. (8.1) and (8.2)

$$\frac{mv^2}{r} = k\frac{e^2}{r^2}$$

or

$$v = \sqrt{\frac{ke^2}{mr}} \tag{8.3}$$

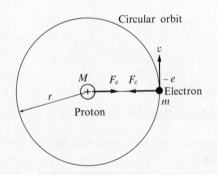

Circular orbit

FIG. 8.1. *The Coulomb force, F_e, equals the centrifugal force, F_c, acting on an electron moving in a circular orbit.*

We are now in a position to calculate the total energy E of the hydrogen atom, which is the sum of the kinetic energy $K(=\frac{1}{2}mv^2)$ and the potential energy $P(=-ke^2/r)$, i.e.,

$$E = K + P = \frac{1}{2}mv^2 + \left(-\frac{ke^2}{r}\right) \tag{8.4}$$

Substituting for v^2 from Eq. (8.3), we get

$$E = \frac{1}{2}\frac{ke^2}{r} - \frac{ke^2}{r} = -\frac{1}{2}\frac{ke^2}{r} \tag{8.5}$$

Thus according to Eq. (8.5), the total energy of the system is negative, and hence the electron is bound to the nucleus, E being the binding energy of the electron. If r decreases, the binding energy increases, making the system more stable. On the other hand, the binding energy decreases with increasing

r, E approaches zero as r approaches infinity and the electron is no longer bound with the nucleus. Knowing the binding energy of an electron in the atom, we may calculate the radius of the electron's orbit from Eq. (8.5). Thus for the hydrogen atom, the measured binding energy E of the electron is -13.58 eV, and from Eq. (8.5) we get the radius of the hydrogen atom to be

$$r = -\frac{ke^2}{2E}$$

$$= -\frac{(8.99 \times 10^9 \text{ newton-m}^2/\text{coulomb}^2)(1.602 \times 10^{-19} \text{ coulomb})^2}{2(-13.58 \text{ eV} \times 1.602 \times 10^{-19} \text{ joule/eV})}$$

$$= 0.53 \times 10^{-10} \text{ m} = 0.53 \text{ Å} \tag{8.6}$$

This value of the atomic radius agrees very well with other experimental determinations. Thus the simple planetary model appears promising. A deeper look reveals many problems; certain experimental facts are not explained by this model. We shall discuss these briefly.

According to classical electromagnetic theory an accelerated charge always radiates electromagnetic waves. (An electric charge at rest produces an electric field, but a moving electric charge produces both an electric field and a magnetic field. If the charge oscillates, i.e., it is accelerated, both the fields at any point will vary periodically, which is equivalent to saying that the charge is emitting electromagnetic waves.) Because the electron in a circular orbit is always accelerated, it will radiate electromagnetic waves. The orbital frequency, and hence the frequency, f, of the waves, is given by

$$f = \frac{\omega}{2\pi} = \frac{v}{2\pi r} \tag{8.7}$$

where ω is the angular frequency. Substituting for v from Eq. (8.3), we get

$$f = \frac{1}{2\pi} \sqrt{\frac{ke^2}{mr^3}} \tag{8.8}$$

With the value of the radius given by Eq. (8.6), one finds the frequency to be $\sim 5 \times 10^{15}$/sec, which lies in the ultraviolet region. If the atom radiates, it loses energy and hence the total energy must decrease. But a decrease in energy according to Eq. (8.5) means that r must decrease (to make E more negative) and hence f continuously increases. From these relations, it can be seen that an electron always finds itself in an orbit of continuously decreasing radius and eventually collapses into the nucleus (Fig. 8.2) in a very short time, $\sim 10^{-8}$ sec (see Problem 8.1). In this process it emits electromagnetic radiation of continuously increasing frequency. But this is in contradiction to the fact that the structure of the atom is stable and does not collapse. Also according to this picture the atom radiates a continuous spectrum, while experimentally it has been established beyond doubt that an atom emits a *discrete spectrum*, i.e., a spectrum consisting of specific frequencies.

In the beginning of the present century, physicists were still looking for a model of the structure of the atom that would lead to the observed facts that atoms are stable and emit discrete spectra. In 1913, Bohr[1] put forth certain postulates which, to a great extent, brought theory into agreement with experimental observations. Before we discuss the Bohr theory, it is essential to review the accumulated results of experiments of atomic spectra.

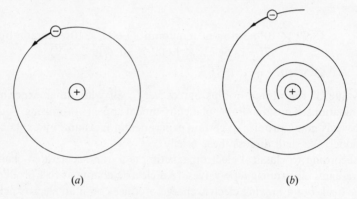

(a)   (b)

FIG. 8.2.   (a) *Stable electron orbit*. (b) *Collapsing electron orbit*.

2.   ATOMIC SPECTRA

The study of spectra involves the measurement of wavelength and the intensity of emitted or absorbed electromagnetic radiation. The instruments used for making visual observation of spectra are called spectroscopes, while the instruments used for the measurements of wavelengths and intensities are called spectrometers. Photographic plates may be used for obtaining permanent records, or one may obtain directly plots of intensity versus wavelengths by means of spectrographs. There are three broad categories of spectra: (1) continuous spectra, (2) discrete (or line) spectra, and (3) band spectra. We shall distinguish between these three in the following.

As we saw in Chapter IV, heated solids emit electromagnetic radiation that consists of all wavelengths, i.e., they emit continuous spectra. The characteristics of the spectra obtained are independent of the type of solid and depend only on its temperature. We were able to explain all the features of this continuous spectra with the help of the quantum theory of radiation without going into the details of the radiation process or the nature of the solid itself. Hence we may conclude that continuous spectra emitted by solids heated to incandescence are due to the collective behavior of a large number of interacting atoms rather than to the behavior of individual atoms.

The discrete, or line, spectrum is the result of the behavior of individual atoms or molecules. The atoms, by colliding with fast electrons or with each other or by some similar process, may have a total energy greater than the normal-state energy and hence are said to be in an *excited state*. The excess energy may be emitted in the form of electromagnetic radiation when the atom returns to its normal state. The electromagnetic radiation emitted in this fashion from atoms consists of a number of discrete wavelengths, producing discrete spectra. Each of these spectral components is called a *line* if a rectangular slit is used, otherwise the shape of each component of the discrete spectrum depends upon the shape of the slit used in the investigation. A discrete spectrum is characteristic of each chemical element, and very small quantities—of the order of micrograms—may be employed for identification of unknown substances.

The excitation of molecules results in a spectrum that consists of bands. Each band is composed of many separate lines very close together. Such bands are due to the rotations and vibrations of molecules. We shall discuss these in detail in Chapter XIV.

We are concerned here mainly with line spectra. The experimental arrangement most commonly used to obtain such a spectrum is shown in Fig. 8.3. The source, S, may be an electric discharge tube containing a monatomic

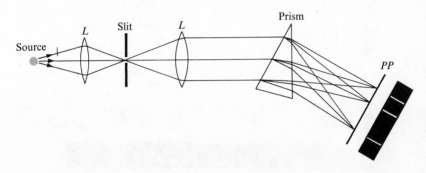

FIG. 8.3. *A typical experimental arrangement for obtaining the line spectrum of an element.*

gas; or an electric arc or electric sparks may be utilized. In some cases, salts of metals under investigation may be continuously heated directly in the flame of a burner. The electromagnetic radiation, after passing through a system of lenses and collimating system, falls on a prism, which produces dispersion and brings to focus different wavelengths at different spots on the photographic plate, PP. A diffraction grating may be used instead of the prism.

Up to this point we have been talking about the discrete emission spectra, but we can obtain another type of spectra: the discrete absorption spectra. To obtain such spectra, white light, which consists of all wavelengths in the visible region, is passed through the vapors of the substance of which the

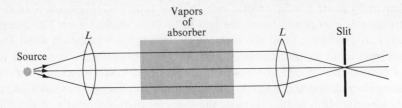

FIG. 8.4. *A typical experimental arrangement for obtaining the absorption spectra of different elements, which are in the form of vapors.*

absorption spectrum is being investigated, as shown in Fig. 8.4. When the resulting beam is analyzed, we find a spectrum consisting of dark lines on a bright background. The wavelengths of the missing lines correspond exactly to the lines obtained in the emission spectrum of the absorber. Figure 8.5

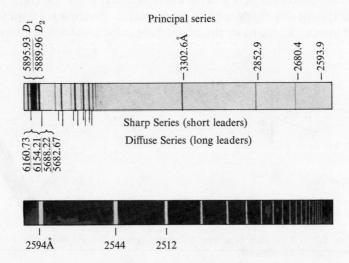

FIG. 8.5. (a) *Emission and* (b) *absorption spectra of sodium.* [*From* Atomic Spectra and Atomic Structure *by Gerhard Herzberg, Dover Publications, Inc., New York, 1944. Reprinted through permission of the publisher.*]

shows the emission and absorption spectrum of sodium. It may be noted that not all the lines in emission spectra necessarily show up in absorption spectra.

We shall now return to the discussion of discrete emission spectra in some detail. In the second half of the nineteenth century, scientists investigated line spectra of many different materials. The purpose was twofold. The accurate measurement of the wavelengths was a helpful addition to chemical analysis. But the main purpose was to accumulate enough data to produce some insight into the structure of the atom. Atomic spectra of each element were found to consist of wavelengths that display some regularities and, in fact, fall into definite sets called the *spectral series*.

The first such series was observed in the spectrum of the hydrogen atom, the simplest of all the atoms, with a single proton as the nucleus and a single electron going around it. The observation was made by J. J. Balmer[2] in 1885. Balmer investigated the characteristics of the visible part of the hydrogen spectrum (shown in Fig. 8.6) and showed that the spectrum could be expressed in the mathematical form

$$\lambda = (3645.6) \frac{n^2}{n^2 - 4} \, \text{Å} \qquad (8.9)$$

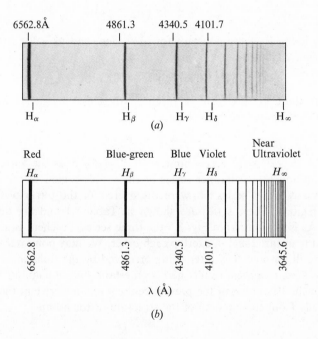

FIG. 8.6. *The visible part of the hydrogen spectrum:* (a) *photograph and* (b) *schematic representation.* [*From* Atomic Spectra and Atomic Structure *by Gerhard Herzberg, Dover Publications, Inc., New York, 1944. Reprinted through permission of the publisher.*]

where λ is the wavelength in Angstrom units (1 Å = 10^{-10} m), and n is a variable integer that can take the values 3, 4, 5, 6, ... For $n = 3$, Eq. (8.9) gives $\lambda = 6562.08$ Å (λ expt. = 6562.10 Å), and this is the H_α line. For $n = 4$,

$\lambda = 4860.80$ Å (λ expt. $= 4861.3$ Å), and this is the H$_\beta$ line. For $n = 5$, $\lambda = 4340$ A (λ expt. $= 4340.5$ Å), and this is the H$_\gamma$ line, and so on. The actual photograph of these lines H$_\alpha$, H$_\beta$, H$_\gamma$, H$_\delta$, . . . , the Balmer series, is shown in Fig. 8.6(a). It may be noted that the spacing between adjacent wavelengths of the series decreases with decreasing wavelengths, and eventually the series of lines converge into the *series limit*, which is reached when $n = \infty$ (or very large) and corresponds to $\lambda = 3645.6$ Å. (The accuracy of wavelength measurement at that time was 1 part in 1000, while at the present time it is possible to measure to 1 part in 100,000.) The discovery of the Balmer series, represented by Eq. (8.9), initiated a search for similar empirical formulae for other series of different spectra. Rydberg[3] in 1896 expressed Eq. (8.9) in a slightly different and more convenient form by using the wave number $\bar{\nu} = 1/\lambda$. The number of waves per centimeter is given by

$$\frac{1}{\lambda} = \bar{\nu} = R_H \left(\frac{1}{2^2} - \frac{1}{n^2} \right) \tag{8.10}$$

where R_H is the Rydberg constant for hydrogen, and its value from recent spectroscopic data is[4]

$$R_H = 109677.576 \pm 0.012 \text{ cm}^{-1} \tag{8.11}$$

The series limit in this form is reached when $n = \infty$, i.e., $1/\lambda = R_H/4$. Equation (8.10) may also be written as

$$\bar{\nu} = T_l - T \tag{8.12}$$

where $T_l = R_H/2^2$ is the series limit while $T = R_H/n^2$ is the variable term.

In addition to the Balmer series in the visible region of the hydrogen spectra, many other series[5-8] were discovered in the ultraviolet and the infrared regions. These series are shown in Table 8.1 and are depicted in Fig. 8.7. As is obvious from Fig. 8.7 the three series, Paschen, Brackett, and Pfund in the infrared region overlap each other. We may point out that these series were discovered only after being predicted by the Bohr theory.

Once these empirical results had been established, the aim of the investigators in the beginning of the present century was to arrive at these results theoretically from some model of the structure of the atom.

3. THE BOHR THEORY OF THE HYDROGEN SPECTRUM

In the last two sections we have acquainted ourselves with two points that must be explained by any satisfactory model of the structure of the atom. First, it must explain the stability of the atom and, secondly, it must explain the observed regularities in the atomic spectra. Niels Bohr, in 1913, initially worked with the Rutherford nuclear model of the atom and then incorporated into Coulomb's and Newton's classical laws the recently discovered Planck's quantum hypothesis of electromagnetic radiation. Even though the path of a

TABLE 8.1

SERIES OF THE HYDROGEN SPECTRUM

Name of the series	Wavelength range	Mathematical form for $\bar{\nu} = \dfrac{1}{\lambda} = R_H\left(\dfrac{1}{n_f^2} - \dfrac{1}{n_2^2}\right)$	Series limit $T_l\left(= \dfrac{R_H}{n_f^2}\right)$
1. Lyman	~940–1216 Å (Ultraviolet)	$\dfrac{1}{\lambda} = R_H\left(\dfrac{1}{1^2} - \dfrac{1}{n^2}\right)$; $n = 2, 3, 4, \ldots$	$\dfrac{R_H}{1^2}$
2. Balmer	~3700–6570 Å (Visible)	$\dfrac{1}{\lambda} = R_H\left(\dfrac{1}{2^2} - \dfrac{1}{n^2}\right)$; $n = 3, 4, 5, \ldots$	$\dfrac{R_H}{2^2}$
3. Paschen	~8460–18,760 Å (Infrared)	$\dfrac{1}{\lambda} = R_H\left(\dfrac{1}{3^2} - \dfrac{1}{n^2}\right)$; $n = 4, 5, 6, \ldots$	$\dfrac{R_H}{3^2}$
4. Brackett	~15,040–40,500 Å (Infrared)	$\dfrac{1}{\lambda} = R_H\left(\dfrac{1}{4^2} - \dfrac{1}{n^2}\right)$; $n = 5, 6, 7, \ldots$	$\dfrac{R_H}{4^2}$
5. Pfund	~23,500–74,600 Å (Infrared)	$\dfrac{1}{\lambda} = R_H\left(\dfrac{1}{5^2} - \dfrac{1}{n^2}\right)$; $n = 6, 7, 8, \ldots$	$\dfrac{R_H}{5^2}$

particle moving in an inverse-square-law force is a conic section, Bohr assumed, for simplicity, the path of the electron around the nucleus to be a circle.

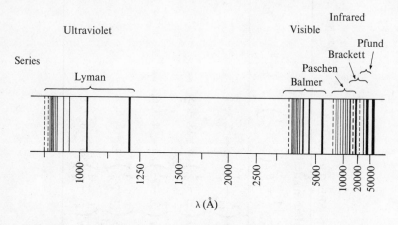

FIG. 8.7. *The relative positions of different lines of the spectral series of hydrogen.*

A. Postulates

Bohr's theory[9] of the hydrogen atom is based on three basic postulates:

POSTULATE 1:   An electron in an atom (i.e., a bound atomic system) can move only in certain circular orbits about the nucleus without radiating. These are called the discrete stationary states of the system.

POSTULATE 2:   Only those stationary states are allowed for which the orbital angular momentum, mvr, of the electron is an integral multiple of $h/2\pi$ (h = Planck's constant), i.e.,

$$mvr = n\frac{h}{2\pi} \tag{8.13}$$

where $n = 1, 2, 3, 4, \ldots$ and n is called the *principal quantum number.*

POSTULATE 3:   When an electron jumps from an initial high-energy state, E_i, to a final low-energy state, E_f, which is an atom undergoing a transition, a photon of energy $h\nu$ is emitted, so that

$$h\nu = E_i - E_f \tag{8.14}$$

There was no justification for the first two postulates at that time, and these were stated arbitrarily. The justification for the third postulate came from Planck's quantum ideas that successfully explained black-body radiation, the photoelectric effect, and the Compton effect. Later developments in wave mechanics eliminated the need for these postulates. A much more detailed and complete theory of atomic structure explains, in addition, many facts that Bohr's theory or its modification could not account for. Before we go ahead with the Bohr theory, we shall see how the simple application of de Broglie's hypothesis results in postulate 2.

Consider a rigid string of length L fixed at both ends. The string can be set into stationary resonance, or standing vibrations, only if L is equal to an integral number of half-wavelengths, $L = n\lambda/2$; see Fig. 8.8(a). If this condi-

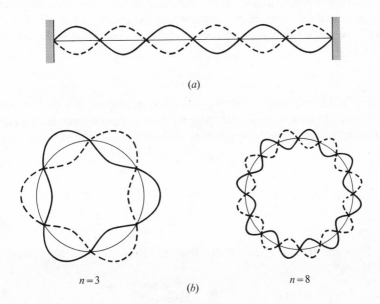

(a)

$n = 3$

$n = 8$

(b)

FIG. 8.8.   (a) *Formation of stationary, or standing, resonance vibrations in a string.* (b) *Formation of stationary, or standing, resonance vibrations on a circular hoop.*

tion is not satisfied, destructive interference will result and the vibrations will stop. If the string is curved into a circle of radius r, and the transverse waves are to be propagated around the circle, the waves will interfere destructively unless the string joins smoothly with itself, i.e., stationary waves will exist only if an integral number of whole wavelengths can be fitted around the circumference; see Fig. 8.8(b). We may state this condition in the form

$$2\pi r = n\lambda \qquad (8.15)$$

According to de Broglie's hypothesis

$$\lambda = h/mv \qquad (8.16)$$

Substituting for λ into Eq. (8.15), we get

$$mvr = n\frac{h}{2\pi}$$

which is Bohr's postulate 2 given by Eq. (8.13). Using $\hbar$ (h-bar) $= h/2\pi$, a symbol more convenient to use, we may write

$$mvr = n\hbar \tag{8.17}$$

B. Energy Levels of the Hydrogen Atom

The above postulates, known as the *quantization rules*, automatically lead to discrete radii and velocities. We assume that the system is quantized, and we proceed with the calculation of these quantities. According to Eq. (8.13) or Eq. (8.17)

$$v_n = \frac{n\hbar}{mr_n} \tag{8.18}$$

where v_n is the tangential velocity of the electron orbiting in a circle of radius r_n. For an electron in a circular motion, the centripetal force is equal to the Coulomb force, and according to Eqs. (8.1) and (8.2), (Fig. 8.1),

$$\frac{mv_n^2}{r_n} = k\frac{e^2}{r_n^2} \tag{8.19}$$

Substituting for v_n form Eq. (8.18) into Eq. (8.19) and simplifying

$$r_n = \frac{n^2\hbar^2}{kme^2} \tag{8.20}$$

Thus the lowest value of the Bohr orbit is obtained by substituting $n = 1$, i.e.,

$$r_1 = \frac{\hbar^2}{kme^2} \tag{8.21}$$

This is the radius of the lowest energy state of the hydrogen atom, and it yields, after substituting for $\hbar$, k, m, and e,

$$r_1 = 0.528 \text{ Å } (=0.528 \times 10^{-10} \text{ m}) \tag{8.22}$$

which agrees well with the experimentally determined value of the diameter of the hydrogen atom equal to 1 Å. Combining Eqs. (8.20) and (8.21),

$$r_n = n^2 r_1 \tag{8.23a}$$

i.e., the possible stationary orbits of the electrons in the hydrogen atoms are

$$r_n = r_1, 4r_1, 9r_1, \ldots \tag{8.23b}$$

as shown in Fig. 8.9.

Substituting Eq. (8.23) into Eq. (8.18), we may calculate the tangential speeds of the electrons in the allowed orbits, i.e.,

$$v_n = \frac{n\hbar}{m(n^2 r_1)} = \frac{1}{n}\left(\frac{\hbar}{mr_1}\right) \tag{8.24}$$

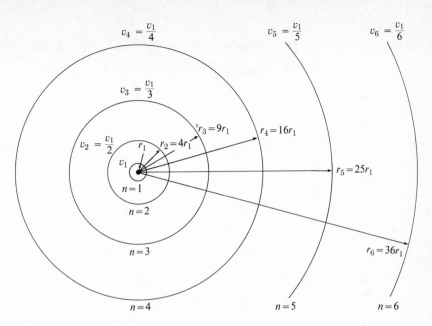

FIG. 8.9.   *The possible stationary orbits of an electron in the hydrogen atom.*

or substituting for r_1 from Eq. (8.21)

$$v_n = \frac{1}{n}\left(\frac{ke^2}{\hbar}\right) \tag{8.25}$$

For $n = 1$

$$v_1 = \frac{\hbar}{mr_1} = \frac{ke^2}{\hbar} \tag{8.26}$$

which is the velocity of the electron in the lowest allowed Bohr orbit. Thus from Eq. (8.25)

$$v_n = \frac{v_1}{n} \tag{8.27a}$$

or the velocities of the electrons in different Bohr orbits are

$$v_n = v_1, \frac{v_1}{2}, \frac{v_1}{3}, \dots \tag{8.27b}$$

and are shown in Fig. 8.10. The ratio of the maximum speed v_1 to the speed of light c, is called the *fine-structure constant*, α, i.e.,

$$\alpha = \frac{v_1}{c} = \frac{ke^2}{\hbar c} = \frac{1}{137.0388} \tag{8.28}$$

Our next task is to calculate the energies corresponding to the Bohr stationary orbits. The total energy E_n of an electron in an orbit of radius r_n

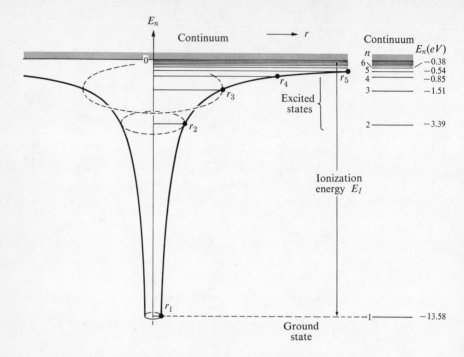

FIG. 8.10. *The possible energy states of the hydrogen atom corresponding to different values of the quantum number n.*

with velocity v_n is equal to the sum of kinetic energy K and the potential energy P

$$E_n = \frac{1}{2} m v_n^2 + \left(-\frac{ke^2}{r_n}\right)$$

Substituting for v_n from Eq. (8.19) into the above equation (or from Eq. (8.5)), gives

$$E_n = -\frac{1}{2} \frac{ke^2}{r_n} \tag{8.29}$$

or because from Eq. (8.23a), $r_n = n^2 r_1$,

$$E_n = -\frac{1}{n^2} \left(\frac{ke^2}{2r_1}\right) \tag{8.30}$$

Also if we substitute for r_1 from Eq. (8.21)

$$E_n = -\frac{1}{n^2} \left(\frac{k^2 e^4 m}{2\hbar^2}\right) \tag{8.31}$$

If we represent

$$E_I = \frac{ke^2}{2r_1} = \frac{k^2 e^4 m}{2\hbar^2} \tag{8.32}$$

then

$$E_n = -\frac{E_I}{n^2} \tag{8.33}$$

As is obvious from Eq. (8.33), for $n = 1$, $E_1 = -E_I$, i.e., $-E_I$ is the energy of the system in the lowest allowed state, and hence is the maximum binding energy of the electron in the hydrogen atom. The energy E_I is called the *ionization energy*. It is the amount of energy needed to completely remove (or detach) the electron from the hydrogen atomic system. In addition to the lowest energy state also known as the *ground state* or *normal state* of the atom, for which $n = 1$ in the hydrogen atom, the hydrogen atom may exist in any of the many states corresponding to $n = 2, 3, 4, 5, \ldots$. The binding energies for these states (including the ground state) according to Eq. (8.33), are:

$$E_n = -E_I, -\frac{E_I}{4}, -\frac{E_I}{9}, -\frac{E_I}{16}, \ldots \tag{8.34}$$

The different states corresponding to different values of the quantum number n are shown in Fig. 8.11. The ground-state energy may be calculated from Eq. (8.32) by substituting the values of k, e, m, and $\hbar$; i.e.,

$$E_1 = -E_I = -13.58 \text{ eV} \tag{8.35}$$

Combining Eq. (8.35) with Eq. (8.33) one may calculate E_n. The different values of E_n are shown in Fig. 8.11.

The states other than the ground state in which the system can exist are the *excited states* of the atom. $E_n = 0$ is achieved for $n = \infty$. The energy difference between this and the ground state, $-E_1$, i.e., $0 - (-E_1) = E_1(= 13.58$ eV), is the ionization energy. The energy that would be needed to change the system from its ground state to one of the excited states, i.e., $(E_n - E_1)$ is the *excitation energy*. For example, the excitation energy for $n = 2$ is $[-(E_I/4) - (-E_I/1)] = [-(E_I/4) + E_I] = \frac{3}{4}E_I$.

C. Hydrogen Emission Spectrum

Knowing the discrete energy states of the hydrogen atom as given by Eqs. (8.31) or (8.33), and making use of the Bohr postulate 3, we are in a position to derive theoretically the hydrogen spectrum. According to postulate 3, if the system exists initially in an energy state E_i (other than the ground state) it will move, or jump, to a final energy state $E_f(E_f < E_i)$ and in doing so, the difference in the energy of the two states will be emitted in the form of a single photon, or quantum of energy $h\nu$, such that

$$h\nu = E_i - E_f \tag{8.36}$$

where ν is the frequency of the photon, or of the electromagnetic radiation, emitted. E_i and E_f are given, according to Eq. (8.33), as

$$E_i = -\frac{E_I}{n_i^2}, \qquad E_f = -\frac{E_I}{n_f^2} \tag{8.37}$$

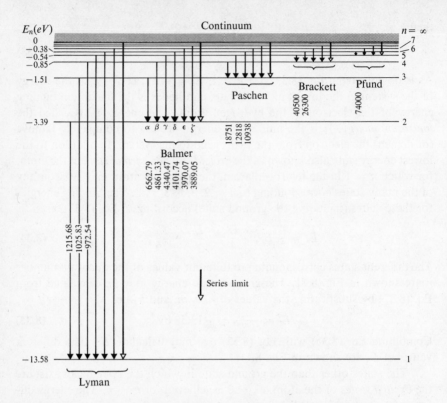

FIG. 8.11. *The energy-level diagram of the hydrogen atom showing the possible transitions corresponding to different series. The numbers along the transitions are wavelengths.*

Therefore

$$\nu = \frac{E_i - E_f}{h} = \frac{(-E_I/n_i^2) - (-E_I/n_f^2)}{h}$$

or

$$\nu = \frac{E_I}{h}\left(\frac{1}{n_f^2} - \frac{1}{n_i^2}\right) \tag{8.38}$$

Because $\nu = \dfrac{c}{\lambda}$, the wave number $\bar{\nu} = \dfrac{1}{\lambda}$ is

$$\bar{\nu} = \frac{1}{\lambda} = \frac{E_I}{hc}\left(\frac{1}{n_f^2} - \frac{1}{n_i^2}\right)$$

$$\bar{\nu} = \frac{1}{\lambda} = R\left(\frac{1}{n_f^2} - \frac{1}{n_i^2}\right) \tag{8.39}$$

where R is the Rydberg constant given, after substituting for E_I from Eq. (8.32), by

$$R = \frac{E_I}{hc} = \frac{k^2 e^4 m}{4\pi \hbar^3 c} = 1.0974 \times 10^{-3} \text{ Å}^{-1} \tag{8.40}$$

which agrees very well with the value of R_H for hydrogen found experimentally[10] and given by Eq. (8.11), i.e.,

$$R_H(\text{expt}) = 109677.576 \pm 0.012 \text{ cm}^{-1}$$

Equation (8.39) is the basic equation and is similar in form to Eq. (8.10) and other equations in Table 8.1. Hence by assigning different values to n_i and n_f, all the series of the hydrogen spectrum in Table 8.1 are accountable and clearly demonstrated in Fig. 8.11. The vertical lengths of the transitions are proportional to the energies of the photons emitted.

A small volume of hydrogen gas at room temperature contains many billions of hydrogen atoms, all of which are in the ground state. These atoms can change to different excited states in the presence of an electrical discharge, as mentioned earlier. Once in excited states, these atoms return to the ground state or to lower excited states by emitting photons of different energies. As shown in Table 8.1, if the final-state quantum number $n_f = 1$ and $n_i(=n) = 2, 3, 4, 5, \ldots$, we get the Lyman series; if $n_f = 2$ and $n_i = 3, 4, 5, \ldots$, we get the Balmer series and similarly, other series. It may be pointed out that the Lyman, Brackett, and Pfund series were actually predicted first by this theory and were then found experimentally, thereby pointing to the success of the theory.

It is not impossible to cause thermal excitation of hydrogen atoms by collisions between them instead of by electrical discharge, but the temperatures needed to achieve this are very high. For example, at room temperature the average kinetic energy of the atoms is $\frac{3}{2}kT = 1/25$ eV while the energy of the transition from $n = 1$ to $n = 2$ (or $E_2 - E_1$) is $-3.40 - (-13.58) \simeq 10.2$ eV. In order to achieve thermal energies of the order of 10 eV or more, the temperature of the atoms will have to be greater than 10^5 °K. For example, if there are N_0 atoms at T °K of which N_1 are in energy state $n = 1$, and N_2 are in energy state $n = 2$, then according to the Boltzmann distribution

$$N_1 = N_0 e^{-E_1/kT}$$

or

$$N_2 = N_0 e^{-E_2/kT}$$

For these two states to be equally probable, or

$$\frac{N_1}{N_2} = 1 = e^{-E_1/kT}/e^{-E_2/kT}$$

we find (for $E_2 - E_1 \simeq 10$ eV)

$$T \simeq 10^5 \text{ °K}$$

Finally, if the electromagnetic radiation of all wavelengths is passed through hydrogen gas, we get the absorption spectrum. The radiation absorbed by atoms in the ground state leaves them in excited states. The missing radiation (equal to the difference in the two discrete energy-levels) appears as a dark line on a bright background. Excited atoms emit radiation within

$\sim 10^{-8}$ second, and return then to the lower states. The intensity of this emitted radiation is isotropic and hence does not lighten the dark absorption line enough so as to return it to its original intensity.

4. IMPROVEMENT AND EXTENSION OF THE BOHR MODEL

In this section, we shall modify the Bohr theory in order to take into account the nuclear mass. We shall also discuss the isotopic shift which led to the discovery of deuterium, and finally the extension will be made to the hydrogenic (or hydrogen-like) atoms.

A.   Correction for Nuclear Motion

In previous derivations, it was assumed that the nucleus was at rest while the electron moved in a circular motion around the nucleus. This condition could be true only if the mass of the nucleus were infinite. This assumption of infinite mass is valid relative to the mass of the electron because the mass of the hydrogen nucleus, a proton, is about 1837 times the mass of the electron. With the development of very precise instruments, it is possible to measure small differences in wavelengths, and it becomes very important to take into account the nuclear mass while making theoretical calculations.

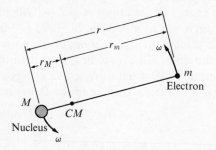

FIG. 8.12.   *Motion of an electron and the nucleus of an atom about their common center of mass.*

Let the mass of the nucleus be M. As shown in Fig. 8.12, r_M and r_m are the distances of the nucleus and the electron from the center of mass, CM. Both the electron and the nucleus revolve around the center of mass with the same angular velocity $\omega(=v/r)$. From the definition of the center of mass

$$Mr_M = mr_m \qquad (8.41)$$

and

$$r = r_M + r_m \qquad (8.42)$$

Solving these equations

$$r_m = \frac{M}{M+m}\, r \quad \text{and} \quad r_M = \frac{m}{M+m}\, r \tag{8.43}$$

The total angular momentum L of the system is now given by the sum of the electron and the nucleus angular momenta, instead of just the electron, i.e.,

$$L = mr_m^2\omega + Mr_M^2\omega \tag{8.44}$$

Substitution for r_m and r_M from Eq. (8.43), yields

$$L = m\left(\frac{M}{M+m}\right)^2 r^2\omega + M\left(\frac{m}{M+m}\right)^2 r^2\omega$$

or

$$L = \left(\frac{mM}{M+m}\right) r^2\omega \tag{8.45}$$

If we define a quantity, the "reduced mass μ," as

$$\frac{1}{\mu} = \frac{1}{M} + \frac{1}{m}$$

or

$$\mu = \frac{Mm}{M+m} \tag{8.46}$$

then Eq. (8.45) takes the form

$$L = \mu r^2\omega \tag{8.47}$$

Thus the Bohr second postulate may be restated as

$$\mu r^2\omega = n\hbar \tag{8.48}$$

which is the same expression as in Eq. (8.13) except that the electron mass m, is replaced by the *reduced mass*, μ.

Equation (8.19) for the force balance must now be modified to take into account the nuclear motion, i.e.,

$$\frac{mv^2}{r_m} = k\frac{e^2}{r^2}$$

or

$$mr_m\omega^2 = k\frac{e^2}{r^2} \tag{8.49}$$

Note that the centrifugal force depends upon the distance r_m of the electron from the center of mass while the Coulomb force still depends upon the distance r between the electron and the nucleus. Substituting for r_m in Eq. (8.49) from Eq. (8.43), we get

$$\frac{Mm}{(M+m)}\, r\omega^2 = k\frac{e^2}{r^2}$$

or

$$\mu r \omega^2 = k \frac{e^2}{r^2} \tag{8.50}$$

The two basic equations, (8.48) and (8.50), are exactly the same as before, (Eqs. (8.13) and (8.19), respectively), except m has been replaced by μ. This means that the results of the theory of the hydrogen atom derived in the last section can be taken over by replacing m by μ. Thus the expression for the energy levels given by Eq. (8.31) takes the form

$$E_n = -\frac{1}{n^2} \left(\frac{k^2 e^4 \mu}{2\hbar^2} \right) \tag{8.51}$$

It is usual to denote the value of the Rydberg constant by R_∞ (R-infinity) if we assume that the nuclear mass is infinite; and if we use the reduced mass, the Rydberg constant is denoted by R_M. Thus without mass correction Eq. (8.39) is given by

$$\bar{\nu}_u = \frac{1}{\lambda_u} = R_\infty \left(\frac{1}{n_f^2} - \frac{1}{n_i^2} \right) \tag{8.52}$$

where the subscript u means uncorrected. While the expression corrected for nuclear mass is

$$\bar{\nu} = \frac{1}{\lambda} = R_M \left(\frac{1}{n_f^2} - \frac{1}{n_i^2} \right) \tag{8.53}$$

where

$$R_\infty = \frac{k^2 e^4 m}{4\pi \hbar^3 c} = 1.0973731 \times 10^{-3} \, \text{A}^{-1}$$

and

$$R_M = \frac{k^2 e^4 \mu}{4\pi \hbar^3 c} = 1.0967758 \times 10^{-3} \, \text{A}^{-1} \tag{8.54}$$

The value of R_M is exactly in agreement with the experimentally determined value. The value of R_M is always less than R_∞, i.e.,

$$\frac{R_M}{R_\infty} = \frac{\mu}{m} = \frac{M}{M + m} = \left(\frac{1}{1 + \frac{m}{M}} \right) \tag{8.55a}$$

or

$$R_M = R_\infty \left(\frac{\mu}{m} \right) = R_\infty \left(\frac{M}{M + m} \right) \tag{8.55b}$$

For the case of the hydrogen atom

$$R_M = R_\infty \left(\frac{1836}{1837} \right) = 0.99945 \, R_\infty \tag{8.55c}$$

i.e., R_M is less than R_∞ by 0.055 percent, while the energies E_n from Eq. (8.51) increase by 0.055 percent. This correction is very important for light-weight atoms and is clearly demonstrated in connection with the discovery of deuterium. It may further be pointed out from Eq. (8.55a) that as $M \to \infty$, $\mu \to m$ and $R_M \to R_\infty$.

B. Discovery of Deuterium

Application of the finite nuclear mass correction to the Rydberg constant led to an important discovery, that of an isotope of hydrogen. Natural hydrogen consists of two isotopes. One isotope, which has a proton as its nucleus and one electron, is called hydrogen, and is denoted by H^1. The other isotope, which has a neutron and a proton as its nucleus and an electron, known as heavy hydrogen, or the deuterium atom, is denoted by H^2 or sometimes by D; the nucleus of the deuterium is called a deuteron. The mass of the hydrogen nucleus is 1.007825 U while the mass of the deuterium nucleus is 2.01410 U. The natural abundance of H^2 in hydrogen is approximately one part in 6000. The original existence of the two isotopes was suggested by Birge and Menzel[11] (1931) while the actual experimental discovery was made by Urey, Brickwedde, and Murphy[12] (1932).

Before discussing the experimental details, let us see what differences are expected in the optical spectra of the two isotopes. From Eqs. (8.54) and (8.55) the two Rydberg constants are given by

$$R_{H^1} = R_\infty \left(\frac{M_{H^1}}{M_{H^1} + m_e} \right) \qquad R_{H^1} = 1.09678 \times 10^{-3} \, A^{-1}$$

$$R_{H^2} = R_\infty \left(\frac{M_{H^2}}{M_{H^2} + m_e} \right) \qquad R_{H^2} = 1.09707 \times 10^{-3} \, A^{-1}$$

Because of the small difference in the two Rydberg constants, the spectral lines due to these two isotopes will be slightly shifted. For example, in the case of the H^1 isotope the H_α line has a wavelength 6562.80 Å, while the H_α line of the H^2 isotope has a wavelength of 6561.01 Å. The difference is $H_\alpha^1 -$ $H_\alpha^2 = 1.79$ Å (see Fig. 8.13). Similarly, the calculated difference $H_\beta^1 - H_\beta^2 =$

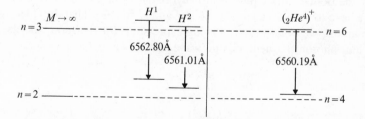

FIG. 8.13.   *The energy levels of hydrogen and deuterium for $n = 2$ and $n = 3$, and of $({}_2He^4)^+$ for $n = 4$ and $n = 6$. The levels shown dotted are without the nuclear-mass correction, while continuous lines are levels after correcting for nuclear mass.*

1.326 Å. These differences, though very small, are easily measured because high-resolution spectrometers are capable of measuring wavelength differences of the order of 0.001 Å. Thus the existence of deuterium could be established if one could observe a spectral series very close to the hydrogen spectral series. The actual experiments were done by Urey, et al[12]. The 21-foot concave grating used had a dispersion of 1.3 Å/mm. The source was an electrical discharge. The lines of the Balmer series were photographed. Because of the small abundance of H^2 in natural hydrogen (0.015 percent) the lines were very faint. In order to obtain samples richer in H^2, liquid hydrogen was evaporated. Being lighter, H^1 evaporated faster, leaving behind the H^2-rich hydrogen. With these samples, the photographs of the Balmer series[12,13] showed, $H^1_\alpha - H^2_\alpha = 1.791$ Å; $H^1_\beta - H^2_\beta = 1.313$ Å; $H^1_\gamma - H^2_\gamma = 1.176$ Å; and $H^1_\delta - H^2_\delta = 1.088$ Å, which compare favorably with the theoretically predicted values of 1.793 Å, 1.326 Å, 1.185 Å, and 1.119 Å, respectively. Thus the existence of H^2 was established.

C. Hydrogenic Atoms or Hydrogen-Like Ions

The Bohr theory of the hydrogen atom can be easily extended to other atoms or ions that have only a single effective electron irrespective of the charge on the nucleus. Such atoms are called hydrogenic atoms or hydrogen-like ions. Thus Bohr's theory will correctly predict the spectra of the ions like He^+, singly-ionized helium; Li^{++}, doubly-ionized lithium; and Be^{+++}, triple-ionized beryllium. In such cases, if the charge on the nucleus is Ze, where Z is the atomic number of the nucleus, the Coulomb law takes the form $F_e = ke(Ze)/r^2$, and the equation for the force balance with nuclear-mass correction, Eq. (8.50), takes the form

$$\mu r\omega^2 = k\frac{Ze^2}{r^2} \qquad (8.56)$$

while the Bohr postulate, $\mu r^2\omega = n\hbar$, remains unchanged. Thus in order to apply the Bohr-theory equations for hydrogen spectra to hydrogen-like ions, all we have to do is to change e^2 to Ze^2 and e^4 to Z^2e^4. Therefore, for hydrogenic atoms, we obtain the following expressions for the radii, speeds, energies, and photon frequencies, and wave numbers as

$$r_n = \frac{n^2\hbar^2}{k\mu(Ze^2)}$$

$$v_n = \frac{k(Ze^2)}{n\hbar}$$

$$E_n = -\frac{1}{n^2}\frac{\mu k^2(Z^2e^4)}{2\hbar^2} \qquad (8.57)$$

$$\nu = \frac{c}{\lambda} = cZ^2 R_M \left(\frac{1}{n_f^2} - \frac{1}{n_i^2} \right)$$

$$\bar{\nu} = \frac{1}{\lambda} = Z^2 R_M \left(\frac{1}{n_f^2} - \frac{1}{n_i^2} \right) \tag{8.57}$$

As is obvious, the energy levels are lowered by a factor Z^2 (a factor of 4 for He⁺, 9 for Li⁺⁺, etc.), as shown in Fig. 8.14. Similarly the corresponding photon frequencies are increased by a factor of Z^2, i.e., the lines of hydrogenic atoms are shifted towards the ultraviolet. We note from Fig. 8.14 (also see

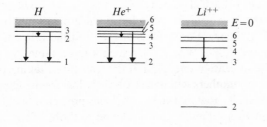

FIG. 8.14.   *The energy levels of hydrogen, singly ionized He (He⁺), and doubly ionized Li (Li⁺⁺). Note that the wavelengths of some transitions in different atoms are the same.*

Fig. 8.13) that certain lines in different hydrogenic atoms have almost the same frequencies and show similar series, except for a small difference due to their Rydberg constants. Such transitions are shown in Fig. 8.14, while the correction due to the difference in nuclear mass is shown in Fig. 8.13 in the case of H¹, H², and He⁺.

5. THE BOHR CORRESPONDENCE PRINCIPLE

We have seen that whenever we are dealing with problems in the microscopic region, we have to use the quantum theory, which developed through the introduction of the Planck constant h. The angular momentum $\hbar$, used in Bohr theory and in other problems, is so small in magnitude that it will not be observed in macroscopic experiments. However, Bohr[14] stated in 1923, in the limit the predictions of the quantum theory for the behavior of any physical system must correspond to the predictions of classical physics for the same system. We may ask what is the limit, or under what circumstance, will the Bohr atom behave classically? One may set an obvious limit: that if the diameter of the Bohr orbit is about 1 mm, the atom should behave according to the classical theory. For the size of the orbit the value of the quantum number, n, is about 5,000. When n has such a large value, the energy levels lie just below the ionization energy, and the transitions taking place between such high quantum numbers will have extremely low frequencies or very long wavelengths. We shall show that the frequencies predicted by the Bohr theory for such large quantum numbers are the same as those predicted by classical theory.

We showed that according to classical electromagnetic theory an electron in a circular orbit around the nucleus has a frequency f given by Eq. (8.8), i.e.,

$$f = \frac{1}{2\pi} \sqrt{\frac{ke^2}{mr^3}} \tag{8.58}$$

Thus the electron will give out radiation of frequency f or its harmonics, $2f, 3f, \ldots$.

Now according to the Bohr theory,

$$\nu = cR\left(\frac{1}{n_f^2} - \frac{1}{n_i^2}\right)$$

may be written as

$$\nu = cR\left(\frac{n_i^2 - n_f^2}{n_i^2 n_f^2}\right)$$

or

$$\nu = cR\left(\frac{(n_i + n_f)(n_i - n_f)}{n_i^2 n_f^2}\right) \tag{8.59}$$

For n very large, let $n_i \simeq n_f = n$ and $n_i - n_f = \Delta n$; Eq. (8.60) takes the form

$$\lim_{n \to \infty} \nu = \frac{2cR}{n^3} \Delta n \tag{8.60}$$

Substituting for R from Eq. (8.40), and r given by Eq. (8.20), we get

$$\lim_{n \to \infty} \nu = \frac{2c}{n^3} \frac{k^2 e^4 m}{4\pi \hbar^3 c} \Delta n$$

$$= \frac{1}{2\pi} \sqrt{\frac{ke^2}{m} \frac{\frac{1}{n^6 \hbar^6}}{k^2 m^3 e^6}} \, \Delta n$$

$$= \frac{1}{2\pi} \sqrt{\frac{ke^2}{mr^3}} \, \Delta n \qquad (8.61)$$

which for $\Delta n = 1$ agrees with the frequency predicted by classical theory and given by Eq. (8.59). Also Eq. (8.61), for $\Delta n = 2, 3, 4, \ldots$, gives the same harmonics as the classical theory.

Hence, we have shown that in the limit of the large quantum number n, the Bohr theory gives the same result as classical theory. We may point out that such a correspondence exists in the case of black-body radiation as well in the limit of long wavelength and low frequencies.

6. THE FRANCK-HERTZ EXPERIMENT

Within less than a year of the publication of the Bohr theory, one of the most direct proofs of the existence of discrete energy states was demonstrated in 1914 by Franck and Hertz[15] by their experiments on critical potentials: Neutral atoms are made to collide with fast-moving electrons (or atoms or molecules). If in such a collision the exchange of energy is only the energy of translation, the collision is elastic, and the atom is not excited, while the electron changes its direction of motion. For sufficiently high-energy electrons, on the other hand, the collision may be inelastic, in which case the electron may lose part or all of its energy in increasing the potential energy of the neutral atom, i.e., in causing the excitation of the atom. The experiment of Franck and Hertz consists of showing that only those inelastic collisions take place that leave excited atoms in discrete-energy states corresponding to those predicted by Bohr.

The experimental arrangement of Franck and Hertz is shown in Fig. 8.15. A tube is filled at low pressure with the vapors of the element under investigation. The electrons emitted from the heated filament, F, are accelerated through the vapor toward the grid, G, and the plate, P. The distances between F, G, and P, and the vapor pressure in the tube are adjusted in such a way that the mean free path of the electron is much smaller than the distance FG, while it is slightly larger than the distance GP. Any electrons reaching the plate will register current in the current-measuring device, I, an ammeter or galvanometer.

An electron starting from rest at F will have fallen through a potential V when it reaches G. The velocity of the electron is given by the relation

$$Ve = \frac{1}{2} mv^2 \qquad (8.62)$$

As the potential V is increased, the kinetic energy $\frac{1}{2}mv^2$ of the electron also

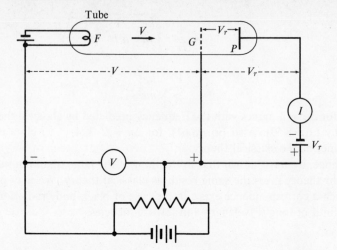

FIG. 8.15. *The Franck-Hertz experimental setup for demonstrating the existence of discrete energy levels.*

increases. As the potential V is increased, more and more electrons reach the plate indicating an increase in the current as shown in Fig. 8.16. For low V the only collisions taking place are elastic. As V increases, the kinetic energy of the electrons approaching G also increases. If this kinetic energy is nearly equal to the first excitation energy of the neutral atoms, inelastic collisions will take place near the grid. The electrons, after losing most of their energy in exciting the atoms, will not be able to cross the retarding potential V_r between G and P. This will be indicated by a sharp drop in the current, as shown in Fig. 8.16. With further increase in V, the electrons suffering their first inelastic collisions will still have enough energy left to reach P against V_r. This

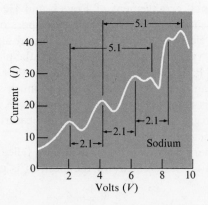

FIG. 8.16. *The current, I, versus potential, V, in the Franck-Hertz experiment using sodium vapors.*

will be indicated once again by an increase in the current. Eventually the next drop in current takes place when the electrons have twice the first excitation energy, i.e., the electron loses all its energy in exciting two different neutral atoms of the same element to their first excited states. As an example, let us calculate V for the case of sodium vapors. As we shall see in Chapter IX, the most prominent transition in sodium is between the first excited state and the ground state, corresponding to a wavelength of 5893 Å. (Actually this is the mean of two close transitions of wavelengths 5890 Å and 5896 Å.) The potential V needed for the electron to have enough kinetic energy $\frac{1}{2}mv^2$ to raise the neutral sodium atom from the ground state to the first excited state may be calculated as follows:

$$\frac{1}{2} mv^2 = Ve = h\nu = \frac{hc}{\lambda}$$

$$V = \frac{hc}{e\lambda} = \frac{6.625 \times 10^{-34} \text{ joule-sec} \times 3 \times 10^8 \text{ m/sec}}{1.602 \times 10^{-19} \text{ coulomb} \times 5893 \times 10^{-10} \text{ m}} \qquad \textbf{(8.63)}$$

$$= 2.1 \text{ volts}$$

Another possible inelastic collision is the case where the colliding electron has enough energy to completely ionize the atom. For sodium the ionization potential is -5.13 eV. Thus if the discrete energy levels do exist, we should see drops in currents at intervals of 2.1 volts (corresponding to first excitation) and 5.13 volts (corresponding to the complete ionization of the atom). This is clearly demonstrated in Fig. 8.16, and confirms the existence of discrete levels.

In the original experiments of Franck and Hertz, mercury vapors were used for which the decreases in current took place at intervals of 4.9 volts, corresponding to the first excited state of mercury.

7.　EXTENSION OF QUANTIZATION RULES

It was natural that success of Bohr theory should lead to a search for quantization rules for other systems. Wilson[16] and Sommerfeld[17] postulated independently that to quantize any atomic system, each degree of freedom must be quantized separately, or, in a more general way, and making use of the concept of phase space, we may state this Wilson-Sommerfeld quantization rule in the following form:

For any physical system whose coordinates are periodic functions of time, there exists corresponding to each coordinate separately a quantum condition that may be stated, in the form of phase-integral, as

$$\oint P_i \, dq_i = n_i h \qquad \textbf{(8.64)}$$

where p_i is the momentum associated with the coordinate q_i and n_i is a corresponding quantum number and takes on integral values. $\oint$ means that the integration takes place over one complete period of the coordinate q_i. The quantity $\oint p_i \, dq_i$ is called the *phase integral* or *action integral* and the meaning of this will become clear as we apply this to a few simple examples.

A. Circulation Motion

Consider the case of the Bohr atom, i.e., an electron of mass m moving with velocity v (or angular velocity ω) in a circle of radius r around the nucleus, as shown in Fig. 8.17. The position of the electron may be completely speci-

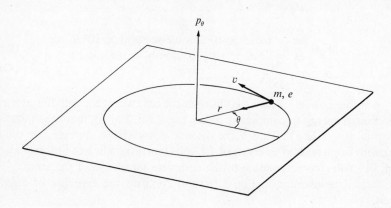

FIG. 8.17.   *An electron moving in a circular orbit has angular momentum* $p_\theta = mr^2(d\theta/dt)$ *but has zero radial momentum.*

fied by the polar coordinates r and θ. The momentum associated with θ is the angular (or azimuthal) momentum $p_\theta = mr^2(d\theta/dt) = mr^2\omega$. The momentum associated with the radial coordinate r is the radial momentum $p_r = m(dr/dt) = 0$, because r is constant and dr/dt is zero. Thus we have to consider only the angular momentum. The phase integral, Eq. (8.64), takes the form

$$\oint p_\theta \, d\theta = n_\theta h$$

i.e.,

$$p_\theta 2\pi = n_\theta h \qquad (8.65)$$

If we write $p_\theta = mr^2\omega = mrv$ and $n_\theta = n$, we get

$$mvr = nh/2\pi \qquad (8.66)$$

where $n = 1, 2, 3, \ldots$, which is Bohr's condition.

B. Simple Harmonic Oscillator

Consider a simple harmonic oscillator consisting of a particle of mass m and angular frequency $\omega(=2\pi\nu)$ such that its displacement x is given by

$$x = x_0 \sin \omega t \tag{8.67}$$

where x_0 is the amplitude of the oscillation. The total energy E, which is the sum of the kinetic energy and the potential energy, may be written as

$$E = \frac{1}{2} m\dot{x}^2 + \frac{1}{2} m\omega^2 x^2 \tag{8.68}$$

Let us introduce the momentum $p = m\dot{x}$ and rewrite Eq. (8.68) in the following form

$$E = \frac{p^2}{2m} + \frac{1}{2} m\omega^2 x^2$$

or

$$\frac{x^2}{2E/m\omega^2} + \frac{p^2}{2mE} = 1 \tag{8.69}$$

which is the equation in the XY plane of an ellipse with semimajor axis a and semiminor axis b given by

$$a = \sqrt{\frac{2E}{m\omega^2}} \quad \text{and} \quad b = \sqrt{2mE} \tag{8.70}$$

and the motion of the particle at any instant is completely given by the point (x, p) in a two-dimensional plot as shown in Fig. 8.18.

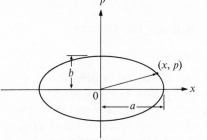

Fig. 8.18. *The two-dimensional motion of a particle in an elliptical path is represented by the coordinates (x, p).*

The integral of Eq. (8.64) is easy to evaluate if we remember that the area of an ellipse is given by πab, i.e.,

$$\oint p_i \, dq_i = \oint p \, dx = \pi ab = nh \tag{8.71}$$

Substituting for a and b from Eq. (8.70) into Eq. (8.71)

$$\oint p\, dx = \pi \sqrt{\frac{2E}{m\omega^2}}\ \sqrt{2mE} = \frac{2\pi E}{\omega} = \frac{E}{\nu} = nh$$

or

$$E = nh\nu \tag{8.72}$$

which is the Planck quantization condition. $\oint p\, dx = nh$ gives a set of ellipses for $n = 1, 2, 3, 4, 5, \ldots$, and the areas between any of these two ellipses is h, i.e., the phase space is divided into elliptical annuli of equal areas h as shown in Fig. 8.19.

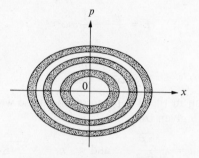

FIG. 8.19. *The set of ellipses calculated from $\oint p\, dx = nh$ for different values of n resulting in the phase space that is divided into elliptical annuli of equal areas h.*

8. SOMMERFELD'S ELLIPTIC ORBITS

A. Quantization Conditions

The first main objection raised to the Bohr theory of the hydrogen atom was its limitation to circular orbits. For any bound system (i.e., the total energy of the system being negative) under the attractive inverse-square-law of force, as is the case here, the general shape of the orbit should be elliptical. If we assume this to be the case, the problem changes from one degree of freedom to two degrees of freedom. As shown in Fig. 8.20, for a circular orbit there is azimuthal (or tangential) velocity only, while for an elliptical orbit we have both azimuthal velocity A and the radial velocity R.

Thus according to Sommerfeld[18], we should start with the assumption that the electron in an atom is moving in an elliptical orbit. Using polar coordinates, we have two degrees of freedom, and the position of the electron at any instant may be described by (r, θ) (see Fig. 8.21). The nucleus is located at one focus of the ellipse. Corresponding to the two degrees of freedom there

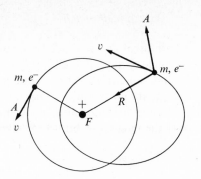

FIG. 8.20.   *As shown in this figure, a particle moving in a circular orbit has azimuthal (or tangential) velocity only, while for an elliptical orbit it has both azimuthal velocity A and radial velocity R.*

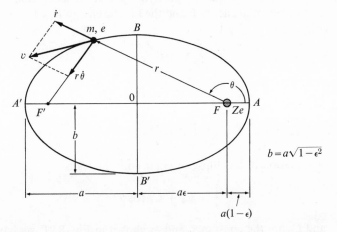

FIG. 8.21.   *The polar coordinates (r, θ) of an electron moving in an elliptical path around the nucleus. The nucleus is located at one focus of the ellipse.*

are two velocities, the azimuthal velocity $r\dot{\theta}$ and the radial velocity $\dot{r}$, and hence we may define two independent momenta, the angular (or azimuthal) momentum p_θ and the radial momentum p_r

$$p_\theta = mr^2\dot{\theta} \tag{8.73}$$

$$p_r = m\dot{r} \tag{8.74}$$

According to the quantum condition given by Eq. (8.64), for these two independent momenta, we have the following two quantum conditions

$$\oint p_\theta \, d\theta = n_\theta h \tag{8.75}$$

$$\oint p_r \, dr = n_r h \tag{8.76}$$

where n_θ and n_r are the azimuthal and the radial quantum numbers, respectively. Note that Bohr's single quantum condition given by Eq. (8.13) is replaced here by two quantum conditions. Also a close look at Eq. (8.75) reveals that it gives the Bohr quantum condition. According to Kepler's second law (for elliptical orbits) the angular momentum p_θ remains constant throughout the motion. Therefore the integral of Eq. (8.75) takes the form

$$\oint p_\theta \, d\theta = \int_0^{2\pi} p_\theta \, d\theta = 2\pi p_\theta = 2\pi m r^2 \dot\theta = n_\theta h \tag{8.77}$$

B. Energies of the States

Our main task is to evaluate the integral of Eq. (8.76) and to find the expression for the energy levels of the hydrogen atom using Sommerfeld's method[19]. The potential energy V and the kinetic energy K of the system are given by (Fig. 8.22)

$$V = -k \frac{Ze^2}{r} \tag{8.78}$$

$$K = \frac{1}{2} m v^2 = \frac{1}{2} m(\dot r^2 + r^2 \dot\theta^2)$$

$$= \frac{1}{2m} \left(p_r^2 + \frac{p_\theta^2}{r^2} \right) \tag{8.79}$$

The general equation of an ellipse in polar coordinates is

$$\frac{1}{r} = C_1 + C_2 \cos \theta \tag{8.80}$$

where C_1 and C_2 are the constants, and as shown in Fig. 8.21, we have

$$\begin{aligned}
OF &= a\epsilon \\
AF &= a(1 - \epsilon) \\
A'F &= a(1 + \epsilon) \\
OB = OB' = b &= a\sqrt{1 - \epsilon^2}
\end{aligned} \tag{8.81}$$

where a and b are the semimajor and semiminor axes, respectively, and ϵ is the eccentricity of the ellipse.

The constants C_1 and C_2 may be evaluated by substituting $\theta = 0°$ and $\theta = \pi$ in Eq. (8.80) when the electron is at A and A', respectively, and using the values of r from Eq. (8.81). Thus the general equation of the ellipse, Eq. (8.80), takes the form

$$\frac{1}{r} = \frac{1 + \epsilon \cos \theta}{a(1 - \epsilon^2)} \tag{8.82}$$

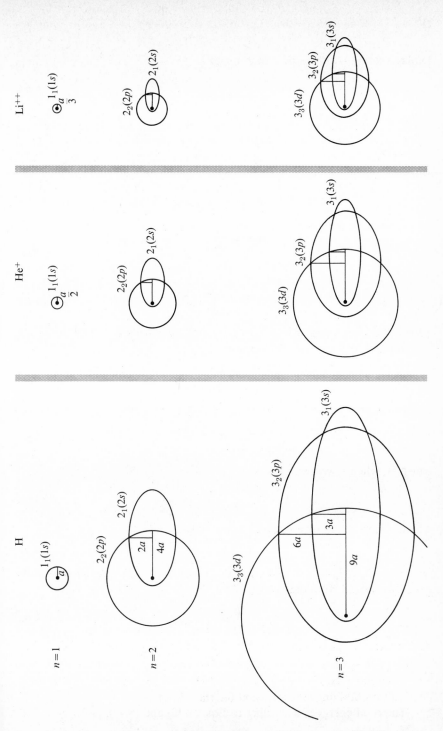

FIG. 8.22. *The different possible paths of the electrons in H, He⁺, and Li⁺⁺ for n = 1, 2, and 3. (The diagrams are drawn to a relative scale.)*

Differentiating r with respect to θ, we get

$$-\frac{1}{r^2}\frac{dr}{d\theta} = -\frac{\epsilon \sin \theta}{a(1 - \epsilon^2)} \tag{8.83}$$

Dividing Eq. (8.83) by Eq. (8.82)

$$\frac{1}{r}\frac{dr}{d\theta} = \frac{\epsilon \sin \theta}{1 + \epsilon \cos \theta} \tag{8.84}$$

Also,

$$p_r = m\dot{r} = m\frac{dr}{dt} = m\frac{dr}{d\theta}\frac{d\theta}{dt} = m\frac{dr}{d\theta}\dot{\theta} \tag{8.85}$$

or, substituting for $\dot{\theta}$ from Eq. (8.73),

$$p_r = \frac{p_\theta}{r^2}\frac{dr}{d\theta} \tag{8.86}$$

Also

$$dr = \frac{dr}{d\theta}d\theta \tag{8.87}$$

Substituting for p_r and dr into Eq. (8.76), and then using Eq. (8.84) for $dr/d\theta$, and noting that p_θ is constant, we get

$$p_\theta \epsilon^2 \int_0^{2\pi} \frac{\sin^2 \theta}{(1 + \epsilon \cos \theta)} d\theta = n_r h \tag{8.88}$$

Substituting for $p_\theta = n_\theta h/2\pi$ (from Eq. (8.77)), and integrating by parts, we get

$$\frac{1}{\sqrt{1 - \epsilon^2}} - 1 = \frac{n_r}{n_\theta} \tag{8.89}$$

which is, when rewritten,

$$1 - \epsilon^2 = \frac{n_\theta^2}{(n_\theta + n_r)^2} = \frac{b^2}{a^2} \tag{8.90}$$

where n_θ and n_r can take integral values only. Let

$$n_\theta + n_r = n \tag{8.91}$$

where $n = 1, 2, 3, 4, \ldots$, and n is called the *total* (or *principle*) *quantum number*. Thus Eq. (8.90) reduces to

$$\frac{b}{a} = \frac{n_\theta}{n} \tag{8.92}$$

This relation is important because it states that out of all the classically permitted ellipses, only those are allowed for which the ratio of the semimajor and semiminor axes is given by Eq. (8.92). We shall discuss this in more detail after obtaining an expression for the energy.

The total energy E according to Eqs. (8.78) and (8.79), is

$$E = K + V = \frac{1}{2m}\left(p_r^2 + \frac{p_\theta^2}{r^2}\right) - k\frac{Ze^2}{r} \tag{8.93}$$

or, substituting for p_r from Eq. (8.86),

$$E = \frac{1}{2m}\left[\left(\frac{p_\theta}{r^2}\frac{dr}{d\theta}\right)^2 + \frac{p_\theta^2}{r^2}\right] - k\frac{Ze^2}{r} \tag{8.94}$$

Solving for $(1/r)(dr/d\theta)$, we get

$$\left(\frac{1}{r}\frac{dr}{d\theta}\right)^2 = \left(\frac{2mE}{p_\theta^2}\right)r^2 + \left(\frac{2mkZe^2}{p_\theta^2}\right)r - 1 \tag{8.95}$$

Eliminate θ between Eq. (8.82) and Eq. (8.84) and write in the form

$$\left(\frac{1}{r}\frac{dr}{d\theta}\right)^2 = -\frac{r^2}{a^2(1-\epsilon^2)} + \frac{2r}{a(1-\epsilon^2)} - 1 \tag{8.96}$$

Compare coefficients of r^2 and r in Eqs. (8.95) and (8.96):

$$\frac{2mE}{p_\theta^2} = -\frac{1}{a^2(1-\epsilon^2)} \tag{8.97}$$

and

$$\frac{mkZe^2}{p_\theta^2} = \frac{1}{a(1-\epsilon^2)} \tag{8.98}$$

Using Eqs. (8.77), (8.90) and (8.92), we obtain by solving the above equations.

$$a = \frac{h^2}{4\pi^2 mkZe^2}(n_\theta + n_r)^2 = n^2\frac{h^2}{4\pi^2 mkZe^2} \tag{8.99}$$

and dividing Eq. (8.97) by Eq. (8.98)

$$E = -\frac{2\pi^2 mk^2 Z^2 e^4}{h^2(n_\theta + n_r)^2} = -\frac{1}{n^2}\frac{2\pi^2 mk^2 Z^2 e^4}{h^2} = -\frac{kZe^2}{2a} \tag{8.100}$$

If we use $h/2\pi = \hbar$, $n = n_r + n_\theta$; the radius of the first Bohr orbit $a_1 = \hbar^2/k\mu e^2$ (where we have replaced m by the reduced mass μ); and Eq. (8.92), we get

$$a = \frac{n^2\hbar^2}{\mu kZe^2} = a_1\frac{n^2}{Z} \tag{8.101}$$

$$b = \frac{n_\theta}{n}a = a_1\frac{n_\theta n}{Z} \tag{8.102}$$

$$E = -\frac{2\pi^2\mu k^2 Z^2 e^4}{(n_\theta + n_r)^2 h^2} = -\frac{1}{n^2}\frac{\mu k^2 Z^2 e^4}{2\hbar^2} \tag{8.103}$$

where the principal quantum number n can take the values

$$n = 1, 2, 3, 4, \ldots \tag{8.104a}$$

and the angular quantum number n_θ takes the values

$$n_\theta = 1, 2, \ldots, n \tag{8.104b}$$

while the radial quantum number n_r takes the values

$$n_r = 0, 1, 2, \ldots, (n-1) \tag{8.104c}$$

Note that $n_r = 0$ only when $n = 1$ and $n_\theta = 1$.

We make the following observations at this point. First of all Eq. (8.103) for E is identical with Eqs. (8.51) and (8.57). Thus nothing new has been obtained concerning the energy of different levels corresponding to different values of n. Secondly, in Eq. (8.104b), n_θ cannot take the value zero. If $n_\theta = 0$ were possible, it would mean that $b = 0$ (Eq. (8.102)), and the ellipse would reduce to a straight line. This implies that the electron would pass through the force center (the nucleus in this case) twice in one period. This is not possible, and hence the value of $n_\theta = 0$ is completely neglected. (In many texts k is used instead of n_θ.)

C. Form of the Elliptic Orbits

As we have seen from Eq. (8.100) and Eq. (8.103), the energy of the hydrogen-like atom is determined by n, the total quantum number, and is a function of the major axis $2a$, independent of the shape of the ellipse. This means that for a given n value, an electron can move in different elliptical orbits for which the major and the minor axis are given by Eqs. (8.101) and (8.102), but for all these elliptical orbits the energy of the state is the same. Such states are called *degenerate states*. For example, for $n = 1$, $n_r = 0$, and $n_\theta = 1$, which means that $a = b$ and we have a circular orbit. For $n = 2$, we can have either $n_r = 0$, and $n_\theta = 2$, which is a circle; or $n_r = 1$ and $n_\theta = 1$, which is an ellipse with $b = a/2$; but both have the same energy. For $n = 3$, we have the following three combinations: $n_\theta = 3, 2, 1$; and $n_r = 0, 1, 2$, corresponding to one circle and two ellipses with $b = \frac{2}{3}a$, and $\frac{1}{3}a$, all three of which have the same energy. These three cases are shown in Fig. (8.22).

The value of a increases as n^2. If we want to draw the corresponding orbits for different hydrogen-like atoms, the value of a decreases as $1/Z$ and the corresponding values of b will decrease by the same proportion. The paths of the orbits for He^+ and Li^{++} (and also for H) are shown in Fig. 8.22.

In general any orbit is denoted by two quantum numbers n and n_θ. Thus the orbit for which $n = 2$, and $n_\theta = 1$, will be written as 2_1. Similarly for $n = 3$, and $n_\theta = 3$, it will be 3_3. In the more modern notation of quantum mechanics, n_θ has been replaced by another quantum number l, called the *orbital quantum number*, defined (using $k = n_\theta$) as

$$l = k - 1 \qquad\qquad (= n_\theta - 1) \qquad\qquad \textbf{(8.105)}$$

and for a given n, l can take the values

$$l = 0, 1, 2, 3, \ldots, \qquad\qquad (n - 1) \qquad\qquad \textbf{(8.106)}$$

Also the state $l = 0$ is denoted by s; $l = 1$ by p; $l = 2$ by d; $l = 3$ by f; and so on as shown.

$$l = 0\ 1\ 2\ 3\ 4\ 5\ 6\ 7 \ldots$$

$$\text{notation} = s\ p\ d\ f\ g\ h\ i\ j \ldots$$

The naming as s, p, d, $f \ldots$ for $l = 0, 1, 2, 3, 4, \ldots$ goes back to the discovery of *s*harp, *p*rincipal, *d*iffused, and *f*undamental series, respectively, in alkali spectra, as we shall discuss in Chapter X. Thus in this notation a state with $n = 2$, $l = 0$, will be the 2s state. A state for which $n = 3$, $l = 2$, will be the 3d state. In Fig. 8.22 all the orbits are marked with both notations. If these diagrams are extended further, we will have for $n = 4$ the following four states, 4s, 4p, 4d, and 4f. Similarly for $n = 5$ we will have 5s, 5p, 5d, 5f, and 5g. The states 2s and 2p have the same energy; the states 3s, 3p, and 3d have the same energy; and so on.

One may question why if the use of Sommerfeld elliptical orbits has not resulted in any new levels, what is the advantage of the model? For a given n we have only one energy state (the same as the corresponding Bohr's state) even though the electron has a choice of moving in n differently shaped orbits, i.e., the states are degenerate and nothing new will be observed in the spectra. But if the degeneracy can be removed, one might hope to learn something new about the atomic spectra.

9. SOMMERFELD'S RELATIVITY CORRECTION

The degeneracy of a level can be removed by applying a relativistic correction to the changing electron mass as was originally done by Sommerfeld[20]. Contrary to the Bohr circular orbit, the velocity of the electron in an elliptical orbit is not constant as may be understood in the following manner: The potential energy of the electron is the greatest when it is farthest from the nucleus and is smallest when closest to the nucleus. Because the total energy is constant, correspondingly the kinetic energy will be the greatest near the nucleus. This means that the electron speeds up when it nears the nucleus and slows down as it moves away. The electron mass m changes according to $m = m_0 / \sqrt{1 - v^2/c^2}$, where m_0 is the rest mass. This change will be more marked in the more elliptic orbit. The increase in the mass of the electron as it approaches the nucleus has the effect of throwing the electron off its path and this orientation keeps on changing every time the electron passes near the nucleus. The path of the electron has been calculated by Sommerfeld[20,21] and is a rosette as shown in Fig. 8.23, which is an ellipse whose major axis precesses slowly in the plane of the ellipse about an axis through one of the foci. Such precession is also observed in the solar system, in which the orbit of the planet Mercury precesses. The speed of precession is equal to the rate at which the major axis of the ellipse turns around the nucleus. The speed of precession depends upon how close the electron comes to the nucleus. Hence, the precession speed is different for different elliptical paths even for the same value of n. This results in the removal of degeneracy of a given energy state, because different elliptical shapes will have slightly different energies.

Thus, according to Sommerfeld, relativistic correction makes the system nondegenerate. Therefore, for $n = 1$, there is only one level. For $n = 2$, there

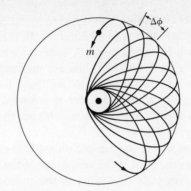

FIG. 8.23. *Application of the relativistic mass-correction to the motion of an electron around the nucleus results in a rosette path.*

are two levels with slightly different energies. For $n = 3$, there are 3 different levels with different energies, and so on (Fig. 8.24). The energies of these levels are given by[22]

$$E = -\frac{\mu k^2 Z^2 e^4}{2n^2 \hbar^2} \left[1 + \frac{\alpha^2 Z^2}{n} \left(\frac{1}{n_\theta} - \frac{3}{4n} \right) \right] \qquad (8.107)$$

or the change in energy due to relativistic correction is

$$\Delta E = -\frac{\mu k^2 Z^4 e^4}{2n^3 \hbar^2} \alpha^2 \left(\frac{1}{n_\theta} - \frac{3}{4n} \right) \qquad (8.108a)$$

where α is the fine-structure constant given by

$$\alpha = \frac{e^2}{\hbar c} = 7.297 \times 10^{-3} \simeq \frac{1}{137} \qquad (8.108b)$$

The separations in Fig. 8.24 for the hydrogen atom are exaggerated and are not to scale. Of all the transitions shown between different levels, the dotted ones are not observed and can be shown to be theoretically not allowed. Also the H_α line (from $n = 3$ to $n = 2$) now shows up as a close triplet instead of a single transition. The transitions, shown as solid lines, seem to follow the rules given below, called the *selection rules*,

$$n_{\theta_i} - n_{\theta_f} = \pm 1 \qquad (8.109a)$$

or

$$\Delta n_\theta = \Delta l = \pm 1 \qquad (8.109b)$$

and only those transitions are allowed for which Eq. (8.109) holds. Other levels and transitions may be drawn with the help of Eqs. (8.108), (8.109), and (8.104) or (8.106).

The type of spectra shown in Fib. 8.24 is the *fine structure*. Though the transitions are very close, with instruments of very high resolution it was possible to measure their separations. The fine structure of the Balmer lines and some lines of ionized helium have been carefully observed. There seems to be a good qualitative agreement between the predicted and the experimental values of the separation in this simple case. But with this model it is impossible for one to account for other observed complex spectra, and hence one must look for the explanation somewhere else. The introduction of the intrinsic angular momentum, or spin[23], of the electron explained complex spectra and had far-reaching consequences in explaining all spectra.

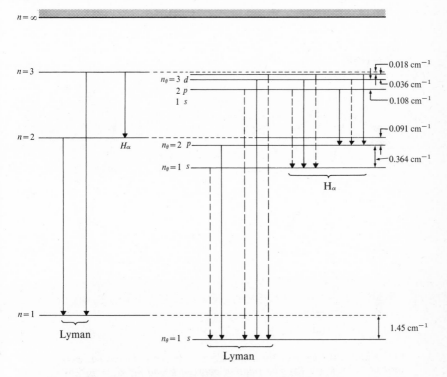

FIG. 8.24. *The fine structure of hydrogen resulting from the removal of degeneracy by applying the relativistic correction. Dotted transitions are not allowed by the selection rules.*

10. SPACE QUANTIZATION

In the Bohr-Sommerfeld model of the hydrogen atom, the motion of the electron was limited to two degrees of freedom. The energy of the system was determined by n, while the shape of the orbit was determined by any two of the three quantum numbers n; k; or n_θ; and n_r. The limitation of the motion of the electron to two degrees of freedom was "unnatural" and should not have been imposed. This means that the Wilson-Sommerfeld quantum condition would require three quantum numbers to completely describe any energy state. But the use of the three quantum numbers does not change the size and shape or energy of the system as with the Bohr-Sommerfeld model. However, the introduction of a third quantum number enables one to determine the orientation of the orbits with respect to some fixed direction in space.

An arbitrarily fixed axis can be set up in space in the following fashion. Assume that the atom is positioned in an external magnetic field H along a vertical Z-axis as shown in Fig. 8.25(b). This results in the precession of the

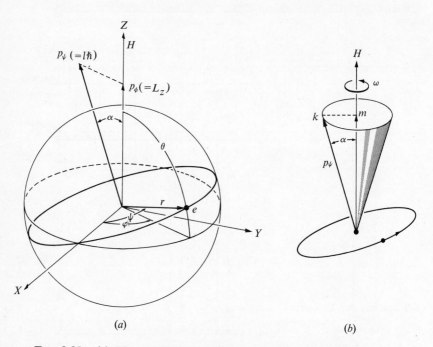

(a)   (b)

FIG. 8.25.   (a) *The position of an electron in three dimensions as described by* (r, θ, ϕ). *(b) The relation between* k *and* m; $p_\phi = p_\psi \cos \alpha$.

plane of the orbit with frequency ω about the axis H in a manner similar to a mechanical top precessing in a gravitational field. The orbital angular momentum vector $\boldsymbol{p}_\psi$ generates a cone about H as shown. The third quantum condition requires that the orientation of the orbit is space-quantized and that the angle α shown can take only certain discrete values as we shall see. The frequency of precession ω depends upon H. This will mean that the energy of the system will also change because of H. But if the strength of H is continuously decreased and brought close to zero, we still have the fixed axis in space and the energy of the system is the same as it was before applying the magnetic field.

The position of the electron in two dimensions was described by (r, θ).

In the present situation let us replace (r, θ) by (r, ψ). In three dimensions the position of the electron is described by (r, θ, ϕ) as shown in Fig. 8.25(a). Because the total energy and the potential energy remain the same and if T_2 and T_3 are the total energies in two- and three-dimensions, respectively, we may write

$$T_2 = \frac{1}{2} m\dot{r}^2 + \frac{1}{2} mr^2\dot{\psi}^2 - \frac{Ze^2}{r}$$
$$= \frac{1}{2}(p_r\dot{r} + p_\psi\dot{\psi}) - \frac{Ze^2}{r} \tag{8.110}$$

with quantum conditions

$$\oint p_r\, dr = rh$$
$$\oint p_\psi\, d\psi = kh \tag{8.111}$$

and

$$T_3 = \frac{1}{2}(p_r\dot{r} + p_\theta\dot{\theta} + p_\phi\dot{\phi}) - \frac{Ze^2}{r} \tag{8.112}$$

with the quantum conditions

$$\oint p_r\, dr = rh$$
$$\oint p_\theta\, d) = th$$
$$\oint p_\psi\, d\psi = mh \tag{8.113}$$

Equating Eqs. (8.110) and (8.112)

$$p_r\dot{r} + p_\psi\dot{\psi} = p_r\dot{r} + p_\theta\dot{\theta} + p_\phi\dot{\phi}$$
$$p_\psi \frac{d\psi}{dt} = p_\theta \frac{d\theta}{dt} + p_\phi \frac{d\phi}{dt} \tag{8.114}$$

or

$$p_\psi\, d\psi = p_\theta\, d\theta + p_\phi\, d\phi \tag{8.115}$$

using Eqs. (8.111) and (8.113) we get

$$\oint p_\psi\, d\psi = \oint p_\theta\, d\theta + \oint p_\phi\, d\phi \tag{8.116}$$

or

$$kh = th + mh$$

or

$$k = t + m \tag{8.117}$$

The projection p_ϕ of the total angular momentum p_ψ (which is constant) on the Z axis is given by

$$p_\phi = p_\psi \cos \alpha \tag{8.118}$$

or

$$\cos \alpha = \frac{p_\phi}{p_\psi} = \frac{mh}{kh} = \frac{m}{k} \tag{8.119}$$

where m is the *magnetic quantum number* and takes the values (for a given k value) of

$$m = \pm 1, \pm 2, \pm 3, \ldots, \pm k \tag{8.120}$$

While for a given n, the azimuthal quantum number k takes the values

$$k = 1, 2, 3, \ldots, n \tag{8.121}$$

Knowing n, k, and m the orbit of the electrons can be completely specified.

Thus for $n = 3$, $k = 1, 2, 3$; while for $k = 1$, $m = \pm 1$, $k = 2$, $m = \pm 1$, ± 2; and for $k = 3$, $m = \pm 1, \pm 2, \pm 3$. These values are illustrated in Fig. 8.26. As we shall see later, these states can actually be detected if the degen-

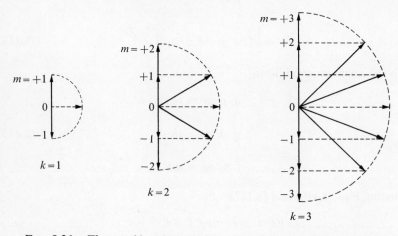

FIG. 8.26. *The possible values of magnetic quantum number m for different values of k.*

eracy is removed by applying an external magnetic field. Note that $m = 0$ is not allowed in this model, but according to quantum mechanics it is allowed. Actually, for a given l

$$m_l = 0, \pm 1, \pm 2, \ldots, \pm l \tag{8.122}$$

11. SUCCESSES AND LIMITATIONS OF THE OLD QUANTUM THEORY

There is no doubt as to the successes of the old quantum theory as seen in the previous sections where the Bohr and Bohr-Sommerfeld models of hydrogen-like atoms are used in explaining many aspects of atomic spectra. The basic assumption of nonradiating stationary orbits, quantization of angular momentum, quantization of bound energy states, and transitions between these states led to the following successes of the Bohr theory:

1. It correctly accounted for the Balmer and other series of the hydrogen spectra, both emission and absorption.
2. It correctly predicted the value of the radius of the hydrogen atom.
3. It satisfactorily explained ionization and excitation potentials.

Further modification, making use of the Wilson-Sommerfeld quantization rules, led to the formulation of the Bohr-Sommerfeld model of the hydrogen atom that further added to the success of the old quantum theory in the following directions:

4. It accounted satisfactorily for some observed fine-structure in the case of the hydrogen atom (after degeneracy was removed by introducing relativity).
5. Introduction of the space quantization explained satisfactorily many aspects of the spectra when the atoms are in a magnetic field (normal Zeeman effect), which will be discussed later.

Though the old quantum theory was able to explain many aspects of atomic spectra that could not be accounted for by classical theory, there are many features of observed spectra that remained unexplained:

1. It fails to account for the observed spectra of complex atoms. Even the spectrum of as simple an atom as the neutral helium atom cannot be explained. The theory is really applicable only to hydrogen-like atoms, such as Li, Na, Cl, Rb, Cs, He$^+$, Li^{++} etc.
2. It offers no method for calculating the rate of transitions, thus the intensities of the spectral lines cannot be calculated.
3. It does not explain some of the finer details of the atomic spectra such as the doublet fine structure in alkali metals.
4. Some complicated splittings observed under a magnetic field (anomalous Zeeman effect) could not be accounted for.

In 1925 the introduction of quantum theory by Schrödinger and its application to atomic spectra was amazingly successful in predicting the quantum numbers and explaining many other aspects of atomic spectra.

PROBLEMS

1. According to the classical model discussed in Section 8.1 the electron in any circular orbit is unstable and will finally collapse into the nucleus as shown in Fig. 8.2. If the electron in the hydrogen atom starts from $r = 0.53$ Å, how long will it take for the electron to collapse into the nucleus (the proton)?

2. In Problem 1, can you suggest a way to calculate the intensity as a function of (a) radius, and (b) time, during the process of collapse?

3. Calculate the frequencies and the wavelengths according to Eq. (8.8) for $r = 0.1$ Å, 0.50 Å, 1.0 Å, 10 Å, and 100 Å. Identify the regions to which these frequencies belong.

4. Show that the gravitational attraction between an electron and a proton in the hydrogen atom separated by a distance $r = 0.53$ Å is negligible as compared to the electrostatic attraction between them.

5. An electron in a hydrogen atom is moving in the first Bohr orbit. Calculate (a) the current due to this moving electron, and (b) the magnitude and direction (with reference to the angular momentum direction) of the magnetic field at the center.

6. What are the values of the quantum number n if the radius of the electron orbit in the hydrogen atom is 0.0001 mm, 0.01 mm, 1 mm, 1 cm, and 10 cm? What are the energies associated with these levels? Which of these orbits (or systems) would you treat classically and which quantum mechanically?

7. Calculate the energies of the photons emitted in the following transitions:
   (a) $n_i = 11$ to $n_f = 10$, and
   (b) $n_i = 101$ to $n_f = 100$.
   Compare the frequencies of these transitions with those of the classical circular orbital frequencies.

8. Express in terms of energy the shortest and the longest wavelength limits of different series in the hydrogen atom. What is the energy range of the visible spectrum (say, from 3800 Å to 7700 Å)?

9. The wavelength of the first line in the Lyman series is 1215.7 Å, and the Balmer Series limit is 3645.6 Å. From this data calculate the ionization energy of the hydrogen atom in (a) eV, and (b) joules.

10. Show that if we take into consideration the recoil energy of the atom, the actual energy of any photon emitted between the two states is not $h\nu$ but $h\nu - (h\nu)^2/2Mc^2$, where M is the mass of the atom. Calculate this for the first line of the Lyman series. How does this correction compare with the nuclear-mass correction for this line?

11. Corresponding to the first three lines (H_α, H_β, and H_γ) of the Balmer series, calculate the momentum of the photons and the recoil energies of the hydrogen atoms.

12. Calculate the de Broglie wavelength of the electron in the first Bohr orbit of the hydrogen atom and show that this is equal to the circumference of this circular orbit.

13. Prove the following relation:

$$\lambda_n = n\lambda_1$$

where λ_n and λ_1 are the de Broglie wavelengths of the electron in the nth and 1st Bohr orbits of the hydrogen atom. Also what is the ratio of this circumference of the nth orbit and λ_n.

14. Prove the following relations for α ($= v_1/c$) the fine structure constant
   (a) $\alpha = ke^2/\hbar c$
   (b) $\alpha = 4\pi a_0 R_\infty$, where a_0 is the first Bohr orbit radius, and
   (c) $\alpha = \lambda_c/a_0$, where λ_c is the Compton wavelength (of the electron) divided by 2π.

15. If the average lifetime of an excited atomic state is 10^{-8} sec, calculate the widths of the first three excited states of the hydrogen atom by using the wavelengths of different transitions and the uncertainty principle. How many revolutions do the electrons make in these orbits before emitting photons?

16. Draw an approximate energy-level diagram of Be^{+++}.

17. Draw an approximate energy-level diagram of C^{+++++}.

18. Calculate the wavelengths of the first four lines of the Balmer series in H^2. Find the difference in the wavelengths of these and the corresponding lines in H^1.

19. Plot the Rydberg constant, R_M, for H^1 and for the hydrogen-like ions He^+, Li^{++}, Be^{+++}, B^{++++}, C^{+++++}, etc., versus M and estimate the value of M for which $R_M \simeq R_\infty$. What is R_∞ from this graph?

20. Find the number of lines in the visible spectrum of the following: **(a)** H^1, **(b)** He^+, and **(c)** Li^{++}.

21. Tritium is an isotope of hydrogen whose nuclear mass is three times that of the ordinary hydrogen. If tritium is excited, what will be the wavelength of the first three lines (H_α, H_β, H_γ) of the Balmer series? How do these compare with the corresponding wavelengths observed in H^1 and H^2?

22. Consider the following pairs of transitions (see Fig. 8.15).
(a) $n_i = 3$ to $n_f = 2$ in H^1, and $n_i = 6$ to $n_f = 4$ in He^+;
(b) $n_i = 3$ to $n_f = 1$ in H^1, and $n_i = 6$ to $n_f = 2$ in He^+.
Compare the wavelengths of these transitions with and without the nuclear-mass corrections.

23. Consider the following transitions: **(a)** $n_i = 2$ to $n_f = 1$ in H^1; **(b)** $n_i = 4$ to $n_f = 2$ in He^+; and **(c)** $n_i = 6$ to $n_f = 3$ in Li^{++}. Compare the wavelengths of these transitions with and without the nuclear-mass corrections.

24. The μ-meson is a particle of mass 207 times the mass of an electron, i.e., $m_\mu = 207 m_e$, and has the same charge as the electron. A μ-meson with a proton forms a μ-mesonic atom just as the electron with a proton forms a hydrogen atom.
(a) Derive an expression for the radii and energies of the different Bohr orbits of a μ-mesonic atom.
(b) Compare the size of the first two orbits of the μ-mesonic atom with that of the hydrogen atom.
(c) Compare the speeds of the μ-mesons in the first two orbits of the μ-mesonic atom with that of the electron.
(d) Compare the energies of the transitions $n_i = 3$ to $n_f = 2$, and $n_i = 2$ to $n_f = 1$ in the μ-mesonic atom with that of the hydrogen atom.
(e) What is the ionization energy of the μ-mesonic atom?

25. The positron is a particle of the same mass as the electron except that it has a unit positive charge. An electron and a positron from a positronium atom in which the positron takes the place of the proton. (Note that we must use reduced mass. Also, it may be noted that the positronium atom is not stable.)
(a) Derive an expression for different energy levels of the positronium atom.
(b) Calculate the energies of the transitions $n_i = 3$ to $n_f = 2$; and $n_i = 2$ to $n_f = 1$. Compare the wavelengths of these transitions with the corresponding transitions in the hydrogen atom.
(c) Calculate the ionization energy of the positronium atom.

26. Calculate the possible wavelengths absorbed by
(a) hydrogen,
(b) singly ionized helium, and
(c) doubly ionized lithium.

27. An electron at zero energy combines with a helium nucleus at rest and forms a He^+ ion. What is the energy of the photon emitted in the process of combination?

28. Show that in a hydrogen-like ion the speed of an electron in the lowest energy state may be expressed as $\alpha c Z$, where α is the fine-structure constant ($\sim 1/137$), and c is the velocity of light. According to this if $Z > 137$, the speed of the electron will be greater than the speed of light! How do you explain this?

29. Potassium vapors are used in the Franck-Hertz experiment. If the binding energies of the ground state and the first excited state are 4.3 eV and 2.7 eV, respectively, at what voltages should we expect to see dips in the current versus voltage plot?

30. What is the minimum potential difference through which electrons must be accelerated so that when they cause inelastic collisions with hydrogen atoms in the ground state, (a) the hydrogen atoms are left in the first excited state, and (b) the hydrogen atoms are completely ionized?

31. What should be the kinetic energy of the hydrogen atom so that when it collides head-on with another hydrogen atom in the ground state, the ground-state hydrogen atom will be completely ionized?

32. The average thermal kinetic energy of the atoms in a gas is $\frac{3}{2}kT$, and these atoms can be utilized to cause excitation and ionization by thermal collisions. What should be the temperature of the hydrogen gas so that the hydrogen atoms are
    (a) excited to the first state, and
    (b) completely ionized by thermal collisions?

33. Derive Eq. (8.68).

34. Show that the condition $\oint p\,dx = nh$ gives a set of ellipses and the area between any of these two ellipses is h.

35. Derive Eq. (8.82) from Eq. (8.80).

36. In Figure 8.23 show that $\Delta\phi = (2\pi/\theta) - 2\pi$.

37. Using the relativistically corrected Sommerfeld formula, calculate the energies of different levels for $n = 2$, $n = 3$, and $n = 4$. Using the selection rules draw all the possible transitions between $n_i = 4$ to $n_f = 3$, and $n_i = 4$ to $n_f = 2$. Calculate the frequencies and the wave numbers of the allowed transitions.

38. What are the values of k and m (also l and m_l) for the following values of n,

$$n = 3, 4, \text{ and } 5$$

Draw the diagrams and calculate the values of θ for different values of k and m.

REFERENCES

1. Bohr, N., *Phil. Mag.*, **26**, 476, (1913).

2. Balmer, J. J., *Wied. Ann.*, **25**, 80, (1885).

3. Rydberg, J. R., *Astrophys. J.*, **4**, 91, (1896).

4. Cohen, E. R., and J. W. M. DuMond, *Revs. Mod. Phys.*, **37**, 537, (1965).

5. Kayser, H., *Handbuch der Spectroscopie*, Vol. I, pp. 3–128, 1900.

6. Balmer, J. J., *Wied. Ann.*, **25**, 80, (1885).

7. Paschen, F., *Ann. Physik*, **60**, 405, (1919).

8. Paschen, F., *Ann. Physik*, **63**, 201, (1920).

9. Bohr, N., *Phil. Mag.*, **26**, 1, (1913), and **27**, 506, (1914).

10. Birge, R. T., *Phys. Rev. Sup.*, **1**, 1, (1929).

11. Birge, R. T., and D. H. Menzel, *Phys. Rev.*, **37**, 1669, (1931).

12. Urey, H. C., F. G. Brickwedde, and G. M. Murphy, *Phys. Rev.*, **40**, 1, (1932).

13. Lewis, G. N., and F. H. Spedding, *Phys. Rev.*, **43**, 964, (1933); also Spedding, F. H., C. D. Shane, and N. S. Grace, *Phys. Rev.*, **44**, 58, (1933).

14. Van Vleck, J. H., *Bull. Nat. Res. Coun.*, **54**, 205, (1926).

15. Franck, J., and G. Hertz, *Verhandl. deut. physik Ges.*, **16**, 457, 512, (1912).

16. Wilson, W., *Phil. Mag.*, **29**, 795, (1915).

17. Sommerfeld, A., *Ann. Physik.*, **51**, 1, (1916).

18. Sommerfeld, A., *Atomic Structure and Spectral Lines*, London: Methuen, 1929.

19. Sommerfeld, A., *Atomic Structure and Spectral Lines*, p. 467, London: Methuen, 1923; also Ruark, A. E., and H. C. Urey, *Atoms, Molecules, and Quanta*, p. 132, New York: McGraw-Hill Book Co., 1930.

20. Stern, O., *Zeit. fur Physik*, **7**, 249, (1921).

21. Gerlach, W., and O. Stern, *Zeit. fur Physik*, **8**, 110, (1921).

22. Gerlach, W., and O. Stern, *Zeit. fur Physik*, **9**, 349, (1922).

23. Stern, O., *Zeit. fur Physik*, **41**, 563, (1927).

SUGGESTIONS FOR FURTHER READING

1. White, H. E., *Introduction to Atomic Spectra*, Chaps. I, II, III, and VI, New York: McGraw-Hill, 1934.

2. Herzberg, G., *Atomic Spectra and Atomic Structure*, Chap. I, New York: Dover Publications, 1944.

3. Melissinos, A. C., *Experiments in Modern Physics*, Chap. 2, New York: Academic Press, 1966.

4. Richtmyer, F. K., E. H. Kennard, T. Lauritsen, and Cooper, *Introduction to Modern Physics*, 6th ed., Chap. 5, New York: McGraw-Hill, 1955.

5. Eisberg, R. M., *Fundamentals of Modern Physics*, Chap. 5, New York: John Wiley & Sons, 1961.

IX

The Quantum Theory of
One-Electron Atoms

1. INTRODUCTION

Even though the Bohr and Sommerfeld theories had been valid for simple cases, both theories had one flaw: so many assumptions about the quantum numbers were required. The advent of quantum mechanics changed this picture altogether. After de Broglie[1] proposed the quantum hypothesis in 1924, Schrödinger[2] developed wave, or quantum, mechanics, (and Heisenberg[3] set forward the theory of matrix mechanics), to solve the one-electron atom problem with amazing success. Starting with the assumption of the validity of the Schrödinger wave equation, its solution automatically leads to the discrete bound-energy states and to all of the several quantum numbers introduced in the previous chapter. The theory is in excellent agreement with experimental observations, and the theory can be further extended to more complicated systems.

2. SCHRÖDINGER'S WAVE EQUATION FOR A SYSTEM OF TWO PARTICLES[4]

Consider a simple system consisting of two particles of masses m_1 and m_2, located at (x_1, y_1, z_1) and (x_2, y_2, z_2), respectively. This system will be equivalent to the simplest atomic system consisting of a nucleus and a single electron. The total energy E_T, which is the sum of the kinetic and potential energies of the system, is given by

$$\frac{1}{2m_1}(p_{x_1}^2 + p_{y_1}^2 + p_{z_1}^2) + \frac{1}{2m_2}(p_{x_2}^2 + p_{y_2}^2 + p_{z_2}^2)$$
$$+ V(x_1, y_1, z_1 ; x_2, y_2, z_2 ; t) = E_T \quad (9.1)$$

where $p_{x_1}, \ldots, p_{z_2}$ are the components of linear momenta and $V(x_1, y_1, z_1 ; x_2, y_2, z_2 ; t)$ is the potential energy between the two particles. We shall be interested in the systems in which the potential energy is time independent and is a function only of the distance between the two particles, i.e.,

$$V = V(x_1, y_1, z_1 ; x_2, y_2, z_2) \quad (9.2)$$

Replacing the linear momenta components by their respective quantum mechanical operators, i.e., $p_x \rightarrow -i\hbar \, (\partial/\partial x)$, etc., and E_T by $i\hbar(\partial/\partial t)$; and introducing the time-dependent wave function ϕ of the system given by

$$\phi = \phi(x_1, y_1, z_1 ; x_2, y_2, z_2 ; t) \quad (9.3)$$

Equation (9.1) takes the form

$$-\frac{\hbar^2}{2m_1} \nabla_1^2 \phi - \frac{\hbar^2}{2m_2} \nabla_2^2 \phi + V\phi = i\hbar \frac{\partial \phi}{\partial t} \quad (9.4)$$

where

$$\nabla_1^2 = \frac{\partial^2}{\partial x_1^2} + \frac{\partial^2}{\partial y_1^2} + \frac{\partial^2}{\partial z_1^2}$$

$$\nabla_2^2 = \frac{\partial^2}{\partial x_2^2} + \frac{\partial^2}{\partial y_2^2} + \frac{\partial^2}{\partial z_2^2}$$

Instead of dealing with the coordinates $x_1, \ldots, z_2$, it is advantageous to deal with *relative coordinates* and *center-of-mass coordinates*. We define relative coordinates, x, y, z, by the relations

$$x = x_1 - x_2$$
$$y = y_1 - y_2 \quad (9.5)$$
$$z = z_1 - z_2$$

and center-of-mass coordinates, X, Y, Z, by

$$(m_1 + m_2)X = m_1 x_1 + m_2 x_2$$
$$(m_1 + m_2)Y = m_1 y_1 + m_2 y_2 \quad (9.6)$$
$$(m_1 + m_2)Z = m_1 z_1 + m_2 z_2$$

Substituting Eqs. (9.5) and (9.6) into Eq. (9.4) we obtain

$$-\frac{\hbar^2}{2M}\left[\frac{\partial^2\phi}{\partial X^2} + \frac{\partial^2\phi}{\partial Y^2} + \frac{\partial^2\phi}{\partial Z^2}\right] - \frac{\hbar^2}{2\mu}\left[\frac{\partial^2\phi}{\partial x^2} + \frac{\partial^2\phi}{\partial y^2} + \frac{\partial^2\phi}{\partial z^2}\right] + V\phi = i\hbar\frac{\partial\phi}{\partial t} \quad (9.7)$$

where $M = m_1 + m_2$ is the mass at the center of mass, and μ is the reduced mass of the system: $\mu = m_1 m_2/(m_1 + m_2)$.

Two separations of Eq. (9.7) can now be carried out. First, the time-dependent part of the wave equation can be extracted. Further, if we assume that V is a function of the relative coordinates only, a second separation can be made into a product of functions of the relative coordinates and the center-of-mass coordinates. Substituting for ϕ (see Eqs. (6.70) and (6.74))

$$\phi(x_1, y_1, z_1 ; x_2, y_2, z_2 ; t) = \phi(x, y, z; X, Y, Z ; t)$$

$$= \psi(x, y, z)\chi(X, Y, Z) \exp\left[-iE_T t/\hbar\right] \qquad (9.8)$$

and splitting E_T into $E_T = E + E'$, we get

$$-\frac{\hbar^2}{2\mu} \nabla^2\psi + V\psi = E\psi \qquad (9.9)$$

and

$$-\frac{\hbar^2}{2M} \nabla^2\chi = E'\chi \qquad (9.10)$$

where

$$\nabla^2\psi = \frac{\partial^2\psi}{\partial x^2} + \frac{\partial^2\psi}{\partial y^2} + \frac{\partial^2\psi}{\partial z^2}$$

$$\nabla^2\chi = \frac{\partial^2\chi}{\partial X^2} \quad \frac{\partial^2\chi}{\partial Y^2} \quad \frac{\partial^2\chi}{\partial Z^2} \qquad (9.11)$$

Note that the separation of Eq. (9.7) into the two Eqs. (9.9) and (9.10) is always possible if the potential V depends only on the coordinates of one particle relative to the other, i.e., only on the distance between the two particles. Equation (9.10) tells us that the center of mass of the system of two particles moves as a free particle of mass $(m_1 + m_2)$, i.e., because in this equation V is zero, it describes the translation motion of the system and is not of much interest. Equation (9.9) describes the relative motion of the two particles and is the same as the motion of a single particle that has a reduced mass, μ, that moves in an external potential V. This equation represents the behavior of the system as viewed from the center of mass, and evidently it is the only equation of interest in this case. Rewriting Eq. (9.9), we have

$$\left(\frac{\partial^2\psi}{\partial x^2} + \frac{\partial^2\psi}{\partial y^2} + \frac{\partial^2\psi}{\partial z^2}\right) + \frac{2\mu}{\hbar^2} (E - V)\psi = 0 \qquad (9.12)$$

where ψ and V are functions of relative coordinates x, y, and z only.

3. THE SCHRÖDINGER WAVE EQUATION AND ITS SOLUTION FOR ONE-ELECTRON ATOMS[5,6]

Consider the one-electron atom consisting of a nucleus of mass M, charge Ze^+, and located at (x_1, y_1, z_1); and an electron of mass m, with charge e^-, located at (x_2, y_2, z_2). As explained in the previous section, the motion can be split into the motion of the center of mass and the motion of the electron relative to the nucleus. The first one corresponds to the translational motion of the atom and is of no interest. The Schrödinger wave equation for the relative motion in relative coordinates, x, y, z, to be solved is given by Eq. (9.12), i.e.,

$$\left(\frac{\partial^2\psi}{\partial x^2} + \frac{\partial^2\psi}{\partial y^2} + \frac{\partial^2\psi}{\partial z^2}\right) + \frac{2\mu}{\hbar^2}(E - V)\psi = 0$$

where the reduced mass μ is given by

$$\mu = \frac{Mm}{M + m} \tag{9.13}$$

where M is the mass of the nucleus and m is the mass of the electron; and the interaction potential $V(x, y, z)$ between the electron and the nucleus is given by

$$V = -\frac{Ze^2}{\sqrt{x^2 + y^2 + z^2}} \tag{9.14}$$

It is not very profitable to solve Eq. (9.12) in rectangular coordinates to describe the motion of the electron. Two different sets of coordinates, polar and parabolic, however, have been used to successfully describe the motion of the electron; spherical polar coordinates are the more commonly used, and we shall write Eq. (9.12) in these coordinates. As shown in Fig. 9.1, the rec-

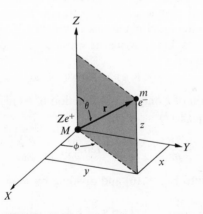

FIG. 9.1.   *Relation between the rectangular coordinates* (x, y, z) *and spherical polar coordinates* (r, θ, ϕ) *of an electron with respect to the nucleus at the origin.*

tangular coordinates (x, y, z) of the electron have to be replaced by the spherical polar coordinates (r, θ, ϕ), where:

r = length of the radius vector from the nucleus to the electron
  = $\sqrt{x^2 + y^2 + z^2}$
θ = the angle between r and the $+Z$ axis, called the zenith angle
  = $\cos^{-1}(z/\sqrt{x^2 + y^2 + z^2}) = \cos^{-1}(z/r)$

ϕ = angle between the projection of the radius vector in the xy plane and the $+X$ axis measured in a counterclockwise direction, called the azimuth angle
= $\tan^{-1}(y/x)$

The coordinates (x, y, z) are related to (r, θ, ϕ) by these relations (as seen from Fig. 9.1):

$$x = r \sin \theta \cos \phi$$
$$y = r \sin \theta \sin \phi \qquad (9.15)$$
$$z = r \cos \theta$$

Making use of the relations of Eq. (9.15), the Schrödinger wave equation, Eq. (9.12), takes the following form in spherical polar coordinates[7], by changing $\psi(x, y, z)$ to $\psi(r, \theta, \phi)$:

$$\frac{1}{r^2} \frac{\partial}{\partial r}\left(r^2 \frac{\partial \psi}{\partial r}\right) + \frac{1}{r^2 \sin \theta} \frac{\partial}{\partial \theta}\left(\sin \theta \frac{\partial \psi}{\partial \theta}\right)$$
$$+ \frac{1}{r^2 \sin^2 \theta} \frac{\partial^2 \psi}{\partial \phi^2} + \frac{2\mu}{\hbar^2} [E - V(r)]\psi = 0 \qquad (9.16)$$

Note that the potential $V(r)$ is a function of the radial distance only and has no angular dependence.

Equation (9.16) is still not in a convenient form to be solved. If $V(r)$ is a function of the radial distance, r, only, a further separation into three independent ordinary differential equations is possible by using the method of separation of variables. Let us write the wave function $\psi(r, \theta, \phi)$ as a product of three wave functions

$$\psi(r, \theta, \phi) = R(r)\Theta(\theta)\Phi(\phi) \qquad (9.17)$$

where R is a function of r only, Θ is a function of θ only, and Φ is a function of ϕ only. From Eq. (9.17)

$$\frac{\partial \psi}{\partial r} = \Theta\Phi \frac{\partial R}{\partial r}, \qquad \frac{\partial \psi}{\partial \theta} = R\Phi \frac{\partial \Theta}{\partial \theta}, \qquad \frac{\partial^2 \psi}{\partial \phi^2} = R\Theta \frac{\partial^2 \Phi}{\partial \phi^2} \qquad (9.18)$$

Substituting these into Eq. (9.16) and dividing by $R\Theta\Phi$, we get

$$\left[\frac{1}{r^2 R} \frac{\partial}{\partial r}\left(r \frac{\partial R}{\partial r}\right) + \frac{1}{r^2(\sin \theta)\Theta} \frac{\partial}{\partial \theta}\left(\sin \theta \frac{\partial \Theta}{\partial \theta}\right) + \frac{1}{r^2(\sin^2 \theta)\Phi} \frac{\partial^2 \Phi}{\partial \phi^2}\right]$$
$$+ \frac{2\mu}{\hbar^2} [E - V(r)] = 0 \qquad (9.19)$$

Multiplying both sides by $r^2 \sin^2 \theta$ and rearranging, the equation becomes:

$$-\frac{\sin^2 \theta}{R} \frac{\partial}{\partial r}\left(r \frac{\partial R}{\partial r}\right) - \frac{\sin \theta}{\Theta} \frac{\partial}{\partial \theta}\left(\sin \theta \frac{\partial \Theta}{\partial \theta}\right) - \frac{2\mu}{\hbar^2} r^2 \sin^2 \theta [E - V(r)] = \frac{1}{\Phi} \frac{\partial^2 \Phi}{\partial \phi^2}$$
$$(9.20)$$

The left side of this equation is a function of r and θ, while the right side is a function of ϕ only. This is possible only if both are equal to a constant, say $-m^2$. Hence, instead of Eq. (9.20), we get the following two equations

$$\frac{1}{\Phi}\frac{d^2\Phi}{d\phi^2} = -m^2 \tag{9.21}$$

and

$$-\frac{\sin^2\theta}{R}\frac{\partial}{\partial r}\left(r\frac{\partial R}{\partial r}\right) - \frac{\sin\theta}{\Theta}\frac{\partial}{\partial\theta}\left(\sin\theta\frac{\partial\Theta}{\partial\theta}\right) - \frac{2\mu}{\hbar^2}r^2\sin^2\theta\,[E - V(r)] = -m^2 \tag{9.22}$$

Dividing both sides of Eq. (9.22) by $\sin^2\theta$ and rearranging:

$$\frac{1}{R}\frac{\partial}{\partial r}\left(r^2\frac{\partial R}{\partial r}\right) + \frac{2\mu r^2}{\hbar^2}[E - V(r)] = \frac{m^2}{\sin^2\theta} - \frac{1}{\Theta\sin\theta}\frac{\partial}{\partial\theta}\left(\sin\theta\frac{\partial\Theta}{\partial\theta}\right) \tag{9.23}$$

Once again because the left side is a function of r only, and the right side is a function of θ only, each must be equal to a constant, say $l(l + 1)$; we could have chosen some constant other than $l(l + 1)$, but we did this as a convenience. Any other constant chosen will have to be equal to $l(l + 1)$, eventually, to satisfy the equations

$$\frac{m^2}{\sin^2\theta} - \frac{1}{\Theta\sin\theta}\frac{d}{d\theta}\left(\sin\theta\frac{d\Theta}{d\theta}\right) = l(l + 1) \tag{9.24}$$

and

$$\frac{1}{R}\frac{d}{dr}\left(r^2\frac{dR}{dr}\right) + \frac{2\mu r^2}{\hbar^2}[E - V(r)] = l(l + 1) \tag{9.25}$$

Equations (9.21), (9.24), and (9.25) are the three required ordinary differential equations (instead of one partial differential equation) that are written in the form

$$\frac{d^2\Phi}{d\phi^2} + m^2\Phi = 0 \tag{9.26}$$

$$\frac{1}{\sin\theta}\frac{d}{d\theta}\left(\sin\theta\frac{d\Theta}{d\theta}\right) + \left[l(l + 1) - \frac{m^2}{\sin^2\theta}\right]\Theta = 0 \tag{9.27}$$

$$\frac{1}{r^2}\frac{d}{dr}\left(r^2\frac{dR}{dr}\right) + \frac{2\mu}{\hbar^2}\left[E - V(r) - \frac{l(l + 1)}{r^2}\right]R = 0 \tag{9.28}$$

Thus our problem of solving the one-electron atom reduces to solving the above three equations and the determination of the constants m^2 and $l(l + 1)$. Remembering that the wave functions must be well behaved, i.e., the wave function and its derivative must be continuous and single-valued, one can easily solve the problem. This will be our next step.

A.   The Angular Factor Φ of the Eigenfunction ψ

To get an expression for $\Phi(\phi)$ we have to find the solution of the differential Eq. (9.26). Using the subscript m with Φ, Eq. (9.26) has the solution of the form

$$\Phi_m(\phi) = Ae^{im\phi} \tag{9.29}$$

where A is a normalization constant. The value of m can be evaluated by making use of the fact that $\Phi_m(\phi)$ should be single-valued. Accordingly, for the azimuthal angles 0 and 2π, we get

$$\Phi_m(0) = \Phi_m(2\pi)$$

i.e.,

$$Ae^{im0} = Ae^{im2\pi}$$

or

$$1 = \cos m2\pi + i \sin m2\pi$$

Hence m, the *magnetic quantum number*, can take the following values

$$m = 0, \pm1, \pm2, \pm3, \ldots \tag{9.30}$$

The orthogonality condition

$$\int_0^{2\pi} \Phi_{m'}^* \Phi_m \, d\phi = \delta_{m'm} \tag{9.31a}$$

(where the Dirac delta $\delta_{m'm} = 0$ if $m' \neq m$, and $\delta_{m'm} = 1$, if $m' = m$) reduces to the following, if the orthogonal set is normalized to unity,

$$\int_0^{2\pi} \Phi_m^* \Phi_m \, d\phi = 1 \tag{9.31b}$$

Because $\Phi_{m'}^* = Ae^{-im'\phi}$, we get for Eq. (9.31a)

$$A^2 \int_0^{2\pi} e^{i(m-m')\phi} \, d\phi = \begin{cases} 0 & \text{for } m \neq m' \\ 2\pi A^2 & \text{for } m = m' \end{cases} \tag{9.32}$$

From Eqs. (9.32) and (9.31b) for $m' = m$, we get

$$A = \frac{1}{\sqrt{2\pi}} \tag{9.33}$$

Thus combining Eqs. (9.29), (9.30), and (9.31), we have the final solution

$$\Phi_m(\phi) = \frac{1}{\sqrt{2\pi}} e^{im\phi} \tag{9.34}$$

B. The Angular Factor Θ of the Eigenfunction ψ

The solution of Eq. (9.27) is not so simple. It is convenient to introduce a new variable ξ

$$\xi = \cos \theta \tag{9.35}$$

and Eq. (9.27) takes the form

$$\frac{d}{d\xi}\left[(1 - \xi^2)\frac{d\Theta}{d\xi}\right] + \left[l(l + 1) - \frac{m^2}{1 - \xi^2}\right]\Theta = 0 \tag{9.36}$$

This differential equation is solved by considering its behavior at points $\xi = \cos \theta = \pm1$, and then finding the power-series solution. The final solution is given by[9,10], after adding the subscript lm to Θ,

$$\Theta_{lm}(\theta) = B \sin^m \theta \cdot P_l^m(\cos \theta) \tag{9.37}$$

where B is the normalization constant. $P_l^m(\cos \theta)$ are the *associated Legendre polynomials* defined as

$$P_l^m(\cos \theta) = (-1)^l \frac{\sin^{|m|} \theta}{2^l l!} \frac{d^{l+|m|}}{(d \cos \theta)^{l+|m|}} \sin^{2l} \theta \qquad (9.38)$$

These functions are listed in several sources [11] and some of these are given in Table 9.1(a). These polynomials vanish unless $|m| \leqslant l$, i.e.,

$$m = -l, -(l-1), -(l-2), \ldots, -1, 0, 1, \ldots, (l-1), l \qquad (9.39)$$

or

$$m = 0, \pm 1, \pm 2, \ldots, \pm l$$

TABLE 9.1(a)
EXPRESSIONS FOR THE VALUES OF
ASSOCIATED LEGENDRE POLYNOMIALS

Electron state	l	m	$P_l^m(\xi)$ $\xi = \cos \theta$
s	0	0	1
p	1	1	1
	1	0	ξ
d	2	2	3
	2	1	3ξ
	2	0	$\frac{1}{2}(\xi^2 - 1)$
f	3	3	15
	3	2	15ξ
	3	1	$\frac{3}{2}(5\xi^2 - 1)$
	3	0	$\frac{1}{2}(5\xi^2 - 3\xi)$

Hence, for a given value of l, m can take $(2l + 1)$ different values. Even though m can be zero, or a positive or negative integer; l must be a positive integer. l is called the *orbital quantum number*.

The orthogonality condition for the associated Legendre polynomials given in Eq. (9.37) takes the form

$$\int_0^{2\pi} \Theta_{l'm}^* \Theta_{lm} \sin \theta \, d\theta = B^2 \begin{cases} 0, & \text{for } l' \neq l \\ \dfrac{2 \cdot (l+m)!}{(2l+1)(l-m)!} & \text{for } l' = l \end{cases} \qquad (9.40)$$

Furthermore, if this set is normalized to unity, i.e.,

$$\int \Theta_{lm}^* \Theta_{lm} \sin \theta \, d\theta = 1 \qquad (9.41)$$

and combined with Eq. (9.40), we get for B

$$B = \sqrt{\frac{(2l+1) \cdot (l-m)!}{2(l+m)!}} \qquad (9.42)$$

Thus from Eqs. (9.37), (9.39), and (9.42), the solution for Θ_{lm} is given by

$$\Theta_{lm} = \sqrt{\frac{(2l+1)(l-m)!}{2(l+m)!}} \, \sin^m \theta \, P_l^m(\cos \theta) \qquad (9.43)$$

where $P_l^m(\cos \theta)$ and m are given by Eq. (9.38) and Eq. (9.39), respectively; while

$$l = 0, 1, 2, 3, 4, \ldots$$

Some of these functions are given in Table 9.1(b). Upper limit on the value of the orbital quantum number, l, will result from the solution of $R(r)$.

TABLE 9.1(b)
VALUES OF THE SPHERICAL HARMONICS $Y_l^m(\theta, \phi) = \Theta(\theta)\Phi(\phi)$

Electron state l	m	$\Phi(\phi)$	$\Theta(\theta)$	$Y_l^m(\theta, \phi) = \Theta(\theta)\Phi(\phi)$
0	0	$\frac{1}{\sqrt{2\pi}}$	$\frac{1}{\sqrt{2}}$	$\frac{1}{\sqrt{4\pi}}$
1	0	$\frac{1}{\sqrt{2\pi}}$	$\frac{\sqrt{6}}{2}\cos\theta$	$\sqrt{\frac{3}{4\pi}}\cos\theta$
	±1	$\frac{1}{\sqrt{2\pi}}e^{\pm i\phi}$	$\frac{\sqrt{3}}{2}\sin\theta$	$\sqrt{\frac{3}{8\pi}}\sin\theta e^{\pm i\phi}$
2	0	$\frac{1}{\sqrt{2\pi}}$	$\frac{\sqrt{10}}{4}(3\cos^2\theta-1)$	$\sqrt{\frac{5}{16\pi}}(3\cos^2\theta-1)$
	±1	$\frac{1}{\sqrt{2\pi}}e^{\pm i\phi}$	$\frac{\sqrt{15}}{2}\sin\theta\cos\theta$	$\sqrt{\frac{15}{8\pi}}\cos\theta\sin\theta e^{\pm i\phi}$
	±2	$\frac{1}{\sqrt{2\pi}}e^{\pm 2i\phi}$	$\frac{\sqrt{15}}{4}\sin^2\theta$	$\sqrt{\frac{15}{32\pi}}\sin^2\theta e^{\pm 2i\phi}$
3	0	$\frac{1}{\sqrt{2\pi}}$	$\sqrt{\frac{7}{8}}(5\cos^3\theta-3\cos\theta)$	$\sqrt{\frac{7}{16\pi}}(2\cos^3\theta-3\cos\theta\sin^2\theta)$
	±1	$\frac{1}{\sqrt{2\pi}}e^{\pm i\phi}$	$\sqrt{\frac{21}{32}}\sin\theta(5\cos^2\theta-1)$	$\sqrt{\frac{21}{64\pi}}\sin\theta(5\cos^2\theta-1)e^{\pm i\phi}$
	±2	$\frac{1}{\sqrt{2\pi}}e^{\pm 2i\phi}$	$\sqrt{\frac{105}{4}}\sin^2\theta\cos\theta$	$\sqrt{\frac{105}{32\pi}}\sin^2\theta\cos\theta e^{\pm 2i\phi}$
	±3	$\frac{1}{\sqrt{2\pi}}e^{\pm 3i\phi}$	$\sqrt{\frac{35}{32}}\sin^3\theta$	$\sqrt{\frac{35}{64\pi}}\sin^3\theta e^{\pm 3i\phi}$

C.   The Radial Factor, R, of the Eigenfunction ψ [12,13]

The radial wave equation to be solved is given by Eq. (9.25), which may be rewritten in the following form:

$$\frac{1}{r^2}\frac{d}{dr}\left(r^2\frac{dR}{dr}\right) + \frac{2\mu}{\hbar^2}\left[E - V(r) - \frac{l(l+1)\hbar^2}{2\mu r^2}\right]R = 0 \qquad (9.25)$$

where the potential energy $V(r) = -Ze^2/r$. To solve this equation for R we shall again impose the condition that R must be finite and continuous everywhere. It is easier to solve Eq. (9.25) if we make the following substitution

$$R = \frac{u}{r} \qquad (9.44)$$

for which it reduces to

$$\frac{d^2u}{dr^2} + \frac{2\mu}{\hbar^2}\left[E + \frac{Ze^2}{r} - \frac{l(l+1)\hbar^2}{2\mu r^2}\right]u = 0 \qquad (9.45)$$

The equation is further simplified if we make the substitutions

$$r = \frac{\hbar^2}{2\mu Ze^2}(n\rho) = \frac{a_0}{2Z}(n\rho) \qquad (9.46)$$

and

$$E = \pm\frac{\mu Z^2 e^4}{2n^2\hbar^2} \qquad (9.47)$$

where a_0 is the radius of the first Bohr orbit

$$a_0 = \frac{\hbar^2}{\mu e^2} = 0.53 \times 10^{-8}\ \text{cm} \qquad (9.48)$$

The resulting equation, after these substitutions, is

$$\frac{d^2u}{d\rho^2} + \left(\pm\frac{1}{4} + \frac{n}{\rho} - \frac{l(l+1)}{\rho^2}\right)u = 0 \qquad (9.49)$$

Thus the problem reduces to finding the values of n and its relation to l. (The radial wave function will be written as R_{nl} and will not depend upon m.) The radial Eq. (9.49) must hold at $\rho \to \infty$ and $\rho \to 0$. For $\rho \to \infty$, Eq. (9.49) reduces to

$$\frac{d^2u}{d\rho^2} \pm \frac{u}{4} = 0 \qquad (9.50)$$

For the positive sign in Eq. (9.50), the solutions are

$$C'\sin\frac{\rho}{2} \quad \text{and} \quad C\cos\frac{\rho}{2} \qquad (9.51)$$

These correspond to the continuum of energy states above the series limit.
    For the negative sign in Eq. (9.50), the solutions are

$$D'e^{+\rho/2} \qquad (9.52a)$$

and

$$De^{-\rho/2} \qquad (9.52b)$$

As $\rho \rightarrow \infty$, the solution $De^{+\rho/2}$ diverges thereby violating the condition that ψ must be finite, and hence we must disregard this solution.

For $\rho \rightarrow 0$, the power series gives two possible solutions for Eq. (9.49),

$$E\rho^{+l} \tag{9.53a}$$

and

$$F\rho^{-l-1} \tag{9.53b}$$

where E and F are constants. Of these two, only $E\rho^{+l}$ satisfies the condition that the radial wave function vanishes as $\rho \rightarrow 0$.

Thus the radial wave function R_{nl} for the negative sign in Eq. (9.49) is the product of Eqs. (9.52b) and (9.53b), for $\rho \rightarrow 0$ and $\rho \rightarrow \infty$, respectively, or $DE\, e^{-\rho/2}\rho^{+l}$ and a power series, which will give the solution for R_{nl} for ρ between 0 and ∞. The complete solution[12,13] is found to be

$$R_{nl} = N_{nl}\rho^{+l}e^{-\rho/2} \cdot L_{n+l}^{2l+1}(\rho) \tag{9.54}$$

where N_{nl} is the normalization constant, and $L_{n+l}^{2l+1}(\rho)$ are the associated Laguerre polynomials[11]. Some of these are listed in Table 9.2. These polynomials vanish unless

$$n = 1, 2, 3, \ldots, \infty \tag{9.55}$$

where n is called the *principal, or total, quantum number*. For a given n

$$l = 0, 1, 2, 3, \ldots, (n-1) \tag{9.56}$$

Using the normalization condition

$$\int R_{nl}^{*}R_{nl}4\pi r^2\, dr = 1 \tag{9.57}$$

we get[13]

$$N_{nl} = \sqrt{\frac{4(n-l-1)!Z^3}{[(n+l)!]^3 n^4 a_0^3}} \tag{9.58}$$

Thus the complete solution of the radial part R_{nl} of the wave function ψ is found by combining Eqs. (9.46), (9.54), (9.55), (9.56), and (9.58):

$$R_{nl} = \sqrt{\frac{4(n-l-1)!Z^3}{[(n+l)!]^3 n^4 a_0}}\left(\frac{2Zr}{na_0}\right)^l \cdot \exp\left(\frac{-Zr}{na_0}\right) \cdot L_{n+l}^{2l+1}\left(\frac{2Zr}{na_0}\right) \tag{9.59}$$

where a_0 is the first Bohr-orbit radius while n and l are positive integers given by Eqs. (9.55) and (9.56). A few values of L_{n+l}^{2l+1} and R_{nl} are given in Table 9.2.

D. Summary of Eigenfunctions, Eigenvalues, and Quantum Numbers

We are now in a position to compare the conclusions of quantum mechanics with those of the Bohr and Sommerfeld theories. From Eq. (9.17), the wave function may be written as

$$\psi_{nlm}(r, \theta, \phi) = R_{nl}(r)\Theta_{lm}(\theta)\Phi_m(\phi) \tag{9.60}$$

TABLE 9.2

THE EXPRESSIONS FOR LAGUERRE POLYNOMIALS
AND RADIAL WAVE-FUNCTIONS

Electron state	n	l	Laguerre polynomials $L_{n+l}^{2l+1}(\rho)$ $\rho = r/2a_0$	Radial wave function, $R_{nl}(r)$
$1s$	1	0	$-1!$	$\dfrac{2}{a_0^{3/2}}\, e^{-r/a_0}$
$2s$	2	0	$2\rho - 4$	$\dfrac{1}{2\sqrt{2}\, a_0^{3/2}} \left(2 - \dfrac{r}{a_0}\right) e^{-r/2a_0}$
$2p$	2	1	$-3!$	$\dfrac{1}{2\sqrt{6}\, a_0^{3/2}} \left(\dfrac{r}{a_0}\right) e^{-r/2a_0}$
$3s$	3	0	$-3\rho^2 + 18\rho - 18$	$\dfrac{2}{81\sqrt{3}\, a_0^{3/2}} \left(27 - \dfrac{18r}{a_0} + \dfrac{2r^2}{a_0^2}\right) e^{-r/3a_0}$
$3p$	3	1	$24\rho - 96$	$\dfrac{4}{81\sqrt{6}\, a_0^{3/2}} \left(6 - \dfrac{r}{a_0}\right) \dfrac{r}{a_0} e^{-r/3a_0}$
$3d$	3	2	$-5!$	$\dfrac{4}{81\sqrt{30}\, a_0^{3/2}} \left(\dfrac{r^2}{a_0^2}\right) e^{-r/3a_0}$
$4s$	4	0	$4\rho^3 - 48\rho^2 + 144\rho - 96$	$\dfrac{1}{96 a_0^{3/2}} \left(24 - \dfrac{18r}{a_0} + \dfrac{3r^2}{a_0^2} - \dfrac{r^3}{8a_0^3}\right) e^{-r/4a_0}$
$4p$	4	1	$-60\rho^2 + 600\rho - 1200$	$\dfrac{3}{96\sqrt{15}\, a_0^{3/2}} \left(20 - \dfrac{5r}{a_0} + \dfrac{r^2}{4a_0^2}\right)\left(\dfrac{r}{2a_0}\right) e^{-r/4a_0}$
$4d$	4	2	$720\rho - 5760$	$\dfrac{5}{96\sqrt{5}\, a_0^{3/2}} \left(6 - \dfrac{r}{2a_0}\right)\left(\dfrac{r}{2a_0}\right)^2 e^{-r/4a_0}$
$4f$	4	3	$-7!$	$\dfrac{1}{96\sqrt{35}\, a_0^{3/2}} \left(\dfrac{r}{2a_0}\right)^3 e^{-r/4a_0}$

Sometimes the wave function ψ is also written as the product of two wave functions

$$\psi_{nlm}(r, \theta, \phi) = R(r) Y_l^m(\theta, \phi)$$

where $Y_l^m(\theta, \phi)$ are the *spherical harmonics* and are given by Table 9.1(b)

$$Y_l^m(\theta, \phi) = \Theta(\theta)\Phi(\phi)$$

Substituting the values of R_{nl}, Θ_{lm}, and Φ_m from Eqs. (9.34), (9.43), and (9.59), the eigenfunctions of the one-electron atom may be written as

$$\psi_{nlm} = \sqrt{\frac{4(n-l-1)!Z^3}{[(n+l)!]^3 n^4 a_0^3}} \left(\frac{2Zr}{na_0}\right)^l \exp\left(\frac{-Zr}{na_0}\right) L_{n+l}^{2l+1}\left(\frac{2Zr}{na_0}\right)$$

$$\times \sqrt{\frac{(2l+1)(l-m)!}{2(l+m)!}} \sin^m \theta \, P_l^m(\cos\theta) \cdot \frac{e^{im\phi}}{\sqrt{2\pi}} \quad (9.61)$$

From the orthogonality property of each component wave-function, we are led to the following orthogonality condition for the complete wave function

$$\int \psi_{n'l'm'}^* \psi_{nlm} \, dv = \begin{cases} 0 & \text{for } n' \neq n, \, l' \neq l, \, m' \neq m \\ 1 & \text{for } n' = n, \, l' = l, \, m' = m \end{cases} \quad (9.62)$$

where dv is a small volume element $4\pi r^2 \sin\theta \, d\theta \, d\phi$. The quantum numbers n, l, and m must satisfy the following conditions otherwise the eigenfunction will vanish:

The total quantum number, n; the orbital quantum number, l; and the magnetic quantum number, m; are all integers given by the following

$$n = 1, 2, 3, 4, \ldots, \infty \quad (9.63a)$$

For a given n, l can take n values given by

$$l = 0, 1, 2, 3, \ldots, (n-1) \quad (9.63b)$$

For a given l, m can take $(2l+1)$ values given by

$$m = -l, -(l-1), \ldots, -1, 0, 1, \ldots, (l-1), l \quad (9.63c)$$

These are the quantum numbers that were arbitrarily assumed in the Bohr and Sommerfeld theories and in space quantization described in Chapter VIII. A further condition for nonvanishing eigenfunctions is also imposed on the energy eigenvalues given by Eq. (9.47), which for the bound states are

$$E_n = -\frac{1}{n^2} \frac{\mu Z^2 e^4}{2\hbar^2} \quad (9.64)$$

where $n = 1, 2, \ldots, \infty$, and is identical to the expression given in Eq. (8.57), which was obtained from the Bohr theory. [Note that $k = (1/4\pi\epsilon_0)$ was taken to be unity in $V = -Ze^2/r$ and hence does not occur in this expression.] Thus the Schrödinger wave equation for one-electron atoms leads to the correct energy eigenvalues and quantum numbers.

Furthermore, it is also clear that for a given value of n there are many values of l and m, i.e., for a given n there are several different eigenfunctions. But the energy is determined by n only, and all these different eigenfunctions have the same energy. Thus the eigenfunctions are degenerate. The number of degenerate states for different values of n are given in Table 9.3. For example, $n = 2$, $l = 0, 1$; for $l = 0$, $m = 0$; and for $l = 1$, $m = 1, 0, -1$, which means when denoting the state by (n, l, m), we have $(2, 0, 0)$, $(2, 1, 1)$, $(2, 1, 0)$, and $(2, 1, -1)$, i.e., four-fold degeneracy. It is obvious from Table 9.3, that for a given n, there is n^2-fold degeneracy. The degeneracy due to m comes

TABLE 9.3

POSSIBLE STATES† OF A ONE ELECTRON ATOM

n	l	nl	m	Number of degenerate eigenfunctions (n, l, m) for a given n equals n^2†
1	0	$1s$	0	$(1, 0, 0)$ $\left.\right\}$ 1
2	0	$2s$	0	$(2, 0, 0)$
	1	$2p$	$-1, 0, 1$	$(2, 1, -1), (2, 1, 0), (2, 1, 1)$ $\left.\right\}$ 4
3	0	$3s$	0	$(3, 0, 0)$
	1	$3p$	$-1, 0, 1$	$(3, 1, -1), (3, 2, 0), (3, 1, 1)$
	2	$3d$	$-2, -1, 0, 1, 2$	$(3, 2, -2), (3, 2, -1), (3, 2, 0), (3, 2, 1), (3, 2, 2)$ $\left.\right\}$ 9
4	0	$4s$	0	$(4, 0, 0)$
	1	$4p$	$-1, 0, 1$	$(4, 1, -1), (4, 1, 0), (4, 1, 1)$
	2	$4d$	$-2, -1, 0, 1, 2$	$(4, 2, -2), (4, 2, -1), (4, 2, 0), (4, 2, 1), (4, 2, 2)$
	3	$4f$	$-3, -2, -1, 0, 1, 2, 3$	$(4, 3, -3), (4, 3, -2), (4, 3, -1), (4, 3, 0), (4, 3, 1), (4, 3, 2), (4, 3, 3)$ $\left.\right\}$ 16

† The degeneracy will be doubled, i.e., $2n^2$ by the introduction of electron spin.

whenever the potential depends upon r only, while the particular form of potential dependence, ($\propto (1/r)$ in this case) leads to l-fold degeneracy.

We may point out that the degeneracy will be doubled, i.e., $2n^2$ by the introduction of electron spin as we shall see later in Sec. 7. This occurs because the electron spin may be aligned parallel or antiparallel to orbital motion.

4. ELECTRON PROBABILITY DENSITY

According to quantum mechanics, we talk in terms of probabilities, and hence we are interested in calculating the electron probability density. Unlike the Bohr theory, the electron cannot be imagined to be moving in some definite orbit. Instead we can only calculate the most probable position. Thus if the state of an electron is denoted by the quantum numbers n, l, and m, then its eigenfunction ψ_{nlm} is

$$\psi_{nlm} = R_{nl}\Theta_{lm}\Phi_m \tag{9.65}$$

while $\psi^*\psi$, called the probability density of the electron, is given by

$$\psi^*_{nlm}\psi_{nlm} = R^*_{nl}R_{nl} \cdot \Theta^*_{lm}\Theta_{lm} \cdot \Phi^*_m\Phi_m \tag{9.66}$$

Thus if $dv = r^2 \sin\theta\, dr\, d\theta\, d\phi$ is a small volume element in spherical polar coordinates, $\psi^*\psi\, dv$ gives the probability of finding the electron in a small volume dv at (r, θ, ϕ). Because $\int \psi^*\psi\, dv$ must be equal to unity, i.e.,

$$\int \psi^*\psi\, dv = \int_0^\infty \int_0^{2\pi} \int_0^\pi \psi^*_{nlm}\psi_{nlm}r^2 \sin\theta\, dr\, d\theta\, d\phi = 1 \tag{9.67}$$

and the electron (or its charge) is imagined to be spread over all space, hence $\psi^*\psi$ is then called the *charge density*. In order to see how the charge density varies with r, θ, and ϕ, we have to calculate $\psi^*\psi$ from Eq. (9.66). It is easier to get some meaningful interpretation if we consider R^*R, $\Theta^*\Theta$, and $\Phi^*\Phi$ separately, and then combine to get an overall picture.

Accordingly, $\Phi^*\Phi$ gives the probability density, $\psi^*\psi$, as a function of ϕ only, i.e., $\Phi^*\Phi$ gives the probability of finding the electron at an angle ϕ. $\Theta^*\Theta$ gives the probability density, $\psi^*\psi$, as a function of θ only, i.e., $\Theta^*\Theta$ gives the probability of finding the electron at an angle θ. R^*R gives the probability density, $\psi^*\psi$, as a function of r only, i.e., R^*R is the probability of finding the electron at r.

A. Probability Interpretation of $\Phi^*_m\Phi_m$

We are interested in finding the product $\Phi^*_m(\phi)\Phi_m(\phi)\, d\phi$, which is defined as the probability of finding an electron between the angles ϕ and $(\phi + d\phi)$. Using the value of $\Phi_m(\phi)$ from Eq. (9.34),

$$\Phi_m^*(\phi)\Phi_m(\phi) = \frac{1}{\sqrt{2\pi}} e^{-im\phi} \frac{1}{\sqrt{2\pi}} e^{im\phi} = \frac{1}{2\pi} \qquad (9.68)$$

which states that the probability density $\Phi_m^*\Phi_m$ is independent of angle ϕ, i.e., it is constant for all values of ϕ between 0 and 2π as shown in Fig. 9.2. The

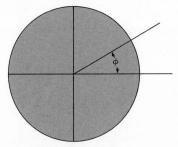

FIG. 9.2.   *The shaded area represents the probability-density distribution* $\Phi_m^*\Phi_m$, *i.e., the probability density distribution,* $\psi^*\psi$, *as a function of* ϕ *only, and is the same at all the angles.*

probability of finding an electron between ϕ_1 and $(\phi_1 + d\phi)$, and at any other angle between ϕ_2 and $(\phi_2 + d\phi)$ are the same, i.e.,

$$\Phi_m^*(\phi_1)\Phi_m(\phi_1)\,d\phi = \Phi_m(\phi_2)\Phi_m(\phi_2)\,d\phi = d\phi/2\pi \qquad (9.69)$$

where ϕ_1 and ϕ_2 may have any values between 0 and 2π.

B.   Probability Interpretation of $\Theta_{lm}^*\Theta_{lm}$

The probability of finding an electron between the angles θ and $(\theta + d\theta)$ is given by $\Theta_{lm}^*(\theta)\Theta_{lm}(\theta) \sin\theta\, d\theta$. The wave functions Θ_{lm} are given by Eq. (9.43). The values of the probability densities $\Theta_{lm}^*\Theta_{lm} = (\Theta_{lm})^2$ and the sum of all the substates, i.e.,

$$\sum_{m=-l}^{m=+l} (\Theta_{lm})^2$$

for different electrons are given in Table 9.4.

The plots of $\Theta_{lm}^*(\theta)\Theta_{lm}(\theta)$ for different values of l and m are drawn in terms of a polar diagram in Fig. 9.3. The origin $r = 0$ is located at the center of the nucleus while the Z axis is along the direction from which θ is measured. We may note several characteristics from these diagrams:

1.   The length of the vector r from the origin to the point on the curve gives the probability density $\Theta_{lm}^*(\theta)\Theta_{lm}(\theta)$ at that particular angle.
2.   Because the probability density $\Phi_m^*\Phi_m$ does not have any angular dependence, the angular dependence of the probability density $\psi_{nlm}^*\psi_{nlm}$ comes through $\Theta_{lm}^*\Theta_{lm}$. (Note that $R(r)$ does not have any angular dependence either.) Thus if we rotate these polar diagrams about the Z axis through 360° (from $\phi = 0$

TABLE 9.4

EXPRESSIONS FOR THE PROBABILITY DENSITY FACTOR $\Theta_{lm}^{*}\Theta_{lm}$

Electron state	l	m	$\Theta_{lm}(\theta)$	$(\Theta_{lm})^2$	$\sum\limits_{m=-l}^{m=+l}(\Theta_{lm})^2$
s	0	0	$\dfrac{1}{\sqrt{2}}$	$\dfrac{1}{2}$	$\dfrac{1}{2}$
p	1	1	$\dfrac{\sqrt{3}}{2}\sin\theta$	$\dfrac{3}{4}\sin^2\theta$	$\dfrac{3}{2}$
	1	0	$\dfrac{\sqrt{6}}{2}\cos\theta$	$\dfrac{6}{4}\cos^2\theta$	
d	2	2	$\dfrac{\sqrt{15}}{4}\sin^2\theta$	$\dfrac{15}{16}\sin^4\theta$	$\dfrac{5}{2}$
	2	1	$\dfrac{\sqrt{15}}{2}\sin\theta\cos\theta$	$\dfrac{15}{4}\sin^2\theta\cos^2\theta$	
	2	0	$\dfrac{\sqrt{10}}{4}(3\cos^2\theta-1)$	$\dfrac{10}{16}(9\cos^4\theta-6\cos^2\theta+1)$	
f	3	3	$\sqrt{\dfrac{35}{32}}\sin^3\theta$	$\dfrac{35}{32}\sin^6\theta$	$\dfrac{7}{2}$
	3	2	$\sqrt{\dfrac{105}{16}}\sin^2\theta\cos\theta$	$\dfrac{105}{16}\sin^4\theta\cos^2\theta$	
	3	1	$\sqrt{\dfrac{21}{32}}\sin\theta(5\cos^2\theta-1)$	$\dfrac{21}{32}\sin^2\theta(25\cos^4\theta-10\cos^2\theta+1)$	
	3	0	$\sqrt{\dfrac{7}{8}}(5\cos^3\theta-3\cos\theta)$	$\dfrac{7}{8}(25\cos^6\theta-30\cos^4\theta+9\cos^2\theta)$	

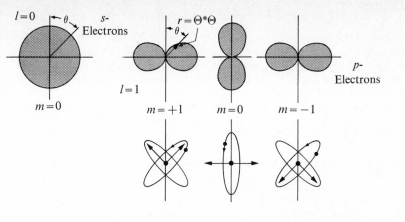

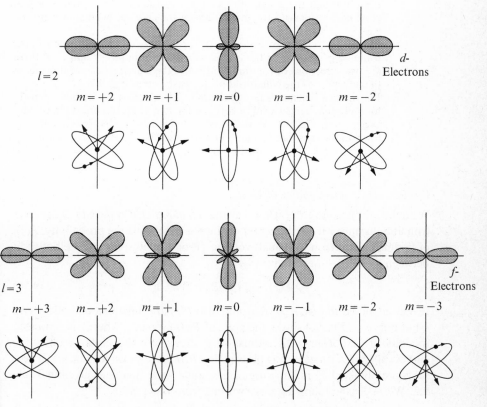

FIG. 9.3. *The polar plots of the probability-density distribution factor,*
$\Theta^*_{lm}(\theta)\Theta_{lm}(\theta)$ $\{= |[\Theta_{lm}(\theta)]^2|\}$, *as a function of the angle θ for s-, p-, d-,*
and f-electrons. The length of the vector **r** *from the origin to the point on*
the curve gives the probability density $\Theta^*\Theta$ at that particular angle. Also
shown are the equivalent classical orbits. [*Printed with permission from*
White, H. E., Introduction to Atomic Spectra, *p. 63. New York:*
McGraw-Hill Book Company, 1934.]

to $\phi = 2\pi$), we will get the complete angular dependence of $\psi^*_{nlm}\psi_{nlm}$. Hence for any point on this surface given by (r, θ, ϕ), the magnitude of r will be equal to $\Theta^*_{lm}\Theta_{lm}\Phi^*_m\Phi_m$ at angles θ and ϕ, i.e., it is the angular probability density of $\psi^*_{nlm}\psi_{nlm}$ (see Fig. 9.3).

3. In the particular case of $n = 1, l = 0, m = 0$, the value of $\Theta^*_{00} \times \Theta_{00} = \frac{1}{2}$ (from the table), which is independent of θ. Because θ varies from 0 to π, the polar diagram will be a half circle. But if we take θ and ϕ together and rotate them about the Z axis through 2π, we get a sphere shown in Fig. 9.3. This implies a spherically symmetric charge probability-density.

4. For values other than $l = 0$, we may make the following generalization:

   (i) For $m = 0$, the charge density is greatest in the direction of the poles, i.e., along $\theta = 0$ and $\theta = \pi$. This implies that the exponent of $e^{im\phi}$ is zero, no motion dependence on ϕ, and the electron orbit is only in one meridian plane through the Z axis. For this $m = 0$ value the interpretation is in good agreement with the orientation of the classical orbit shown in Fig. 9.3.

   (ii) For $|m| = l$, i.e., $m = +l$ or $-l$, the probability density is greatest in the plane perpendicular to the Z axis. Corresponding to $e^{il\phi}$ and $e^{-il\phi}$ there are two directions of rotation, and hence there are two classical orbits in the direction of the equatorial plane, as shown in Fig. 9.3.

   (iii) For the case when m is not equal to 0, $+l$, or $-l$, the probability density for a given l changes with m between the two limits discussed above, and as shown in Fig. 9.3. As the value of m increases, $\Theta^*\Theta$ becomes greater towards the equatorial plane. The two classical orbits each corresponding to $e^{im\phi}$ and $e^{-im\phi}$ are shown in each case.

C. Probability Interpretation of $R^*_{nl}R_{nl}$

We define the quantity $R^*_{nl}(r)R_{nl}(r)$ as the *radial probability density* of the electron at a distance r from the center of the nucleus; while the probability, $P(r)$, of finding the electron in a small volume dV of a small spherical shell of radii between r and $(r + dr)$, is given by

$$P(r) = R^*_{nl}(r)R_{nl}(r)4\pi r^2 \, dr \qquad (9.70)$$

It may be noted that R_{nl}, $R^*_{nl}R_{nl}$, and also $P(r)$ are functions of both n and l, but not of m. Fig. 9.4 shows the plots of $R_{nl}(r)$ versus r, where r is expressed in units of first Bohr-orbit radius. Also shown are the plots (broken-line curves) of $R^*_{nl}R_{nl}$ versus r. The plots of $4\pi r^2 R^*_{nl}R_{nl}$ are shown in Fig. 9.5. These plots are obtained by making use of the radial wave functions given in Table 9.2. We make the following observations from these plots.

1. Figure 9.4 shows that R_{nl} and also R^2_{nl} has a maximum at $r = 0$ (i.e., at the nucleus) for all s-states; while for all other states $p, d, f, \ldots$, the functions R_{nl} are zero at $r = 0$. The plots of $P(r)$ shown in Fig. 9.5 reveal that $P(r)$ are zero at $r = 0$ for all values of $s, p, d, f, g, \ldots$ states. Thus for s-state, even though R_{nl} is not zero at $r = 0$, the probability of finding the electron at the nucleus itself is zero.

2. Figure 9.5 shows that for each eigenstate the probability $P(r)$ has high values only within certain ranges of r. These restricted values of the ranges within which the electron will be found most frequently are called *shells*. The concept of the

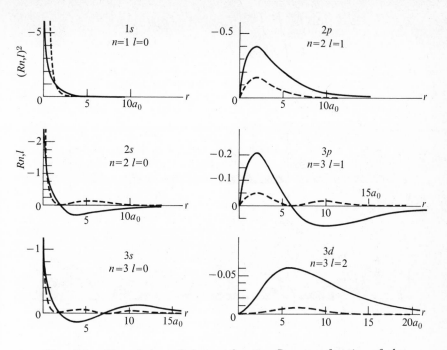

FIG. 9.4. *Plot of the radial wave function R_{nl} as a function of the electron-nuclear distance, r, for various states in the hydrogen atom. The distance r is in units of the Bohr radius $a_0 = \hbar^2/me^2 = 0.53$ Å. Also shown are the plots of $(R_{nl})^2 = R_{nl}^* R_{nl}$ (broken-line curves) as a function of electron-nuclear distance.* [*Printed with permission from H. E. White,* Introduction to Atomic Spectra, *p. 67. New York: McGraw-Hill Book Company, 1934.*]

shell comes from the fact that the electron eigenstates with common n values have similar probability distributions independent of the values of l and m. Thus the eigenstates of electrons with the same n but different l and m constitute a shell. The energies of the eigenstates in a given shell all have the same energy E_n given by Eq. (9.64).

3. The plots in Fig. 9.5 clearly show that the probability densities $P(r)$ for each eigenstate are zero both at $r = 0$ and $r = \infty$, as expected; but $P(r)$ is also zero at distances between $r = 0$ and $r = \infty$. This means that the electron can be found on either side of some point, say on either side of $r = 2a_0$ but not at $r = 2a_0$. This difficulty is overcome by introducing the concept of the spinning electron.

4. We shall now proceed to calculate the expectation value of r. We shall see below that $\bar{r}$ primarily depends upon the value of n, with a small l dependence. Hence for different values of n, the values of $\bar{r}_{nl}$ obtained correspond to the radial electron-nuclear distance, or we may say that $\bar{r}_{nl}$ represent the characteristic radii of the shells. Thus, using the method given by Waller[14]

$$\bar{r}_{nl} = \int_0^\infty \psi_{nlm}^* r \psi_{nlm} \, dr = \int_0^\infty r P(r) \, dr$$

$$= \int_0^\infty \int_0^\pi \int_0^{2\pi} \psi_{nlm}^* r \psi_{nlm} r^2 \sin\theta \, d\theta \, d\phi \, dr$$

$$= 4\pi \int R_{nl}^*(r) R_{nl}(r) r^3 \, dr$$

or

$$\bar{r}_{nl} = \frac{n^2 a_0}{Z} \left\{ 1 + \frac{1}{2} \left[1 - \frac{l(l+1)}{n^2} \right] \right\} \tag{9.71}$$

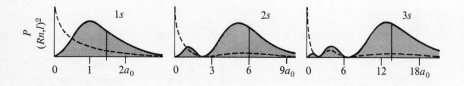

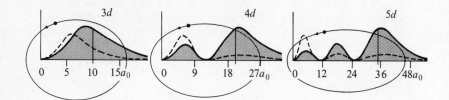

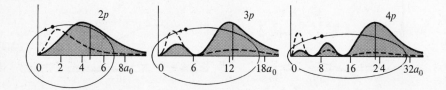

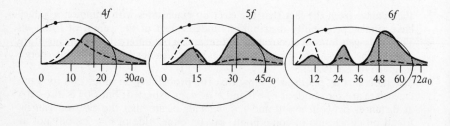

$\longrightarrow r \longrightarrow$

FIG. 9.5. *Plots of the probability density factor* $(R_{nl})^2$, *broken-line curves, and the probability-density distribution function* $P = 4\pi r^2 (R_{nl})^2$, *shaded areas, as a function of the electron-nuclear distance r (r is in units of the first Bohr orbit radius* a_0). *Also shown for comparison are the classical electron orbits. The distance between the two vertical lines is the average electron-nuclear distance.* [*Printed with permission from White, H. E.*, Introduction to Atomic Spectra, *p. 68. New York: McGraw-Hill Book Company, 1934.*]

While the radii of the Bohr circular orbits of the atom are given by

$$r_{\text{Bohr}} = n^2 \frac{a_0}{Z} \qquad (9.72)$$

In Eq. (9.71), the presence of the factor $\frac{1}{2}$ and $1/n^2$ in the second term on the right side means that $\bar{r}_{nl}$ depends primarily upon the first term only, and this compares well with the Bohr-orbit radius given by Eq. (9.72). It is also obvious from Fig. 9.5 that the $1s$, $2p$, $3d$, and $4f$ states have single maxima at $r = a_0$, $4a_0$, $9a_0$, and $16a_0$, which are exactly equal to r_{Bohr} given by Eq. (9.72). On the other hand, the orbits drawn in this figure (Fig. 9.5) using Eq. (9.71) show a better agreement, in general, with experiment.

We may also point out that the value of $\bar{r}$ obtained by using the Bohr-Sommerfeld model is given by

$$\bar{r} = \frac{n^2 a_0}{Z} \left[1 + \frac{1}{2} \left(1 - \frac{k^2}{n^2} \right) \right] \qquad (9.73)$$

Thus if we replace k by $l(l + 1)$, Eq. (9.73) becomes identical with the quantum mechanical result of Eq. (9.71). We shall see that this replacement comes quite naturally while obtaining the expression for orbital angular momentum according to quantum mechanics. As is noticed in the diagrams for $l = 0$, i.e., the s-orbit, according to Bohr it will not be possible because of the resulting straight-line passing through the nucleus. But this difficulty is overcome in quantum mechanics; $l = 0$ is possible because as is obvious from Fig. 9.5, a state with zero angular-momentum has zero probability at the nucleus.

5. Lastly, we shall discuss a special case of the $1s$-state for $Z = 1$. According to quantum mechanics from Eq. (9.71) the value of $\bar{r} = 1.5a_0$, while from Eq. (9.72), $r_{\text{Bohr}} = a_0$. This may seem contradictory because the energy levels are the same for both the quantum mechanical orbit and the Bohr orbit. This apparent discrepancy disappears if we realize that the energy E_n depends upon $1/r$ and not r. Thus the average value of $\langle 1/r_{nl} \rangle$ should be the same as $1/r_0$, and this is the case.

D.   A General Probability Interpretation of $\psi_{nlm}^* \psi_{nlm}$

We would like now to know the probability density $\psi_{nlm}^* \psi_{nlm}$ given by

$$\psi_{nlm}^* \psi_{nlm} = (R_{nl}^* R_{nl}) \cdot (\Theta_{lm}^* \Theta_{lm}) \cdot (\Phi_m^* \Phi_m) \qquad (9.74)$$

The value of the wave function ψ_{nlm} is given by Eq. (9.61), and these do form an orthogonal set satisfying the condition in Eq. (9.62). Our problem is to plot the probability density given by Eq. (9.74). The plots of $\psi_{nlm}^* \psi_{nlm}$ (and not $\psi_{nlm}^* \psi_{nlm} \, dv$) are shown [15] in Fig. 9.6. The wave function ψ does not have any ϕ-dependence but has quite a complicated r- and θ-dependence. Figure 9.6 shows the probability densities as functions of r and θ for different atomic states. A three-dimensional picture of ψ^2 can be imagined by rotating a particular plot about a vertical axis, because there is no ϕ dependence, i.e., figures in three dimensions are symmetrical about the Z axis.

The s-states may be pictured as concentric circles. The $2p$-states with $m = +1$ and $m = -1$ (figures are symmetrical for $m = +1$ or -1) look

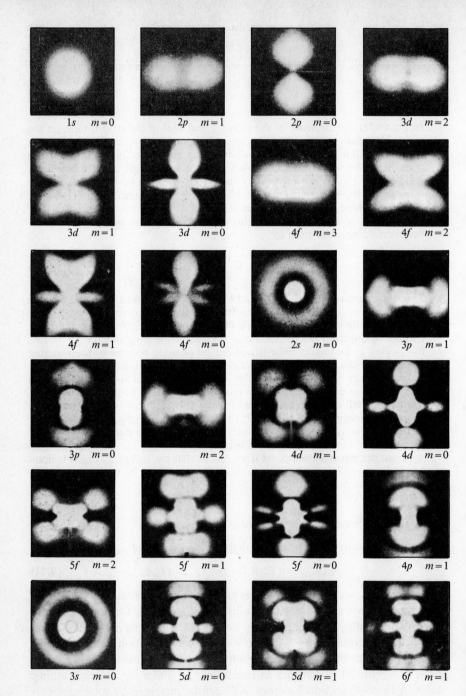

FIG. 9.6. *Photographic representation of the electron cloud, i.e., the electron probability-density distribution* $|\psi|^2 = \psi^*\psi$ *for several energy states of the hydrogen atom. The figure was made by using a spinning mechanical model by White. The scale varies from figure to figure.* [*Printed with permission from White, H. E.,* Introduction to Atomic Spectra, *p. 71. New York: McGraw-Hill Book Company, 1934.*]

more or less like a smoke ring, or a doughnut, in the equatorial plane with its center as the nucleus, the radius being $4r_0$. The $3d$-state with $m = \pm 1$ has the form of two cones with their apexes touching each other at the nucleus; while the $4d$-state for $m = \pm 2$ has two concentric rings. Similar pictures may be imagined for other states.

It may be pointed out that the Z axis (vertical axis) has been chosen arbitrarily. All the states corresponding to a given n are completely degenerate, and there is no way of distinguishing one state from the other unless the degeneracy is removed. Without removing the degeneracy, what one gets for $\psi^*_{nlm}\psi_{nlm}$ in acutal measurement is a spherically symmetric distribution. For example, for $n = 2$, for which the energy is E_2, the measurement will yield

$$\Psi^*_{nlm}\Psi_{nlm} = \frac{1}{4}\Psi^*_{200}\Psi_{200} + \frac{1}{4}\Psi^*_{21-1}\Psi_{21-1} + \frac{1}{4}\psi^*_{210}\psi_{210} + \frac{1}{4}\psi^*_{211}\psi_{211}$$

$$= \frac{\exp(-Zr/a_0)}{128\pi}\left\{\left(\frac{Z}{a_0}\right)^3\left(2 - \frac{Zr}{a_0}\right)^2 + \left(\frac{Z}{a_0}\right)^5 r^2 \right. \tag{9.75}$$

$$\left. \left[\frac{1}{2}\sin^2\theta + \frac{1}{2}\sin^2\theta + \cos^2\theta\right]\right\}$$

$$= \frac{\exp(-Zr/a_0)}{128\pi}\left(\frac{Z}{a_0}\right)^3\left[\left(2 - \frac{Zr}{a_0}\right)^2 + \left(\frac{Zr}{a_0}\right)^2\right]$$

which is a constant for a given r. Of course, if one removes the degeneracy by applying an external field, which results in different energies for different states, then the measurement of the individual state probabilities $\psi^*_{200}\psi_{200}$, $\psi^*_{21-1}\psi_{21-1}$, $\psi^*_{210}\psi_{210}$, and $\psi^*_{211}\psi_{211}$ can be observed for $n = 2$ by making measurements of the energies and the transition rates. Similar considerations apply to other cases as well.

5. ORBITAL ANGULAR MOMENTUM AND SPACE QUANTIZATION ACCORDING TO QUANTUM MECHANICS

By treating the one-electron atom by quantum mechanics, we introduced three quantum numbers n, l, and m. The total quantum number n determined the magnitude of energy corresponding to different n values as given by Eq. (9.64). Our problem at hand is to find the magnitude of the orbital angular momentum corresponding to the orbital quantum number l. We shall also be concerned with finding the physically measurable quantity corresponding to m.

According to classical mechanics the angular momentum **L** of a particle is given by

$$\mathbf{L} = \mathbf{r} \times \mathbf{p} \tag{9.76}$$

or

$$L = rp \sin\theta \tag{9.77}$$

where $\mathbf{p}$ is the linear momentum vector, $\mathbf{r}$ is the distance of the particle from the origin, and θ is the angle between r and p. Writing Eq. (9.76) in the component form

$$L_x = yp_z - zp_y$$
$$L_y = zp_x - xp_z \qquad\qquad \textbf{(9.78)}$$
$$L_z = xp_y - yp_x$$

In order to obtain the quantum operators corresponding to the angular momentum components L_x, L_y, and L_z, we must make the following replacement in the right side of Eq. (9.78) with

$$\mathbf{r} \to \mathbf{r} \qquad \text{and} \qquad \mathbf{p} \to -i\hbar \frac{\partial}{\partial \mathbf{r}}$$

we get the following angular momentum operators for different components

$$L_x = -i\hbar \left(y \frac{\partial}{\partial z} - z \frac{\partial}{\partial y} \right)$$
$$L_y = -i\hbar \left(z \frac{\partial}{\partial x} - x \frac{\partial}{\partial z} \right) \qquad\qquad \textbf{(9.79)}$$
$$L_z = -i\hbar \left(x \frac{\partial}{\partial y} - y \frac{\partial}{\partial x} \right)$$

In order to write these operators in spherical coordinates, we make use of the transformations given by Eq. (9.15), and obtain the following[16]

$$L_x = i\hbar \left(\sin \phi \frac{\partial}{\partial \theta} + \cot \theta \cos \phi \frac{\partial}{\partial \phi} \right)$$
$$L_y = i\hbar \left(-\cos \phi \frac{\partial}{\partial \theta} + \cot \theta \sin \phi \frac{\partial}{\partial \phi} \right) \qquad\qquad \textbf{(9.80)}$$
$$L_z = -i\hbar \frac{\partial}{\partial \phi}$$

The square of the total angular-momentum operator L is given by

$$L^2 = L_x^2 + L_y^2 + L_z^2$$
$$= -\hbar^2 \left[\frac{1}{\sin \theta} \frac{\partial}{\partial \theta} \left(\sin \theta \frac{\partial}{\partial \theta} \right) + \frac{1}{\sin^2 \theta} \frac{\partial^2}{\partial \phi^2} \right] \qquad \textbf{(9.81)}$$

Our interest is to calculate the magnitudes of the total angular momentum and its components for an electron in the atom. This means we have to calculate the expectation values of L_x, L_y, L_z, and L^2. Before doing this, let us say ψ_{nlm} is the wave function of the electron and find the eigenvalues corresponding to the operators in Eqs. (9.80) and (9.81). Remembering that

$$\psi_{nlm} = R_{nl}(r)\Theta_{lm}(\theta)\Phi_m(\phi)$$

we get

$$L_z\psi_{nlm} = R_{nl}(r)\Theta_{lm}L_z\Phi_m(\phi)$$

$$= R_{nl}(r)\Theta_{lm}(\theta)\left\{-i\hbar\frac{\partial}{\partial\phi}\Phi_m(\phi)\right\}$$

and because

$$\Phi_m(\phi) = \frac{1}{\sqrt{2\pi}}e^{im\phi}$$

$$L_z\psi_{nlm} = m\hbar R_{nl}(r)\Theta_{lm}(\theta)\frac{1}{\sqrt{2\pi}}e^{im\phi}$$

or

$$L_z\psi_{nlm} = m\hbar\psi_{nlm} \tag{9.82}$$

Next let us calculate

$$L^2\psi_{nlm} = R_{nl}(r)(-\hbar^2)\left[\frac{\Phi_m(\phi)}{\sin\theta}\frac{d}{d\theta}\left(\sin\theta\frac{d\Theta_{lm}(\theta)}{d\theta}\right) + \frac{\Theta_{lm}(\theta)}{\sin^2\theta}\frac{d^2\Phi_m(\phi)}{d\phi^2}\right]$$

Making use of Eq. (9.21) and Eq. (9.24), i.e.,

$$\frac{1}{\Phi}\frac{d^2\Phi}{d\phi^2} = -m^2$$

and

$$\frac{m^2}{\sin^2\theta} - \frac{1}{\Theta\sin\theta}\frac{d}{d\theta}\left(\sin\theta\frac{d\Theta}{d\theta}\right) = l(l+1)$$

we get,

$$L^2\psi_{nlm} = R_{nl}(r)(-\hbar^2)\Phi_m(\phi)[-l(l+1)\Theta_{lm}(\theta)]$$

or

$$L^2\psi_{nlm} = l(l+1)\hbar^2\psi_{nlm} \tag{9.83}$$

Unlike L_z and L^2, the operation of L_x and L_y on ψ_{nlm} does not give the same ψ_{nlm}, i.e.,

$$L_x^2\psi_{nlm} \neq \text{constant } \psi_{nlm} = \text{constant } \psi_{n'l'm'}$$

$$L_y^2\psi_{nlm} \neq \text{constant } \psi_{nlm} = \text{constant } \psi_{n'l'm'} \tag{9.84}$$

With the help of Eqs. (9.82), (9.83), and (9.84), it is easy now to calculate the expectation values as follows (using the orthogonality property Eqs. (9.62) and (9.67))

$$\overline{L^2} = \iiint \psi_{nlm}^* L^2\psi_{nlm}r^2\sin\theta\,dr\,d\theta\,d\phi$$

$$= l(l+1)\hbar^2\iiint \psi_{nlm}^*\psi_{nlm}r^2\sin\theta\,dr\,d\theta\,d\phi$$

or

$$L^2 = l(l+1)\hbar^2 \tag{9.85}$$

and

$$\bar{L}_z = \iiint \psi_{nlm}^* L_z \psi_{nlm} r^2 \sin\theta \, dr \, d\theta \, d\phi$$

$$= m\hbar \iiint \psi_{nlm}^* \psi_{nlm} r^2 \sin\theta \, dr \, d\theta \, d\phi$$

or

$$\bar{L}_z = m\hbar \tag{9.86}$$

Similarly

$$\bar{L}_x = \iiint \psi_{nlm}^* L_x \psi_{nlm} r^2 \sin\theta \, dr \, d\theta \, d\phi = 0 \tag{9.87}$$

and

$$\bar{L}_y = \iiint \psi_{nlm}^* L_y \psi_{nlm} r^2 \sin\theta \, dr \, d\theta \, d\phi = 0 \tag{9.88}$$

The result of any measurement should be the expectation value. An electron in any definite eigenstate, ψ_{nlm}, has a definite energy E_n. Also from Eqs. (9.85) to (9.88), the electron has a definite value of total angular momentum L given by

$$L = \sqrt{l(l+1)}\hbar \tag{9.89}$$

and a definite value for the z component of angular momentum

$$L_z = m\hbar \tag{9.90}$$

On the other hand, the average values of $\bar{L}_x$ and $\bar{L}_y$ are zero. This means that the orbital angular-momentum vector orientation is constantly changing, resulting in the fluctuation of L_x and L_y in such a way that $\bar{L}_x = 0$ and $\bar{L}_y = 0$.

Hence for an orbital quantum number l, the length of the orbital angular momentum in units of $\hbar$ is $L/\hbar = \sqrt{l(l+1)}$. For a given l, m can take the value $-l, -(l-1), \ldots, -1, 0, 1, \ldots, (l-1), l$, or the values of L_z in units of $\hbar$ are

$$L_z/\hbar = -l, -(l-1), \ldots, -1, 0, 1, \ldots, (l-1), l$$

The angular momentum $L/\hbar$ and its space quantization $L_z/\hbar$ are shown in a vector diagram in Fig. 9.7(a). While the rotation in the form of a cone is shown in Fig. 9.7(b). The angle of the cone is defined by

$$\cos\theta = \frac{L_z}{L} = \frac{m}{\sqrt{l(l+1)}} \tag{9.91}$$

The maximum value the angle θ can take is $\cos\theta = (l/\sqrt{l(l+1)})$, which means, as shown in Fig. 9.7, that $\mathbf{L}$ can never completely align itself in the direction of the Z axis. Classically, complete alignment is possible as was shown in Chapter VIII.

We may also point out that the space quantization according to the rule $L = \sqrt{l(l+1)}\hbar$ is not a unique property of the Coulomb potential but is a characteristic of any potential that is a function of the radial coordinate, r, only.

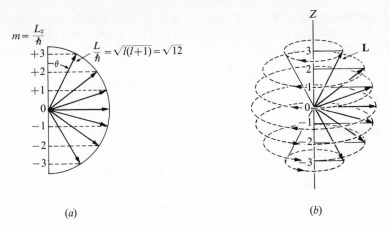

$$m = \frac{L_z}{\hbar}$$

$$\frac{L}{\hbar} = \sqrt{l(l+1)} = \sqrt{12}$$

(a)   (b)

FIG. 9.7.   *Illustration of* (a) *the space quantization of the orbital angular momentum for the case of l = 3, and* (b) *constant precession of the angular momentum vector*, **L**, *about the Z axis.*

Lastly, we may point out that for $n = 1$, $l = 0$, $L = \sqrt{0(0 + 1)}\hbar = 0$, i.e., the orbital angular momentum for $n = 1$ state is zero. This is in complete contradiction to the Bohr theory where it is not possible to have an orbit with zero angular momentum. According to quantum mechanics, the orbit for $l = 0$ will not necessarily be a straight line, because the electron does not move in a definite orbit. (Notice that in the Bohr theory the state corresponding to $l = 0$ (the s-orbit) is not possible because this gives zero angular momentum and therefore an orbit path passing through the nucleus. This difficulty is overcome in quantum mechanics, however, and states having zero angular momentum have a probability density of zero at the nucleus [see Fig. 9.5].) The orbital quantum number k of the Bohr-Sommerfeld model is replaced in quantum mechanics by l, where

$$k - 1 = l \qquad\qquad (9.92)$$

while the magnitude of the orbital angular momentum $k\hbar$ is replaced in quantum mechanics by $\sqrt{l(l + 1)}\hbar$.

6.   ORIGIN OF SPECTRAL LINES AND SELECTION RULES

In the previous sections we have been dealing with eigenvalue problems of the state functions that vary with spatial coordinates but remain constant in time. The eigenfunctions correctly describe the "stationary" states of the atom, and the atom when in these states does not radiate or absorb radiation. As we saw earlier the agreement between quantum theory and experimental observation is good. As a natural extension of the quantum theory one would like to explain with its help the origin of spectral lines and the selection rules. In order to calculate the *transition rates*, i.e., the probability that an atom will change from a quantum state of initial energy E_i to a quantum state of final energy E_f, we have to make use of the *perturbation theory* [17,18]. The rigorous treatment of spontaneous emission is based on the theory of quantum electrodynamics, which is outside the scope of this book.

A. Origin of Spectral Lines

We shall briefly introduce perturbation theory, which is based on the time-dependent Schrödinger wave equation. For a wave function $\Psi(x, y, z; t)$, the Schrödinger wave equation is given by

$$H\Psi = i\hbar \frac{\partial \Psi}{\partial t} \tag{9.93}$$

where H is the Hamiltonian operator, and the wave function Ψ is given by

$$\Psi(x, y, z; t) = \psi(x, y, z)e^{-i(E/\hbar)t} \tag{9.94}$$

Of course, if we substitute Eq. (9.94) into Eq. (9.93), we get the time-independent S.W.E.,

$$H\psi = E\psi \tag{9.95}$$

However, Eq. (9.94) gives only one of many possible solutions of Eq. (9.93), and a more general solution is obtained by substituting a linear combination of eigenfunctions ψ_n, each with an amplitude a_n and the corresponding eigenvalue E_n. We may write

$$\Psi(z, y, z; t) = a_1\psi_1 \exp\left[-i(E_i/\hbar)t\right] + a_2\psi_2 \exp\left[-i(E_2/\hbar)t\right] + \ldots$$

i.e.,

$$\Psi(x, y, z; t) = \sum_n a_n\psi_n \exp\left[-i(E_n/\hbar)t\right] \tag{9.96}$$

Suppose a system (say an atom) is initially in a definite energy state E_i corresponding to the Hamiltonian H_0 and eigenfunction ψ_i. In this case only the coefficient a_i is nonzero in Eq. (9.96), i.e.,

$$\Psi = a_i\psi_i \exp\left[-i(E_i/\hbar)t\right] \tag{9.97}$$

and the corresponding probability density, (or the density of the charge distribution of the atom), is given by

$$\Psi^*\Psi = a_i^* a_i \psi_i^* \psi_i \tag{9.98}$$

Note that $\Psi^*\Psi$ is constant in time, corresponding to the stationary state of the system and hence there will be no emission or absorption of radiation. This means that an atom cannot radiate as long as it is in such an eigenstate.

Let us now assume that the system is in a state i at $t = 0$, with the Hamiltonian H_0. At $t = 0$, we apply a perturbing interaction energy H', which is supposed to be small compared with the original unperturbed Hamiltonian H_0. We may now write the total Hamiltonian H as

$$H = H_0 + H' \tag{9.99}$$

The result of applying a small perturbation H' is to add a contribution from the state with energy E_f to the initial state with energy E_i corresponding to the Hamiltonian H_0. Thus the wave function of the system (or the atom) corresponding to Hamiltonian H is

$$\Psi = a_i \psi_i \exp\left[-(E_i/\hbar)t\right] + a_f \psi_f \exp\left[-i(E_f/\hbar)t\right] \tag{9.100}$$

and the corresponding probability density is

$$\Psi^*\Psi = a_i^* a_i \psi_i^* \psi_i + a_f^* a_f \psi_f^* \psi_f + a_i^* a_f \psi_i^* \psi_f \exp\left[i(E_i - E_f)t/\hbar\right]$$
$$+ a_f^* a_i \psi_f^* \psi_i \exp\left[-i(E_i - E_f)t/\hbar\right] \tag{9.101}$$

The first two terms on the right are constant in time, while the last two terms oscillate with the frequency $\omega(=2\pi\nu)$

$$\omega = \frac{E_i - E_f}{\hbar} \tag{9.102}$$

We may interpret Eq. (9.101) in the following manner: To start with, at $t = 0$, $a_f = 0$, and hence $\Psi^*\Psi = a_i^* a_i \psi_i^* \psi_i$ is a constant, and hence the atom does not radiate. As the time passes on, a_i decreases and a_f increases. Eventually when $a_i = 0$, $\Psi^*\Psi = a_f^* a_f \psi_f^* \psi_f$ is a constant, and hence the atom again does not radiate because it is in a stationary state. But when the atom is still in a state described by Eq. (9.100), it is capable of radiation because the corresponding probability density, and hence the charge distribution, given by Eq. (9.101), oscillates with frequency given by Eq. (9.102). The oscillating charge distribution during the transition from one state, i, to the other state, f, emits a quantum of electromagnetic radiation of frequency ν given by Eq. (9.102), agreeing with the Bohr theory.

To be more specific let us write the probability of finding the system in another state f at time t. This probability depends upon the square of the quantity called the *matrix element*[18], H'_{if}, of the operator H' for the transition from state i to state f. The matrix element H'_{if} may be written in Dirac's notation as

$$H'_{if} = \langle i|H'|f \rangle \equiv \int \psi_f^* H' \psi_i \, dv \tag{9.103}$$

Thus the probability of transition per unit time, P_{if}, from state i to state f is proportional to the square of the matrix element H'_{if}, i.e.,

$$P_{if} \propto |H'_{if}|^2 \tag{9.104}$$

Because the system is in a finite bound state,

$$\psi_i^* \psi_f = \psi_f^* \psi_i \qquad \text{and} \qquad a^*b = b^*a$$

and hence

$$H'_{if} = H'^{*}_{fi} \tag{9.105}$$

i.e.,

$$P_{if} = P_{fi} \tag{9.106}$$

which implies that for the perturbation operator H', the probabilities of forward and reverse reaction are the same. Thus the process involves finding H' and then calculating the matrix elements given by Eq. (9.103). If the matrix elements are nonvanishing, the transition is *allowed*. If the matrix elements vanish, the transition is *forbidden*.

Thus we may summarize the above discussion: If the position or the charge distribution or some other property of the atom remains constant in time, i.e., the expectation value is constant, the atom will not radiate. But if by applying some perturbing force the average value of some property of the atom starts oscillating with time, it will emit (or absorb) radiation of the frequency of its oscillations given by Eq. (9.102).

B. Electromagnetic Transitions and Selection Rules[19]

In our discussion of atomic spectra we are interested in the interaction of electromagnetic radiation with atoms. Thus the perturbing interaction is electromagnetic in nature. The transition rates and the selection rules can be derived for the induced absorption and induced emission with the help of the method outlined above. The difficulty may arise in the case of spontaneous emission because it looks as if there will be no perturbing electromagnetic field that will produce the mixing of the wave functions and will result in an oscillatory probability density. But the difficulty is overcome by the theory of quantum electrodynamics[20]. According to this theory both the electromagnetic field and the atom are quantized. Even when the electromagnetic field is in the lowest energy state, the electromagnetic field has a zero point energy (which is not zero), and hence there is always some electromagnetic radiation (oscillators) present. There will be, therefore, an interaction (or exchange of energy) between the atom and the photons of the electromagnetic radiation field, providing the perturbing field. The selection rules derived for spontaneous emission are the same as those for induced absorption and will be discussed below.

Let us assume that a single electron bound in an atom absorbs the incident radiant energy by the interaction of the electromagnetic wave. The most important term in this interaction described by the perturbing field is due to the electric dipole interaction energy given by

$$H' = -\mathbf{p}\mathbf{E} = +e\mathbf{r}\mathbf{E} \tag{9.107}$$

where $\mathbf{p} = -e\mathbf{r}$ is the instantaneous dipole moment of the electron at distance $\mathbf{r}$, $\mathbf{E}$ is the electric-field vector of the incident wave. Because the wavelength of the incident wave ($\lambda \sim 10^3 \text{ Å}$) is much larger than the size of the atom ($r \sim 1$ Å), the magnitude of **E** may be assumed to be constant over the whole atom. Thus by combining Eq. (9.103) and Eq. (9.107),

$$H_{i_f} = \int \psi_f^* H' \psi_i \, dv = eE \int \psi_f^* r \psi_i \, dv \qquad (9.108)$$

It is convenient to deal with one component of the dipole moment at a time. Let us say that we are considering the x component of the dipole moment in which case r is replaced by x, and E by E_x. Replacing the rectangular coordinates by spherical coordinates

$$x = r \sin \theta \cos \phi$$
$$y = r \sin \theta \sin \phi$$
$$z = r \cos \theta \qquad (9.109)$$
$$dv = r^2 \sin \theta \, dr \, d\theta \, d\phi$$

and using the hydrogen atom wave functions

$$\psi_i = \psi_{n,l,m} = R_{n,l}(r)\Theta_{l,m}(\theta)\Phi_m(\phi)$$
$$\psi_f = \psi_{n',l',m'} = R_{n',l'}(r)\Theta_{l',m'}(\theta)\Phi_{m'}(\phi) \qquad (9.110)$$

Equation (9.109) takes the form

$$H_{if,x} = eE_x \iiint \psi_{n',l',m'}^* r \sin \theta \cos \phi \, \psi_{n,l,m} r^2 \sin \theta \, dr \, d\theta \, d\phi$$
$$\qquad (9.111)$$
$$= eE_x \int_0^\infty r^3 R_{n',l'}^* R_{n,l} \, dr \int_0^\pi \Theta_{l',m'}^* \Theta_{l,m} \sin^2 \theta \, d\theta \int_0^{2\pi} \Phi_{m'}^* \Phi_m \cos \phi \, d\phi$$

If any one of these integrals vanish, the transition probability will be zero. We shall consider these three separately.

(i) *Selection Rules for m.* Considering only the third integral, and using the wave function

$$\Phi_m = \frac{1}{\sqrt{2\pi}} \exp{(im\phi)}$$

and noting that $\cos \phi = (e^{i\phi} + e^{-i\phi})/2$, we get

$$\int_0^{2\pi} \Phi_{m'}^* \Phi_m \cos \phi \, d\phi = \frac{1}{4\pi} \int_0^{2\pi}$$
$$\{\exp{[-i(m' - m + 1)\phi]} + \exp{[-i(m' - m - 1)\phi]}\} \, d\phi \qquad (9.112)$$

Because m, m' are integers, therefore $(m' - m + 1)$ and $(m' - m - 1)$ are equal to 0 or to an integer, say k. But

$$\int_0^{2\pi} e^{-ik\phi} = \int_0^{2\pi} \cos k\phi \, d\phi - i \int_0^{2\pi} \sin k\phi \, d\phi = 0$$

for $k = \pm 1, \pm 2, \pm 3, \ldots$. Therefore, Eq. (9.112) is zero unless

$$m' - m + 1 = 0 \quad \text{and} \quad m' - m = 1 = 0$$

i.e.,

$$\Delta m = m' - m = \pm 1 \qquad (9.113)$$

The same selection rule is obtained for the y component as well, i.e.,

$$H_{if,x} \neq 0, \qquad H_{if,y} \neq 0, \qquad \text{if } \Delta m = \pm 1$$

But for the z component

$$H_{if,z} = \int_0^\infty r^3 R_{n',l}^* R_{n,l} \, dr \int_0^\pi \Theta_{l',m'}^* \Theta_{l,m} \sin \theta \cos \theta \, d\theta \int_0^{2\pi} \Phi_{m'}^* \Phi_m \, d\phi \qquad \textbf{(9.114)}$$

The third integral is

$$\int_0^{2\pi} \Phi_{m'}^* \Phi_m \, d\phi = \frac{1}{2\pi} \int_0^{2\pi} \exp\left[-i(m'-m)\phi\right] d\phi$$

Because m' and m are integers, it is zero unless

$$m' - m = 0 \qquad \textbf{(9.115)}$$

Combining Eqs. (9.113) and (9.115), the selection rules for m_l are

$$\Delta m = 0, \pm 1 \qquad \textbf{(9.116)}$$

Thus the transition rates given by Eq. (9.111) or Eq. (9.108) will be zero, unless $\Delta m = 0, \pm 1$.

(ii) *Selection Rules for l.* The selection rules for l may be obtained by evaluating the second integral on the right side of Eq. (9.111). Before we can do this we have to reconsider the definition of odd and even parity as given in Chapter VI. We had concluded that under the reflection of coordinates, the wave functions that satisfy the condition

$$\psi(-x, -y, -z) = +\psi(x, y, z) \qquad \textbf{(9.117)}$$

are of even parity, and the wave functions that satisfy the condition

$$\psi(-x, -y, -z) = -\psi(x, y, z) \qquad \textbf{(9.118)}$$

are of odd parity. Because we have been dealing with spherical coordinates, we shall express the above definitions in a slightly different form. Under reflection, i.e., under the change of signs of the rectangular coordinates, the spherical coordinates change as shown in Fig. 9.8, and are mathematically expressed as

$$r \rightarrow r, \qquad \theta \rightarrow (\pi - \theta), \qquad \phi \rightarrow (\pi + \phi) \qquad \textbf{(9.119)}$$

Thus in the hydrogen atom wave functions given by Eq. (9.110), the Θ and Φ parts of the wave function have the following relations under reflection.

$$\Phi_m(\pi + \phi) = (-1)^{|m|} \Phi_m(\phi) \qquad \textbf{(9.120)}$$

and

$$\Theta_{l,m}(\pi - \theta) = (-1)^{l+|m|} \Theta_{l,m}(\theta) \qquad \textbf{(9.121)}$$

while the radial part $R_{n,l}(r)$ does not change. Hence combining Eqs. (9.120) and (9.121) with R_{nl}, we get

$$R_{n,l}(r)\Theta_{l,m}(\pi - \theta)\Phi_m(\pi + \phi) = (-1)^{l+|m|}(-1)^{|m|} R_{n,l}(r) \times \Theta_{l,m}(\theta)\Phi_m(\phi)$$

$$\textbf{(9.122)}$$

or in short,

$$\psi_{n,l,m}(r, \pi - \theta, \pi + \phi) = (-1)^l \psi_{n,l,m}(r, \theta, \phi) \qquad (9.123)$$

From Eq. (9.123), we draw the following conclusion:

For l odd, i.e., $l = 1, 3, 5, 7, \ldots$, ψ is odd.
For l even, i.e., $l = 0, 2, 4, 6, \ldots$, ψ is even.

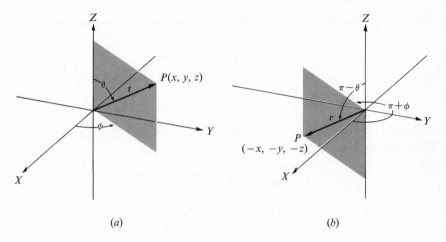

(a)   (b)

FIG. 9.8.   *Relation between rectangular coordinates (x, y, z) and spherical polar coordinates (r, θ, ϕ) of a point P:* (a) *before reflection and* (b) *after reflection, i.e., after the parity operator is applied.*

From Eq. (9.108) because $r(=x, y, \text{ or } z)$ is odd, the matrix element H_{if} is odd if ψ_i and ψ_f both are odd or even. But the odd integral is zero, and hence H_{if} must be even. This is possible, only if ψ_i and ψ_f have different parity, i.e., during the transition the wave function ψ must change parity to give a nonzero value for the transition probability, H_{if}. From Eq. (9.123), this implies that in Eqs. (9.111) or (9.114), l' and l must differ by odd integers, i.e.,

$$\Delta l = l' - l = \pm 1, \pm 3, \pm 5, \ldots$$

But these selection rules combined with the selection rules for m given by Eq. (9.116), limit the change in l to the following, i.e.,

$$\Delta l = \pm 1 \qquad (9.124)$$

(iii) *Selection Rules for n.*   Finally, there is no limit or change in n, i.e., Δn can have any value.

7.   DIRAC'S THEORY AND ELECTRON SPIN[21]

The Schrödinger wave equation that we have been using so far is in the non-relativistic form, i.e., it is not invariant under a Lorentz transformation; and hence it is applicable to only those particles that are moving with velocities small as compared to that of light. The relativistic form of the quantum mechanical equation may be arrived at in the following part. As we shall see, it leads to many interesting consequences.

A. The Klein-Gordon Equation[22]

Consider an electron of rest mass m_0, with total energy E and momentum p. According to relativistic mechanics these quantities are related as

$$E^2 = p^2c^2 + m_0^2c^4 \tag{9.125}$$

By the rules of quantum mechanics, we replace E by $i\hbar(\partial/\partial t)$, and p by $-i\hbar\nabla$, i.e.,

$$p^2 = p_x^2 + p_y^2 + p_z^2 = -\hbar^2\nabla^2 \tag{9.126}$$

and if we let $\Psi(r, t)$ be the wave function on which they operate, we get the following for Eq. (9.125)

$$-\hbar^2 \frac{\partial^2\Psi}{\partial t^2} = -\hbar^2c^2\nabla^2\Psi + m_0^2c^4\Psi$$

or

$$\nabla^2\Psi - \frac{1}{c^2}\frac{\partial^2\Psi}{\partial t^2} = \frac{m_0^2c^2}{\hbar^2}\Psi \tag{9.127}$$

Equation (9.127) is the Klein-Gordon equation.

Note that for $m_0 = 0$, i.e., in the case of a photon, Eq. (9.127) reduces to the wave equation of the electromagnetic field, i.e.,

$$\nabla^2\Psi - \frac{1}{c^2}\frac{\partial^2\Psi}{\partial t^2} = 0 \tag{9.128}$$

B. Dirac's Equation

In 1928 Dirac pointed out that several difficulties are encountered if we apply the second-order Klein-Gordon equation to electrons. Thus in solving the time-dependent Schrödinger equation

$$H\Psi = i\hbar\frac{\partial\Psi}{\partial t} \tag{9.129}$$

where H is, of course, the energy operator corresponding to E in Eq. (9.125), the difficulties arise because of the term E^2, resulting in not only $+ve$ value of E, but also giving $-ve$ value of E, i.e.

$$E = \pm\sqrt{p^2c^2 + m_0^2c^4} \tag{9.130}$$

Dirac overcame this difficulty by postulating that the right side of Eq. (9.130) must have an exact square root. Thus we may take H to be a linear combination of the momentum operators p_x, p_y, p_z and the rest mass m_0, i.e.,

$$H = \sqrt{p^2c^2 + m_0^2c^4} = c(\alpha_1 p_x + \alpha_2 p_y + \alpha_3 p_z + \beta m_0 c)$$
$$= c[(\boldsymbol{\alpha} \cdot \mathbf{p}) + \beta m_0 c] \tag{9.131}$$

where α_1, α_2, α_3, and β are operators that must satisfy some definite conditions. The scalar product $\boldsymbol{\alpha} \cdot \mathbf{p}$ stands for the expression

$$\boldsymbol{\alpha} \cdot \mathbf{p} = \alpha_1 p_x + \alpha_2 p_y + \alpha_3 p_z \tag{9.132}$$

Squaring Eq. (9.131), we find that α_1, α_2, α_3, and β must satisfy the following conditions

$$\left. \begin{array}{cccc} \alpha_1^2 = 1 & \alpha_2^2 = 1 & \alpha_3^2 = 1 & \beta^2 = 1 \\ \alpha_1\alpha_2 + \alpha_2\alpha_1 = 0 & & \alpha_1\beta + \beta\alpha_1 = 0 \\ \alpha_2\alpha_3 + \alpha_3\alpha_1 = 0 & & \alpha_2\beta + \beta\alpha_2 = 0 \\ \alpha_3\alpha_1 + \alpha_1\alpha_3 = 0 & & \alpha_3\beta + \beta\alpha_3 = 0 \end{array} \right\} \tag{9.133}$$

If we solve for α_1, α_2, α_3, and β, it is easy to represent these in terms of matrices of order four; and one of the possible representations is

$$\alpha_1 = \begin{pmatrix} 0 & 0 & 0 & 1 \\ 0 & 0 & 1 & 0 \\ 0 & 1 & 0 & 0 \\ 1 & 0 & 0 & 0 \end{pmatrix} \qquad \alpha_2 = \begin{pmatrix} 0 & 0 & 0 & -i \\ 0 & 0 & i & 0 \\ 0 & -i & 0 & 0 \\ i & 0 & 0 & 0 \end{pmatrix}$$

$$\alpha_3 = \begin{pmatrix} 0 & 0 & 1 & 0 \\ 0 & 0 & 0 & -1 \\ 1 & 0 & 0 & 0 \\ 0 & -1 & 0 & 0 \end{pmatrix} \qquad \beta = \begin{pmatrix} 1 & 0 & 0 & 0 \\ 0 & 1 & 0 & 0 \\ 0 & 0 & -1 & 0 \\ 0 & 0 & 0 & -1 \end{pmatrix} \tag{9.134}$$

We may also write the above matrices in the form of partitioned matrices

$$\boldsymbol{\alpha} = \begin{pmatrix} 0 & \boldsymbol{\sigma} \\ \boldsymbol{\sigma} & 0 \end{pmatrix} \qquad \beta = \begin{pmatrix} 1 & 0 \\ 0 & -1 \end{pmatrix} \tag{9.135}$$

where the vector notation $\boldsymbol{\alpha}$ denotes the three matrices α_1, α_2, α_3. $\boldsymbol{\sigma}$ has three components of 2×2 matrices, while 0 and 1 are zero and unit matrices of order two, i.e.,

$$\sigma_1(=\sigma_x) = \begin{pmatrix} 0 & 1 \\ 1 & 0 \end{pmatrix}, \quad \sigma_2(=\sigma_y) = \begin{pmatrix} 0 & -i \\ i & 0 \end{pmatrix}, \quad \sigma_3(=\sigma_z) = \begin{pmatrix} 1 & 0 \\ 0 & -1 \end{pmatrix} \tag{9.136}$$

$$0 = \begin{pmatrix} 0 & 0 \\ 0 & 0 \end{pmatrix} \quad \text{and} \quad 1 = \begin{pmatrix} 1 & 0 \\ 0 & 1 \end{pmatrix} \tag{9.137}$$

Matrices σ_x, σ_y, and σ_z are called Pauli's spin matrices.

Now for the free particle of energy E, its solutions according to Eq. (9.129) may be written as

$$\Psi(\mathbf{r}, t) = \Psi(\mathbf{r})e^{-i(Et)/\hbar} \tag{9.138}$$

If we combine Eqs. (9.129), (9.131), and (9.138), we obtain the following wave equation for the free particle, Dirac's equation,

$$c[(\boldsymbol{\alpha} \cdot \mathbf{p}) + \beta m_0 c]\Psi(\mathbf{r}) = E\Psi(\mathbf{r})$$

or

$$(-i\hbar c\boldsymbol{\alpha}\cdot\boldsymbol{\nabla} + \beta m_0 c^2)\Psi(\mathbf{r}) = E\Psi(\mathbf{r}) \qquad (9.139)$$

where

$$\boldsymbol{\alpha}\cdot\boldsymbol{\nabla} = \alpha_1\frac{\partial}{\partial x} + \alpha_2\frac{\partial}{\partial y} + \alpha_3\frac{\partial}{\partial z} \qquad (9.140)$$

Because, as shown in Eq. (9.134), α_1, α_2, α_3, β are 4×4 matrices, the wave function $\psi(r)$ must be a four-component wave function, i.e., a column matrix of the form

$$\psi(\mathbf{r}) = \begin{pmatrix} \psi_1(\mathbf{r}) \\ \psi_2(\mathbf{r}) \\ \psi_3(\mathbf{r}) \\ \psi_4(\mathbf{r}) \end{pmatrix} \qquad (9.141)$$

Hence combining Eqs. (9.139) and (9.141), we find the following four equations.

$$(E - m_0 c^2)\psi_1 + i\hbar c\,\frac{\partial\psi_3}{\partial z} + i\hbar c\left(\frac{\partial}{\partial x} - i\,\frac{\partial}{\partial y}\right)\psi_4 = 0$$

$$(E - m_0 c^2)\psi_2 + i\hbar c\left(\frac{\partial}{\partial x} + i\,\frac{\partial}{\partial y}\right)\psi_3 - i\hbar c\,\frac{\partial\psi_4}{\partial z} = 0$$

$$i\hbar c\,\frac{\partial\psi_1}{\partial z} + i\hbar c\left(\frac{\partial}{\partial x} - i\,\frac{\partial}{\partial y}\right)\psi_2 + (E + m_0 c^2)\psi_3 = 0 \qquad (9.142)$$

$$i\hbar c\left(\frac{\partial}{\partial x} + i\,\frac{\partial}{\partial y}\right)\psi_1 - i\hbar c\,\frac{\partial\psi_2}{\partial z} + (E + m_0 c^2)\psi_4 = 0$$

Thus we have overcome the difficulty of the square root requirement by replacing one equation by four equations given by Eq. (9.142). We shall now discuss two physically interesting results derived from Dirac's theory.

C. The Electron Spin

Even though we have used a special representation in arriving at Dirac's equation, the special properties derived from these equations are independent of the representation. The most important property of elementary particles such as the electron, proton, and the like, is that each has an intrinsic angular momentum, usually called intrinsic spin or, simply, spin (intrinsic in the sense that the particle is spinning about its own axis and is not to be confused with the orbital motion). This spin may be derived simply from the study of the Hamiltonian. Considering the electron as an example, the Hamiltonion is given by Eq. (9.131),

$$H = c\boldsymbol{\alpha}\cdot\mathbf{p} + \beta m_0 c^2 \qquad (9.143)$$

An important property of any operator f is that its time rate of change is related to the Hamiltonian H by the following relation[23]

$$i\hbar\,\frac{\partial f}{\partial t} = [Hf - fH] \qquad (9.144)$$

If the operator f corresponds to a quantity that is a constant of motion, then according to the classical theory $\partial f/\partial t = 0$ and hence

$$Hf - fH = 0 \tag{9.145}$$

Equation (9.145) says that the operators f and H commute with each other.

According to classical theory, we know that the z component of the orbital angular momentum, L_z, given by

$$L_z = xp_y - yp_x$$

is a constant of motion. We now show that L_z does not commute with the relativistic Hamiltonian H given by Eq. (9.144) and hence is not a constant of motion. Thus for $f = L_z$

$$
\begin{aligned}
L_z H - H L_z &= (xp_y - yp_x)(c\boldsymbol{\alpha} \cdot \mathbf{p} + \beta m_0 c^2) - (c\boldsymbol{\alpha} \cdot \mathbf{p} + \beta m_0 c^2)(xp_y - yp_x) \\
&= -c\hbar^2 \left(x\frac{\partial}{\partial y} - y\frac{\partial}{\partial x} \right)\left(\alpha_1 \frac{\partial}{\partial x} + \alpha_2 \frac{\partial}{\partial y} + \alpha_3 \frac{\partial}{\partial z} \right) \\
&\quad - c\hbar^2 \left(\alpha_1 \frac{\partial}{\partial x} + \alpha_2 \frac{\partial}{\partial y} + \alpha_3 \frac{\partial}{\partial z} \right)\left(x\frac{\partial}{\partial y} - y\frac{\partial}{\partial x} \right) \\
&= -c\hbar^2 \left(\alpha_2 \frac{\partial}{\partial x} - \alpha_1 \frac{\partial}{\partial y} \right) \\
&= -i\hbar c(\alpha_2 p_x - \alpha_1 p_y)
\end{aligned}
\tag{9.146}
$$

or

$$i\hbar \frac{\partial L_z}{\partial t} = L_z H - H L_z = -i\hbar c(\alpha_2 p_x - \alpha_1 p_y) \neq 0 \tag{9.147}$$

In order to make it zero, we will have to add some quantity to this equation so as to find the corresponding constant of motion in relativistic mechanics. Consider an operator $\frac{1}{2}\hbar\sigma_z$, and let us calculate

$$
\begin{aligned}
i\hbar \frac{\partial(\frac{1}{2}\hbar\sigma_z)}{\partial t} &= \frac{1}{2}\hbar\sigma_z H - H\frac{1}{2}\hbar\sigma_z \\
&= c\hbar^2 \left(\alpha_2 \frac{\partial}{\partial x} - \alpha_1 \frac{\partial}{\partial y} \right) \\
&= i\hbar c(\alpha_2 p_x - \alpha_1 p_y) \neq 0
\end{aligned}
\tag{9.148}
$$

But, adding Eqs. (9.147) and (9.148), we get

$$i\hbar \frac{\partial}{\partial t}\left(L_z + \frac{1}{2}\hbar\sigma_z \right) = \left(L_z + \frac{1}{2}\hbar\sigma_z \right) H - H\left(L_z + \frac{1}{2}\hbar\sigma_z \right) \tag{9.149}$$

$$= 0$$

Equation (9.149) reveals that in relativistic mechanics L_z is not a constant of motion but $L_z + (1/2)\hbar\sigma_z$ is, because it commutes with H. Similar results may be derived for the x and y components. Hence, in general

$$\mathbf{L} + \frac{1}{2}\hbar\boldsymbol{\sigma} \tag{9.150}$$

is a constant of motion; $\frac{1}{2}\hbar\sigma$ is interpreted as the intrinsic spin of the particle, an electron in this case. From the properties of σ, we may say that the magnitude of the spin angular momentum is $\frac{1}{2}\hbar$. This $\frac{1}{2}\hbar$ combines with the orbital angular momentum (which has a magnitude $\sqrt{l(l+1)}\hbar$) to give the total angular momentum of the particle; which then is a constant of motion. We may point out that in the nonrelativistic limit both $\mathbf{L}$ and $\frac{1}{2}\hbar\sigma$ are separate constants of motion.

As we shall see in the next chapter the above predictions of the theory have been experimentally verified.

D. Particles and Antiparticles

Equation (9.125) $E = \pm\sqrt{p^2c^2 + m_0^2c^4}$ was interpreted by Dirac as meaning that a particle can have energy either $E > m_0c^2$, or $E < -m_0c^2$, in order to satisfy the above equation. As shown in Fig. 9.9 the region of energy between

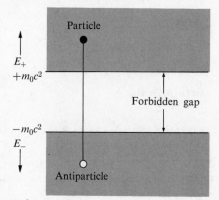

FIG. 9.9. *According to Dirac an electron may have energy equal to either $<-m_0c^2$ or $>m_0c^2$, while the region in between is forbidden as shown. Creation of particle and antiparticle pair is also demonstrated.*

m_0c^2 and $-m_0c^2$ is called the forbidden region. It was also postulated that the energy states with $E < -m_0c^2$ are all filled. But if we supply an energy greater than $2m_0c^2$ to the particle in the negative energy state, the particle may be raised to the positive energy state, leaving a hole behind. The hole left behind is identified with the antiparticle. Thus for every particle, there is an antiparticle. These predictions are more firm than stated here. For example, if we have a particle with intrinsic spin $\frac{1}{2}\hbar\sigma_z$, along the Z axis, the spin might point along the $+Z$ axis or $-Z$ axis; while its antiparticle lying in the negative energy states will also have these two choices. As a matter of fact, the four Dirac's equations given by (9.142) represent these four states of the particle and the antiparticle in the order mentioned above.

The electron is a particle of mass $m_0 = 0.51$ MeV and charge $-1e$, its antiparticle, called the positron with a mass $m_0 = 0.51$ MeV and charge $+1e$, has been discovered. As a matter of fact for every particle, there has been discovered an antiparticle[24].

PROBLEMS

1. Quantum mechanical calculations give the following expression for the average value of r in the hydrogen-like atoms

$$\langle r \rangle = r_{av} = \frac{n^2 a_0}{Z} \left[1 + \frac{1}{2} \left\{ 1 - \frac{l(l+1)}{n^2} \right\} \right]$$

Taking $n = 1, 2, 3$, calculate r_{av} for all possible states. How do these values compare with the corresponding Bohr radii? List these in the order of increasing r_{av} and compare with those obtained in the Bohr-Sommerfeld theory.

2. Show that the normalization condition for $\psi_{n_l m_l}$ requires that

$$\int_0^\infty |R_{nl}|^2 r^2 \, dr = 1$$

3. For $n = 1, 2, 3$, what are the values of r for which the probability of finding the electron is zero.

4. Show, by direct substitution into Eq. (9.36), that

$$\Theta_{20}(\theta) = \sqrt{\frac{5}{8}} (3 \cos^2 \theta - 1)$$

is a solution of Schrödinger's angular equation. Also show that this wave function is normalized.

5. Show, by direct substitution into Eq. (9.43), that

$$R_{10}(r) = \frac{2}{a_0^{3/2}} \exp \left[-r/a_0 \right]$$

is a solution of Schrödinger's radial equation.

6. Show that the wave functions $Y_l^m (= \Theta(\theta)\Phi(\phi))$ are orthogonal and normalized, i.e.,

$$\int_0^\pi \int_0^{2\pi} Y_l^{m*} Y_{l'}^{m'} \, d\Omega = \delta_{ll'} \delta_{mm'}$$

where $\delta_{ll'} = 0$ if $l \neq l'$ (orthogonality condition) and $\delta_{ll'} = 1$ if $l = l'$ (normalization condition), similarly $\delta_{mm'} = 0$ if $m \neq m'$ and $= 1$ if $m = m'$; and $d\Omega = \sin \theta \, d\theta \, d\phi$.

7. Show that the Legendre polynomials of degree l contain only even or odd powers of ξ according to whether l is even or odd.

8. Using the definition of the associated Legendre functions show that their parity is given by $(-1)^{l+m}$.

9. In spherical coordinates, the parity operator corresponds to changing r, θ, ϕ to r, $\pi - \theta$, $\pi + \phi$. Using this show that the parity of $Y_l^{m_l}$ functions is $(-l)^l$.

10. By direct calculations show that the wave functions $Y_l^{m_l}$ are proper functions of the operators L_z and L_z^2.

11. We have shown that an atomic electron has a precisely defined angular mo-

mentum even though its angular position at any time is not always well defined. Explain.

12. Derive Eqs. (9.80) from (9.79) by substituting the values of x, y, and z given by Eq. (9.15) and the values of $\partial/\partial x$, $\partial/\partial y$, and $\partial/\partial z$ by making use of relations of the form

$$\frac{\partial}{\partial x} = \frac{\partial r}{\partial x}\frac{\partial}{\partial r} + \frac{\partial \theta}{\partial x}\frac{\partial}{\partial \theta} + \frac{\partial \phi}{\partial x}\frac{\partial}{\partial \phi} \; ; \text{etc.}$$

13. Derive Eq. (9.81).

14. Substituting the values of L_x and L_y, show that

$$L_x \pm iL_y = \hbar e^{\pm i\phi}\left(\pm\frac{\partial}{\partial \theta} + i \cot \theta \frac{\partial}{\partial \phi}\right)$$

and also prove that

$$(L_x \pm iL_y)Y_l^m = \hbar\sqrt{(l \mp m)(l \pm m + 1)}\,Y_l^{m-1}$$

15. Show that $\psi(r) = K(e^{-ur})/r$, where K is a constant and $u = m_0 c/\hbar$, is a solution of the Klein-Gordon equation. (Note that ψ in this form represents the nuclear force according to Yukawa's meson theory.)

REFERENCES

1. de Broglie, L., *Phil. Mag.*, **47**, 466, (1924); *Ann. Physik*, **3**, 22, (1925).

2. Schrödinger, E., *Ann. Physik*, **79**, 361, 489, 734, (1926); *Phys. Rev.*, **28**, 1049, (1926).

3. Heisenberg, W., *Zeit. fur Phys.*, **33**, 879, (1925).

4. Bethe, H., and E. Salpeter, *Quantum Mechanics of One- and Two-Electron Atoms*, Berlin: Springer, 1959.

5. Tralli, N., and F. R. Pomilla, *Atomic Theory*, Chap. 5, New York: McGraw-Hill Book Company, 1969.

6. Shore, B. W., and D. H. Menzel, *Atomic Spectra*, Chap. III, New York: John Wiley & Sons, Inc., 1968.

7. Morse, P. M., and H. Feshbach, *Methods of Theoretical Physics*, Chap. I, New York: McGraw-Hill Book Company, 1953; also, Menzel, D. H., *Mathematical Physics*, Sec. 32, New York: Dover Publications, Inc., 1961.

8. Dirac, P. A. M., *The Principles of Quantum Mechanics*, 3d ed., Sec. 15, New York: Oxford Univ. Press, 1947.

9. Morse, P. M., and H. Feshbach, *Methods of Theoretical Physics*, New York: McGraw-Hill Book Company, 1953; Courant, R., and D. Hilbert, *Methods of Mathematical Physics*, Vol. I, New York: Interscience, 1953.

10. Margenau, H., and G. M. Murphy, *The Mathematics of Physics and Chemistry*, 2nd ed., D. Van Nostrand Co., Inc., Princeton, N. J., 1956.

11. Abramowitz, M. A., and I. A. Stegun (eds.), *Handbook of Mathematical Functions* (Natl. Bur. Stds. Appl. Math. Series 55), Washington, D. C., 1964.

12. Shore, B. W., and D. H. Menzel, *Atomic Spectra*, Sec. 3.11, New York: John Wiley & Sons, Inc., 1968, and other references given there.

13. Schiff, L. I., *Quantum Mechanics*, 3rd ed., New York: McGraw-Hill Book Company, 1969.

14. Waller, I., *Zeit. fur Physik*, **38**, 635, (1926).

15. Slater, J. C., *Phys. Rev.*, **37**, 482, (1931); also, White, H. E., *Phys. Rev.*, **37**, 1416, (1931).

16. Dicke, R. H., and J. M. Wittke, *Quantum Mechanics*, Chap. 9, Reading, Mass.: Addison-Wesley Publishing Co., Inc., 1960.

17. Schrödinger, E., *Ann. Physik*, **80**, 437, (1926).

18. Powell, J. L., and B. Crasemann, *Quantum Mechanics*, Chap. 11, Reading, Mass.: Addison-Wesley Publishing Co., Inc., 1961.

19. Einstein, A., *Zeit. fur Physik*, **18**, 121, (1917); Dirac, P. A. M., *Proc. Roy. Soc.*, **A114**, 243, (1927); also Tralli, N., and F. R. Pomilla, *Atomic Theory*, Sec. 5-12, 5-13, New York: McGraw-Hill Book Company, 1969.

20. Heitler, W., *The Quantum Theory of Radiation*, 3rd ed., New York: Oxford Univ. Press, 1953.

21. Dirac, P. A. M., *Proc. Roy. Soc.*, **A117**, 610, (1928).

22. Dirac, P. A. M., *The Principles of Quantum Mechanics*, 4th ed., Chap. 11, New York: Oxford Univ. Press, 1957.

23. Powell, J. L., and B. Crasemann, *Quantum Mechanics*, p. 181, Reading, Mass.: Addison-Wesley Publishing Co., Inc., 1961.

24. Arya, A. P., *Fundamentals of Nuclear Physics*, p. 296 and Ch. XV. Boston, Mass.: Allyn and Bacon, Inc., 1966.

SUGGESTIONS FOR FURTHER READING

1. White, H. E., *Introduction to Atomic Spectra*, Chaps. IV, IX. New York: McGraw-Hill Book Company, Inc., 1934.

2. Herzberg, G., *Atomic Spectra & Atomic Structure*, Chap. I. New York: Dover Publications, Inc., 1944.

3. Livesey, D. L., *Atomic and Nuclear Physics*, Chap. 7. Waltham, Mass.: Blaisdell Publishing Company, 1966.

4. Eisberg, R. M., *Fundamentals of Modern Physics*, Chap. 10. New York: John Wiley & Sons, Inc., 1961.

5. Slater, J. C., *Quantum Theory of Matter*, 2nd ed., New York: McGraw-Hill Book Company, 1968.

6. Shore, B. W., and D. H. Menzel, *Principles of Atomic Spectra*, New York: John Wiley & Sons, Inc., 1968.

7. Powell, J. L., and B. Crasemann, *Quantum Mechanics*, Chap. 7. Reading, Mass.: Addison-Wesley Publishing Company, Inc., 1961.

8. Tralli, N., and F. R. Pomilla, *Atomic Theory, An Introduction to Wave Mechanics*, New York: McGraw-Hill Book Company, 1969.

9. Schiff, L. I., *Quantum Mechanics*, 2nd ed., Chaps. IV, X, XII. New York: McGraw-Hill Book Company, 1955.

10. See also Chap. VI, Suggestions for Further Reading, 6 through 14.

X

One-Valence Electron Atoms
and the Effects of Magnetic Fields

1. ATOMIC VECTOR MODELS

Since the formulation of the Bohr theory of the hydrogen atom several atomic vector models have been proposed to explain various aspects of atomic spectra, among them being: (a) the Bohr-Sommerfeld model[1], (b) the Landé model[2], (c) the Sommerfeld (or old quantum-mechanical) model[3], and (d) the quantum mechanical (or wave mechanical) model[4].

Since the development of quantum mechanics, the quantum mechanical model has been used almost exclusively because it frequently offers the most accurate answers to many different questions. One of the disadvantages of the quantum-mechanical model, however, is that its solutions must be interpreted in terms of probabilities, which is not the most useful of concepts. It is sometimes much easier to think in terms of the old quantum-theory model of Sommerfeld, which offers a simple vector model of the atom. In our following discussions of atomic spectra, both the Sommerfeld and the quantum mechanical models will be utilized. The Sommerfeld model will be used whenever we are visualizing the general aspects of atomic phenomena, while in actual calculations the quantum-mechanical model will be used. The Landé model will not be discussed, but the Bohr-Sommerfeld model will be referred to occasionally. Table 10.1 gives values of the orbital (or azimuthal) angular momentum (expressed in units of $\hbar$) according to the

TABLE 10.1

VALUES OF THE ORBITAL (OR AZIMUTHAL)
ANGULAR MOMENTA ACCORDING TO DIFFERENT MODELS

Electron notation			Quantum-mechanical model:	Old quantum-mechanical, or Sommerfeld, model:	Bohr-Sommerfeld model:
n	l	nl	$\sqrt{l(l+1)} = L/\hbar$	$l = (k-1) = L/\hbar$	$k = L/\hbar$
1	0	$1s$	0	0	1
2	0	$2s$	0	0	1
	1	$2p$	$\sqrt{2}$	1	2
3	0	$3s$	0	0	1
	1	$3p$	$\sqrt{2}$	1	2
	2	$3d$	$\sqrt{6}$	2	3
4	0	$4s$	0	0	1
	1	$4p$	$\sqrt{2}$	1	2
	2	$4d$	$\sqrt{6}$	2	3
	3	$4f$	$\sqrt{12}$	3	4

quantum mechanical and the Sommerfeld model, together with the commonly used electron notation. Also shown, for comparison, are the values of k according to the Bohr-Sommerfeld model. Figure 10.1 shows the corresponding orbits for $n = 3$ for the three models.

According to the Bohr-Sommerfeld model, the principal quantum-number n determines the energy of the state; n and the azimuthal quantum-number k together determine the size and shape of the orbit, while the magnetic quantum-number m determines the orientation in space. The magnitudes of the orbital (or azimuthal) angular momentum and its z component are given by $k\hbar$ and $m\hbar$, respectively. In order to be in accord with the quantum-mechanical model (old as well as new), k must be replaced by l. According to the Sommerfeld model, the orbital quantum-number l is given by $l = k - 1$, and the magnitude of the orbital angular-momentum vector, $\mathbf{L}$, is $l\hbar$. According to the quantum-mechanical model the orbital quantum number l is related to k by the same relation, i.e., $l = k - 1$, but the magnitude of the orbital angular momentum vector is L, where $L = \sqrt{l(l+1)}\,\hbar$. Hence according to quantum mechanics

$$P_l \, (= P_\theta) = |\mathbf{L}| = L = \sqrt{l(l+1)}\,\hbar \qquad (10.1)$$

It is a common practice to refer to the value of the orbital angular momentum as $l\hbar$ but in actual numerical calculations we use the value $L = \sqrt{l(l+1)}\,\hbar$. As is obvious, for very large values of l, $\sqrt{l(l+1)}$ approaches l. The values of the z components, $L_z = m_l\hbar$ (from here on, we shall be using m_l instead of m), are the same according to these two models, as shown in Fig. 10.2. Thus

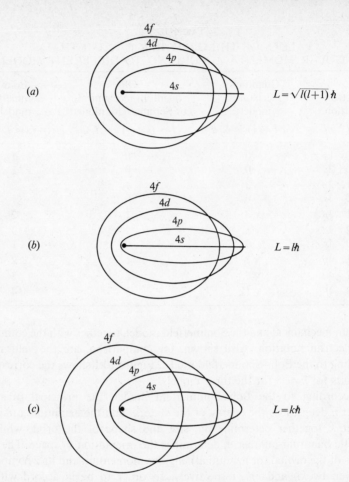

$$L = \sqrt{l(l+1)}\,\hbar$$

$$L = l\hbar$$

$$L = k\hbar$$

FIG. 10.1.   *The possible orbits of an electron for n = 3 according to* (a) *the quantum-mechanical model;* (b) *the old quantum-mechanical, or Sommerfeld, model; and* (c) *the Bohr-Sommerfeld model.*

we may conclude that even though the magnitudes of the orbital angular momenta are different according to these two models, the following relations are good for both:

$$n = 1, 2, 3, 4, \ldots, \infty$$

for a given n,

$$l = 0, 1, 2, 3, \ldots, (n-1)$$

and for a given l, m_l has the values

$$m_l = -l, -(l-1), \ldots, -2, -1, 0, 1, 2, \ldots, (l-1)\ l$$

It must be remembered that the interpretation and use of the quantities L and L_z as vectors as shown in Fig. 10.2 is just a convenient method of

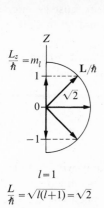
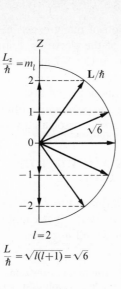
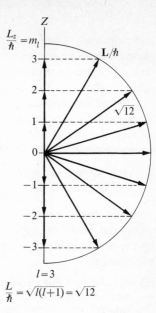

(a)

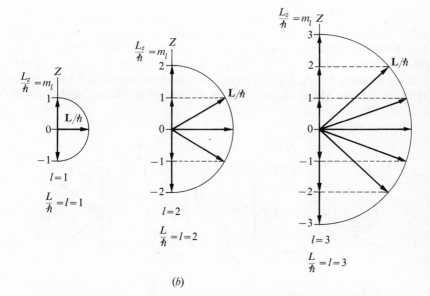

(b)

FIG. 10.2. The space quantization of orbital angular-momentum according to (a) the quantum-mechanical model, and (b) the Sommerfeld model.

341

representation in the interpretation of many experimental results to be discussed later. The actual motion of the electrons in an atom must be interpreted in terms of probabilities as in Fig. 9.7 and not as a motion in definite orbits as shown in Fig. 10.1.

Before we proceed with the discussion of atomic spectra, it is necessary to introduce the concept of spin angular-momentum associated with the electron and the spin quantum-number associated with it.

2. THE SPINNING ELECTRON AND THE TOTAL ANGULAR-MOMENTUM VECTOR

There are many aspects of atomic spectra associated not only with complex atoms but also with hydrogen-like atoms that cannot be explained entirely by the three quantum numbers n, l, and m_l. Some of the phenomena to be explained are:

(a) the observed fine structure, i.e., the many transitions that seem to be singlets when observed with low- or medium-resolution spectroscopes are actually doublets or triplets when observed with high-resolution equipment;
(b) the number of transitions observed when atoms are placed in an external magnetic field (known as the Zeeman effect) are many more than can be accounted for.

Thus it was necessary to associate some other angular momentum with the electron in the atom. This new angular momentum property was assigned to the electron in 1925 by Uhlenbeck and Goudsmit[5] and, independently, by Bichowsky and Urey[6]. According to them, an atomic electron in any state is assumed to be spinning about its own mechanical axis as a planet spins, or rotates, about its own axis, as shown in Fig. 10.3(a), and, thus, in

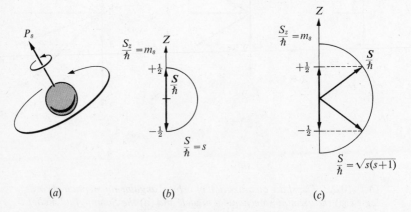

(a)   (b)   (c)

FIG. 10.3.   (a) *The spin of an electron about its own axis.* (b) *Space quantization of S according to the Sommerfeld model, resulting in $m_s = \pm\frac{1}{2}$.* (c) *Space quantization of S according to the quantum-mechanical model, resulting in $m_s = \pm\frac{1}{2}$.*

addition to the orbital angular-momentum, an electron is assigned a *spin angular-momentum*. In order to explain the doublet fine-structure in alkali metals and other observations, to be discussed later in this chapter, it is sufficient to assign spin angular-momentum p_s of only one-half a quantum unit of angular momentum, i.e.,

$$S(=p_s) = |\mathbf{S}| = s\hbar = \frac{1}{2}\hbar \qquad (10.2)$$

where s is called the spin quantum-number. Once again, as with other quantum numbers, S is space quantized, and m_s can take only one of two values:

$$m_s = +\frac{1}{2} \quad \text{or} \quad -\frac{1}{2} \qquad (10.3)$$

as shown in Fig. 10.3(b) and (c); m_s is called the *spin magnetic-quantum number*. Figure 10.3(b) and Fig. 10.3(c) show the space quantization according to the Sommerfeld and quantum-mechanical models, respectively. As shown in Fig. 10.3(c), for correct values of the magnitude according to quantum mechanics, we must use the value S, as

$$S = \sqrt{s(s+1)}\,\hbar = \sqrt{\frac{1}{2}\left(\frac{1}{2}+1\right)}\,\hbar = \frac{\sqrt{3}}{2}\hbar \qquad (10.4)$$

A direct experimental proof as to the existence of electron spin and its space quantization was given in an experiment by Stern and Gerlach to be discussed later in this chapter.

Thus the electron has two angular momenta, the orbital angular-momentum **L** and the spin angular-momentum **S**. These two angular momenta combine together to give the *total angular momentum* **J**, i.e.,

$$\mathbf{J} = \mathbf{L} + \mathbf{S}$$

where the magnitude of **J** is given by

$$|\mathbf{J}| = J = \sqrt{j(j+1)}\,\hbar \qquad (10.5)$$

Because **L** and **S** are both quantized, **J** must also be quantized; j is called the *total angular-momentum-quantum number*. With respect to the direction of the orbital angular momentum vector **L**, **S** can take two values: either parallel to it or antiparallel to it (exact alignment is not possible according to quantum mechanics). Hence, j can have the two values:

$$j = l + \frac{1}{2}$$

and

$$j = l - \frac{1}{2} \qquad (10.6)$$

Thus for $l = 1$, $j = 3/2$ or $1/2$; $l = 2$ gives $j = 5/2$ or $3/2$; while for $l = 0$, we get $j = 1/2$. Thus all the l-states are doublets with total angular momentum quantum number $j = l + 1/2$ and $j = l - 1/2$ except for the s-state ($l = 0$), which is a singlet with $j = 1/2$. Figure 10.4 illustrates the coupling between L and S according to the Sommerfeld model while Fig. 10.5 demon-

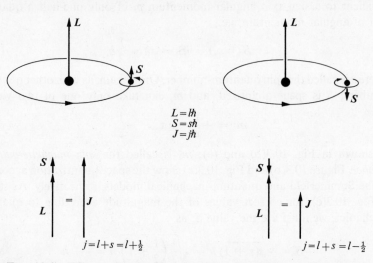

$$L = l\hbar$$
$$S = s\hbar$$
$$J = j\hbar$$

$$j = l + s = l + \tfrac{1}{2}$$

$$j = l + s = l - \tfrac{1}{2}$$

FIG. 10.4.   *The coupling between the vectors L and S according to the Sommerfeld model (old quantum model). Note that $L = l\hbar$ and $S = s\hbar$.*

strates the quantum mechanical coupling scheme. We may once again note that it is convenient to use l, s, and j as quantum numbers, but in actual calculations we must use the wave-mechanically correct values of L, S, and J, where (with angular momentum in units of $\hbar$)

$$\frac{L}{\hbar} = \sqrt{l(l + 1)}$$

$$\frac{S}{\hbar} = \sqrt{s(s + 1)} \tag{10.7}$$

$$\frac{J}{\hbar} = \sqrt{j(j + 1)}$$

For example, for an s-electron, (not to be confused with the spin quantum number s), $l = 0$, $s = 1/2$, $j = 1/2$ we get $L/\hbar = 0$, $S/\hbar = \sqrt{\tfrac{1}{2}(\tfrac{1}{2} + 1)} = \sqrt{3}/2$ and $J/\hbar = \sqrt{\tfrac{1}{2}(\tfrac{1}{2} + 1)} = \sqrt{3}/2$. For a p-electron, $l = 1$, $s = 1/2$, $j = 3/2$ or $1/2$, we get $L/\hbar = \sqrt{l(l + 1)} = \sqrt{2}$, $S/\hbar = \sqrt{\tfrac{1}{2}(\tfrac{1}{2} + 1)} = \sqrt{3}/2$; while $J/\hbar$ has two values $\sqrt{\tfrac{3}{2}(\tfrac{3}{2} + 1)} = \sqrt{15}/2$ and $\sqrt{\tfrac{1}{2}(\tfrac{1}{2} + 1)} = \sqrt{3}/2$. Similarly, for a d-electron, $l = 2$, $s = 1/2$, $j = 5/2$ or $3/2$; while $J/\hbar$ has the two values $\sqrt{\tfrac{5}{2}(\tfrac{5}{2} + 1)} = \sqrt{35}/2$ and $\sqrt{\tfrac{3}{2}(\tfrac{3}{2} + 1)} = \sqrt{15}/2$. In the same manner we can calculate $J/\hbar$ for higher orbital angular-momentum states.

Because of the quantization of L and S, the angular momenta add together only at certain angles. Using Fig. 10.5 and the law of cosines we can calculate the angle θ between L and S at which these two vectors add. Thus from Fig. 10.5

$$J^2 = L^2 + S^2 + 2LS \cos \theta \qquad (10.8)$$

or

$$j(j + 1)\hbar^2 = l(l + 1)\hbar^2 + s(s + 1)\hbar^2 + 2\sqrt{l(l + 1)}\sqrt{s(s + 1)}\,\hbar^2 \cos \theta \quad (10.9)$$

cancelling $\hbar^2$ and rewriting Eq. (10.9),

$$\cos \theta = \frac{j(j + 1) - l(l + 1) - s(s + 1)}{2\sqrt{l(l + 1)}\sqrt{s(s + 1)}} \qquad (10.10)$$

Thus for $l = 1, s = 1/2, j = 3/2$ or $1/2$. If $j = 3/2$, $\cos \theta = 1/\sqrt{6}$ or $\theta = 66°$, and if $j = 1/2$, $\cos \theta = 2/\sqrt{6}$ or $\theta = 145°$.

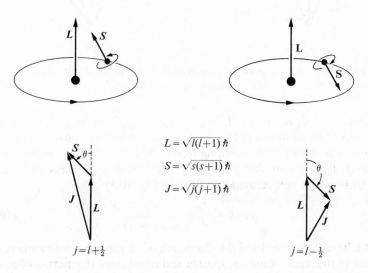

$$L = \sqrt{l(l+1)}\,\hbar$$
$$S = \sqrt{s(s+1)}\,\hbar$$
$$J = \sqrt{j(j+1)}\,\hbar$$

$$j = l + \tfrac{1}{2} \qquad\qquad j = l - \tfrac{1}{2}$$

FIG. 10.5.   *The coupling between the vectors* L *and* S *according to the quantum mechanical (wave mechanical) model. Note that* $L = \sqrt{l(l + 1)}\,\hbar$ *and* $S = \sqrt{s(s + 1)}\,\hbar$.

Because L and S both show space quantization, J must also show space quantization. Both L and S precess about J in a manner shown in Fig. 10.6(a). Furthermore, in the presence of an arbitrary axis, J will precess about this axis, say, the Z axis, as shown in Fig. 10.6(b). The space quantization rule requires that for a given j, the J vector precesses about the Z axis in such a manner so that the z component, J_z, resulting from the projection of J along the Z axis is given by

$$p_{jz} = J_z = m_j\hbar \qquad (10.11)$$

where m_j is the total magnetic quantum number which can take the following $(2j + 1$ values, each differing by unity, i.e.,

$$m_j = -j, -(j - 1), \ldots, (j - 1), j \qquad (10.12)$$

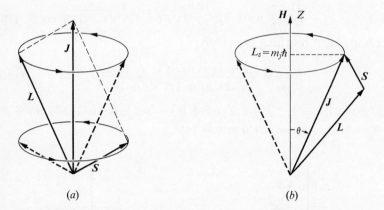

(a) (b)

FIG. 10.6.   (a) *The precession of both* **L** *and* **S** *about* **J**. (b) *The space quantization of the total angular-momentum vector* **J**.

Thus for $j = 1/2$, $m_j = +1/2$, $-1/2$; for $j = 3/2$, $m_j = 3/2$, $1/2$, $-1/2$, $-3/2$ and so on as shown in Fig. 10.7. Note that only the quantum mechanical picture is shown, and according to this **J** (as was the case with **L** and **S**) can never align exactly along the Z axis. The relation between m_j and j is given by (θ not to be confused with that in Fig. 10.5)

$$\cos \theta = \frac{J_z}{J} = \frac{m_j}{\sqrt{j(j + 1)}} \qquad (10.13)$$

We have now completed the discussion of all the quantum numbers that are used in the study of atomic spectra and result from the motion of atomic electrons. To summarize:

(a)   The total quantum-number, n, which determines the energy of the state, can take the values:

$$n = 1, 2, 3, 4, 5, \ldots, \infty$$

(b)   The orbital quantum-number, l, which determines the magnitude of the orbital angular-momentum, and, which for a given value of n, can take the values:

$$l = 0, 1, 2, 3, 4, \ldots, n - 1$$

(c)   The orbital magnetic quantum-number, m_l, which determines the z component of the orbital angular-momentum also determines the orientation of the orbital motion. For a given value of l, m_l can take the following $(2l + 1)$ values:

$$m_l = -l, -(l - 1), \ldots, -2, -1, 0, +1, +2, \ldots, (l - 1), l$$

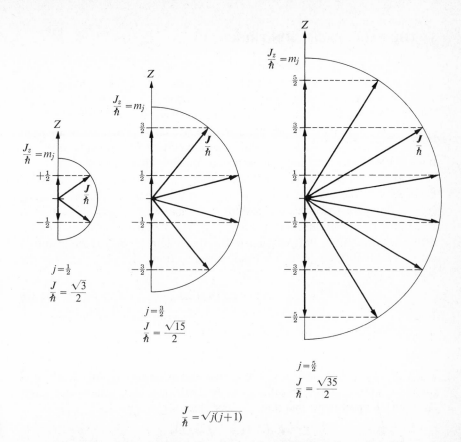

FIG. 10.7.   *The possible values of m_j for different values of j. The figure is drawn according to the quantum-mechanical model for which $J = \sqrt{j(j+1)}\,\hbar$.*

(d)   Each electron has an intrinsic angular momentum $\sqrt{s(s+1)}\,\hbar$, where the spin quantum-number, s, has only one value $s = \tfrac{1}{2}$, while m_s can take $(2s+1) = 2$ values, i.e.,

$$m_s = +\frac{1}{2} \quad \text{or} \quad -\frac{1}{2}$$

(e)   The total angular momentum quantum-number j can take two values $l + \tfrac{1}{2}$ and $l - \tfrac{1}{2}$. For a given value of j, m_j can take $(2j+1)$ values, i.e.,

$$m_j = -j, -(j-1), \ldots, -1, 0, +1, \ldots, (j-1), j$$

Before we examine the experimental proof of these quantization rules, out of necessity we must consider the Pauli exclusion principle. Because in any atom, except hydrogen, there are more than one electron, we must assign some order to the electrons inside the atom. The Pauli exclusion principle leads us to that order.

3. THE PAULI EXCLUSION PRINCIPLE

All electrons in any one state are identical with respect to their mass, charge, spin, and magnetic moment. An atom with many electrons is equivalent to a system containing many indistinguishable identical particles. Although we have all the quantum numbers needed to identify the quantum state of an electron, one question remains unanswered: Are all the electrons in an atom in one quantum state or in different quantum states? Experimental observations led W. Pauli[7] to state an exclusion principle that answered this.

Let us consider a system of N noninteracting, identical, indistinguishable particles. Let the wave functions of each of these particles be $\psi_\alpha(1)$, $\psi_\beta(2)$, $\psi_\gamma(3)$, . . . where 1 denotes the position coordinates (x_1, y_1, z_1) of particle 1, 2 denotes the position coordinates (x_2, y_2, z_2) of particle 2, etc.; while α denotes the quantum state of particle 1 in the system, β denotes the quantum state of particle 2, etc. Thus the total wave function $\psi(1, 2, 3, . . . , N)$ of the system is given by

$$\psi(1, 2, 3, . . . , N) = \psi_\alpha(1)\psi_\beta(2)\psi_\gamma(3) . . . \psi_\nu(N) \tag{10.14}$$

For simplicity let us assume that the system consists of only two noninteracting, identical particles for which Eq. (10.14) reduces to

$$\psi_{\alpha\beta}(1, 2) = \psi_\alpha(1)\psi_\beta(2) \tag{10.15}$$

$\psi_{\alpha\beta}(1, 2)$ means that particle 1 is in a quantum-state α, and particle 2 is in a quantum-state β. If the positions of the two identical particles are interchanged, the new wave function of the system is given by

$$\psi_{\alpha\beta}(2, 1) = \psi_\alpha(2)\psi_\beta(1) \tag{10.16}$$

i.e., particle 2 is in quantum-state α, while particle 1 is in quantum-state β. Because the particles are identical, the exchange of their positions should not change the probability density of the system, i.e., from Eq. (10.15) and Eq. (10.16)

$$|\psi_{\alpha\beta}(1, 2)|^2 = |\psi_{\alpha\beta}(2, 1)|^2 \tag{10.17}$$

Therefore, either

$$\psi_{\alpha\beta}(2, 1) = +\psi_{\alpha\beta}(1, 2) \tag{10.18}$$

or

$$\psi_{\alpha\beta}(2, 1) = -\psi_{\alpha\beta}(1, 2) \tag{10.19}$$

Equation (10.18) states that if identical particles are exchanged, the exchanged wave function is the same as the initial wave function, while according to Eq. (10.19) the exchanged wave function has an opposite sign. The wave functions that do not change sign on exchange of positions are called *symmetric*, while those that do change sign are called *antisymmetric* wave functions. The probability density, however, according to Eq. (10.17) is not changed whether the wave function is symmetric or antisymmetric.

For a system of two identical particles, it is impossible to find out whether the particles are in such states that the system is described by the wave function $\psi_{\alpha\beta}(1, 2)$ given by Eq. (10.15) or that the system is described by the wave function $\psi_{\alpha\beta}(2, 1)$ given by Eq. (10.16). We may say that there is equal likelihood that the system is to be found in state $\psi_{\alpha\beta}(1, 2)$ and state $\psi_{\alpha\beta}(2, 1)$. Thus the linear combinations of these two wave functions should yield the eigenfunctions of the system. Two such linear combinations are possible. The *symmetric eigenfunction* ψ_S

$$\psi_S = \frac{1}{\sqrt{2}} [\psi_{\alpha\beta}(1, 2) + \psi_{\alpha\beta}(2, 1)] \tag{10.20}$$

and the *antisymmetric eigenfunction* ψ_A

$$\psi_A = \frac{1}{\sqrt{2}} [\psi_{\alpha\beta}(1, 2) - \psi_{\alpha\beta}(2, 1)] \tag{10.21}$$

where the factor $1/\sqrt{2}$ is the necessary normalization factor. Even though ψ_A changes sign with the exchange of particles, both ψ_A and ψ_S are the solutions of the Schrödinger equation. The total energy of the system corresponding to $\psi_{\alpha\beta}(1, 2)$ is the same as that corresponding to $\psi_{\alpha\beta}(2, 1)$ and hence the states are degenerate. This is called the *exchange degeneracy*.

Thus we conclude that the wave function of the two noninteracting identical particles is either symmetric or antisymmetric. In a real system of interacting identical particles, such as electrons in an atom, one would like to know if the eigenfunctions of the system have definite symmetry, either symmetric or antisymmetric. Quantum mechanics is unable to answer this question, and we must look for the answer elsewhere.

Before the application of quantum mechanics, Pauli, in 1925, from the analysis of experimental data of the energy levels of certain atoms, stated: *No two electrons in any multi-electron atom can be in the same quantum state.* This is known as the *Pauli exclusion principle*, and it means that all the electrons in any atom are in different quantum states. If this were not so, say, for a system of two particles, $\alpha = \beta$, then from Eq. (10.21)

$$\psi_A = \frac{1}{\sqrt{2}} [\psi_{\alpha\alpha}(1, 2) - \psi_{\alpha\alpha}(2, 1)]$$

$$= \frac{1}{\sqrt{2}} [\psi_\alpha(1)\psi_\alpha(2) - \psi_\alpha(2)\psi_\alpha(1)] \tag{10.22}$$

$$= 0$$

i.e., ψ_A, the antisymmetric eigenfunction, vanishes if we assume that the two particles can be in the same quantum state. Thus for ψ_A to be nonvanishing, $\alpha \neq \beta$, i.e., the Pauli exclusion principle must be obeyed for identical particles. Accordingly, we may summarize: *The eigenfunction of the system containing several electrons, such as electrons in an atom, must be antisymmetric.*

Equation (10.21) may be written in the determinant form as

$$\psi_A = \frac{1}{\sqrt{2}} \left[\psi_{\alpha\beta}(1, 2) - \psi_{\alpha\beta}(2, 1) \right]$$

$$= \frac{1}{\sqrt{2}} \left[\psi_\alpha(1)\psi_\beta(2) - \psi_\beta(1)\psi_\alpha(2) \right]$$

or

$$\psi_A = \frac{1}{\sqrt{2}} \begin{pmatrix} \psi_\alpha(1) & \psi_\alpha(2) \\ \psi_\beta(1) & \psi_\beta(2) \end{pmatrix} \tag{10.23}$$

The antisymmetric eigenfunction for the system of N noninteracting identical particles may be written by the extension of Eq. (10.23) in the form of a scalar determinant

$$\psi_A = \frac{1}{\sqrt{N!}} \begin{pmatrix} \psi_\alpha(1) & \psi_\alpha(2) & \ldots & \psi_\alpha(N) \\ \psi_\beta(1) & \psi_\beta(2) & \ldots & \psi_\beta(N) \\ \ldots & \ldots & \ldots & \ldots \\ \ldots & \ldots & \ldots & \ldots \\ \psi_\nu(1) & \psi_\nu(2) & \ldots & \psi_\nu(N) \end{pmatrix} \tag{10.24}$$

Notice that ψ_A given by Eq. (10.24) will vanish if any two particles are in the same quantum state, i.e., for ψ_A to be nonvanishing all the quantum states $\alpha, \beta, \gamma, \ldots, \nu$ are nonidentical.

Thus far we have established that for several electrons in an atom that constitutes a system of identical particles, the wave function of the system must be antisymmetric, i.e., no two electrons in an atom can be in the same quantum state. Our next problem is to designate the state of an electron in an atom. The position of the electron in an atom is given by three coordinates, x, y, z (or r, θ, ϕ), and its spin state. Thus an electron in a given quantum state is described completely by a set of four quantum numbers. In the presence of a strong magnetic field, the set of four quantum numbers used are n, l, m_l, and m_s; while in a weak field or in no field, the set of four quantum numbers used are n, l, j, and m_j. We may imagine an atom in a magnetic field, which is then reduced to zero in intensity; we then have a preferred direction but no field. Hence, we may use either of the two sets to specify the state of an electron in an atom. We may then restate the Pauli exclusion principle as: *No two electrons in an atom may have identical values for a set of four quantum numbers* $(n, l, m_l, m_s;$ *or* $n, l, j, m_j)$.

Thus, for example, the helium atom has two electrons; for both electrons, three quantum numbers are the same $n = 1$, $l = 0$, $m_l = 0$. For the Pauli exclusion principle to be true, the fourth quantum number, m_s, must differ for the two electrons, i.e., $m_s = +\frac{1}{2}$ for one electron and $m_s = -\frac{1}{2}$ for the other electron. If both electrons had $m_s = \frac{1}{2}$, the ground state of helium will have a total spin quantum number of unity. But the transitions to and from the ground state with a spin of unity have not been observed, and hence m_s for the two electrons is not the same. The ground-state spin of the helium atom is zero, and the quantum states of the two electrons are $(1, 0, 0, \frac{1}{2})$ and $(1, 0, 0, -\frac{1}{2})$. Observations like these in experimental data led Pauli to state his exclusion principle. We can extend the exclusion principle to many more particles other than electrons.

Any system of identical particles each having a spin $\frac{1}{2}$ has an antisymmetric wave function with respect to the exchange of two particles in the system. All such systems obey the Pauli exclusion principle. Particles with spin $\frac{1}{2}$ are called *Fermi particles*, or *fermions*, because the system of Fermi particles obeys Fermi-Dirac statistics. Other examples of fermions obeying the Pauli exclusion principle are protons, neutrons, and μ-mesons.

Any system of identical particles each having a 0 or integral spin-value has a symmetric wave function with respect to the exchange of any two particles in the system. Such systems do not obey the Pauli exclusion principle. Particles with 0 or integral spin value are called *Bose particles* or *bosons*, because the system of Bose particles obeys Bose-Einstein statistics. Examples of Bose particles are photons, helium atoms, α-particles, and π-mesons.

4. ELECTRON CONFIGURATIONS

To determine the electronic structures of atoms, we must assign quantum states to the electrons in a given atom, for which we use two principles:

(1) Any system of particles must be stable when its total energy is negative.
(2) The use of the Pauli exclusion principle avoids the assignment of more than one electron into a given quantum state.

In assigning quantum states, we shall use the four quantum numbers n, l, m_l, and m_s ; (although the use of the other set, n, l, j, and m_j, gives the same results). The electrons that have the same principal quantum-number n are said to be in the same *group*, *shell*, or *energy level*. For a given value of n, those electrons that have the same value of l are said to be in the same *subgroup*, *subshell*, or *sublevel*. We should note that the differences in the energies of the different n-states are much greater than the energy differences for different l values in a given group. In the discussion of the periodic table and x-rays, $n = 1$ is denoted K shell, $n = 2$ is L shell, $n = 3$ is M shell, $n = 4$ is N shell, etc.

We shall now start with the calculation of the total number of electrons in different quantum states in a given shell and subshell. For a given value of l, m_l has $(2l + 1)$ different values, and for each m_l there are two different values of m_s $(= \pm \frac{1}{2})$. Thus in a given subgroup, there are $2(2l + 1)$ combinations of l, m_l, and m_s, none of which have all the same three quantum numbers. For a given n there are n different values of l, 0, 1, 2, $\ldots$, $n - 1$.

Thus the total number of different quantum states, N_t, for a given n are given by

$$N_t = \sum_{l=0}^{n-1} 2(2l + 1)$$

$$= 2[1 + 3 + 5 + 7 + \ldots + (2n - 1)]$$

$$= 2\left[n\left\{\frac{1 + (2n - 1)}{2}\right\}\right]$$

$$= 2n^2$$

$$(10.25)$$

Table 10.2 gives the quantum numbers n, l, m_l, and m_s for different quantum states in different shells. For a given quantum state, found in the column at the left, one reads horizontally across to find the quantum numbers, n, l, m_l, and m_s, in that order. As is obvious from this table, no two quantum states have all four quantum numbers the same. One of the facts that is obvious from this table is that the sums of m_l and m_s are zero for any complete subgroup or subshell, i.e., $\Sigma m_l = 0$ and $\Sigma m_s = 0$; which means $s = 0$ and $l = 0$, and hence $j = 0$.

Using Table 10.2, quantum states may be determined for the electrons of any complex atom. For the hydrogen atom where $Z = 1$, the value of $N_t = 1$ read across identifies the quantum state of the electron as $(1, 0, 0, \frac{1}{2})$. For nitrogen where $Z = 7$, all of the quantum states up to and including $N_t = 7$ are the quantum states of the seven electrons of the nitrogen atom. Similarly for sodium, where $Z = 11$, all of the quantum states up to and including $N_t = 11$ are the quantum states of the 11 electrons of the sodium atom. The normal, or ground, state of an atom described by the quantum numbers of each electron in that atom is the electron configuration of that atom.

An abbreviated form in which to give the values of these states is the following. For hydrogen, for example, we write the ground state configuration as $1s^1$, which means $n = 1$ (the first number); $l = 0$ (the letter s stands for $l = 0$); and the superscript gives the number of electrons in the substate, which in this case denotes that there is only one electron in this substate. For nitrogen, for which $Z = 7$, we write $1s^2 2s^2 2p^3$, which means there are two electrons in the $n = 1$, $l = 0$ state; two electrons in $n = 2$, $l = 0$ state; and three electrons in $n = 2$, $l = 1$ state. Similarly, the electron configuration of sodium, for which $Z = 11$, is given by

$$1s^2 2s^2 2p^6 3s^1$$

which says that the first two shells and their subshells are completely filled with 10 electrons while the eleventh electron of sodium is in the $n = 3$, $l = 0$ state. The electron configurations of the atoms that correspond to the closing of the subshell and shell are shown in the column at the right in Table 10.2.

The corresponding number of electrons in each of these atoms may be read from the column at the left.

Another convenient display of electron configuration is an energy level diagram with $m_s = +\frac{1}{2}$ pointing up and $m_s = -\frac{1}{2}$ pointing down. A representation corresponding to Table 10.2 is shown in Fig. 10.8. As examples, the electron configurations of $_1$H, $_7$N, and $_{11}$Na are shown in Fig. 10.9.

The actual order of the levels that gives the minimum energy for the atoms to be stable is

$$1s^2 2s^2 2p^6 3s^2 3p^6 4s^2 3d^{10} 4p^6 5s^2 4d^{10} 5p^6 6s^2 4f^{14} 5d^{10} 6p^6 7s^2 6d^{10}$$

and note that it does not follow the sequence of increasing n and l values.

5. THE SPECTRA OF ALKALI METALS

We have been discussing in detail both the theoretical as well as the experimental aspects of the hydrogen spectrum. It is natural to extend the results of wave mechanics in order to explain the experimentally observed spectra of complex atoms. But mathematical difficulties prohibit us from making exact quantum mechanical calculations for atoms other than hydrogen and helium. Our first attempt will be to explain the optical spectra of the alkali metals, which are the simplest of all, after the hydrogen atom. The discussion will be carried out under the following subheadings:

A. The General Characteristics of the Energy Levels of Alkali Atoms
B. Penetrating and Nonpenetrating Orbits; Quantum Defect and Screening Parameter
C. Fine Structure of Alkali-Type Spectra Due to Spin-Orbit Coupling
D. Summary of the Selection Rules and the Intensity Rules

A. The General Characteristics of the Energy Levels of Alkali Atoms

The alkali metals that make up the first group of the periodic table, together with hydrogen are: hydrogen, H, ($Z = 1$); lithium, Li, ($Z = 3$); sodium, Na, ($Z = 11$); potassium, K, ($Z = 19$); rubidium, Rb, ($Z = 37$); and cesium, Cs, ($Z = 55$). Even though the atoms of these elements contain different numbers of electrons, they have one important common factor that becomes obvious in examining the normal configurations of these atoms, as shown in Table 10.3. The last electron of each atom is in the s-state ($l = 0$ state); $1s$, $2s$, $3s$, $4s$, $5s$, and $6s$, respectively, for H, Li, Na, K, Rb, and Cs. These s-states are the ground states of these atoms. The electron in the ground state is called the valence electron (in chemistry) or the optical electron (in spectroscopy). In each of these atoms, all the electrons, except the optical electron, form completely filled shells or subshells, and hence do not contribute to the spin, orbital, or total angular-momenta of the atom. Each alkali atom, there-

TABLE 10.2
NUMBER OF QUANTUM STATES IN DIFFERENT SHELLS

Quantum states, N_l, or number of electron	n	l	m_l	m_s	Number of electrons in the subshell N_l	Number of electrons in the closed shell	Electron configuration at closed shells and subshells
1	1	0	0	$+\tfrac{1}{2}$			
2	1	0	0	$-\tfrac{1}{2}$	2	2	$1s^2$
3	2	0	0	$+\tfrac{1}{2}$			
4	2	0	0	$-\tfrac{1}{2}$	2		$1s^2 2s^2$
5	2	1	-1	$+\tfrac{1}{2}$			
6	2	1	-1	$-\tfrac{1}{2}$			
7	2	1	0	$+\tfrac{1}{2}$			
8	2	1	0	$-\tfrac{1}{2}$			
9	2	1	$+1$	$+\tfrac{1}{2}$			
10	2	1	$+1$	$-\tfrac{1}{2}$	6	8	$1s^2 2s^2 2p^6$
11	3	0	0	$+\tfrac{1}{2}$			
12	3	0	0	$-\tfrac{1}{2}$	2		$1s^2 2s^2 2p^6 3s^2$
13	3	1	-1	$+\tfrac{1}{2}$			
14	3	1	-1	$-\tfrac{1}{2}$			
15	3	1	0	$+\tfrac{1}{2}$			
16	3	1	0	$-\tfrac{1}{2}$			

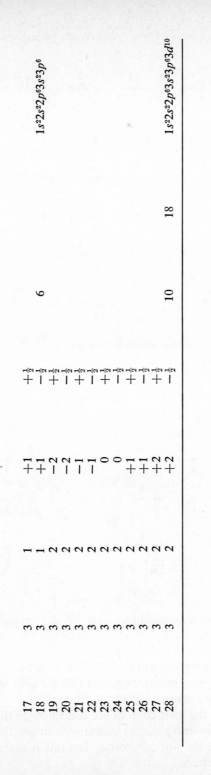

17	3	1	+1	$+\frac{1}{2}$			
18	3	1	+1	$-\frac{1}{2}$	6	18	$1s^22s^22p^63s^23p^6$
19	3	2	-2	$+\frac{1}{2}$			
20	3	2	-2	$-\frac{1}{2}$			
21	3	2	-1	$+\frac{1}{2}$			
22	3	2	-1	$-\frac{1}{2}$			
23	3	2	0	$+\frac{1}{2}$			
24	3	2	0	$-\frac{1}{2}$	10		
25	3	2	+1	$+\frac{1}{2}$			
26	3	2	+1	$-\frac{1}{2}$			
27	3	2	+2	$+\frac{1}{2}$			
28	3	2	+2	$-\frac{1}{2}$		10	$1s^22s^22p^63s^23p^63d^{10}$

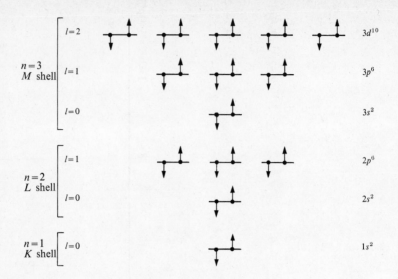

FIG. 10.8. *Electron configurations in atoms.*

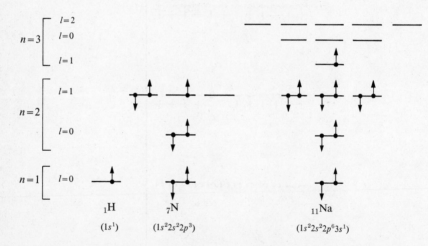

FIG. 10.9. *Electron configurations of $_1H$, $_7N$, and $_{11}Na$ atoms.*

fore, consists of (i) the nucleus, (ii) the "inert" core of electrons that does not contribute to the angular momentum, and (iii) the optical, or the valence, electron in one of the *s* states.

The electrons in the inert core do not contribute to the atomic spectra, however, even at low energies, the *s*-electron outside the core is readily excited and produces the optical spectra. For this reason, the *s*-electron is called the optical electron.

TABLE 10.3

ELECTRON CONFIGURATIONS FOR THE ALKALI ATOMS AND HYDROGEN IN NORMAL STATES

Element	K	L	M	N	O	P	Singly ionized alkaline-earth
	$l = 0$	0 1	0 1 2	0 1 2 3	0 1 2 3 4	0 1 2 3 4 5	
$_1$H	**1s**						$_2$He$^+$
$_3$Li	$1s^2$	**2s**					$_4$Be$^+$
$_{11}$Na	$1s^2$	$2s^2\ 2p^6$	**3s**				$_{12}$Mg$^+$
$_{19}$K	$1s^2$	$2s^2\ 2p^6$	$3s^2\ 3p^6$	**4s**			$_{20}$Ca$^+$
$_{37}$Rb	$1s^2$	$2s^2\ 2p^6$	$3s^2\ 3p^6\ 3d^{10}$	$4s^2\ 4p^6$	**5s**		$_{38}$Sr$^+$
$_{55}$Cs	$1s^2$	$2s^2\ 2p^6$	$3s^2\ 3p^6\ 3d^{10}$	$4s^2\ 4p^6\ 4d^{10}$	$5s^2\ 5p^6\ .\ .\ .$	**6s**	$_{56}$Ba$^+$

The elements in the second group of the periodic table, the alkaline-earth elements, together with helium, are He ($Z = 2$), Be ($Z = 4$), Mg ($Z = 12$), Ca ($Z = 20$), Sr ($Z = 38$), and Ba ($Z = 56$). If these atoms are singly ionized, i.e., He$^+$, Be$^+$, Mg$^+$, Ca$^+$, Sr$^+$, and Ba$^+$, they will have configurations similar to corresponding alkali metals as shown in Table 10.3. Thus these singly ionized atoms should show spectra similar to the alkali metals.

Figure 10.10 clearly illustrates the differences between these four types of atoms

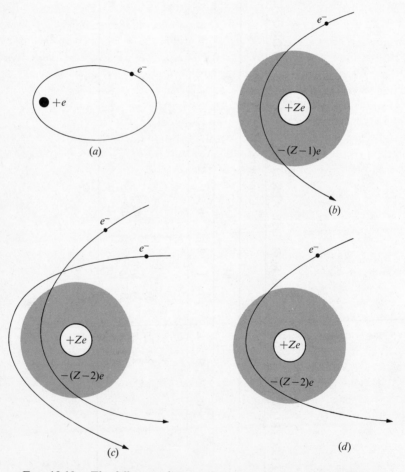

FIG. 10.10. *The differences between four types of atoms:* (a) *the hydrogen atom,* (b) *the alkali-metal atoms,* (c) *the alkaline-earth atoms, and* (d) *the singly ionized alkaline-earth atoms. The nucleus is surrounded by a core of electrons, the shielding electrons, that provides a shield between the nucleus and the optical electrons.*

(a) the hydrogen atom,
(b) the alkali-metal atoms,
(c) the alkaline-earth atoms, and
(d) the singly ionized alkaline-earth atoms.

In contrast to the hydrogen atom, in the alkali-metal atoms the optical electron moves in the net field of the nucleus of charge $+Ze$ and a charge of $-(Z - 1)e$ due to the shielding electrons. This shielding of the nucleus causes shifts in the energy levels of the same n but different l, as we shall discuss later. For the sake of comparison, Fig. 10.10(c) illustrates the alkaline-earth atom in which there are two optical electrons moving in the net field due to the nuclear charge $+Ze$ and the charge $-(Z - 2)e$ of the shielding electrons. If the alkaline-earth atom is singly ionized, as shown in Fig. 10.10(d), there is now only one optical electron; this parallels the condition of the alkali-metal atom shown in Fig. 10.10(b) except that the shielding is due to $(Z - 2)$ electrons instead of $(Z - 1)$ electrons. Thus except for the relative differences in the energies, the alkali-metal atoms and singly ionized alkaline earths show similar spectra. If we stretch our imagination still further, we may say that the spectra of doubly ionized atoms of boron or aluminum will be very similar to the spectra discussed above, and so on.

Before proceeding further we may generalize the notation commonly used for complex atoms. The following identification scheme is used to denote orbital angular momentum quantum states

$$l = 0, 1, 2, 3, 4, 5, 6, 7, \ldots$$
$$\text{letter notation} = S, P, D, F, G, H, I, J, \ldots$$

(10.26)

The letter is always preceded by a number that indicates the value of the principal quantum number, n. Thus, for example, $1S$ stands for $n = 1, l = 0$; $3S$ stands for $n = 3, l = 0$; $4P$ stands for $n = 4, l = 1$; $3D$ stands for $n = 3$, $l = 2$, and so on.

In our preliminary discussion, let us neglect the relativistic effects and the spin-orbit coupling effect. Neglecting the spin-orbit effect means that we are assuming that the electron has no intrinsic spin angular-momentum, i.e., instead of $s = \frac{1}{2}$, we assume $s = 0$. If these two assumptions are made, the energy level diagram of sodium, which is typical of the alkali metals, along with the possible transitions between levels, is as shown in Fig. 10.11(a). The energy levels are shown as horizontal lines. For comparison the energy-level diagram of hydrogen is shown in Fig. 10.11(b). As is obvious, any n-level of hydrogen is degenerate as shown at the extreme right of the diagram, i.e., for a given n, all corresponding orbital states have the same energy. In the case of sodium, the degeneracy has been removed, i.e., different orbital states of a given n have different energies as shown in Fig. 10.11(a). The reason for the removal of this degeneracy in the case of sodium is that the effect of electron shielding as shown in Fig. 10.10(b) differs for different orbital states. The effect depends upon the shape of the orbit (according to classical theory)

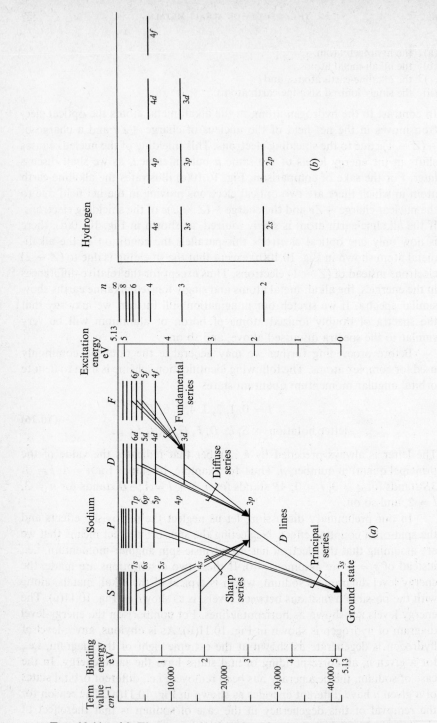

FIG. 10.11. (a) *The energy level diagram of sodium (neglecting spin and relativistic corrections) is indicated by the short horizontal lines. The slant lines are the possible transitions between different levels.* (b) *The energy level diagram of hydrogen.*

or the probability density (according to the wave mechanics) of the optical, or ground, state electron. For sodium the first two shells corresponding to $n = 1$ and $n = 2$ are completely filled with a total of ten electrons, denoted by $1s^2 2s^2 2p^6$, while the eleventh electron is in the $3S$ state, which is the ground state of the sodium atom. Any excitation will result in the transformation of the $3S$ electron to higher energy levels like $3P$, $4S$, $3D$, $4P$, $5S$, etc. The following features, to be justified later, may be deduced from the energy-level diagram of sodium.

(i) In a given n level, if the degeneracy is removed, the S-levels go down in energy much deeper than the P-levels, the P-levels more than D-levels, and the D-levels more than F-levels.

(ii) With increasing values of n, the corresponding depressions become smaller and smaller. Thus, for example, $5D$ and $5F$ levels of sodium coincide closely with the $n = 5$ level of hydrogen, and $6D$ and $6F$ with the $n = 6$ level, and so on. That is, in going from more elliptical s-orbits (S-states) to the less elliptical or more circular p-, d-, f-orbits (or P, D, F states), the levels approach those of the hydrogen atom.

Once the electron reaches one of the excited states, it comes to the ground state through different transitions. All such transitions must follow certain selection rules. Only those transitions are possible for which l changes by unity, i.e.,

$$\Delta l = \pm 1 \qquad\qquad (10.27)$$

which means according to the law of conservation of angular momentum, the photon must carry away a unit angular-momentum equal to $\hbar$ $(= h/2\pi)$. There is no restriction on the change in the value of n in any transition. This results in the transitions shown in Fig. 10.11(a). These transitions may be classified into the following four groups:

principal series	$nP \rightarrow 3S$	$n = 3, 4, 5, \ldots$	(P-series)
sharp series	$nS \rightarrow 3P$	$n = 4, 5, 6, \ldots$	(S-series)
diffuse series	$nD \rightarrow 3P$	$n = 3, 4, 5, \ldots$	(D-series)
fundamental series	$nF \rightarrow 3D$	$n = 4, 5, 6, \ldots$	(F-series)

$$(10.28)$$

Of these transitions, $3P \rightarrow 3S$ yields the most intense yellow D-lines of sodium. The labeling of the levels as S, P, D, and F and classifying the transitions as principal, sharp, diffuse, and fundamental is based on the terms used in spectroscopy. The lines of the S-series were found to be relatively sharp, and hence the name sharp series. The lines of the P-series were found both in emission and absorption spectra for relatively small excitation energies, and hence the name principal series. The lines of the D-series were found to be rather diffused and hence the name diffused series. The lines of the F-series lie in the infrared with the frequencies lower than any other series, and they come close to the frequencies of the fundamental hydrogen atom, and hence the name fundamental series.

We may point out that all these S-, P-, D-, and F-states are actually doublet levels as we shall find out when we discuss fine structure. Before going into fine structure we shall discuss how the shielding by the electrons has resulted in the removal of degeneracy of a level with same n but different l values.

B.   Penetrating and Nonpenetrating Orbits[8, 9]

In order to calculate the energy levels of sodium and other alkali-metal atoms, some model of the atom that is like hydrogen is required. Referring once again to Fig. 10.10(b), we see that the nucleus of charge $+Ze$ is surrounded by a core of $(Z - 1)$ electrons, which forms closed shells and subshells, while the single electron moves inside and outside the core. This makes the system seem hydrogen-like in that the system consists of a singly charged nucleus, equal to the net charge of the nucleus and the core of electrons, and a single valence electron.

According to the quantum-mechanical model, we first calculate the probability charge-density distribution for the neutral alkali atom and then calculate the relative distribution or probability density of the single valence electron. Detailed calculations have been made by Hartree[10] by using successive approximations leading to the method of a self-consistent field. Using this method, Hartree calculated the radial density-distribution for each core electron of a given alkali atom. The resulting electric field of all the core electrons must provide for solutions of the Schrödinger wave equation that will give a distribution of electrons that reproduces the field. Without going into the details of the calculations, we present the results in the form of plots in Fig. 10.12. The shaded areas in this figure show the probability charge-density distribution, $4\pi r^2 \psi^* \psi$, for core electrons of different alkali atoms, and the distribution for the valence electron in the normal state in each case. The humps in the core distribution correspond to the location of the K-, L-, M-, N-, O-shell electrons. The heavy dot on each horizontal axis shows the extremity of the classical orbit. Calculations similar to those of Hartree have been made by Pauling[11] who calculated these plots using hydrogen wave-functions and approximate methods, and also by Thomas[12] who used statistical methods.

Returning to the Hartree method, let us take the specific example of sodium shown in Fig. 10.13, where, in addition to the core radial probability-density distribution shown shaded, the distribution of the valence electron in the $3s$, $3p$, and $3d$ states is also shown. Equivalent to this quantum-mechanical model, the classical model is shown in Fig. 10.14. As is obvious from Fig. 10.13, the $3s$-electron penetrates into the shaded area, which is the nuclear core probability-density distribution, much more than the $3p$ electron, while as compared to the $3s$ and $3p$, the penetration of the $3d$ is almost negligible. Thus we classify the $3s$ and $3p$ as penetrating orbits, and the $3d$ as a nonpenetrating orbit. This is more obvious from the classical picture in Fig. 10.14.

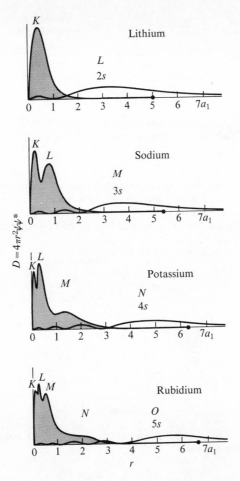

FIG. 10.12.   *The probability charge-density distribution, $4\pi r^2 \psi^* \psi$, for the core electrons (shaded areas) and the valence electrons in the normal state of different alkali atoms. [Printed with permission from White, H. E.,* Introduction to Atomic Spectra, *p. 101. New York: McGraw-Hill Book Company, 1934.]*

Because the $3d$ does not penetrate into the core, if the electron is in the $3d$ state, the system is almost hydrogen-like. Due to penetration, the effective charge for the $3s$ and $3p$ orbits is more than the hydrogen atom charge $(+e)$, and hence the orbits are greatly reduced in size radially. This means that the deviation from the hydrogen-like system results in more negative energy; the more the deviation, the deeper will be the depression of the level from the corresponding hydrogen level. Thus for any value of n, the lower l values will have more negative energies, e.g., the S-state lies lower than the P-state,

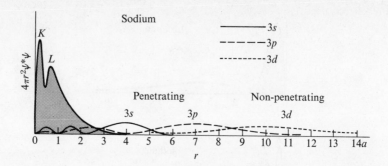

FIG. 10.13.   *The core radial probability-density distribution, shaded area, and the distribution of valence electrons in the 3s-, 3p-, and 3d-states for sodium.* [*Printed with permission from White, H. E.,* Introduction to Atomic Spectra, *p. 103. New York: McGraw-Hill Book Company, 1934.*]

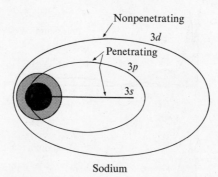

FIG. 10.14.   *The classical model of the core and the valence-electron distribution for sodium.*

the *P*-state lies lower than the *D*-state, and so on. That such is actually the case is seen from the energy-level diagram of sodium in Fig. 10.11(a).

We now turn our attention to the nonpenetrating orbits, which are defined as those orbits for which the experimentally observed energies are nearly equal to the corresponding hydrogen-atom orbits. For such states the orbital quantum number *l* is nearly equal to the total quantum number *n*. The best example is offered by the 4*f*, 5*f*, etc., states in Fig. 10.11(a), which come close to the corresponding hydrogen levels. In general, even for the nonpenetrating orbits there is always a small depression of the levels (and hence the term values are generally greater than for the hydrogen atom). This difference has been explained by Born and Heisenberg[13] as being due to the polarization of the core by the valence electron. The valence electron pulls (attracts) the nucleus while it pushes away (repels) the core electrons. The net result is a decrease in the total energy of the system. Such calculations of the polarization effect have been made by Pauling and Goudsmit[14], and by Van Vleck and N. G. Whitelaw[15] for the alkali metals and are in agreement with the experimental results.

The only difference between the penetrating and nonpenetrating orbits is that the term values of the penetrating orbits are significantly different from those of hydrogen. The term values may be calculated both according to classical[14,16,17] as well as quantum-mechanical[18,19] methods. Both these methods use the idealized model first suggested by Schrödinger[20]. According to this model the core electrons are imagined as distributed uniformly over the surface of one or more concentric spheres. Let us imagine the core electrons as distributed uniformly on a sphere of radius ρ; $Z_i e$ will be the effective nuclear charge inside the charged shell, and $Z_o e$ will be the effective nuclear charge outside the charged shell. Accordingly, the potential energy of the valence electron outside and inside the shell will be

$$V_o = -\frac{Z_o e^2}{r} \qquad \text{for } r > \rho$$

and

$$V_i = -\frac{Z_i e^2}{r} + \frac{Z_i e^2}{\rho} - \frac{Z_o e^2}{\rho} \qquad \text{for } r < \rho \qquad (10.29)$$

Without going into mathematical details, given elsewhere[9,14,16,17,18], we shall briefly state the results of both the classical and quantum-mechanical methods.

The term value ($T_n = -E/hc$) of a level in the hydrogen atom is given by

$$T_n = \frac{R_H}{n^2} \qquad (10.30)$$

where R_H is the Rydberg constant. The energy of the nth hydrogen level is given by

$$E_n = -R_H \frac{ch}{n^2} \qquad (10.31)$$

We may write a similar expression for an alkali atom in the form

$$E_n = -R \frac{ch}{n^2_{\text{eff}}} \qquad (10.32)$$

where n_{eff} is called the *effective quantum-number*, which is not an integer, and the values of n_{eff} are such as to yield the correct value of the energy levels; n_{eff} and n are related by

$$n_{\text{eff}} = n - \mu \qquad (10.33)$$

where μ is called the *quantum defect*, which may be calculated by classical theory[14,16,17]. The calculations show that for a given atom, the value of the quantum defect, μ, is a function of the orbital quantum number, l, and is almost independent of the total quantum number, n. This is illustrated in Table 10.4 in the case of penetrating orbits in lithium and sodium. The

TABLE 10.4

EXPERIMENTAL VALUES OF THE QUANTUM DEFECT, μ, FOR
PENETRATING ORBITS IN Li AND Na[23]

Element	Term (electron)	$n = 2$	$n = 3$	$n = 4$	$n = 5$	$n = 6$	$n = 7$	Mean value of μ
$_3$Li	S (s)	0.41	0.40	0.35	0.35	0.35	0.35	0.36
$_{11}$Na	S (s)	—	1.373	1.357	1.352	1.349	1.348	1.35
	P (p)	—	0.883	0.867	0.862	0.859	0.858	0.86
	D (d)	—	0.010	0.011	0.013	0.011	0.009	0.01
	F (f)	—	—	0.000	−0.001	−0.008	−0.012	∼0

quantum defects for sodium may be calculated by fitting Eq. (10.32) to the experimentally observed energy levels, and the mean values are given in Table 10.4. It may be pointed out that Eq. (10.32), written in the form

$$E_n = -\frac{Rch}{(n - \mu)^2} \qquad (10.34)$$

is similar in form to the empirical Rydberg series formula for the alkali atoms.

The Hartree method of self-consistent field theory has been applied with quantum mechanics in calculating the quantum defects. The agreement with the experimentally observed values for μ is excellent.

Another approach to the calculation of the energy levels of alkali atoms involves the use of the variational method in quantum mechanics[21] in conjunction with the idealized model of Schrödinger discussed above. The Schrödinger wave equation is solved for a hydrogen-like atom with the following conditions imposed: The quantum number n is not changed to fit the data. The wave functions used are similar to the hydrogen wavefunctions for different states except that Z is not a constant but is replaced by a quantity $(Z - \sigma)$, where σ is called the *screening constant*. The value of the parameter σ is obtained by varying the quantity $(Z - \sigma)$ (by the variational method) until a minimum energy is obtained[22]. In view of the use of the penetrating and nonpenetrating orbits, the nuclear charge is effectively screened by the core electrons, and the use of the screening constant, σ, has much more significance than the use of the effective quantum number, n_{eff}. The theoretically calculated values of σ for different states yield the term values that are in agreement with experimentally observed values.

Once again we may remind ourselves that the terms *penetrating orbit* and *nonpenetrating orbit* are used as a convenience in describing not easily visualized probability-density distributions in quantum mechanics.

C. Fine Structure Due to Spin-Orbit Coupling

In the discussion of the atomic spectra of sodium, so far we have neglected the intrinsic spin of the valence electron. Many of the transitions that according to the level scheme shown in Fig. 10.11 are singlets, when observed with a high-resolution spectroscope appear as close doublets. For example, Fig. 10.15 shows the spectrum of sodium, from which it is obvious that the

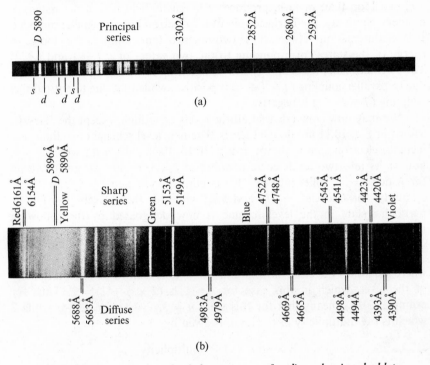

FIG. 10.15. *A photograph of the spectrum of sodium showing doublet fine structure.*

$3P \rightarrow 3S$ transition is not a singlet transition but is a close doublet with wavelengths 5889.9 Å and 5895.9 Å. Thus in order to explain the observed doublet structure we must modify our theory by including electron spin.

The electron has a spin angular-momentum of $S (= \sqrt{s(s + 1)}\hbar$, where $s = 1/2)$ which will couple with its orbital angular-momentum, $L (= \sqrt{l(l + 1)}\hbar)$, resulting in a total angular-momentum, $J (= \sqrt{j(j + 1)}\hbar)$. The total angular-momentum quantum number j can take the following two values, provided $l \neq 0$,

$$j = l + \frac{1}{2} \quad \text{and} \quad j = l - \frac{1}{2}$$

and it takes only one value, $j = 1/2$, if $l = 0$. Thus each l-level is split into two levels except for the S ($l = 0$) level, which is still a singlet. The coupling of the spin and the orbital angular-momenta of the valence electron results in the change in the energy of the two states corresponding to $j = l + \frac{1}{2}$ (parallel coupling) and $j = l - \frac{1}{2}$ (antiparallel coupling).

The origin of the interaction energy may be explained briefly in the following manner. An electron in an orbital path is equivalent to current in a closed loop that, in turn, produces a magnetic field with a net magnetic moment. Similarly, the intrinsic spin of the electron has a magnetic moment. It is the interaction between these two magnets that results in the change of energy of the states corresponding to the two values of j: $l + \frac{1}{2}$ and $l - \frac{1}{2}$. The calculations of exact energy will be taken up later. The change in energy due to parallel coupling ($j = l + \frac{1}{2}$) is positive, while that due to antiparallel coupling ($j = l - \frac{1}{2}$) is negative.

We may now conclude that all the levels of sodium, except the S-levels, shown in Fig. 10.11 are doublet levels. The new level scheme of sodium that includes electron spin is shown in Fig. 10.16. Each P-level for which $l = 1$, now splits into two levels corresponding to $j = 3/2$ and $1/2$; each D-level for which $l = 2$, splits into two levels corresponding to $j = 5/2$ and $3/2$. Similarly, for F-levels $j = 7/2$ and $5/2$; while for the S-levels, $j = 1/2$. A particular state in the level scheme is now designated by the following notation

$$n\ ^{2s+1}L_j$$

where s denotes the electron spin and $(2s + 1)$ is defined as the multiplicity of the level, which in this case for $s = \frac{1}{2}$ is $(2 \times \frac{1}{2} + 1) = 2$. Thus for example, $3^2P_{3/2}$ means that for this state $n = 3$, $l = 1$, and $j = \frac{3}{2}$, while 2 which is the multiplicity of the level, is given by

$$2 \times \text{spin} + 1 = \text{multiplicity}$$

means that the electron spin is $1/2$. We read $3^2P_{3/2}$ the three-doublet-P-three-half state. The other member of the doublet is $3^2P_{1/2}$. For convenience in Fig. 10.16, the different L-states are grouped under different columns. Note that even though the S-states are singlet, to be consistent they are written as doublets, i.e., as $^2S_{1/2}$. We shall see that under the influence of the magnetic field, the degeneracy is removed and the S-states really split into doublet levels. The spin-orbit energy separation is very small for the D- and F-levels and hence are not shown split. The spin-orbit splitting introduces much smaller energy shifts as compared to the removal of l-degeneracy.

The energy level diagrams of the alkali atoms are shown, with spin-orbit interaction included, in Fig. 10.17 for Li, Na, K, Rb, and Cs. The hydrogen levels are shown on the extreme right. The general features of the splitting due to the spin-orbit coupling, which may be calculated theoretically, are summarized in the following:

(i) For a given alkali atom, the doublet separation decreases with increasing n. This is illustrated in Fig. 10.18 and Table 10.5(a).

(ii) Within each element, for a given n, P-doublets are wider than D-doublets; D-doublets are wider than F-doublets, and so on, i.e., the separation decreases with increasing l. This is illustrated in Fig. 10.18 and Table 10.5(b).

(iii) The doublet separation increases with increasing Z as shown in Fig. 10.17 for $2p$, $3p$, $4p$, $5p$, and $6p$ doublet separations of Li, Na, K, Rb, and Cs, respectively. These separations are given in Table 10.5(c).

(iv) Finally, the doublet separations are larger in the ionized alkaline-earth atoms than the corresponding doublets in the alkali-metal atoms. This is illustrated in Table 10.5(d).

The transitions between the states of sodium that are classified as the sharp, principal, diffuse, and fundamental series are denoted by the following notations

sharp series $\qquad n^2S_{1/2} \quad \rightarrow 3^2P_{3/2,1/2};\ n = 4, 5, 6, \ldots$; doublets

principal series $\quad n^2P_{3/2,1/2} \rightarrow 3^2S_{1/2};\qquad n = 3, 5, 6, \ldots$; doublets

diffuse series $\qquad n^2D_{5/2,3/2} \rightarrow 3^2P_{3/2,1/2};\ n = 3, 4, 5, \ldots$; triplet

fundamental series $n^2F_{7/2,5/2} \rightarrow 3^2D_{5/2,3/2};\ n = 4, 5, 6, \ldots$; triplets

$$\text{(10.35)}$$

The transitions corresponding to the first member of the principal series, i.e., $3^2P_{3/2} \rightarrow 3^2S_{1/2}$, and $3^2P_{1/2} \rightarrow 3^2S_{1/2}$ are the prominent sodium D-line doublet with wavelengths 5889.9 Å and 5895.9 Å. It may be noted that both the diffuse and fundamental series originate at doublet levels and end at doublet levels. Therefore, one would expect these series to be doublets and quartets—not triplets. They are triplets because the transitions $n^2D_{5/2} \rightarrow 3^2P_{1/2}$, and $n^2F_{7/2} \rightarrow 3^2D_{3/2}$ in which j changes by 2 units are prohibited by the selection rules as we shall discuss below.

D. The Selection Rules and the Intensity Rules

The transitions between different levels shown in Fig. 10.16 are governed by certain selection rules that may be derived by the quantum-mechanical method outlined in Chapter IX. Only those electron transitions that obey the following selection rules are allowed, all others being forbidden:

(i) The orbital quantum number l must change by unity, i.e.,

$$\Delta l = \pm 1$$

This means that the initial levels have parity opposite to those of the final levels. The conservation of momentum implies that a photon emitted in an electron jump carries away with it one unit ($1\hbar$) of angular momentum.

(ii) The total quantum number j obeys the following rules:

$$\Delta j = 0, \pm 1 \qquad \text{but} \qquad j = 0 \text{ to } j = 0 \text{ is forbidden}$$

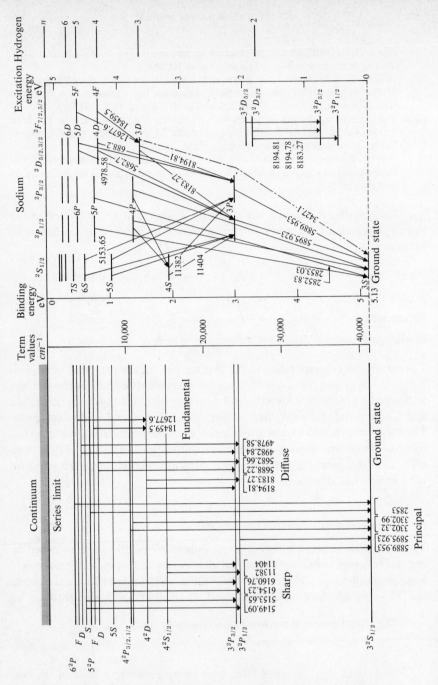

FIG. 10.16. *The energy levels and the possible transitions in the sodium atom. (Two different representations are shown.)*

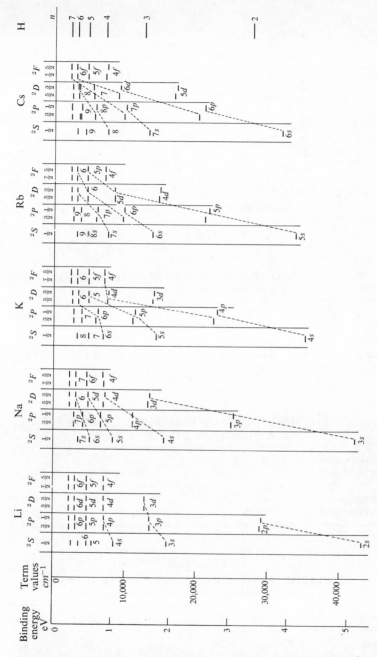

FIG. 10.17. *The energy-level diagrams, taking into account spin-orbit interactions, for Li, Na, K, Rb, and Cs.*

371

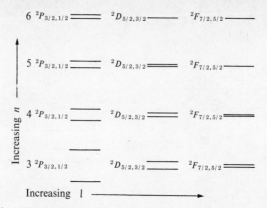

FIG. 10.18. *The decrease in the doublet separation with increasing n for a given alkali-metal atom.*

TABLE 10.5(a)

SPLITTING DUE TO SPIN-ORBIT INTERACTION
AS A FUNCTION OF n IN SODIUM

Subshell		$3p$	$4p$	$5p$	$6p$
Spin-orbit⎫ Splitting⎬	in cm^{-1}	17.19	6.15	2.46	1.40
	in eV	21.3×10^{-4}	7.63×10^{-4}	3.05×10^{-4}	1.74×10^{-4}

TABLE 10.5(b)

SPLITTING DUE TO SPIN-ORBIT INTERACTION
AS A FUNCTION OF l IN SODIUM

l value and doublet state	1 $^2P_{3/2,1/2}$	2 $^2D_{5/2,3/2}$	3 $^2F_{7/2,5/2}$
Relative fine-structure splitting	$\sim 2 \times 10^{-3}$ eV ~ 6 Å	$\sim 6 \times 10^{-6}$ eV ~ 0.02 Å	$\lesssim 10^{-9}$ eV $\lesssim 10^{-9}$ Å

TABLE 10.5(c)

SPLITTING DUE TO SPIN-ORBIT INTERACTION
AS A FUNCTION OF Z FOR $l = 1$

Atom	$_3$Li	$_{11}$Na	$_{19}$K	$_{37}$Rb	$_{55}$Cs
Subshell	$2p$	$3p$	$4p$	$5p$	$6p$
Spin orbit Splitting in eV	0.42×10^{-4}	21×10^{-4}	72×10^{-4}	295×10^{-4}	687×10^{-4}

TABLE 10.5(d)

SPLITTING DUE TO SPIN-ORBIT INTERACTION
IN ALKALI-METAL AND SINGLY-IONIZED
ALKALINE-EARTH ATOMS FOR THE FIRST
MEMBER OF THE PRINCIPAL SERIES

Atom	Li	Na	K	Rb	Cs
Splitting in cm^{-1}	0.338	17.2	57.9	237.7	554.0
	Be$^+$	Mg$^+$	Ca$^+$	Sr$^+$	Ba$^+$
Splitting in cm^{-1}	6.61	91.5	223.0	800.0	1691.0

Thus the selection rules for j do not allow the transitions $^2D_{5/2} \rightarrow {}^2P_{1/2}$, and $^2F_{7/2} \rightarrow {}^2D_{3/2}$ as shown in Fig. 10.19.

(iii)   There is no restriction on the change in n.

The forbidden transitions only mean that the probability for such an event is small. In practice there are occasional violations of the above selection rules. A particular transition that is forbidden according to the selection rules is shown as dotted in Fig. 10.16 and is between the states $3^2D \rightarrow 3^2S$ in which l changes by two units; i.e., $\Delta l = 2$. The intensity (the rate of transition) of this transition is, of course, very small.

Not all the lines (frequencies) observed in a spectrum of a given element have the same intensities. There are certain rules that govern the relative intensities, and we shall discuss these in the particular case of fine-structure

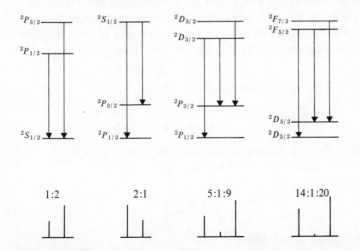

FIG. 10.19.   *The relative intensities of transitions between the doublet states.*

doublets, although the rules may be easily applied to other cases. The following two rules give the qualitative magnitude of the intensities of the doublet lines.

(i)   In any given doublet, the line for which j and l change in the same way is the stronger.

(ii) If there is more than one line for which j and l change in the same manner, the line with the largest value of j is the stronger.

As an example of (i), consider the transitions $^2P_{3/2} \rightarrow {}^2S_{1/2}$ for which j and l change by 1, and $^2P_{1/2} \rightarrow {}^2S_{1/2}$ for which l changes by 1 but j by 0. Hence the first transition is stronger than the second, as shown in Fig. 10.19. As an application of (ii), consider the transitions $^2D_{5/2,3/2} \rightarrow {}^2P_{3/2,1/2}$. For $^2D_{5/2} \rightarrow {}^2P_{3/2}$, both j and l change by 1; for $^2D_{3/2} \rightarrow {}^2P_{1/2}$ both j and l change by 1, while for $^2D_{3/2} \rightarrow {}^2P_{3/2}$, l changes by 1 but j by 0. Hence the above three transitions are in the order of decreasing intensity, as shown in Fig. 10.19.

The quantitative rules for intensity were first discovered by Burger, et al[24], and may be stated as below in terms of the statistical weight. For a state with quantum number j, its *statistical weight* or quantum weight may be defined as being equal to $(2j + 1)$, and *the sum of the intensities of those lines of a doublet that start or end from a common level are proportional to their quantum weights.*

This rule can be understood by considering the two examples mentioned above. For the transitions $^2P_{3/2} \rightarrow {}^2S_{1/2}$, and $^2P_{1/2} \rightarrow {}^2S_{1/2}$, which start from $j = 3/2$ and $j = 1/2$, the respective quantum weights are $2 \times (3/2) + 1 = 4$ and $2 \times (1/2) + 1 = 2$, respectively. Thus the intensities would be in the ratio of 2:1 as shown in Fig. 10.19; and these agree with the experimental values. Consider now the transitions $^2D \rightarrow {}^2P$ (Fig. 10.19), i.e., $^2D_{5/2} \rightarrow {}^2P_{3/2}$; $^2D_{3/2} \rightarrow {}^2P_{3/2}$; and $^2D_{3/2} \rightarrow {}^2P_{1/2}$. Let the intensities of these three transitions be denoted by X, Y, and Z, respectively. The fourth transition, $^2D_{5/2} \rightarrow {}^2P_{1/2}$, is not allowed and hence its intensity may be taken to be zero. Schematically, we write the intensity rule for this case in the following form:

$$
\begin{array}{r|cc}
 & P_{3/2} & {}^2P_{1/2} \\
\text{quantum weights} \rightarrow & 4 & 2 \\
\downarrow & & \\
\hline
{}^2D_{5/2} \quad 6 & X & 0 \\
{}^2D_{3/2} \quad 4 & Y & Z \\
\end{array}
$$

From the above rule, the sum of the intensities starting from $^2D_{5/2}$ is $X + 0$, and this is related to the sum of the intensities starting from $^2D_{3/2}$ of $Y + Z$ in the ratio of 6:4, i.e.,

$$\frac{X + 0}{Y + Z} = \frac{6}{4} \qquad\qquad (10.36)$$

Similarly, ending with P-levels

$$\frac{X + Y}{0 + Z} = \frac{4}{2} \qquad\qquad (10.37)$$

Solving Eqs. (10.36) and (10.37) gives

$$X = 9, \qquad Y = 1, \qquad \text{and} \qquad Z = 5$$

These relative intensities are shown in Fig. 10.19.

This rule may be extended to many other cases, but one must remember that the rule does not always apply.

6. MAGNETIC MOMENT DUE TO ELECTRON ORBITAL MOTION

In order to verify the rules of space quantization, atoms must be placed in an external magnetic field that fixes the direction of the arbitrary Z axis. Before we can investigate the effects of the external magnetic field, it is necessary to understand the magnetic properties associated with the motion of the electrons in the atoms. The results derived here and in the following sections could be derived directly from quantum mechanics, but the classical method using Bohr-type orbits has the advantage of being easily visualized. We will start with the discussion of the orbital motion of the electron, then examine the spin motion, and later we shall combine these two to find the total magnetic moment of the atom.

Consider an electron moving under a central inverse-square-law force in an elliptical orbit; see Fig. 10.20(a). The motion of the electron in the orbit is equivalent to a closed loop carrying current. The current through this loop is given by

$$i = \frac{1}{c} \frac{e}{T} \tag{10.38}$$

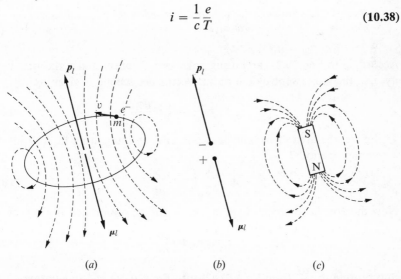

$$(a) \qquad\qquad\qquad (b) \qquad\qquad\qquad (c)$$

FIG. 10.20.   (a) *The orbital motion of an electron is equivalent to a current loop as shown.* (b) *Dipole equivalent of a current loop.* (c) *A permanent-magnet equivalent of a current loop.*

where i is the current in electromagnetic units, e is the charge of the electron in electrostatic units, T is the time period of the electron in its orbit, and c, the velocity of light, is equal to the ratio of the em (electromagnetic) to es (electrostatic) unit of charge. As we know, at large distances from the loop the field due to the loop is the same as that of a magnetic dipole located at the center of the loop. Figure 10.20(b) is the dipole equivalent of the current loop. The loop behaves like a small permanent magnet as the one shown in Fig. 10.20(c). According to Ampere's theorem [25], the current in the loop gives rise to a magnetic moment, μ_l, given by

$$\mu_l = \text{current} \times \text{area enclosed by the loop} = iA \qquad (10.39)$$

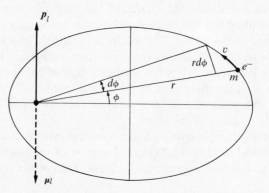

FIG. 10.21. *Evaluation of the area enclosed in the elliptical path of an electron, using polar coordinates.*

According to Fig. 10.21, and using polar coordinates r and ϕ, the areal velocity, i.e., the area swept by the radius vector per second is given by

$$\frac{1}{2} r \cdot r \frac{d\phi}{dt} = \frac{1}{2} r^2 \frac{d\phi}{dt} \qquad (10.40)$$

Therefore, the area of the ellipse is obtained by integrating Eq. (10.40) over a complete period T

$$A = \frac{1}{2} \int_0^T r^2 \frac{d\phi}{dt} \, dt \qquad (10.41)$$

Now the angular momentum p_l is a constant of motion and is given by

$$p_l = mr^2 \frac{d\phi}{dt} \qquad (10.42)$$

Substituting for $\frac{d\phi}{dt}$ from Eq. (10.42) into Eq. (10.41) and integrating,

$$A = \frac{1}{2} \frac{p_l}{m} T \qquad (10.43)$$

Combining Eqs. (10.43), (10.38), and (10.39), we get

$$\mu_l = \frac{e}{2mc}\, p_l \qquad (10.44)$$

Because $p_l = L = \sqrt{l(l+1)}\,\hbar$, we may rewrite Eq. (10.44)

$$\mu_l = \frac{e}{2mc}\, L \qquad (10.45)$$

or

$$\mu_l = \frac{e}{2mc}\, \sqrt{l(l+1)}\,\hbar = \frac{eh}{4\pi mc}\, \sqrt{l(l+1)} \qquad (10.46)$$

According to Eq. (10.46) the magnetic moment associated with the orbital motion of electron has the following values. For $l = 0$, $\mu_l = 0$; $l = 1$, $\mu_l = \sqrt{2}\,(eh/4\pi mc)$; $l = 2$, $\mu_l = \sqrt{6}\,(eh/4\pi mc)$. The quantity $(eh/4\pi mc)$ is made up of universal constants and is used as a unit for the magnetic moment. This quantity, $(eh/4\pi mc)$, is the *Bohr magneton*, μ_B, and its numerical value is[26]

$$\mu_B = \frac{eh}{4\pi mc} = 0.92732 \times 10^{-20}\ \text{erg/gauss} \qquad (10.47)$$

Equation (10.45) may now be written in vector form as

$$\boldsymbol{\mu}_l = -\frac{e}{2mc}\, \mathbf{L} = -\frac{\mu_B}{\hbar}\, \mathbf{L} \qquad (10.48)$$

The negative sign is included because of the negative charge of the electron; the direction of $\boldsymbol{\mu}_l$ is opposite to that of $\mathbf{L}$ as shown in Fig. 10.20.

At this point we shall introduce another important quantity called variously the *Landé g-factor*, *g-factor*, or the *gyromagnetic ratio*. According to Eq. (10.44), the quantity μ_l/p_l is a constant and is equal to $e/2mc$. This may also be written in the form

$$\frac{\mu_l}{p_l} = g_l\, \frac{e}{2mc} \qquad (10.49)$$

where g_l, the Landé g-factor, is a new constant. The g-factor in this case is unity, but there will be many applications (in motions other than orbital) where it will not be unity. Equation (10.48) is a special case of the following equation with $g_l = 1$.

$$\frac{\mu_l/\mu_B}{L/\hbar} = g_l \qquad (10.50)$$

Equation (10.50) is a general definition of the gyromagnetic ratio, g: *the ratio of the magnetic moment expressed in units of Bohr magnetons to the orbital angular-momentum expressed in units of $\hbar$.* In this particular case of the orbital motion of the electron, $g = g_l = 1$.

7. MAGNETIC MOMENT DUE TO ELECTRON SPIN

An electron spins about its own axis and has an intrinsic spin angular momentum of $(\sqrt{3}/2)\hbar$. Because of this motion, the electron should behave as a tiny magnet, as shown in Fig. 10.22, and should possess a magnetic mo-

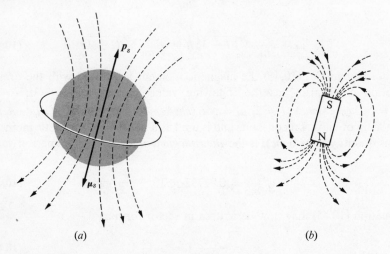

(a)   (b)

FIG. 10.22.   (a) *An electron spinning about its own axis is equivalent to a tiny magnet as shown in* (b).

ment. Once again, because of the negative charge, the directions of the spin angular-momentum and the spin magnetic-moment are opposite (see Fig. 10.22). However, because of the lack of knowledge about the structure of the electron and its charge distribution, it becomes impossible to calculate the magnetic moment in a manner similar to that for the orbital motion. From Eq. (10.49) or Eq. (10.50) we may write a similar expression for the spinning motion of the electron, i.e.,

$$\mu_s = g_s \frac{e}{2mc} p_s \tag{10.51}$$

where μ_s is the spin magnetic-moment, g_s is the spin g-factor, and p_s is the spin angular-momentum given by

$$p_s = S = \sqrt{s(s+1)}\,\hbar \tag{10.52}$$

Combining Eqs. (10.51) and (10.52),

$$\mu_s = g_s \frac{eh}{4\pi mc} \sqrt{s(s+1)} \tag{10.53}$$

or, in vector form,

$$\mu_s = -g_s \frac{\mu_B}{\hbar} S \tag{10.54}$$

Because the value of s is $\frac{1}{2}$ for a single electron, the only unknown is g_s. In order for these results to be in agreement with experiment, it is necessary to assign a value of 2 for g_s (or precisely $g_s = 2.002319230$). Thus Eq. (10.54) may be written as (similar to Eq. (10.50))

$$\frac{\mu_s/\mu_B}{S/\hbar} = g_s = 2 \tag{10.55}$$

Note that the gyromagnetic ratio g_s is twice the gyromagnetic ratio g_l, i.e.,

$$g_s = 2g_l \tag{10.56}$$

For $s = \frac{1}{2}$ and $g_s = 2$, from Eq. (10.53), we get the following value of the magnetic moment for a spinning electron:

$$\mu_s = 2 \cdot \frac{eh}{4\pi mc} \sqrt{\frac{1}{2}\left(\frac{1}{2} + 1\right)} = \sqrt{3}\,\mu_B = 1.62 \times 10^{-20}\,\text{erg/gauss} \tag{10.57}$$

8.   PRECESSION OF A CHARGED PARTICLE IN AN EXTERNAL MAGNETIC FIELD

We shall show that the effect of a uniform magnetic field on a charged body that has angular momentum is to cause the angular-momentum vector to precess uniformly with an angular frequency known as the Larmor frequency. This motion is similar to that of a mechanical top that precesses in a gravitational field. Thus an electron moving in an orbit in the presence of a uniform magnetic field will be expected to precess as shown in Fig. 10.23. This pre-

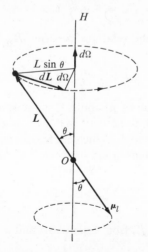

Fig. 10.23. *Precession of an orbiting electron in an external uniform magnetic field.*

cession, the *Larmor precession*, is superimposed on the already-existing orbital angular-motion; the relation expressing the frequency of precession is *Larmor's theorem*. Our aim in this section is, first, to derive the Larmor theorem[27], and, second, to calculate the change in the energy of the system when placed in a uniform field.

The motion of an electron in an orbit may be replaced by a dipole of magnetic moment μ_l. Thus there will be an interaction between μ_l and the applied magnetic field H. Because the applied magnetic field is uniform, there will be no net forces acting on the dipole; but there will be a net torque on the dipole. This torque is equal to the time rate of change of the angular momentum, i.e.,

$$\frac{d\mathbf{L}}{dt} = \mathbf{N} \tag{10.58}$$

But the torque N is given by[28]

$$N = \mu_l H \sin \theta$$

or

$$\mathbf{N} = \mu_l \times \mathbf{H} \tag{10.59}$$

Also from Eq. (10.49),

$$\mu_l = -g_l \frac{e}{2mc} \mathbf{p}_l = -g_l \frac{\mu_B}{\hbar} \mathbf{L}$$

Combining this with Eqs. (10.58) and (10.59), we get

$$\frac{d\mathbf{L}}{dt} = -g_l \frac{\mu_B}{\hbar} \mathbf{L} \times \mathbf{H}$$

or

$$d\mathbf{L} = -g_l \frac{\mu_B}{\hbar} \mathbf{L} \times \mathbf{H}\, dt \tag{10.60}$$

Figure 10.23 illustrates the relations between $d\mathbf{L}$, $\mathbf{L}$, and $\mathbf{H}$. Note that in scalar form

$$dL = g_l \frac{\mu_B}{\hbar} LH\, dt \sin \theta \tag{10.61}$$

The rate of precession of μ_l about $\mathbf{H}$ is the same as that of $\mathbf{L}$ about $\mathbf{H}$, because μ_l is proportional to $\mathbf{L}$. Thus we may consider $\mathbf{L}$ instead of μ_l. Note that $d\mathbf{L}$ is perpendicular to $\mathbf{L}$, which means that as the vector rotates, its magnitude remains constant while its direction changes. In a time dt, the vector $\mathbf{L}$ rotates through an angle $d\Omega$ and according to Fig. 10.23

$$d\Omega = \frac{dL}{L \sin \theta} \tag{10.62}$$

Substituting the value of $d\mathbf{L}$ from Eq. (10.61) and noting that $\mu_B/\hbar = e/2mc$, we get

$$d\Omega = g_l \frac{\mu_B}{\hbar} \frac{LH\, dt \sin \theta}{L \sin \theta} = g_l \frac{e}{2mc} H\, dt$$

and writing $d\Omega/dt = \omega_L$ = the angular frequency of precession, or the Larmor precessional angular frequency,

$$\omega_L = \frac{d\Omega}{dt} = g_l \frac{e}{2mc} H \qquad (10.63)$$

Because for the orbital motion of an electron, $g_l = 1$,

$$\omega_L = \frac{e}{2mc} H \qquad (10.64)$$

and the frequency ν_L is

$$\nu_L = \frac{e}{4\pi mc} H \qquad (10.65)$$

Equation (10.64) is the statement of Larmor's theorem. Note that the precessional frequency is independent of the magnitude of the angular momentum vector and is a function only of the charge and mass of the particle and the magnitude of the applied field H. If $H = 0$, $\omega_L = 0$.

A similar expression may be obtained for the spinning motion of the electron. For an expression similar to that of Eq. (10.63)

$$\omega_s = g_s \frac{e}{2mc} H \qquad (10.66)$$

For a spinning electron $g_s = 2$, hence

$$\omega_s = \frac{e}{mc} H \qquad (10.67)$$

A comparison of Eq. (10.67) with Eq. (10.64) shows that $\omega_s = 2\omega_L$, i.e., the spin vector precesses twice as fast as the orbital vector.

We shall now proceed with the calculation of the change in the energy, ΔE, when such a dipole system with magnetic moment μ_l is placed in an external uniform magnetic-field, H, as shown in Fig. 10.24. ΔE is a completely orientational potential-energy. As a matter of convenience and convention, assume that when μ_l is at 90° to H, ΔE is equal to zero, while the potential energy at any other angle, θ, is calculated by finding the amount of external work that must be done to rotate the dipole from $\theta = 90°$ to $\theta°$, i.e.,

$$\Delta E = \int_{90°}^{\theta°} N \, d\theta$$

Substituting for N from Eq. (10.59) and integrating

$$\Delta E = \int_{90°}^{\theta°} \mu_l H \sin \theta \, d\theta = -\mu_l H \cos \theta$$

i.e.,

$$\Delta E = -\mu_l \cdot H \qquad (10.68)$$

For $\theta = 0°$, $\Delta E = -\mu_l H$, i.e., the change in energy is minimum when μ_l is parallel to H. For $\theta = 180°$, $\Delta E = \mu_l H$, i.e., it is maximum. Suppose that when the magnetic field is applied the μ_l is found at an angle θ, and if μ_l is to be aligned along H so that the system has minimum energy, this energy must be dissipated. The absence of any mechanism for the removal of this energy stops the natural tendency of μ_l to align itself along **H**, thereby making μ_l precess around **H**, with θ and ΔE remaining fixed for a particular set of dipoles. The quantization of **L** leads to the quantization of μ_l, and hence the precession of μ_l around **H** takes place only at certain angles.

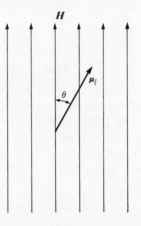

Fig. 10.24. *A dipole system with magnetic moment, μ_1, placed in an external uniform magnetic field, **H**.*

In actual experiments one does not check the space quantization of **L** directly—only through the quantization of μ_l. The same is true of **S** as well as **J**. The above remarks will be helpful in Secs. 10 to 14 for the proof of space quantization.

9. THE ELECTRON SPIN-ORBIT INTERACTION

We are now in a position to calculate the magnitude of the spin-orbit inter-action—the magnitude of the doublet separation—that results in the fine structure as discussed in Sec. 5. We have seen that the doublets separation varies from member to member, which means that it depends upon the quantum number n; from series to series, upon the quantum number l; and from element to element, upon the atomic number, Z. The doublet separa-tion, therefore, is a function of n, l, and Z.

The calculations of the interaction energy produced with the addition of the electron spin, resulting in spin-orbit coupling, have been made extensively using quantum-mechanical methods by Pauli[29], Darwin[30], Dirac[31], and Gordon[32]. Because the results obtained by using semiclassical methods (the Bohr theory and the theory of relativity) are the same as those obtained from

Dirac's quantum-mechanical calculations, we shall follow the semiclassical treatment[33].

Consider a hydrogen-like atom in which a charge $-e$ is moving with a velocity $\mathbf{v}$ and orbital angular-momentum:

$$\mathbf{L} = m\mathbf{r} \times \mathbf{v} \tag{10.69}$$

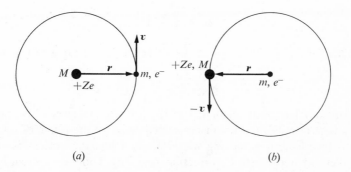

(a)   (b)

Fig. 10.25.   (a) *The nucleus with charge $+Ze$ is at rest while the electron is moving in a circular Bohr orbit with a velocity, v, as observed from the nucleus.* (b) *Motion of the nucleus in a circular Bohr orbit as observed by the electron.*

where $L = \sqrt{l(l+1)}\,\hbar$, and $\mathbf{r}$ is the radius vector as shown in Fig. 10.25(a). We have assumed that the nucleus is at rest. If we make the observation from the electron frame of reference, the electron will be at rest, while the nucleus of charge Ze^+ will be moving with a velocity $-\mathbf{v}$, as shown in Fig. 10.25(b). The nucleus moving with velocity $-\mathbf{v}$ is equivalent to a current element described by current density vector

$$\mathbf{j} = -\frac{Ze\mathbf{v}}{c} \tag{10.70}$$

which according to Ampere's law produces a magnetic field at the position of the electron given by

$$\mathbf{H} = \frac{\mathbf{j} \times \mathbf{r}}{r^3} = \frac{Ze}{cr^3}\mathbf{r} \times \mathbf{v} \tag{10.71}$$

According to Coulomb's law, the electric field $\mathbf{E}$ acting on the electron is given by

$$\mathbf{E} = +\frac{Ze}{r^3}\mathbf{r} \tag{10.72}$$

Combining Eqs. (10.71) and (10.72), we get

$$\mathbf{H} = \frac{\mathbf{E} \times \mathbf{v}}{c} \tag{10.73}$$

which is the general expression for $\mathbf{H}$.

Now combining Eqs. (10.71) and (10.69), we get

$$H = \frac{Ze}{mc} \frac{1}{r^3} L \qquad (10.74)$$

Thus the situation is that we have a spinning electron in the field H given by Eq. (10.74), and hence according to Larmor's theorem or Eq. (10.66), the electron precesses around this field with a frequency ω_p given by

$$\omega_p = g_s \frac{\mu_B}{\hbar} H \qquad (10.75)$$

Substituting for g_s ($=2$), μ_B ($= eh/4\pi mc$) and H from Eq. (10.74), we get

$$\omega_p = 2 \cdot \frac{e}{2mc} \frac{Ze}{mc} \frac{1}{r^3} L = \frac{Ze^2}{m^2 c^2} \frac{1}{r^3} L \qquad (10.76)$$

This frequency has been calculated in the frame of reference in which the electron is at rest. We must transfer this equation to the frame of reference in which the electron is moving with velocity v and the nucleus is at rest. This results in a relativistic correction given by Thomas[34] according to which, in addition to the Larmor precession ω_p, the electron has a relativity precession ω_T which is one half of ω_p and is in the opposite direction, i.e., $\omega_T = -\frac{1}{2}\omega_p$. Thus the resultant precession ω of the spinning electron is

$$\omega = \omega_p + \omega_T = \frac{1}{2} \omega_p = \frac{1}{2} \frac{Ze^2}{m^2 c^2} \frac{1}{r^3} L \qquad (10.77)$$

The interaction energy is orientational potential energy (equal to the kinetic energy of electron's precession around H) and is the product of ω and the projection of the spin angular momentum vector S on L (by substituting from Eqs. (10.53) and (10.67) in $\Delta E = \mu_s \cdot H$):

$$\Delta E_{S \cdot L} = \omega \cdot S \qquad (10.78)$$

where $S = \sqrt{s(s+1)}\,\hbar$. Substituting the value of ω from Eq. (10.77),

$$\Delta E_{S \cdot L} = \frac{Ze^2}{2m^2 c^2} \frac{1}{r^3} L \cdot S = \frac{Ze^2}{2m^2 c^2} \frac{1}{r^3} LS \cos(L, S) \qquad (10.79)$$

Thus in order to know the magnitude of $\Delta E_{S \cdot L}$, we have to calculate the value of $1/r^3$ and $LS \cos(L, S)$. The electron nuclear-distance is a function of Z, n, and l. Because the value of r changes continuously, we simply calculate the average value of $1/r^3$. From quantum mechanics[35], using perturbation theory,

$$\left\langle \frac{1}{r^3} \right\rangle_{av} = \frac{Z^3}{a_0^3 n^3 l(l + \frac{1}{2})(l + 1)} \qquad (10.80)$$

where a_0 is the Bohr radius given by

$$a_0 = \frac{\hbar^2}{me^2} \qquad (10.81)$$

The term $LS \cos (\mathbf{L}, \mathbf{S})$ may be calculated by using the cosine law. If $\mathbf{L}$ and $\mathbf{S}$ precess around $\mathbf{J}$, then from Fig. 10.6(a), we get

$$J^2 = L^2 + S^2 + 2LS \cos (\mathbf{L}, \mathbf{S}) \tag{10.82}$$

or

$$\cos (\mathbf{L}, \mathbf{S}) = \frac{J^2 - L^2 - S^2}{2LS} = \frac{j(j+1) - l(l+1) - s(s+1)}{2\sqrt{l(l+1)}\sqrt{s(s+1)}} \tag{10.83}$$

Therefore, Eq. (10.79) takes the form

$$\Delta E_{\text{S.L}} = \frac{Ze^2}{2m^2c^2} \frac{Z^3}{a_0^3 n^3 l(l+\frac{1}{2})(l+1)} \frac{J^2 - L^2 - S^2}{2} \tag{10.84}$$

Thus the value of the spin-orbit interaction may be calculated from this equation. In an abbreviated form Eq. (10.84) may be written as

$$\Delta E_{\text{S.L}} = a \frac{J^2 - L^2 - S^2}{2} = a\mathbf{L} \cdot \mathbf{S} \tag{10.85}$$

where a is a constant given by

$$a = \frac{Ze^2}{2m^2c^2} \left\langle \frac{1}{r^3} \right\rangle_{\text{av}} \tag{10.86}$$

and $(1/r^3)_{\text{av}}$ is given by Eq. (10.80).

Let us discuss some applications of Eq. (10.85).

(a) Suppose the energy of a level without spin-orbit interaction is E_0. The energy, including spin-orbit interaction, will be

$$E = E_0 + \Delta E_{\text{L.S}} \tag{10.87}$$

Consider the $^2P_{3/2,1/2}$ levels. For $j = 3/2$, $l = 1$, $s = 1/2$, we get

$$E = E_0 + \frac{1}{2} a\hbar^2 = E_0 + \frac{1}{2} A$$

where $A = a\hbar^2$; and for $j = 1/2$, $l = 1$, $s = 1/2$, we get

$$E = E_0 - a\hbar^2 = E_0 - A$$

The splitting of these and some other levels is shown in Fig. 10.26.

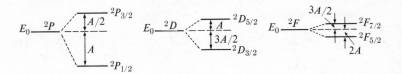

FIG. 10.26. *Fine-structure splitting due to the spin-orbit interaction is shown for the case of doublets levels* $^2P_{3/2,1/2}$; $^2D_{5/2,3/2}$; *and* $^2F_{7/2,5/2}$.

(b) From the following considerations we may get some idea of the value of $\Delta E_{\text{L.S}}$. Let us say $n = 2$, $Z = 1$, and $\langle 1/r^3 \rangle_{\text{av}} \sim (1/2)^3 a_0^3$. Also $\mathbf{S} \cdot \mathbf{L} \approx \hbar^2$. Therefore

$$\Delta E_{S \cdot L} \sim \frac{e^2}{2m^2c^2}\left(\frac{1}{2^3 a_0^3}\right)\hbar^2 \approx 10^{-16} \text{ ergs} \simeq 10^{-4} \text{ eV}$$

as compared to $E_0 \approx -3.4$ eV for the $n = 2$ level of the hydrogen atom.

(c)   Let us calculate the magnitude of $\mathbf{H}$ acting on the spin magnetic-moment μ_s of the electron. Thus

$$\Delta E_{S \cdot L} = \boldsymbol{\mu}_s \cdot \mathbf{H} \approx \mu_s H$$

Because for $s = \frac{1}{2}$, $\mu_s = \sqrt{3}\,\mu_B \simeq \mu_B \simeq 10^{-20}$ erg/gauss and $\Delta E_{S \cdot L}$ from (b) $\sim 10^{-16}$ ergs, therefore,

$$H \simeq \frac{\Delta E_{S \cdot L}}{\mu_B} = \frac{10^{-16} \text{ ergs}}{10^{-20} \text{ ergs/gauss}} = 10^4 \text{ gauss}$$

which is not a weak magnetic field.

(d)   Finally, we may point out that the number of energy levels obtained from the Sommerfeld relativity correction alone are the same as obtained from the above theory where both spin-orbit coupling and relativity corrections have been made. Even though the magnitudes of the two corrections are the same for the case of the hydrogen spectrum, for the alkali atoms and others it is the above theory that correctly predicts the fine-structure separations. For example, in the case of alkali atoms the outer electron is moving very slowly and the Sommerfeld relativistic correction is almost negligible, while experimentally the splitting is readily observed. Only in the case of the hydrogen atom do the two theories agree as shown in Fig. 10.27, and this is a good example of how two incorrect assumptions can lead to the correct result. As a matter of fact, Gordon has shown that Sommerfeld's fine-structure formula for the hydrogen atom may be derived as a special case of Dirac's theory of the hydrogen atom.

Just to give some idea of the energy levels of a hydrogenic atom:

(i)   According to the Bohr theory ($k = 1$ in Gaussian units)

$$E_n = -\frac{\mu k^2 Z^2 e^4}{2n^2 \hbar^2} \tag{10.88}$$

(ii)   According to the Bohr-Sommerfeld model, which takes care of the relativistic correction[36],

$$E_n = -\frac{\mu k^2 Z^2 e^4}{2n^2 \hbar^2}\left[1 + \frac{\alpha^2 Z^2}{n}\left(\frac{1}{n_\theta} - \frac{3}{4n}\right)\right] \tag{10.89}$$

(iii)   According to the Dirac theory, which takes care of both relativity and spin-orbit coupling[31],

$$E_n = -\frac{\mu k^2 Z^2 e^4}{2n^2 \hbar^2}\left[1 + \frac{Z^2 \alpha^2}{n}\left(\frac{1}{j + \frac{1}{2}} - \frac{3}{4n}\right)\right] \tag{10.90}$$

These three for the hydrogen atom are shown in Fig. 10.27. But for any other atom it is Eq. (10.90), i.e., Dirac's theory that agrees with the observed levels.

10.   THE NORMAL ZEEMAN EFFECT

We have frequently talked about the space quantization of orbital angular-momentum, spin angular-momentum, and the total orbital angular-momentum. We shall now start with the task of experimentally proving these quantization rules. The experimental observation of the quantization of orbital angular momentum by applying a magnetic field is classified as the normal Zeeman effect[37] and will be discussed in this section.

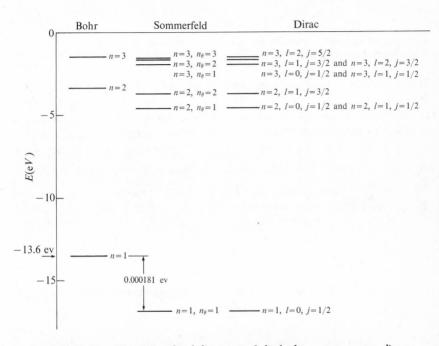

FIG. 10.27. *The energy-level diagrams of the hydrogen atom according to Bohr, Sommerfeld, and Dirac. Note that the displacements between the substates in the Sommerfeld and Dirac levels are exaggerated by a factor of $(137)^2$.* [*From Eisberg, R. M.,* Fundamentals of Modern Physics, *p. 357. New York: John Wiley & Sons, Inc., 1961.*]

Let us assume that we can neglect the spin angular-momentum of an electron or that the total net spin of an atom is zero. Thus we are considering the orbital angular-momentum, **L**, of an atom. According to Eq. (10.48)

$$\boldsymbol{\mu}_l = -\frac{e}{2mc}\,\mathbf{L} \tag{10.48}$$

where $L = \sqrt{l(l+1)}\,\hbar$, and if **L** is quantized, so will be $\boldsymbol{\mu}_l$. If this system is placed in a uniform magnetic field of strength H, the change in energy according to Eq. (10.68) is

$$\Delta E = -\boldsymbol{\mu}_l \cdot \mathbf{H} \tag{10.68}$$

which on combining with Eq. (10.48) gives

$$\Delta E = \frac{e}{2mc}\,\mathbf{L} \cdot \mathbf{H} \tag{10.91}$$

But $\mathbf{L} \cdot \mathbf{H} = LH \cos \theta$, and $L \cos \theta = L_Z$; therefore,

$$\Delta E = \frac{e}{2mc} L_Z H \qquad (10.92)$$

or because $L_Z = m_l \hbar$, we get

$$\Delta E = m_l \mu_B H \qquad (10.93)$$

In terms of Larmor's angular frequency, ω_l, this takes the form

$$\Delta E = m_l \omega_l \hbar \qquad (10.94)$$

Because L has $(2l + 1)$-fold degeneracy, i.e., for a given value of l, m_l can take $(2l + 1)$ values: $-l, -(l - 1), \ldots, -2, -1, 0, 1, 2, \ldots, (l - 1), l$; therefore, from Eq. (10.93), ΔE can also take $(2l + 1)$ values. Thus a state that is in a quantum state l with energy E_0, when placed in a magnetic field H will split into $(2l + 1)$ substates with their energies given by the expression

$$E = E_0 + \Delta E = E_0 + m_l \mu_B H \qquad (10.95)$$

Thus for $l = 0$, $m_l = 0$, and hence $E = E_0$. For $l = 1$, $m_l = -1, 0, +1$, and E can take the following three values

$$E = E_0 - \mu_B H$$

$$E = E_0$$

$$E = E_0 + \mu_B H$$

Similarly for $l = 2$, $m_l = -2, -1, 0, 1, 2$; E will take the following five values

$$E = E_0 - 2\mu_B H$$

$$E = E_0 - \mu_B H$$

$$E = E_0$$

$$E = E_0 + \mu_B H$$

$$E = E_0 + 2\mu_B H$$

These and some other levels are shown in Fig. 10.28. Note that the levels are equally spaced and the magnitude of this equal spacing is a function of H only.

In actual practice one cannot observe the resulting new levels. The only way to get information about the levels is to observe the transitions between the levels. Suppose in the absence of the magnetic field a transition of frequency ν_0 is observed between the initial level of energy E_0^i and the final level of energy E_0^f, i.e.,

$$h\nu_0 = E_0^i - E_0^f \qquad (10.96)$$

If a magnetic field of strength H is applied, the expressions for the energies take the form

$$E^i = E_0^i + \Delta E^i = E_0^i + m_l^i \mu_B H \qquad (10.97)$$

$$E^f = E_0^f + \Delta E^f = E_0^f + m_l^f \mu_B H \qquad (10.98)$$

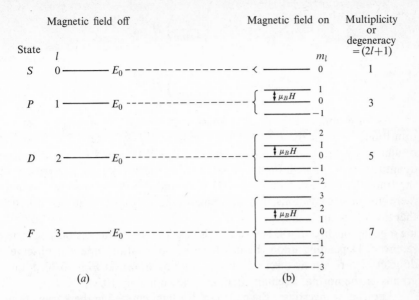

FIG. 10.28.   (a) *Energy levels in the absence of a magnetic field.* (b) *Energy levels in the presence of an external magnetic field.*

Therefore, the frequencies ν of the transitions between the initial and the final states under the influence of a magnetic field are obtained by subtracting Eq. (10.98) from Eq. (10.97), i.e.,

$$h\nu = E^i - E^f = (E_0^i - E_0^f) + (m_l^i - m_l^f)\mu_B H \qquad (10.99)$$

Defining

$$\Delta m_l = m_l^i - m_l^f \qquad (10.100)$$

and using Eq. (10.96), Eq. (10.99) takes the form

$$h\nu = h\nu_0 + \Delta m_l\,\mu_B H \qquad (10.101)$$

Dividing by h,

$$\nu = \nu_0 + \Delta m_l\,\frac{eH}{4\pi mc} \qquad (10.102)$$

Not all the transitions taking place between m_l^i and m_l^f are allowed by the selection rules. The selection rules allow only those for which the change in the magnetic quantum number is 0 or ± 1, i.e.,

$$\Delta m_l = 0,\ \pm 1 \qquad (10.103)$$

Combining Eqs. (10.102) and (10.103) will show that the original transition of frequency ν_0 is replaced by three transitions with the following three frequencies (one decreased, one unchanged, and one increased),

$$\nu = \nu_0 - \left(\frac{e}{4\pi mc}\right) H$$

$$\nu = \nu_0 \tag{10.104}$$

$$\nu = \nu_0 + \left(\frac{e}{4\pi mc}\right) H$$

As an example, Fig. 10.29(a) shows the normal Zeeman effect for the transitions between the $P(l = 1)$ state and the $S(l = 0)$ state. Experimental results verify the frequency relations of Eq. (10.104) and hence the space quantization of l as well. Figure 10.29(b) shows the normal Zeeman pattern of the transitions between the $D(l = 2)$ state and the $P(l = 1)$ state. Actually there are nine transitions, but the magnitudes of the separations are such that they show up as only three groups of different frequencies, each containing a group of three lines. Hence in this case the degeneracy is only partially removed. Depending upon the direction of observation, one will observe a doublet or a triplet as discussed below, and as shown in Fig. 10.30. Photographs of the normal Zeeman effect are shown in Fig. 10.31.

Let us now investigate the nature of the light emitted in these transitions. In the magnetic field H, these spectral lines are polarized as shown in Fig. 10.31.

(a) *When the Zeeman effect is viewed along the direction of the field*, H, which may be achieved through a hole in the pole face, only the two circular components, corresponding to right-handed and left-handed circularly polarized light, are observed. The right-handed components correspond to the transition $\Delta m_l = +1$; while the left-handed components correspond to $\Delta m_l = -1$. Because light is transverse in nature, the electromagnetic field must always have the field vectors **E** and **B** normal to the direction of propagation, and hence (the Z motions) will not emit light in the field direction H. In this case, therefore, we see only a doublet.

(b) *When the Zeeman effect is viewed in a direction normal to the axis of the magnetic field*, H, the electric vector vibrating parallel to the field H (the motion along Z) the light is observed as plane-polarized light, while the two circular motions are observed as plane-polarized light with the electric vector at right angles to the field. In this case, therefore, we see a normal triplet.

The abbreviation p (or π) stands for the vibrations parallel to the field and s (or σ) stands for a vibration normal to the field. These polarization values may be summarized as follows:

$$\text{viewed} \perp \text{to field } H \begin{cases} \Delta m_l = \pm 1; \text{ plane-polarized} \perp \text{to } H; \sigma \text{ components} \\ \Delta m_l = 0; \quad \text{plane-polarized} \parallel \text{to } H; \ \pi \text{ components} \end{cases}$$

$$\text{viewed} \parallel \text{to field } H \begin{cases} \Delta m_l = \pm 1; \text{ circularly polarized;} \quad \sigma \text{ components} \\ \Delta m_l = 0; \quad \text{forbidden;} \qquad\qquad \pi \text{ components} \end{cases}$$

$$\tag{10.105}$$

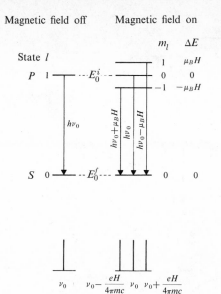

(a)

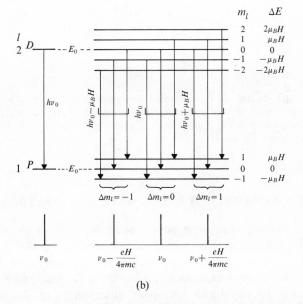

(b)

Fig. 10.29. (a) *The normal Zeeman effect of a transition between the P($l = 1$) state and the S($l = 0$) state. (b) The normal Zeeman effect of a transition between the D($l = 2$) state and the P($l = 1$) state.*

391

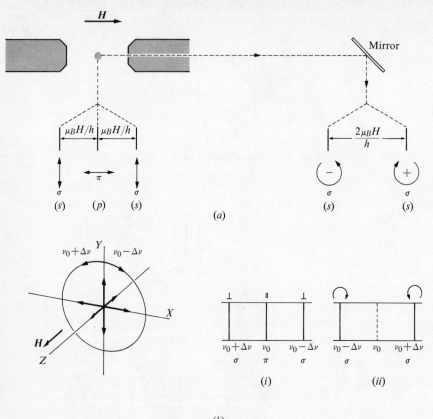

FIG. 10.30.   (a) *An experimental arrangement for observing the normal Zeeman effect both perpendicular and parallel to* **H**. (b) *Graphical representation of splitting in the normal Zeeman effect* (i) *perpendicular to* **H**, *and* (ii) *parallel to* **H**.

11.   THE STERN-GERLACH EXPERIMENT AND ELECTRON SPIN

The Stern-Gerlach experiment offers one of the most direct and convincing proofs of space quantization that limits the possible orientations of angular-momentum and magnetic-moment vectors in a magnetic field. Although the purpose of the original experiment performed by O. Stern and W. Gerlach[38] in 1921 was to investigate the space quantization of the spin angular-momentum vector, the experiment may very well be used to illustrate the space quantization of orbital as well as total angular-momenta vectors.

If an electron has an intrinsic spin angular-momentum, it may be regarded to have an intrinsic magnetic-moment. Thus an atom with such an

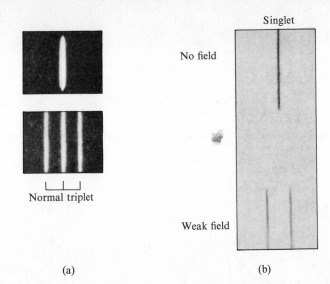

FIG. 10.31.   *Photographs of the normal Zeeman effect viewed* (a) *perpendicular and* (b) *parallel to the magnetic field for Zn and Cd singlets, respectively.* [*Printed with permission from H. E. White,* Introduction to Atomic Spectra, *p. 182. New York: McGraw-Hill Book Company, Inc., 1934.*]

intrinsic magnetic moment will behave like a small magnet. But if such a magnetic dipole is placed in a uniform magnetic field as shown in Fig. 10.32(a) (where $2a$ is the moment arm), the forces at the two poles are equal and opposite, constituting a couple. Because there is no net force, there is no translational motion of the atomic magnet, but because of the net torque there will be a rotational motion. In order to cause translational motion, the dipole magnet must be placed in an inhomogenous magnetic field. Those dipoles that are aligned along H, as shown in Fig. 10.32(b), will have more upward force than downward, because $H_1 > H_2$, or $qH_1 > qH_2$; such dipoles will drift along the $+Z$ axis. Those dipoles that are aligned opposite to H, as shown in Fig. 10.32(c), will drift along the $-Z$ axis.

The force acting on the dipole magnet may be calculated easily. Consider the case of an atom for which $l = 0$ that has only spin angular-momentum. According to Eq. (10.53) or Eq. (10.54)

$$\mu_s = -g_s \frac{eh}{4\pi mc} \sqrt{s(s+1)} = -g_s \frac{\mu_B}{\hbar} S$$

and the change in energy ΔE_s, in a uniform field H, according to Eq. (10.69) is

$$\Delta E_s = -\mu_s \cdot \mathbf{H}$$

Combining these two equations,

$$\Delta E_s = g_s \frac{eh}{4\pi mc} \sqrt{s(s+1)} \cos\theta \; H \tag{10.106}$$

or because $S \cos\theta = \sqrt{s(s+1)}\, \hbar \cos\theta = S_Z = m_s\, \hbar$

$$m_s = \sqrt{s(s+1)} \cos\theta \tag{10.107}$$

we get,

$$\Delta E_s = g_s m_s \frac{eh}{4\pi mc} H \tag{10.108}$$

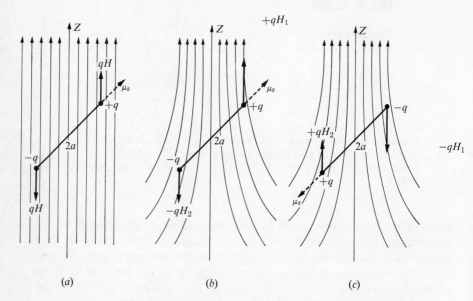

(a)   (b)   (c)

FIG. 10.32.   (a) *Forces acting on a small magnetic dipole when placed in a uniform magnetic field.* (b), (c) *A dipole magnet placed in an inhomogeneous magnetic field as shown will have a translational motion.*

But if the atomic magnet is placed in an inhomogenous magnetic field, the net force acting on the magnet may be calculated by differentiating Eq. (10.108) with respect to z, where the Z axis is the direction of symmetry of the inhomogeneous field as well as the direction of space quantization of electron spin.

$$F_z = -\frac{d}{dz}(\Delta E_s)$$

or

$$F_z = -g_s m_s \frac{eh}{4\pi mc} \frac{dH}{dz} \tag{10.109}$$

and dH/dz is the inhomogeneity of the magnetic field. Thus for the electron spin $s = \frac{1}{2}, m_s = \pm\frac{1}{2}$; and according to Eq. (10.109) the dipoles with $m_s = -\frac{1}{2}$

will drift toward the $+Z$ axis, and the dipoles with $m_s = +\frac{1}{2}$ will drift in the direction of the $-Z$ axis.

The actual experimental arrangement used by Stern and Gerlach is shown in Fig. 10.33. A narrow beam of silver atoms is obtained from an oven 0.

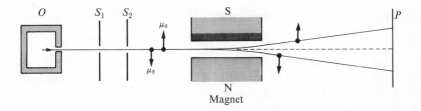

FIG. 10.33.   *The experimental arrangement used by Stern and Gerlach for observing intrinsic spin angular momentum of an electron.*

After passing the collimating slits S_1 and S_2, the beam passes through the inhomogeneous magnetic field, and is received on a photographic plate, P. The shape of the pole faces of the magnet is shown in Fig. 10.34. This form

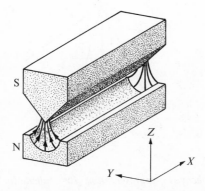

FIG. 10.34.   *The pole faces of a magnet for producing an inhomogeneous field used in the Stern-Gerlach experiment.*

of the inhomogeneous magnetic field satisfies the condition of inhomogeneity in Eq. (10.109), i.e., if the beam of atoms is moving along the X axis, then $\partial H/\partial z = \partial H_z/\partial z$, while $\partial H_z/\partial y = 0$. The impressions obtained on the photographic plates with and without the magnetic field are shown in Fig. 10.35.

For the silver atoms the ground state configuration is $5^2S_{1/2}$. This means that for the valence electron, $l = 0$, $j = s = \frac{1}{2}$, and, therefore, $m_s = \pm\frac{1}{2}$. Thus, according to space quantization, each level should split into two, with

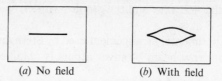

(*a*) No field   (*b*) With field

FIG. 10.35. *Impressions of the beam of silver atoms obtained on the photographic plate in the Stern-Gerlach experiment.* (a) *No field, and* (b) *with field.*

reference to some arbitrary axis in space. The reference axis is the Z axis in this case, and as is obvious from Fig. 10.36(b) for $s = \frac{1}{2}$, the multiplicity is $(2s + 1) = (2 \times \frac{1}{2} + 1) = 2$, with $m_s = -\frac{1}{2}$ or $+\frac{1}{2}$. This confirms qualitatively the space quantization of spin.

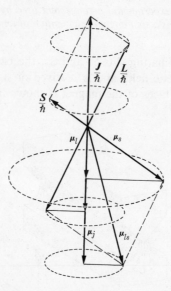

FIG. 10.36. *Schematic representation for calculation of the total angular-momentum vector,* μ_j.

It is also possible to evaluate g_s. Rewriting Eq. (10.109) by making the substitution $F_z = \overline{F}_z$, the average force, $(eh/4\pi mc) = \mu_B$, and $(dH/dz) = (dH_z/dz)$, we get

$$\overline{F}_z = g_s m_s \mu_B \frac{dH_z}{dz} \tag{10.110}$$

By measuring the splitting of the beam, one can calculate $\overline{F}_z$, (dH_z/dz) can be measured, and μ_B is known. Thus one can find the product $g_s m_s$. It has been found that

$$g_s m_s = \pm 1 \tag{10.111}$$

Thus if $m_s = \pm \frac{1}{2}$,

$$g_s = 2 \tag{10.112}$$

i.e., the spin g-factor is twice that of the orbital g-factor as assumed earlier.

Similar experiments have been performed with hydrogen, lithium, sodium, gold, and other atoms; all prove the space quantization of angular momentum. Experiments similar to these can be performed to prove qualitatively the space quantization of L and J vectors. Actually, the atomic-beam methods are used to find the multiplicities by counting the number of splittings, and then the values of s, l, or j may be obtained as the case may be.

12. THE TOTAL MAGNETIC MOMENT OF THE ATOM AND THE LANDÉ g-FACTOR

Before we can investigate the energy levels of an atom placed in an external uniform magnetic field, it is necessary to calculate the magnetic moment μ_j of the atom corresponding to the total angular momentum J of the valence electron, where

$$J = L + S \tag{10.113}$$

As shown in Fig. 10.36, as a result of the interaction between the vectors L and S, these vectors precess about their resultant vector J. According to Eq. (10.48), the magnetic moment due to the orbital motion is

$$\mu_l = -\frac{e}{2mc} L \tag{10.114}$$

The magnetic moment due to the spin of the electron is

$$\mu_s = -2 \frac{e}{2mc} S \tag{10.115}$$

Because of the negative charge, the directions of both μ_l and μ_s are opposite to L and S, respectively, as shown in Fig. 10.36. In this figure the scale chosen is such that the magnitude of the vector μ_l is equal to the magnitude of L. On this scale, because from Eqs. (10.114) and (10.115) the ratio of $\mu_s/S = -(e/mc)$ is twice that of $\mu_l/L = -(e/2mc)$, the length of the vector μ_s should be drawn twice that of S. Because of this relationship the resultant magnetic moment μ_{ls} is not along J as shown. We are interested in calculating μ_j, the magnetic moment along the direction of J. Because L and S precess about J, μ_l and μ_s must also precess about J. We must then resolve both μ_l and μ_s into two components each: $\mu_l \cos (L, J)$ and $\mu_s \cos (S, J)$, which are components parallel to J; and $\mu_l \sin (L, J)$ and $\mu_s \sin (S, J)$, which are components perpendicular to J. $\cos (L, J)$ is the cosine of the angle between L and J, with similar meanings for $\cos (S, J)$, $\sin (L, J)$, and $\sin (S, J)$. Because the perpendicular component of each vector is constantly changing in direction, the value of this perpendicular component averaged over a period of motion will be zero. The effective magnetic moment of the atom, μ_j, will therefore be equal to the sum of the parallel components, i.e.,

$$\mu_j = \mu_l \cos (\mathbf{L}, \mathbf{J}) + \mu_s \cos (\mathbf{S}, \mathbf{J}) \tag{10.116}$$

Substituting for μ_l and μ_s from Eqs. (10.114) and (10.115), and noting that $L = \sqrt{l(l+1)}\,\hbar$ and $S = \sqrt{s(s+1)}\,\hbar$, we get

$$\mu_j = \frac{eh}{4\pi mc} \left[\sqrt{l(l+1)} \cos (\mathbf{L}, \mathbf{J}) + 2\sqrt{s(s+1)} \cos (\mathbf{S}, \mathbf{J}) \right] \tag{10.117}$$

Applying the cosine law to the triangle formed by the three vectors $\mathbf{L}$, $\mathbf{S}$, and $\mathbf{J}$, we get

$$\cos (\mathbf{L}, \mathbf{J}) = \frac{j(j+1) + l(l+1) - s(s+1)}{2\sqrt{j(j+1)}\,\sqrt{l(l+1)}}$$

and

$$\cos (\mathbf{S}, \mathbf{J}) = \frac{j(j+1) + s(s+1) - l(l+1)}{2\sqrt{j(j+1)}\,\sqrt{s(s+1)}} \tag{10.118}$$

Combining Eqs. (10.117) and (10.118), we obtain

$$\mu_j = \frac{eh}{4\pi mc} \frac{3j(j+1) + s(s+1) - l(l+1)}{2\sqrt{j(j+1)}}$$

Multiplying the numerator and denominator of this equation by $\sqrt{j(j+1)}$ and rewriting,

$$\mu_j = \frac{eh}{4\pi mc} \sqrt{j(j+1)} \left[1 + \frac{j(j+1) + s(s+1) - l(l+1)}{2j(j+1)} \right] \tag{10.119}$$

or

$$\mu_j = g\sqrt{j(j+1)} \frac{eh}{4\pi mc} \tag{10.120}$$

where

$$g = 1 + \frac{j(j+1) + s(s+1) - l(l+1)}{2j(j+1)} \tag{10.121}$$

and g is called *the Landé g-factor*[39].

Because $eh/4\pi mc = \mu_B$, we may rewrite Eq. (10.120) as

$$\mu_j = g\mu_B J/\hbar$$

or

$$g = \frac{\mu_j/\mu_B}{\mathbf{J}/\hbar} \tag{10.122}$$

which says that *the Landé g-factor may be defined as the ratio of the magnetic moment of the system, in units of Bohr magneton, to its angular momentum, in units of $\hbar$.*

It may be pointed out that because g is a function of l, s, and j, the splitting of energy levels is also a function of these. If $s = 0$, Eq. (10.121) gives $g = 1$, as it should, and similarly, if $l = 0$, $g = 2$.

13. THE ANOMALOUS ZEEMAN EFFECT

The anomalous Zeeman effect is the splitting of an energy level and the resulting transitions between different states when an atom for which the spin, s, is not zero is placed in a weak magnetic field. The vector diagram is as shown in Fig. 10.37, where **L** and **S** precess rapidly around **J**, while **J** precesses

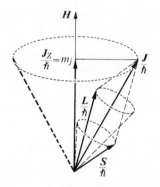

FIG. 10.37. *Vector diagram showing the rapid precession of* **L** *and* **S** *around* **J***, and the slow precession of* **J** *around* **H***.*

slowly around **H**, which is the direction of the external weak magnetic field. The condition that the applied magnetic field be weak is very important. If the applied field is weak as compared to the internal field, (which is due to the spin and orbital motions of the electron), it will insure that **L** and **S** precess around **J** and **J** precesses around **H**. If the applied field is strong, it may break the spin-orbit coupling in which case **J** will have no meaning (it ceases to exist), and we cannot talk of precession of **J** about **H**. In a typical case the weak magnetic field (weak compared to internal field but strong otherwise) is of the order of 30,000 gauss. (The case of a strong magnetic field in which the spin-orbit coupling breaks down is treated in Sec. 14 under the Paschen-Back effect.)

In a magnetic field, the projection of **J** is denoted by $J_Z = m_j\hbar$ and as already noted m_j can take the values: $-j$, $-(j-1)$, $\ldots$, -1, 0, 1, $\ldots$, $(j-1)$, j, which means that the multiplicity is $(2j+1)$. As an example, Fig. 10.38 shows the splitting of levels with $j = 1$ and $j = 5/2$ under the

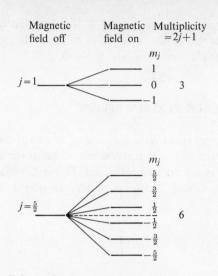

Magnetic   Magnetic   Multiplicity
field off   field on $=2j+1$

FIG. 10.38.   *Splitting (not to scale) of the levels with j = 1 and j = 5/2 under the influence of a weak magnetic field.*

influence of a weak magnetic field. The change in the energy when an atom is placed in an external field is given by

$$\Delta E = \mu_j H \cos (\mathbf{J}, \mathbf{H}) \qquad (10.123)$$

where μ_j is the magnetic moment of the atom given by Eq. (10.120). Hence

$$\Delta E = g\sqrt{j(j + 1)} \, \frac{eh}{4\pi mc} \, H \cos (\mathbf{J}, \mathbf{H}) \qquad (10.124)$$

Because $\sqrt{j(j + 1)} \cos (J, H) = m_j$, the total magnetic quantum number, we may rewrite Eq. (10.124) as

$$\Delta E = g m_j \frac{eh}{4\pi mc} H \qquad (10.125)$$

Dividing both sides by hc, we get the term value T (in cm^{-1}) as

$$T = g m_j \frac{eH}{4\pi mc^2} \qquad (10.126)$$

or

$$T = g m_j \mathsf{L} \qquad (10.127)$$

If H is fixed, and $(e/4\pi mc^2)$ is constant, then ΔE depends only on the product of $g m_j$. The product $(e/4\pi mc^2)H$, which will be a constant in a given magnetic field, is called a *Lorentz Unit* and is denoted by L. Thus the Lorentz unit is a unit of energy for expressing splitting in a magnetic field. As an example, Fig. 10.39 shows the splitting of the $^2P_{3/2}$ state in a weak magnetic field, where the splitting has been expressed in Lorentz units. In this case $j = 3/2$, therefore, $(2j + 1) = [2 \times (3/2) + 1] = 4$, i.e., $m_j = 3/2, 1/2,$

$-1/2$, $-3/2$. The value of g for $^2P_{3/2}$ calculated by substituting $j = 3/2$, $l = 1$, and $s = 1/2$ in Eq. (10.121) can be found:

$$g = 1 + \frac{\frac{3}{2}(\frac{3}{2} + 1) + \frac{1}{2}(\frac{1}{2} + 1) - 1(1 + 1)}{2\frac{3}{2}(\frac{3}{2} + 1)} = \frac{4}{3}$$

Thus for different values of $m_j g$, the splitting in Lorentz units is given by 2, $2/3$, $-2/3$, -2, as shown in Fig. 10.39, on the extreme right.

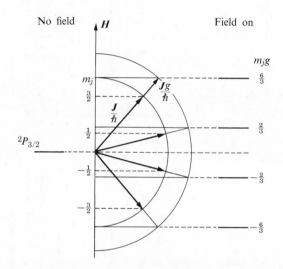

FIG. 10.39. *Graphical representation of the relative splitting (in Lorentz units) of a $^2P_{3/2}$ level in a weak magnetic field.*

In order to understand the patterns obtained in the anomalous Zeeman effect, let us consider a specific example of sodium D-lines, which are the transitions $^2P_{3/2} \rightarrow \, ^2S_{1/2}$ and $^2P_{1/2} \rightarrow \, ^2S_{1/2}$. A sodium flame or arc is placed in a weak magnetic field, and the light emitted is observed with the help of a spectroscope of high resolving power. Under the influence of a magnetic field, the $^2P_{3/2}$ level splits into four levels, the $^2P_{1/2}$ level splits into two levels, and the $^2S_{1/2}$ also splits into two levels as shown in Fig. 10.40. The shorter wavelength transition $^2P_{3/2} \rightarrow \, ^2S_{1/2}$ splits into six lines, while the longer wavelength transition $^2P_{1/2} \rightarrow \, ^2S_{1/2}$ splits into four lines. Table 10.6 shows the values of m_j and gm_j for different levels, i.e., the splitting is expressed in Lorentz units.

Figure 10.40 shows the transitions in a complete anomalous Zeeman pattern of sodium D-lines, and also shows the actual photograph. The transitions are governed by the selection rules in the following:

The theoretically derived selection rules agree completely with experi-

No field   Field on

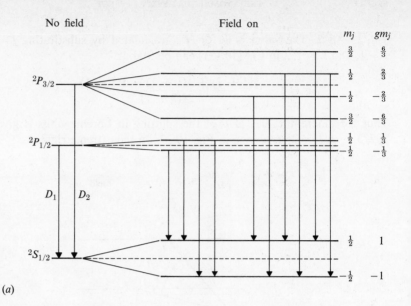

m_j gm_j

$\frac{3}{2}$ $\frac{6}{3}$

$\frac{1}{2}$ $\frac{2}{3}$

$-\frac{1}{2}$ $-\frac{2}{3}$

$-\frac{3}{2}$ $-\frac{6}{3}$

$^2P_{3/2}$

$^2P_{1/2}$

$\frac{1}{2}$ $\frac{1}{3}$

$-\frac{1}{2}$ $-\frac{1}{3}$

D_1 D_2

$^2S_{1/2}$

$\frac{1}{2}$ 1

$-\frac{1}{2}$ -1

(a)

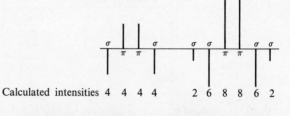

Calculated intensities 4 4 4 4   2 6 8 8 6 2

(b)

Sodium principal doublet

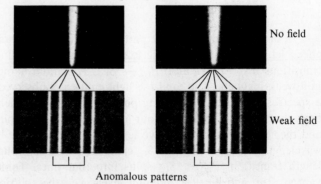

No field

Weak field

(c)   Anomalous patterns

FIG. 10.40. *Anomalous Zeeman effect in sodium D-lines showing* (a) *the levels and the transitions, with and without a field,* (b) *the calculated intensities, and* (c) *photograph (viewed perpendicular to the field).* [*Printed with permission from White, H. E.,* Introduction to Atomic Spectra, *p. 152. New York: McGraw-Hill Book Company, 1934.*]

TABLE 10.6
SPLITTING IN LORENTZ UNITS

State	l	s	j	g	m_j	gm_j
$3\,^2P_{3/2}$	1	$\frac{1}{2}$	$\frac{3}{2}$	$\frac{4}{3}$	$\frac{3}{2}, \frac{1}{2}, -\frac{1}{2}, -\frac{3}{2}$	$2, \frac{2}{3}, -\frac{2}{3}, -2$
$3\,^2P_{1/2}$	1	$\frac{1}{2}$	$\frac{1}{2}$	$\frac{2}{3}$	$\frac{1}{2}, -\frac{1}{2}$	$\frac{1}{3}, -\frac{1}{3}$
$3\,^2S_{1/2}$	0	$\frac{1}{2}$	$\frac{1}{2}$	2	$\frac{1}{2}, -\frac{1}{2}$	$1, -1$

mental observations. In addition to the condition that $\Delta l = \pm 1$, in any transition, the magnetic quantum-number m_j must change by $+1$, 0 or -1:

$$\Delta m_j = 0, \pm 1 \qquad \qquad (10.128)$$

The allowed transitions are shown in Fig. 10.40, for the Zeeman effect of a principal-series doublet.

The polarization rules mentioned earlier and derived from classical, as well as quantum, theory are in agreement with experiment; see Eq. (10.105).

The intensity rules derived for the field free level are easily applied to the case of levels in a weak magnetic field, and may be stated as: The sum of the intensities of all the transitions leaving from (or arriving at) any Zeeman level is equal to the sum of the intensities of all transitions leaving from (or arriving at) any other level having the same n and l values. All the above rules are demonstrated in the Zeeman pattern shown in Fig. 10.40.

14. THE PASCHEN-BACK EFFECT

The condition imposed for observing the anomalous Zeeman pattern of spectral lines was an applied magnetic field that is weak as compared to the internal magnetic field. This in turn implied that the vectors **L** and **S** precess very fast about **J** as compared to the precession of **J** about **H**. In this way we could discuss the pattern in terms of the vector **J** and its projection J_Z. If the magnetic field is continuously increased so that magnetic splitting becomes greater than the multiplet splitting, the precessional frequency of **J** about **H** becomes greater than the precessional frequencies of **L** and **S** about **J**. Under these conditions the motion becomes complicated and the precession of **J** about **H** will be irregular, and, in addition, the perpendicular components of μ_l and μ_s will not cancel when averaged over a period.

If the field is increased further and is made large, the result is that the coupling between **L** and **S** completely breaks down. This means that the **J** disappears completely, while **L** and **S** each precess independently about the magnetic field axis **H**, as shown in Fig. 10.41. F. Paschen and E. Back[40,41] found that whatever may be the Zeeman pattern of the spectral lines in a weak magnetic field, these patterns under the influence of a strong magnetic field always approximate the triplet pattern characteristic of the normal

Zeeman effect. The Paschen-Back effect is thus defined as the observance of patterns of spectral lines under a strong magnetic field.

As shown in Fig. 10.41, the quantum numbers in a strong magnetic

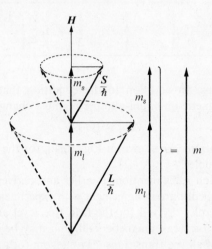

FIG. 10.41.   *Independent precession of* **L** *and* **S** *about* **H** *in the presence of a strong magnetic field.*

field, or in the Paschen-Back effect, are (1) m_l and (2) m_s (instead of j and m_j as in a weak field). (1) m_l is the projection of $\mathbf{L}/\hbar$ on **H** and can take the values $-l, -(l-1), \ldots, -1, 0, 1, \ldots, +l$, i.e., $(2l+1)$ values. (2) m_s is the projection of $\mathbf{S}/\hbar$ on **H** and can take the values $+\frac{1}{2}$ or $-\frac{1}{2}$, i.e., only two values. Because for each value of m_l there are two values of m_s, the total number of levels in a strong magnetic field will be $2(2l+1)$, which is the same number as in a weak field. For example, for an s-electron, $l = 0$, $s = \frac{1}{2}$, accordingly the two states are $(m_l = 0, m_s = +\frac{1}{2})$ and $(m_l = 0, m_s = -\frac{1}{2})$. Similarly, for a p-electron, $l = 1$ and $s = \frac{1}{2}$, there are six possible states $(m_l = +1, m_s = \frac{1}{2})$, $(m_l = 0, m_s = +\frac{1}{2})$, $(m_l = -1, m_s = \frac{1}{2})$, $(m_l = 1, m_s = -\frac{1}{2})$, $(m_l = 0, m_s = -\frac{1}{2})$, and $(m_l = -1, m_s = -\frac{1}{2})$, as illustrated in Fig. 10.42.

The selection rules for the transitions between these levels are the following.

$$\Delta m_l = 0, \pm 1 \quad \text{and} \quad \Delta m_s = 0 \tag{10.129}$$

These selection rules may be derived theoretically and have been experimentally verified.

The total energy of an atom placed in a strong magnetic field consists of three parts: (1) the energy due to the precession of **L** around **H**, (2) the energy due to the precession of **S** about **H**, (3) the interaction energy between **L** and **S**. Even though the vectors **L** and **S** precess independently, the magnetic field produced by one interacts with the field produced by the other. Because the interaction energy between **L** and **S** is very small, in the first approximation we may neglect this. According to Larmor's theorem, the precessional angular velocities ω_l and ω_s about H are

$$\omega_l = \frac{e}{2mc} H \qquad\qquad (10.130)$$

and

$$\omega_s = 2 \frac{e}{2mc} H \qquad\qquad (10.131)$$

Multiplying these angular velocities by the projections of **L** and **S** on **H**, we get the corresponding energies.

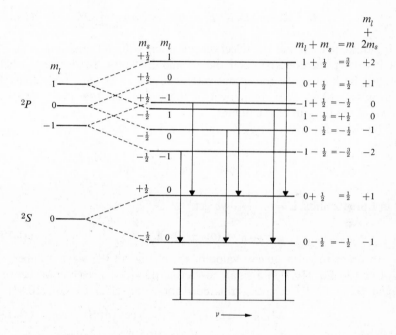

FIG. 10.42.   *The Paschen-Back effect of $^2P \rightarrow {}^2S$ transition, i.e., $^2P \rightarrow {}^2S$ transition in a strong magnetic field.*

Thus the energy due to the precession of **L** around **H** is

$$\Delta E_{\text{L}\cdot\text{H}} = \frac{e}{2mc} HL \cos(\text{L, H}) = m_l \frac{eh}{4\pi mc} H \qquad (10.132)$$

where

$$m_l = L_{Z/\hbar} = \frac{L \cos(\text{L, H})}{h} = \sqrt{l(l+1)} \cos(\text{L, H}). \qquad (10.133)$$

Similarly, the energy due to the precession of $\mathbf{S}$ around $\mathbf{H}$ is

$$\Delta E_{\text{S}\cdot\text{H}} = 2\frac{e}{2mc}HS\cos(\text{S, H}) = 2m_s\frac{eh}{4\pi mc}H \qquad (10.134)$$

where $m_s = S_{Z/\hbar} = S\cos(S, H)/(\hbar) = \sqrt{s(s+1)}\cos(\text{S, H})$. Thus the total change in the energy (neglecting the small interaction energy between $\mathbf{L}$ and $\mathbf{S}$), is given by adding Eqs. (10.132) and (10.134), i.e.,

$$\Delta E_H = \Delta E_{\text{L}\cdot\text{H}} + \Delta E_{\text{S}\cdot\text{H}}$$

or

$$\Delta E_H = (m_l + 2m_s)\frac{eh}{4\pi mc}H \qquad (10.135)$$

Thus the energy of any level in a strong magnetic field is

$$E = E_0 + \Delta E_H = E_0 + (m_l + 2m_s)\frac{eh}{4\pi mc}H \qquad (10.136)$$

Using this equation and the selection rules $\Delta m_l = 0, \pm 1$, and $\Delta m_s = 0$, one obtains the transitions between the ^2P and ^2S states. In this case of the Paschen-Back effect the transitions with equal values of Δm_l nearly coincide. Thus in Fig. 10.42, each component of the triplet has two components as shown at the bottom of the figure.

Dividing Eq. (10.135) by hc and rewriting, the shift in the term value ΔT_H is

$$-\Delta T_H = (m_l + 2m_s)\frac{eH}{4\pi mc^2}\text{ cm}^{-1} \qquad (10.137)$$

or in Lorentz units, $\mathbf{L} = \dfrac{eH}{4\pi mc}$, we get

$$-\Delta T_H = (m_l + 2m_s)\mathbf{L}\text{ cm}^{-1} \qquad (10.138)$$

In order to get a precise value of the change in the wave number, we must add to Eq. (10.138) a small correction due to the interaction between $\mathbf{L}$ and $\mathbf{S}$. In field free-space, this correction according to Eq. (10.85), is

$$-\Delta T_{\text{L}\cdot\text{S}} = \Delta E_{\text{S}\cdot\text{L}}/hc = a'LS\cos(\text{L, S}) \qquad (10.139)$$

where $a' = a/hc$ is constant, given by Eq. (10.86), and $\cos(\text{L, S})$ remains constant. But in the presence of a magnetic field, this is constantly changing, and we must use the average value given by finding the average value of $\cos(\text{L, S})$, i.e.,

$$\langle\cos(\text{L, S})\rangle_{\text{av}} = \cos(\text{L, H})\cos(\text{S, H}) \qquad (10.140)$$

Therefore,

$$\begin{aligned}
-\Delta T_{\text{L}\cdot\text{S}} &= a'LS\langle\cos(\text{L, S})\rangle_{\text{av}} \\
&= a'L\cos(\text{L, H})S\cos(\text{S, H}) \qquad (10.141) \\
&= a'L_Z S_Z = a'm_l m_s
\end{aligned}$$

The total shift in the energy, in units of wave numbers, is given by adding Eqs. (10.138) and (10.141), i.e., ΔT in cm^{-1} becomes

$$-\Delta T = (m_l + 2m_s)\mathbf{L} + am_l m_s \qquad (10.142)$$

and the general expression for any energy level in a strong magnetic field is given by

$$T(\text{cm}^{-1}) = T_0 - (m_l + 2m_s)\mathbf{L} - am_l m_s \qquad (10.143)$$

The levels and the resulting transitions shown at the extreme right of Fig. 10.43 are the ones obtained in Fig. 10.42, except that a small correction given by Eq. (10.141) has been added.

Figure 10.43 shows all the changes in the energy levels and the corre-

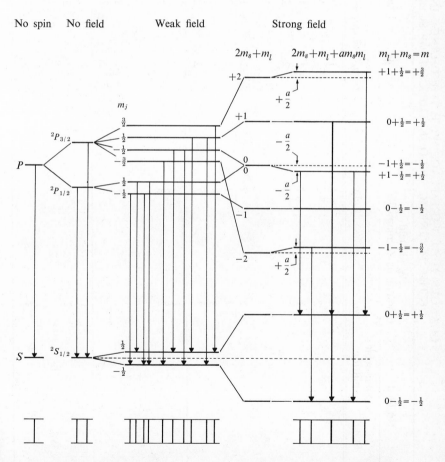

Fig. 10.43. *The changes in the energy levels and the corresponding transitions starting from no spin and no field progressing to a weak field and finally to a strong field.*

TABLE 10.7

CHANGES THAT TAKE PLACE WITH THE CHANGE IN THE STRENGTH OF THE MAGNETIC FIELD IN THE CASE OF SODIUM D-LINES

No field		Weak field (anomalous Zeeman effect)			Strong field (Paschen-Back effect)					
State	Spin-orbit splitting	m_j	g	$m_j g$	m_l	m_s	$m = m_l + m_s$	am_lm_s	$m_l + 2m_s$	$m_l + 2m_s + am_lm_s$
$^2P_{3/2}$	$+\dfrac{a}{2}$	$+\dfrac{3}{2}$	$\dfrac{4}{3}$	$+\dfrac{6}{3}$	$+1$	$+\dfrac{1}{2}$	$+\dfrac{3}{2}$	$+\dfrac{a}{2}$	$+2$	$2+\dfrac{a}{2}$
		$+\dfrac{1}{2}$		$+\dfrac{2}{3}$	0	$+\dfrac{1}{2}$	$+\dfrac{1}{2}$	0	$+1$	$+1$
		$-\dfrac{1}{2}$		$-\dfrac{2}{3}$	-1	$+\dfrac{1}{2}$	$-\dfrac{1}{2}$	$-\dfrac{a}{2}$	0	$-\dfrac{a}{2}$
		$-\dfrac{3}{2}$		$-\dfrac{6}{3}$	$+1$	$-\dfrac{1}{2}$	$+\dfrac{1}{2}$	$-\dfrac{a}{2}$	0	$-\dfrac{a}{2}$
$^2P_{1/2}$	$-a$	$+\dfrac{1}{2}$	$\dfrac{2}{3}$	$+\dfrac{1}{3}$	0	$-\dfrac{1}{2}$	$-\dfrac{1}{2}$	0	-1	-1
		$-\dfrac{1}{2}$		$-\dfrac{1}{3}$	-1	$-\dfrac{1}{2}$	$-\dfrac{3}{2}$	$+\dfrac{a}{2}$	-2	$-2+\dfrac{a}{2}$
$^2S_{1/2}$	0	$+\dfrac{1}{2}$	2	$+1$	0	$+\dfrac{1}{2}$	$+\dfrac{1}{2}$	0	$+1$	$+1$
		$-\dfrac{1}{2}$		-1	0	$-\dfrac{1}{2}$	$-\dfrac{1}{2}$	0	-1	1

sponding transitions starting from no spin and no field to weak field and then to strong field. Table 10.7 shows the corresponding changes in terms of the quantum numbers.

PROBLEMS

1. Calculate the values of the total angular momentum for an f-electron and a g-electron according to (a) the quantum-mechanical model, (b) the Sommerfeld model (vector model) and (c) the Bohr-Sommerfeld model.

2. Calculate the angles between the vectors $\mathbf{L}$ and $\mathbf{S}$ for the f- and g-electrons according to the quantum-mechanical model.

3. Find the angles between the total and the orbital angular-momentum vectors for the following states: (a) $^2D_{3/2}$, (b) $^2D_{5/2}$, (c) $^2F_{5/2}$, and (d) $^2F_{7/2}$.

4. Write the electron configuration of the following: (a) S, (b) Si, (c) Ca, and (d) Br.

5. Write the electron configuration of the following in their ground states: (a) Zn ($Z = 30$), (b) Al ($Z = 13$), (c) Ag ($Z = 47$), and (d) Hg ($Z = 80$). Show diagrammatic representations of the configurations.

6. How many elements would there be if atoms could be formed having electrons with principal quantum-numbers up to $n = 7$? Why are there no stable elements with $Z > 92$?

7. Consider an atom with an electron configuration of $1s^22s^22p^63s^23p^1$. What are the values of l, s, and j and the corresponding angular momenta?

8. Consider an atom with an electron configuration of $1s^22s^22p^63s^23p^64s^23d^1$. What are the values of the quantum numbers l, s, and j and the corresponding angular momenta?

9. What are the four quantum numbers of the third electron in Li ($Z = 3$) for the two lowest excited states? What are the wavelengths of the transitions from these excited states to the ground state?

10. Referring to Fig. 10.14, calculate the value of r_{max} in units of a_0 for the elliptical orbits for Li, Na, K, Rb, and Cs. (Note that $r = r_{max}$ when the energy is all potential, and also at this point the potential energy is equal to the ionization potential.)

11. List all possible transitions that will occur for the sodium atom in the (a) $5P$ state, (b) $5D$ state, and (c) $5F$ state.

12. The sodium D-lines have wavelengths of 5890 Å and 5896 Å. (a) Calculate the wave numbers of these two lines. (b) Calculate the energies in electron volts and ergs of the levels from which transitions start. The ionization energy of sodium is 5.13 eV.

13. The wavelengths of the principal series of a certain element are found to be 6707.8 Å, 3232.6 Å, 2741.3 Å, 2562.5 Å, and 2475.3 Å with a series limit of 43,486 cm^{-1}.
    (a) What are the wavelengths in terms of wave numbers?
    (b) Calculate the ionization potential.
    (c) Calculate the first resonance potential.

14. Assuming $_3$Li to be a hydrogen-like atom, calculate the ionization energy of

the 2s-valence-electron. How does this compare with the experimental value of 5.39 eV? Can you get some idea of the quantum defect from this?

15. Calculate the screening constant and the effective positive charge for the valence electron of sodium ($Z = 11$) when the atom is in the ground state. The ionization energy for the 3s-electron in sodium is 5.14 eV.

16. Why in the absorption spectrum of sodium are only P-series observed? (Calculate the lifetime of the excited state by using the uncertainty principle.)

17. Calculate approximately the wavelength of the $3P \rightarrow 3S$ transition in the singly ionized Mg atom ($Z = 12$), and compare it with the value obtained from the Na atom.

18. The values of the quantum defects for the S-, P-, and D-levels in Li ($Z = 3$) are 0.40, 0.04, and 0.001, respectively. If we want to express an energy-level diagram in terms of the screening constants instead of the quantum defects, what are the values of the screening constants for these levels?

19. The values of the quantum defects for the s-, p-, and d-levels in Na ($Z = 11$) are 1.37, 0.88, and 0.01, respectively. If we want to express an energy-level diagram in terms of the screening constants instead of the quantum defects, what are the values of the screening constants for these levels?

20. The term values of the levels in potassium corresponding to $n = 4$, 5, 6, and 7 are 22,021 cm^{-1}, 10,304 cm^{-1}, 6009 cm^{-1}, and 3934 cm^{-1}, respectively. Transitions between these levels and a level with a term value of 35,006 cm^{-1} form a series. (a) Calculate the wavelength of each line. (b) Calculate the energy of each level in electron volts. (c) Calculate the quantum defects of the initial levels so as to be in agreement with their term values.

21. Derive an expression for μ_l, assuming that the electron is moving in a circular orbit.

22. Show that if a simple electric or magnetic dipole is placed in a uniform field, there is no net force acting on it.

23. Suppose that the electron may be treated as a sphere of radius 3×10^{-13} cm, and the mass and charge of the electron are uniformly distributed over this sphere. (a) If the electron has a spin angular-momentum of $(\sqrt{3/2})\hbar$, what should be the angular velocity of the spinning electron. (b) Calculate the magnetic moment of the electron according to this model and compare it with the correct value.

24. Calculate (a) the electric current and (b) the magnetic dipole-moment of an electron in the hydrogen atom in the first three Bohr orbits, i.e., for $n = 1, 2, 3$.

25. Calculate the precessional frequencies of the s-, p-, d-, and f-electrons when the atoms are placed in a magnetic field of 25,000 gauss.

26. An atom with an angular momentum of $2\hbar$ and magnetic moment of 2 Bohr magnetons is placed in a magnetic field of 1.5 weber/m^2. If the magnetic moment makes an angle of 30°, calculate (a) the torque on the atom and (b) the rate of precession.

27. Calculate the energy difference between the two electron-spin orientations in a magnetic field of flux density B.

28. Radio frequency signals can induce electron-spin transitions to change from a parallel to antiparallel orientation, and vice versa. Calculate the frequency (radio frequency) of a signal that will cause such a transition in a magnetic flux of 0.50 weber/m^2. (This is *spin flip*, or *spin resonance*.)

29. Fine structure can be investigated by means of direct transitions between fine-structure components. These transitions lie in the radio-frequency or micro-wave region. Calculate the frequency that will cause a transition (absorption in this case) between $3^2P_{1/2}$ and $3^2P_{3/2}$ states of sodium. Note that the wavelengths of the transitions $3^2P_{1/2,3/2} \rightarrow 3^2S_{1/2}$ are 5889.95 Å and 5895.92 Å.

30. Show that the spin-orbit splitting energy expression may be written as

$$\Delta E_{S \cdot L} = \frac{1}{2m^2c^2} \frac{1}{r} \frac{dV(r)}{dr} \mathbf{S} \cdot \mathbf{L}$$

where $V(r) = -(1/4\pi\epsilon_0)(e^2/r)$. It may also be written as

$$\Delta E_{S \cdot L} = \frac{1}{2} g_s \frac{e}{2m} \mathbf{S} \cdot \mathbf{H}_l$$

31. The measured separation between the two sodium levels $3^2P_{3/2}$ and $3^2P_{1/2}$ is 5.97 Å. What is the value of the constant a in the expression $\Delta E_{S \cdot L} = a\mathbf{S} \cdot \mathbf{L}$.

32. Calculate the order of the magnetic field that produces spin-orbit splitting in sodium D-lines.

33. Calculate the spin-orbit interactions if $s = \frac{1}{2}$, and $l = 5, 10$, and 20. Show that for large values of l, the spin and the orbital angular-momentum vectors are almost at right angles to each other for both values of $j (=l \pm \frac{1}{2})$.

34. Show that in the case of spin-orbit interactions, m_s and m_l are not valid quantum numbers but m_j is (i.e., L_z and S_z cannot have well-defined values while J_z has a well-defined value).

35. Draw an energy-level diagram for the $4F$ and $3D$ states of an atom placed in a magnetic field assuming that the resultant spin angular momentum is zero. Calculate also the separation between the adjacent normal Zeeman components. The field applied is 1.00 weber/m².

36. Suppose a spectrometer can resolve lines that are separated by 0.05 Å. What should be the value of the magnetic field H in order to see the normal Zeeman components of the transition between $5F$ and $4D$ states.

37. One of the methods by which the value of e/m may be measured is the normal Zeeman effect. Obtain an expression for e/m in terms of B and the separation $(\nu - \nu_0)$ between different components.

38. Consider the classical picture of an electron moving in a circular orbit with an angular frequency ω_0 under the influence of a centripetal force $m\omega_0^2 r$. If a magnetic field of flux density B is applied at right angles to the plane of the orbit, show that the new frequency ω is

$$\omega = \sqrt{\omega_0^2 + (2B/2m)^2} \pm (eB/2\omega)$$

What is the justification for saying that this is almost the same as

$$\omega = \omega_0 \pm (eB/2m)$$

39. Consider the Stern-Gerlach experiment in which silver atoms are heated to 1000° K. A beam of these atoms passes through an inhomogeneous magnetic field of gradient 0.75 (weber/m²)/cm over a distance of 10 cm. The beam passes through another 12 cm of free space (no magnetic field), striking a photographic plate. Calculate the separation between the two lines on the plate. Note that $(1/2)mv^2 = (3/2)kT$. (1 weber/m² = 10^4 gauss)

40. A beam of silver atoms with a velocity of 5×10^4 cm/sec passes through an inhomogeneous magnetic field 10 cm long with a gradient of 0.50 (weber/m²)/cm in a direction perpendicular to the motion of the atoms. Calculate the maximum separation between the two beams just as they emerge from the magnetic field region. (1 weber/m² $= 10^4$ gauss)

41. A beam of hydrogen atoms with velocity 5×10^6 cm/sec passes through a field of gradient 0.50 (weber/m²)/cm for 1 m in a direction perpendicular to this field. Assume that the electron spins are either parallel or antiparallel to this field. Calculate (a) the force exerted on the atoms, and (b) the vertical displacement. (1 weber/m² $= 10^4$ gauss)

42. Show that the total angular-momentum and the total magnetic-moment of an atom with a closed subshell is zero.

43. Suppose the ground state of an atom is $^2F_{7/2}$. Calculate the Landé g-factor and the magnetic moment.

44. Calculate the total angular-momentum and total magnetic-moment of Al ($Z = 13$) in its ground state.

45. Calculate in terms of eV and wave numbers the separation between the Zeeman component of sodium D-lines under the influence of a magnetic field of 25,000 gauss.

46. Draw the anamolous Zeeman pattern of the first three diffused lines of sodium, i.e., $3^2D_{5/2,3/2} \rightarrow 3^2P_{3/2,1/2}$. Assuming that the magnetic field is 30,000 gauss, calculate the frequencies of all the allowed Zeeman components.

47. Draw the energy levels of the states $^2D_{5/2,3/2}$ in (a) a weak field, and (b) in a field very strong compared with the spin-orbit interaction.

48. Consider the transitions $3^2D_{5/2,3/2} \rightarrow 3^2P_{3/2,1/2}$ in sodium. If the magnetic field applied is much stronger than the spin-orbit coupling interaction, draw the possible levels and the transitions (Paschen-Back effect).

49. In Prob. 10.48, if the field is 50,000 gauss, calculate the separations (in eV) of different components and the frequencies of different transitions.

REFERENCES

1. Sommerfeld, A., *Ann. Physik*, **51**, 1, (1916).

2. Back, E., and A. Landé, *Zeemaneffekt and Multiplettstruktur*, Berlin: Springer, 1925.

3. Sommerfeld, A., *Atombau*, 4th ed. Also Pauling and Goudsmit, The Structure of Line Spectra, Ch. II. New York: McGraw-Hill Book Co., 1930.

4. Condon, E. U., and P. M. Morse, *Quantum Mechanics*; see also references in Chap. IX.

5. Uhlenbeck, G. E., and S. Goudsmit, *Physics*, **5**, 266, (1925); *Nature*, **107**, 264, (1920).

6. Bichowsky, F. R., and H. C. Urey, *Proc. Nat. Acad. Sci.*, **12**, 80, (1926).

7. Pauli, W., *Zeit. fur Physik*, **31**, 765, (1925).

8. Dirac, P. A. M., *Proc. Roy. Soc.*, A112, 661, (1926); also W. Heisenberg, *Zeit. fur Physik*, **38**, 411, (1926).

9. White, H. E., *Introduction to Atomic Spectra*, Chap. VII, p. 101. New York: McGraw-Hill Book Company, 1934.

10. Hartree, D. R., *Proc. Camb. Phil. Soc.*, **24**, 89, 111, (1928).

11. Pauling, L., *Proc. Roy. Soc.*, **A114**, 181, (1927).

12. Thomas, L. H., *Proc. Camb. Phil. Soc.*, **23**, 542, (1927).

13. Born, M., and W. Heisenberg, *Zeit. fur Physik*, **23**, 388, (1924).

14. Pauling, L., and S. Goudsmit, *Structure of Line Spectra*, p. 45. New York: McGraw-Hill Book Company, Inc., 1930.

15. Van Vleck, J. H., and N. G. Whitelaw, *Phys. Rev.*, **44**, 551, (1933).

16. Wentzel, G., *Zeit. fur Physik*, **19**, 53, (1923).

17. Van Urk, A. T., *Zeit. fur Physik*, **13**, 268, (1923).

18. Wilson, E. B., *Jour. Chem. Phys.*, **1**, 210, (1933).

19. Slater, J. C., *Phys. Rev.*, **34**, 1293, (1928), and **42**, 33, (1932).

20. Schrödinger, E., *Zeit. fur Physik*, **4**, 347, (1921).

21. Millikan, R. A., and I. S. Brown, *Phys. Rev.*, **23**, 764, (1924); also A. Landé, *Zeit. fur Physik*, **25**, 46, (1924).

22. Schiff, L. I., *Quantum Mechanics*, p. 175. New York: McGraw-Hill Book Company, 1955.

23. Urk, A. Th. Van, *Zeit. fur Physik*, **13**, 268, (1923).

24. Burger, H. C., and H. B. Dorgelo, *Zeit. fur Physik*, **23**, 258, (1924).

25. Slater, J. C., and N. H. Frank, *Electromagnetism*, p. 59. New York: McGraw-Hill Book Company, 1947.

26. Cohen, E. R., and J. W. M. DuMond, *Revs. Mod. Phys.*, **37**, 537, (1965).

27. Goldstein, H., *Classical Mechanics*, p. 176. Reading, Mass.: Addison-Wesley Publishing Co., Inc., 1959.

28. Goldstein, H., *Classical Mechanics*, p. 132. Reading, Mass.: Addison-Wesley Publishing Co., Inc., 1959.

29. Pauli, W., *Zeit. fur Physik*, **43**, 601, (1927).

30. Darwin, C. G., *Proc. Roy. Soc.*, **A116**, 227, (1927), and **A118**, 654, (1928).

31. Dirac, P. A. M., *Proc. Roy. Soc.*, **A117**, 616, (1927), and **A118**, 351, (1928).

32. Gordon, W., *Zeit. fur Physik*, **48**, 11, (1929).

33. White, H. E., *Introduction to Atomic Spectra*, p. 124. New York: McGraw-Hill Book Company, 1934.

34. Thomas, L. H., *Nature*, **117**, 514, (1926).

35. Landé, A., *Zeit. fur Physik*, **25**, 46, (1924).

36. Sommerfeld, A., *Ann. Physik*, **51**, 1, (1916).

37. Zeeman, P., *Phil. Mag.*, **5**, 43, 226, (1897).

38. Stern, O., and W. Gerlach, *Zeit. fur Physik*, **8**, 110, (1921), and **9**, 349, 353, (1922); *Ann. Physik*, **74**, 673, (1924).

39. Landé, A., *Zeit. fur Physik*, **5**, 231, (1921), and **25**, 46, (1924).

40. Paschen, R., and E. Back, *Ann. Physik*, **39**, 897, (1912), and **40**, 960, (1913).

41. Paschen, F., and E. Back, *Physics*, **1**, 261, (1921).

SUGGESTIONS FOR FURTHER READING

1. White, H. E., *Introduction to Atomic Spectra*, Chaps. V, VII, VIII, IX, and X. New York: McGraw-Hill Book Company, 1934.

2. Herzberg, G., *Atomic Spectra and Atomic Structure*, Chap. II. New York: Dover Publications, Inc., 1944.

3. Richtmyer, R. F., E. H. Kennard, and T. Lauritsen, *Introduction to Modern Physics*, 5th ed., Chap. 7. New York: McGraw-Hill Book Company, 1955.

4. Eisberg, R. M., *Fundamentals of Modern Physics*, Chap. 11. New York: John Wiley & Sons, Inc., 1961.

5. Slater, J. C., *Quantum Theory of Matter*, 2nd ed., New York: McGraw-Hill Book Company, 1968.

6. Shore, B. W., and D. H. Menzel, *Principles of Atomic Spectra*, New York: John Wiley & Sons, Inc., 1968.

7. Condon, E. U., and G. H. Shortley, *The Theory of Atomic Spectra*, Cambridge: Cambridge Univ. Press, 1963.

8. Pauling, L., and S. Goudsmit, *The Structure of Line Spectra*. New York: McGraw-Hill Book Company, 1930.

XI

Spectra of Atoms with Two or More Valence Electrons

1. COUPLING SCHEMES FOR ATOMS WITH TWO OR MORE VALENCE ELECTRONS

In the last chapter we investigated atoms with only one valence electron, and we were concerned with the total, orbital, and spin angular-momenta quantum numbers j, l, and s, respectively, which are connected by the relation $\mathbf{J} = \mathbf{L} + \mathbf{S}$, where $J = \sqrt{j(j+1)}\,\hbar$, $L = \sqrt{l(l+1)}\,\hbar$, and $S = \sqrt{s(s+1)}\,\hbar$. In the case of atoms that have more than one valence electron, *each* electron has orbital angular momentum as well as spin angular momentum. Before investigating the energy-level diagrams and the spectra emitted, it is necessary to know something about the way these orbital and spin angular-momenta are coupled to form the resultant angular momentum. Once again it may be assumed that the electrons in completed shells and subshells form an inert core that do not contribute to the total resultant angular-momentum of the atom.

There are two coupling models that we shall discuss: the LS-, or Russell-Saunders, coupling[1], and the jj-coupling[2]. The LS-coupling, which is sometimes called the normal coupling, is valid most of the time for light- and medium-weight atoms, that is, for atoms with low and medium Z. For atoms with high Z, the jj-coupling is more common. The division into these two types of coupling may be explained by the spin-orbit interaction[3], and the electrostatic Coulomb interaction[4] of the electrons outside the core. The Coulomb interaction is much larger than, and should not be confused with,

415

the magnetic interaction due to the spin of the valence electrons. The Coulomb interaction, also called the residual electrostatic interaction, is defined as the difference between the true electrostatic interaction energy and the average value representing the modified field that is used in the Schrödinger wave equation for the many-electron atoms. It so happens that for atoms with low and medium Z, splitting that results from the Coulomb interaction is much greater than the spin-orbit splitting. This leads to the strong coupling between the spin angular-momenta and, also, separately between the orbital angular-momenta of the valence electrons, as we shall explain in the discussion of LS-coupling. On the other hand, for atoms of high Z, the spin-orbit splitting is much larger than the splitting due to the Coulomb interaction. This leads to a strong coupling between the spin and orbital angular-momenta of each valence electron and will be examined in detail in the discussion of jj-coupling.

It may be pointed out that the LS-coupling and the jj-coupling are the two extreme cases. There are situations in which both types of couplings take place, called the intermediate coupling, but these cases are difficult to handle theoretically and will be omitted from further discussions.

A. The LS-, or Russell-Saunders, Coupling[1]

As mentioned earlier, this type of coupling seems to apply most frequently to low and medium Z. In this coupling the orbital angular-momentum vectors $\mathbf{L}_i$ (where $L_i = \sqrt{l_i(l_i + 1)}\,\hbar$) of each valence electron combine together to give a resultant orbital angular-momentum vector $\mathbf{L}_t$ (where $L_t = \sqrt{l_t(l_t + 1)}\,\hbar$). It is assumed that the individual $\mathbf{L}_i$ vectors are so strongly coupled with one another (i.e., they are precessing very fast around $\mathbf{L}_t$) that states with different resultant $\mathbf{L}_t$ have very different energies. Quantum mechanically, l_t can take only integer values. This type of coupling between different $\mathbf{L}_i$ is called the ll-coupling and is written mathematically as

$$\mathbf{L}_1 + \mathbf{L}_2 + \mathbf{L}_3 + \ldots + \mathbf{L}_i = \mathbf{L}_t \tag{11.1a}$$

where

$$|\mathbf{L}_t| = L_t = \sqrt{l_t(l_t + 1)}\,\hbar \tag{11.1b}$$

Some examples of ll-coupling for the case of two-valence electron atoms are shown in Fig. 11.1. Of course if $l_1 = 1$, and $l_2 = 0$, then $l_t = 1$; l_t has only one value. But as we see from Fig. 11.1(a), if $l_1 = 1$ and $l_2 = 1$, then $\mathbf{L}_t = \mathbf{L}_1 + \mathbf{L}_2$, or $l_t = 2, 1, 0$, thus $L_t (= \sqrt{l_t(l_t + 1)}\,\hbar)$ can have three possible values. Similarly, if $l_1 = 2$ and $l_2 = 1$, then as shown in Fig. 11.1(b), $l_t = 3, 2, 1$, thus L_t has three possible values. This process can be extended to the many-electron systems as well as to higher orbital angular-momentum states.

Figure 11.2(a) shows how $\mathbf{L}_1$ and $\mathbf{L}_2$ precess about their resultant vector $\mathbf{L}_t$. The magnitude and direction of $\mathbf{L}_t$ depends upon the magnitudes and the

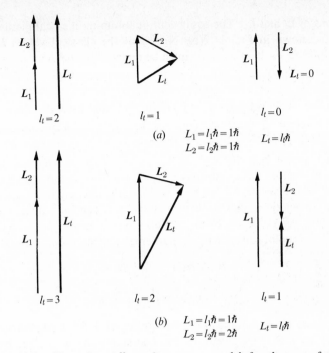

(a) $L_1 = l_1\hbar = 1\hbar$
       $L_2 = l_2\hbar = 1\hbar$ $L_t = l_t\hbar$

(b) $L_1 = l_1\hbar = 1\hbar$
       $L_2 = l_2\hbar = 2\hbar$ $L_t = l_t\hbar$

FIG. 11.1.   *Examples of ll-coupling, vector model, for the case of two-valence electron atoms:* (a) *for* $l_1 = 1$ *and* $l_2 = 1$, *the three possible values are* $l_t = 2, 1, 0$; (b) *for* $l_1 = 1$ *and* $l_2 = 2$, *the three possible values are* $l_t = 3, 2, 1$.

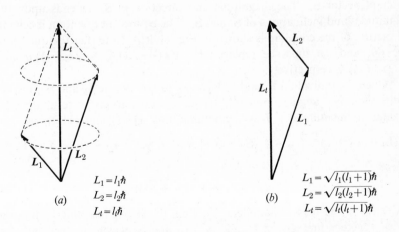

(a) $L_1 = l_1\hbar$
       $L_2 = l_2\hbar$
       $L_t = l_t\hbar$

(b) $L_1 = \sqrt{l_1(l_1+1)}\hbar$
       $L_2 = \sqrt{l_2(l_2+1)}\hbar$
       $L_t = \sqrt{l_t(l_t+1)}\hbar$

FIG. 11.2.   *The precession of* L_1 *and* L_2 *about their resultant vector* L_t.
(a) *The classical picture for which* $L_1 = l_1\hbar$, $L_2 = l_2\hbar$, *and* $L_t = l_t\hbar$.
(b) *The quantum-mechanical picture for which* $L_1 = \sqrt{l_1(l_1 + 1)}\,\hbar$,
$L_2 = \sqrt{l_2(l_2 + 1)}\,\hbar$, *and* $L_t = \sqrt{l_t(l_t + 1)}\,\hbar$.

inclinations of L_1 and L_2. The equivalent quantum-mechanical picture of the coupling is shown in Fig. 11.2(b). Note that the classical values $L_1 = l_1\hbar$, $L_2 = l_2\hbar$ and the resultant $L_t = l_t\hbar$ must be replaced by the quantum-mechanical values $L_1 = \sqrt{l_1(l_1 + 1)}\,\hbar$, $L_2 = \sqrt{l_2(l_2 + 1)}\,\hbar$, and $L_t = \sqrt{l_t(l_t + 1)}\,\hbar$, respectively.

Next we shall investigate ss-coupling. In this case the spin angular momentum vectors S_i (each $= \frac{1}{2}\hbar$ classically and $\sqrt{3}/2\,\hbar$ quantum mechanically) of each electron combine together to give a resultant spin angular momentum vector S_t, where $S_t = \sqrt{s_t(s_t + 1)}\,\hbar$. It is assumed that the individual S_i vectors are so strongly coupled with one another (i.e., they are precessing very fast around S_t) that states with different resultant S_t have very different energies. Quantum mechanically s_t can take integer or half-integer values, each differing by unity. This type of coupling between different S_i is called ss-coupling and is written mathematically as

$$S_1 + S_2 + S_3 + \ldots + S_i = S_t \qquad (11.2a)$$

where

$$|S_t| = S_t = \sqrt{s_t(s_t + 1)}\,\hbar \qquad (11.2b)$$

Some examples of ss-coupling are shown in Fig. 11.3. For two electrons, each with spin $\frac{1}{2}$, $S_t = S_1 + S_2$ gives $s_t = 1$ or 0 as shown in Fig. 11.3(a). For three electrons each with spin $\frac{1}{2}$, $S_t = S_1 + S_2 + S_3$, s_t can take two values, $\frac{3}{2}$ or $\frac{1}{2}$, as shown in Fig. 11.3(b). Similarly, for four electrons s_t can take three values 2, 1, or 0 as shown in Fig. 11.3(c).

Figure 11.4(a) shows how the vectors S_1 and S_2 precess about their resultant vector S_t. The magnitude and direction of S_t depends upon the magnitudes and inclinations of S_1 and S_2. The equivalent quantum mechanical picture of the coupling is shown in Fig. 11.4(b). Note that the quantities $s_1\hbar$, $s_2\hbar$, and $s_t\hbar$ must be replaced by $\sqrt{s_1(s_1 + 1)}\,\hbar$, $\sqrt{s_2(s_2 + 1)}\,\hbar$, and $\sqrt{s_t(s_t + 1)}\,\hbar$, respectively.

Once the individual L_i and S_i have combined to give L_t and S_t, respectively, these two angular momenta further combine to give a resultant total angular momentum J_t. Thus combining Eqs. (11.1) and (11.2), we get,

$$(L_1 + L_2 + \ldots + L_i) + (S_1 + S_2 + \ldots + S_i) = L_t + S_t = J_t \qquad (11.3a)$$

where

$$|J_t| = J_t = \sqrt{j_t(j_t + 1)}\,\hbar \qquad (11.3b)$$

Thus in the Russell-Saunders coupling, the strong coupling vectors are added together first giving L_t and S_t; L_t and S_t which, in turn, are less strongly coupled, give the resultant vector J_t. Each possible value of L_t can combine with each possible value of S_t to give quantized values of J_t. The process of LS-coupling is shown clearly in Fig. 11.5 where L_1 and L_2 are shown precessing around L_t, S_1 and S_2 are precessing around their resultant S_t, while L_t and S_t, in turn, precess comparatively slowly around J_t. An

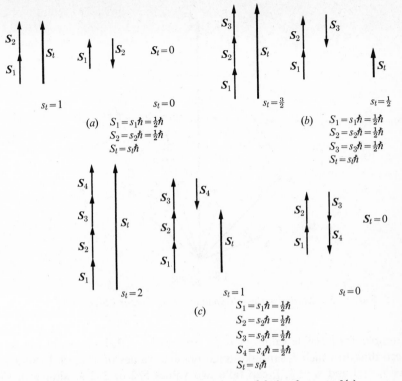

FIG. 11.3.   *Examples of ss coupling, vector model, for the case of* (a) *two electrons:* $s_1 = \frac{1}{2}, s_2 = \frac{1}{2}, s_t = 1, 0$; (b) *three electrons:* $s_1 = s_2 = s_3 = \frac{1}{2}$, $s_t = \frac{3}{2}, \frac{1}{2}$; (c) *four electrons:* $s_1 = s_2 = s_3 = s_4 = \frac{1}{2}, s_t = 2, 1, 0$.

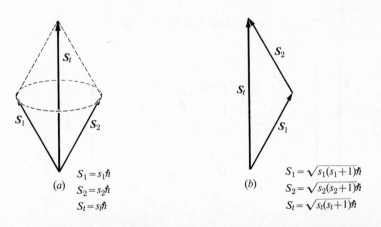

FIG. 11.4.   *The precession of* S_1 *and* S_2 *about their resultant vector* S_t. (a) *The classical picture for which* $S_1 = s_1\hbar$, $S_2 = s_2\hbar$, *and* $S_t = s_t\hbar$. (b) *The quantum-mechanical picture for which* $S_1 = \sqrt{s_1(s_1 + 1)}\hbar$, $S_2 = \sqrt{s_2(s_2 + 1)}\hbar$, *and* $S_t = \sqrt{s_t(s_t + 1)}\hbar$.

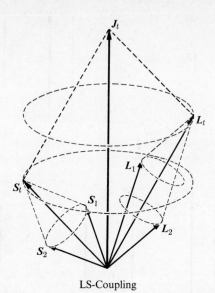

LS-Coupling

FIG. 11.5.   *Model of Russell-Saunders-coupling, or LS-coupling.*

example, for possible values of j_t if $l_t = 2$ and $s_t = 1$, is shown in Fig. 11.6, according to which j_t can take three possible values of 3, 2, or 1. Similarly for $l_t = 2$ and $s_t = \frac{1}{2}$, j_t can take two values 5/2 or 3/2 as shown in Fig. 11.7 together with their equivalent quantum-mechanical pictures. Note that $J_t = \sqrt{j_t(j_t + 1)}\hbar$; j_t can take all possible values from $|l_t - s_t|_{\min}$ to $|l_t + s_t|$ with all the intermediate values differing by unity

$$|l_t - s_t|_{\min} \leqslant j_t \leqslant |l_t + s_t| \qquad (11.4a)$$

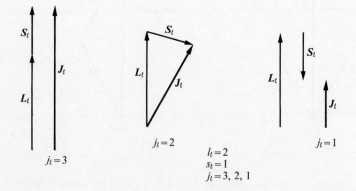

FIG. 11.6.   *For $l_t = 2$ and $s_t = 1$, the possible values of j_t are 3, 2, 1.*

and

$$j_t \text{ has } (2s_t + 1) \text{ values if } s_t < l_t$$
$$j_t \text{ has } (2l_t + 1) \text{ values if } l_t < s_t$$

(11.4b)

We may summarize the following rules about LS-coupling:

(i) All the vectors **L**, **S**, and **J** are quantized.

(ii) l_t is always an integer, while s_t is an integer if the total number of electrons is even, and is a half-integer if the total number of electrons is odd.

(iii) j_t is an integer or half-integer depending upon whether s_t is an integer or half-integer, respectively. The possible values of j_t are given by the relations of Eq. (11.4).

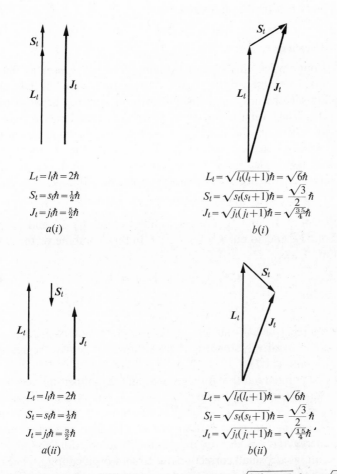

$$L_t = l_t\hbar = 2\hbar$$
$$S_t = s_t\hbar = \tfrac{1}{2}\hbar$$
$$J_t = j_t\hbar = \tfrac{5}{2}\hbar$$

$a(i)$

$$L_t = \sqrt{l_t(l_t+1)}\hbar = \sqrt{6}\hbar$$
$$S_t = \sqrt{s_t(s_t+1)}\hbar = \frac{\sqrt{3}}{2}\hbar$$
$$J_t = \sqrt{j_t(j_t+1)}\hbar = \sqrt{\tfrac{35}{4}}\hbar$$

$b(i)$

$$L_t = l_t\hbar = 2\hbar$$
$$S_t = s_t\hbar = \tfrac{1}{2}\hbar$$
$$J_t = j_t\hbar = \tfrac{3}{2}\hbar$$

$a(ii)$

$$L_t = \sqrt{l_t(l_t+1)}\hbar = \sqrt{6}\hbar$$
$$S_t = \sqrt{s_t(s_t+1)}\hbar = \frac{\sqrt{3}}{2}\hbar$$
$$J_t = \sqrt{j_t(j_t+1)}\hbar = \sqrt{\tfrac{15}{4}}\hbar$$

$b(ii)$

Fig. 11.7. *Two possible values of J_t for $L_t (= \sqrt{l_t(l_t+1)}\,\hbar = \sqrt{6}\,\hbar)$ and $S_t (= \sqrt{s_t(s_t+1)}\hbar = \sqrt{3}\hbar/2)$ where $l_t = 2$ and $s_t = \tfrac{1}{2}$: (a) the classical model, and (b) the quantum-mechanical model.*

Finally, we shall introduce a new notation for the many-valence-electron atoms. The notation of single-valence-electron atoms,

$$l = 0, 1, 2, 3, 4, 5, \ldots$$

$$\text{term: } s, p, d, f, g, h, \ldots$$

is replaced in the many-valence-electron atoms by

$$l_t = 0, 1, 2, 3, 4, 5, \ldots$$

$$\text{term: } S, P, D, F, G, H, \ldots \tag{11.5}$$

When $s_t = 0$, the multiplicity, $r = 2s_t + 1 = 1$, is a singlet. For $s_t = \frac{1}{2}$, $r = 2s_t + 1 = 2$, the multiplicity is a doublet. For $s_t = 1, r = 2s_t + 1 = 3$, the multiplicity is a triplet, and so on.

B. The jj-Coupling

As pointed out earlier, this type of coupling does not appear as frequently as does the LS-coupling, but in many cases, contrary to the LS-coupling, this coupling satisfactorily explains the order of splitting between different energy levels. Whenever the spin-orbit splitting is very large, it means that the interaction between the spin and the orbital angular-momentum vectors of an individual electron is very large. This implies that **L** and **S** of each electron must be coupled together first, giving a resultant **J**, i.e., $\mathbf{J} = \mathbf{L} + \mathbf{S}$. Thus if there are i valence electrons in an atom, we will have

$$\mathbf{L_1} + \mathbf{S_1} = \mathbf{J_1} ; \mathbf{L_2} + \mathbf{S_2} = \mathbf{J_2} , \ldots, \mathbf{L_i} + \mathbf{S_i} = \mathbf{J_i} \tag{11.6}$$

This implies that $\mathbf{L_1}$ and $\mathbf{S_1}$ precess rapidly about $\mathbf{J_1}$, $\mathbf{L_2}$ and $\mathbf{S_2}$ precess rapidly about $\mathbf{J_2}$, and so on. $\mathbf{J_1}, \mathbf{J_2}, \ldots, \mathbf{J_i}$ in turn combine vectorily to give the resultant $\mathbf{J}_t$, i.e.,

$$\mathbf{J_1} + \mathbf{J_2} + \ldots + \mathbf{J_i} = \mathbf{J}_t \tag{11.7a}$$

where

$$|\mathbf{J}_t| = J_t = \sqrt{j_t(j_t + 1)}\, \hbar \tag{11.7b}$$

and j_t takes integer or half-integer values. The precession of $\mathbf{J_1}, \mathbf{J_2}, \ldots, \mathbf{J_i}$, around $\mathbf{J}_t$ is comparatively slow. Figure 11.8 shows a schematic representation of Eqs. (11.6) and (11.7).

It may be pointed out that for a given atom the number of levels obtained will be the same, i.e., the multiplicity of the states will be the same no matter which type of coupling is assumed, but the order of the splitting will be different. In actual practice, in LS-coupling the first correction made to the main energy term is due to the Coulomb interaction and then upon this is superimposed a small correction due to spin-orbit coupling. The reverse procedure is followed in the case of jj-coupling because the correction due to the spin-orbit coupling is larger than the Coulomb interaction correction term. In the case of LS-coupling, the Coulomb interaction between different spin momenta vectors, $\mathbf{S}_i$, is much larger than the Coulomb interaction between different orbital momenta vectors, $\mathbf{L}_i$. All these conclusions will be justified later in this chapter.

2. POSSIBLE TERM TYPES FOR MANY-VALENCE-ELECTRON ATOMS AND THE PAULI EXCLUSION PRINCIPLE[5]

Except for an occasional reference to jj-coupling, we shall be using LS-coupling throughout our further discussions. Reviewing the notation that will be used in designating different terms, we have the following: The total orbital angular-momentum is denoted by the capital letter, the preceding superscript denotes the multiplicity, r, of the level, and the following subscript denotes the total angular-momentum quantum number, j_t. Thus a

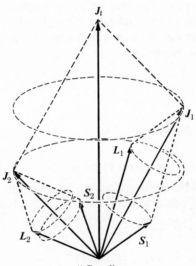

jj-Coupling

FIG. 11.8. *The jj-coupling model showing precession of $\mathbf{L}_i$ and $\mathbf{S}_i$ around $\mathbf{J}_i$, and $\mathbf{J}_i$ around $\mathbf{J}_t$.*

typical term is written in the form $^r L_{j_t}$, where $r = 2s_t + 1$ gives the multiplicity of the term as shown in Table 11.1 for different values of s_t. Because the value of s_t depends upon the number of electrons, it leads to different types of multiplicities of the levels, depending upon the number of valence electrons, as shown in Table 11.2. For an odd number of valence electrons the multiplicity is even, while for an even number of valence electrons the multiplicity is odd.

The Pauli exclusion principle, which states that no two electrons in an atom can have all four quantum numbers identical, will be operative all

TABLE 11.1

MULTIPLICITIES OF THE TERMS FOR
DIFFERENT VALUES OF s_t

Spin s_t	$r = 2s_t + 1$	Multiplicity of terms
0	1	singlets
$\frac{1}{2}$	2	doublets
1	3	triplets
$\frac{3}{2}$	4	quartets
2	5	quintets
$\frac{5}{2}$	6	sextets
3	7	septets
$\cdots$	$\cdots$	$\cdots$

through the discussions. The four quantum numbers to be used are n, l, m_l, and m_s. The use of the exclusion principle eliminates many otherwise allowed terms. Before we can start writing terms, we must distinguish between two different types of electrons:

(a) *Nonequivalent electrons* are those that belong to different (n, l) subgroups; i.e., the several electrons that have at least one of the two quantum numbers n and l different.

(b) *Equivalent electrons* are those that belong to the same (n, l) subgroup; i.e., the electrons that have the same values of n and l.

A. Possible Terms of Nonequivalent Electrons

Because nonequivalent electrons belong to different (n, l) subgroups, the Pauli exclusion principle is automatically satisfied. For two electrons in an atom with different n but, say, $l = 0$ for each, the configuration is written

TABLE 11.2

MULTIPLICITIES OF THE TERMS FOR DIFFERENT
NUMBERS OF ELECTRONS

Number of electrons	Possible values of s_t	Possible multiplicities of the terms
0	0	singlets
1	$\frac{1}{2}$	doublets
2	0, 1	singlets, triplets
3	$\frac{1}{2}, \frac{3}{2}$	doublets, quartets
4	0, 1, 2	singlets, triplets, quintets
5	$\frac{1}{2}, \frac{3}{2}, \frac{5}{2}$	doublets, quartets, sextets
6	0, 1, 2, 3	singlets, triplets, quintets, septets
7	$\frac{1}{2}, \frac{3}{2}, \frac{5}{2}, \frac{7}{2}$	doublets, quartets, sextets, octets
8	0, 1, 2, 3, 4	singlets, triplets, quintets, septets, nonets

as $s \cdot s$ or ss. Two electrons for which $l_1 = 0$ for one and $l_2 = 1$ for the other are denoted by sp. Similarly, sd stands for two nonequivalent electrons with $l_1 = 0$, and $l_2 = 2$; pd stands for $l_1 = 1$ and $l_2 = 2$; pp stands for $l_1 = 1$ and $l_2 = 1$; spd stands for three electrons with $l_1 = 0$, $l_2 = 1$, and $l_3 = 2$, and so on.

In order to calculate the possible number of terms corresponding· to different electron configurations, the possible values of l_t and s_t must first be calculated separately, followed by the vector addition of $\mathbf{L}_t$ and $\mathbf{S}_t$ to get the possible values of $\mathbf{J}_t$.

Consider the case of two electrons with the configuration sp. This means $l_1 = 0$ and $l_2 = 1$, thus $l_t = 1$; and $s_1 = \frac{1}{2}$ and $s_2 = \frac{1}{2}$, thus $s_t = 0$ or 1. These values give $j_t = 1 + 0 = 1$ or $j_t = 1 + 1 = 2, 1, 0$. The term corresponding to $s_t = 0$ is a singlet state $^1P_1$, and the term corresponding to $s_t = 1$ is a triplet state $^3P_{2,1,0}$, i.e., $^3P_2$, $^3P_1$, $^3P_0$. Thus for sp electrons the possible terms are $^1P_1$, $^3P_{2,1,0}$. Similarly for pd electrons, $l_1 = 1$ and $l_2 = 2$, resulting in $l_t = 3, 2, 1$; and $s_1 = \frac{1}{2}$ and $s_2 = \frac{1}{2}$, resulting in $s_t = 0, 1$. For $s_t = 0$ we get singlet states with $j_t = 3, 2, 1$, i.e., $^1F_3$, $^1D_2$, $^1P_1$. For $s_t = 1$ and if $l_t = 1$, $j_t = 2, 1, 0$; if $l_t = 2$, $j_t = 3, 2, 1$, and if $l_t = 3$, $j_t = 4, 3, 2$. These give rise to the following triplet states $^3P_{2,1,0}$, $^3D_{3,2,1}$, and $^3F_{4,3,2}$. Thus for the pd configuration of electrons, the following states are possible.

$$^1P_1, \ ^1D_2, \ ^1F_3, \ ^3P_{2,1,0}, \ ^3D_{3,2,1}, \ ^3F_{4,3,2}$$

These and many other terms corresponding to different configurations are listed in Table 11.3.

For three or more electrons, first the l's of two electrons are added to give a resultant l_{1+2}, then l_3 of the third electron is added to get the resultant

TABLE 11.3
POSSIBLE TERMS OF NONEQUIVALENT ELECTRONS

Electron configuration	Possible terms			
	Singlets	Doublets	Triplets	Quartets
ss	^1S		^3S	
sp	^1P		^3P	
sd	^1D		^3D	
pp	$^1S, \ ^1P, \ ^1D$		$^3S, \ ^3P, \ ^3D$	
pd	$^1P, \ ^1D, \ ^1F$		$^3P, \ ^3D, \ ^3F$	
dd	$^1S, \ ^1P, \ ^1D, \ ^1F, \ ^1G$		$^3S, \ ^3P, \ ^3D, \ ^3F, \ ^3G$	
sss		$^2S, \ ^2S$		^4S
ssp		$^2P, \ ^2P$		^4P
ssd		$^2D, \ ^2D$		^4D
spp		$^2S, \ ^2P, \ ^2D$		$^4S, \ ^4P, \ ^4D$
		$^2S, \ ^2P, \ ^2D$		
spd		$^2P, \ ^2D, \ ^2F$		$^4P, \ ^4D, \ ^4F$
		$^2P, \ ^2D, \ ^2F$		

l_{1+2+3}, and so on, finally arriving at the resultant l_t. A similar procedure is used for spin vectors, i.e., $s_1 + s_2 = s_{1+2}$, $s_{1+2} + s_3$ to get the resultant s_t. Finally l_t and s_t are added to get j_t. Examples of terms corresponding to three-electron systems are also given in Table 11.3.

B. Possible Terms of Equivalent Electrons

As defined earlier, the equivalent electrons are those that have both the quantum numbers n and l the same. For example, the configuration of two electrons each of which has the same n and has $l = 1$, i.e., $l_1 = l_2 = 1$, will be written as np^2. Similarly, the configuration of two equivalent d-electrons will be nd^2. Similarly, four equivalent p-electrons may be written as np^4, and so on. Before calculating the number of possible terms corresponding to any given configuration, one must take into account the Pauli exclusion principle, which is operative in this case, and many of the terms that were possible in the case of nonequivalent electrons will have to be deleted. For equivalent electrons, of the four quantum numbers, n, l, m_l, m_s, two quantum numbers n and l are the same. This leaves us two more quantum numbers, m_l and m_s, with which to construct different possible states. A quantum state resulting from two electrons will be denoted by $(nlm_{l_1}, m_{s_1}; nlm_{l_2}, m_{s_2})$.

Consider the simple example of two valence equivalent s-electrons denoted by the configuration ns^2. Both electrons have the same n and the same $l = 0$, and for each of these $m_l = 0$. Thus three of the four quantum numbers are the same, and hence the fourth quantum number, m_s, must be different for the two electrons; if one has $m_s = +\frac{1}{2}$, the other must be $m_s = -\frac{1}{2}$. The spins of the two electrons, therefore, must be antiparallel. This results only in one possible combination denoted by $(n00, \frac{1}{2}; n00, -\frac{1}{2})$. The total m_{s_t} for this state is given by

$$m_{s_t} = m_{s_1} + m_{s_2} = \frac{1}{2} - \frac{1}{2} = 0 \tag{11.8}$$

which means that $s_t = 0$, i.e., the state is a singlet state. $m_{l_t} = m_{l_1} + m_{l_2} = 0 + 0 = 0$, i.e., $l_t = 0$, which means $j_t = l_t + s_t = 0$. Thus the resultant state is a singlet S-state denoted by $^1S_0$. Thus for two equivalent s-electrons, there is one singlet S-state possible and no triplet S-states, while in the case of nonequivalent electrons both singlets and triplets were possible.

Let us take up a slightly more difficult example. Consider two equivalent p-electrons, i.e., np^2. Accordingly, each electron has the following possible values for m_l and m_s

$$m_{l_1} = m_{l_2} = +1, 0, -1$$

$$m_{s_1} = m_{s_2} = +\frac{1}{2} \text{ or } -\frac{1}{2}$$

There are many possible states of the form $(nlm_{l_1}, m_{s_1}; nlm_{l_2}, m_{s_2})$ that can be formed from different values of $m_{l_1}, m_{l_2}, m_{s_1}, m_{s_2}$. But the Pauli exclusion

TABLE 11.4

POSSIBLE TERMS FOR TWO EQUIVALENT p-ELECTRONS

	m_l (for 1 or 2)						
	$+1$	0	-1	$m_{l_i}=\Sigma m_{l_i}$	$m_{s_i}=\Sigma m_{s_i}$	$m_{j_i}=m_{l_i}+m_{s_i}$	State
	m_s	m_s	m_s				
1	$\tfrac{1}{2}\ -\tfrac{1}{2}$			2	0	2	^1D
2	$\tfrac{1}{2}$	$\tfrac{1}{2}$		1	1	2	^3P
3	$\tfrac{1}{2}$	$-\tfrac{1}{2}$		1	0	1	^1D
4	$-\tfrac{1}{2}$	$+\tfrac{1}{2}$		1	0	1	^3P
5	$-\tfrac{1}{2}$	$-\tfrac{1}{2}$		1	-1	0	^3P
6	$\tfrac{1}{2}$		$\tfrac{1}{2}$	0	1	1	^3P
7	$\tfrac{1}{2}$		$-\tfrac{1}{2}$	0	0	0	^1D
8	$-\tfrac{1}{2}$		$\tfrac{1}{2}$	0	0	0	^3P
9	$-\tfrac{1}{2}$		$-\tfrac{1}{2}$	0	-1	-1	^3P
10		$\tfrac{1}{2}\ -\tfrac{1}{2}$		0	0	0	^1S
11		$\tfrac{1}{2}$	$\tfrac{1}{2}$	-1	1	0	^3P
12		$\tfrac{1}{2}$	$-\tfrac{1}{2}$	-1	0	-1	^1D
13		$-\tfrac{1}{2}$	$+\tfrac{1}{2}$	-1	0	-1	^3P
14		$-\tfrac{1}{2}$	$-\tfrac{1}{2}$	-1	-1	-2	^3P
15			$+\tfrac{1}{2}\ \tfrac{1}{2}$	-2	0	-2	^1D

TABLE 11.5

POSSIBLE TERMS (QUANTUM STATES) OF EQUIVALENT ELECTRONS

Electron configuration	Terms
ns^0	^1S
ns^1	^2S
ns^2	^1S
np^0	^1S
np^1	^2P
np^2	$^1S, {}^1D, {}^3P$
np^3	$^2P, {}^2D, {}^4S$
np^4	$^1S, {}^1D, {}^3P$
np^5	^2P
np^6	^1S
nd^0	^1S
nd^1	^2D
nd^2	$^1S, {}^1D, {}^1G, {}^3P, {}^3F$
nd^3	$^2D, {}^2P, {}^2D, {}^2F, {}^2G, {}^2H, {}^4P, {}^4F$
nd^4	$^1S, {}^1D, {}^1G, {}^1S, {}^1D, {}^1G, {}^1H, {}^1I, {}^3P, {}^3F, {}^3P, {}^3D, {}^3F, {}^3G, {}^3H, {}^5D$
nd^5	$^2D, {}^2P, {}^2D, {}^2F, {}^2G, {}^2H, {}^2S, {}^2D, {}^2F, {}^2G, {}^2I, {}^4P, {}^4F, {}^4D, {}^4G, {}^6S$
nd^6	$^1S, {}^1D, {}^1G, {}^1S, {}^1D, {}^1G, {}^1H, {}^1I, {}^3P, {}^3F, {}^3P, {}^3D, {}^3F, {}^3G, {}^3H, {}^5D$
nd^7	$^2D, {}^2P, {}^2D, {}^2F, {}^2G, {}^2H, {}^4P, {}^4F$
nd^8	$^1S, {}^1D, {}^1G, {}^3P, {}^3F$
nd^9	^2D
nd^{10}	^1S

principle allows only 15 of these; they are shown in Table 11.4. Hence the np^2-electrons can exist in the states $^1S_0$, $^1D_2$, and $^3P_{2,1,0}$, resulting in $1 + 5 + 9 = 15$ states. The possible number of states for many other equivalent electron configurations are shown in Table 11.5.

Before leaving this discussion, we may make the following remarks.

(a) For a closed shell, $l_t = 0$, $s_t = 0$, i.e., $m_{l_t} = 0$ and $m_{s_t} = 0$. This means that the closed shell always forms a $^1S_0$ state, i.e., the same as ns^2-electrons.

(b) The terms of a configuration l^N are the same as those of the configuration l^{r-N}, where r is the maximum number of l-electrons given by $r = 2(2l + 1)$. For example, for $l = 1$, $r = 6$, the terms from the configuration p^2 will be the same as from p^4. Similarly, the terms from the configuration d^2 will be the same as from d^8. These results are illustrated in Table 11.5.

(c) From (b) it can be seen that when less than half of the shell is filled, the multiplets formed from the equivalent electrons are *regular*, but *inverted* if more than half the shell is filled. The meaning of regular and inverted is explained in Sec. 8.

3. LS-COUPLING FOR TWO-VALENCE-ELECTRON ATOMS AND THE LANDÉ INTERVAL RULE[6,7]

The purpose of this section is to calculate the fine structure for the case of two-valence-electron atoms, using LS-coupling. First of all we shall explain the LS-coupling in terms of the vector model. This will be followed by writing the fine-structure term-value for any level. Finally, the Landé interval rule, which gives the relative separation between the fine-structure states of any given level, will be discussed.

A. Vector Model

In order to understand the fine structure of different levels one must use quantum-mechanical methods. But one can even get a reasonably good picture by using the classical vector model, as we have been doing all along.

In order to write the expressions for the interactions between the spin and orbital parts of two-electron systems, we shall make use of the expression derived for one-electron atoms. In the case of one-electron atoms the interaction between the spin angular momentum $\mathbf{S}$ and the orbital angular momentum $\mathbf{L}$ of the valence electron leads to the splitting of different energy levels, P, D, F, etc., into two levels, and the shift of each fine structure level from the original unsplit level is given by Eq. (10.85), i.e.,

$$\Delta E_{\mathbf{S} \cdot \mathbf{L}} = aLS\langle\cos (\mathbf{L}, \mathbf{S})\rangle_{av} = a \frac{(J^2 - L^2 - S^2)}{2} \tag{11.9}$$

where

$$a = \frac{Ze^2}{2m^2c^2} \left\langle \frac{1}{r^3} \right\rangle_{av} = \frac{e^2Z^4}{2m^2c^2a_0^3n^3l(l + \frac{1}{2})(l + 1)} \tag{11.10}$$

In the case of two-electron atoms, we have to consider the interactions between four different angular momenta, L_1, S_1, L_2, and S_2. Considering different possible combinations, we can write six possible interaction terms depending upon the following pairs:

$$(S_1, S_2); \quad (L_1, S_1); \quad (L_1, S_2);$$
$$(L_1, L_2); \quad (L_2, S_2); \quad (L_2, S_1) \quad \text{(11.11)}$$

Corresponding to these six pairs we can write six energy terms similar to the one given by Eq. (11.9), i.e.,

$$\Delta E_1 = a_1 S_1 S_2 \cos (S_1, S_2); \Delta E_3 = a_3 L_1 S_1 \cos (L_1, S_1); \Delta E_5 = a_5 L_1 S_2 \cos (L_1, S_2)$$
$$\Delta E_2 = a_2 L_1 L_2 \cos (L_1, L_2); \Delta E_4 = a_4 L_2 S_2 \cos (L_2, S_2); \Delta E_6 = a_6 L_2 S_1 \cos (L_2, S_1)$$
$$\text{(11.12)}$$

where $a_1, a_2, \ldots, a_6$ are constants properly converted to energy units.

It is easy to see now how the two coupling schemes result from this. In LS-coupling the terms ΔE_1 and ΔE_2 are very large as compared to the terms ΔE_3 and ΔE_4, while ΔE_5 and ΔE_6 are assumed to be comparatively very small, thus leading to the predominantly LS-coupling, as in Fig. 11.5. In jj-coupling, the terms ΔE_3 and ΔE_4 are very large as compared to the terms ΔE_1 and ΔE_2, while ΔE_5 and ΔE_6 are assumed to be comparatively very small, thus leading to the predominantly jj-coupling as shown in Fig. 11.8. In the following discussion we shall be concerned with the most common LS-coupling.

B.   Fine-Structure Energy Levels and Hund's Rule[8]

We start with the assumption that there is exclusively LS-coupling between the two valence electrons of the atom. This means that of the six terms given in Eq. (11.12), only the following four are effective (neglecting ΔE_5 and ΔE_6):

$$\Delta E_1 = a_1 S_1 S_2 \cos (S_1, S_2); \quad \Delta E_3 = a_3 L_1 S_1 \cos (L_1, S_1);$$
$$\Delta E_2 = a_2 L_1 L_2 \cos (L_1, L_2); \quad \Delta E_4 = a_4 L_2 S_2 \cos (L_2, S_2) \quad \text{(11.13)}$$

Referring to Fig. 11.5 and applying the cosine law,

$$S_t^2 = S_1^2 + S_2^2 + 2 S_1 S_2 \cos (S_1, S_2)$$
$$L_t^2 = L_1^2 + L_2^2 + 2 L_1 L_2 \cos (L_1, L_2)$$

we can write the expressions for ΔE_1 and ΔE_2 in Eq. (11.13) as

$$\Delta E_1 = \frac{1}{2} a_1 (S_t^2 - S_1^2 - S_2^2) \quad \text{(11.14)}$$

and

$$\Delta E_2 = \frac{1}{2} a_2 (L_t^2 - L_1^2 - L_2^2) \quad \text{(11.15)}$$

Because the angles between (L_1, S_1) and (L_2, S_2) are constantly changing, we must use the average values of the cosines in ΔE_3 and ΔE_4. Assuming that the precession of L_1, S_1; and L_2, S_2 are much more rapid than that of

L_t and S_t around J_t, we will find the cancellation of normal components, and we may write

$$\langle \cos (L_1, S_1) \rangle_{av} = \cos (L_1, L_t) \cdot \cos (L_t, S_t) \cdot \cos (S_t, S_1) \quad \textbf{(11.16)}$$

and then using the cosine law, this takes the form

$$\langle \cos (L_1, S_1) \rangle_{av} = \frac{L_t^2 + L_1^2 - L_2^2}{2L_1L_t} \cdot \frac{J_t^2 - L_t^2 - S_t^2}{2L_tS_t} \cdot \frac{S_t^2 + S_1^2 - S_2^2}{2S_tS_1} \quad \textbf{(11.17)}$$

Similarly

$$\langle \cos (L_2, S_2) \rangle_{av} = \frac{L_t^2 + L_2^2 - L_1^2}{2L_2L_t} \cdot \frac{J_t^2 - L_t^2 - S_t^2}{2L_tS_t} \cdot \frac{S_t^2 + S_2^2 - S_1^2}{2S_tS_2} \quad \textbf{(11.18)}$$

Thus we may write

$$\Delta E_3 + \Delta E_4 = a_3 L_1 S_1 \langle \cos (L_1, S_1) \rangle_{av} + a_4 L_2 S_2 \langle \cos (L_2, S_2) \rangle_{av} \quad \textbf{(11.19)}$$

Substituting from Eqs. (11.17) and (11.18) in Eq. (11.19), we get

$$\Delta E_3 + \Delta E_4 = \frac{1}{2} A(J_t^2 - L_t^2 - S_t^2) = A \cdot L_t S_t \cos (L_t, S_t) \quad \textbf{(11.20)}$$

where A is given by

$$A = a_3 c_3 + a_4 c_4$$

$$= a_3 \left[\frac{S_t^2 + S_1^2 - S_2^2}{2S_t^2} \cdot \frac{L_t^2 + L_1^2 - L_2^2}{2L_t^2} \right] + a_4 \left[\frac{S_t^2 + S_2^2 - S_1^2}{2S_t^2} \cdot \frac{L_t^2 + L_2^2 - L_1^2}{2L_t^2} \right]$$

$$\textbf{(11.21)}$$

The equivalent expressions for Eqs. (11.14), (11.15), and (11.20) in terms of different quantum numbers are given by

$$\Delta E_1 = \frac{1}{2} a_1 [s_t(s_t + 1) - s_1(s_1 + 1) - s_2(s_2 + 1)] \quad \textbf{(11.22)}$$

$$\Delta E_2 = \frac{1}{2} a_2 [l_t(l_t + 1) - l_1(l_1 + 1) - l_2(l_2 + 1)] \quad \textbf{(11.23)}$$

$$\Delta E_3 + \Delta E_4 = \frac{1}{2} A[j_t(j_t + 1) - l_t(l_t + 1) - s_t(s_t + 1)] \quad \textbf{(11.24)}$$

Thus if E_0 is the energy of a given level without the fine structure correction, then the energy E with the fine structure correction is given by

$$E = E_0 + \Delta E_1 + \Delta E_2 + \Delta E_3 + \Delta E_4 \quad \textbf{(11.25)}$$

In order to calculate the fine structure terms one must know the values of a_1, a_2, and A. If the interactions were completely magnetic in nature, then the expressions for a_1, a_2, a_3, a_4 could be written similar to the one given in Eq. (11.10). But it was mentioned in the beginning of this chapter that although the spin-orbit interactions are magnetic in character, the strong spin-spin and orbit-orbit interactions are due to the residual Coulomb, or electrostatic, interactions.

In order to be consistent with the experimental observation that the singlet levels lie always higher than the triplet, the strong electrostatic interaction between S_1 and S_2 must result in the coefficient a_1 in Eq. (11.22) being negative. Thus for $s_1 = \frac{1}{2}$, $s_2 = \frac{1}{2}$, $s_t = 0$ and 1; and Eq. (11.22) gives

$$\Delta E_1 = -\frac{3}{4} a_1 \qquad \text{for} \qquad s_t = 0 \qquad\qquad \textbf{(11.26)}$$

and

$$\Delta E_1 = \frac{1}{4} a_1 \qquad \text{for} \qquad s_t = 1 \qquad\qquad \textbf{(11.27)}$$

i.e., because a_1 is negative, ΔE_1 is positive for $s_t = 0$, and negative for $s_t = 1$, as shown in Fig. 11.9. That the coefficient a_1 is negative is shown by Heisenberg[9] as the resultant of the resonance electrostatic-interaction phenomena.

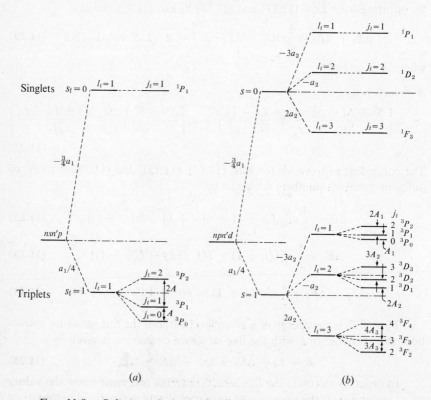

FIG. 11.9. *Splitting of energy levels due to the interaction energies between two valence electrons in a typical LS-coupling configuration:* (a) *nsn'p electrons, and* (b) *npn'd electrons.*

As the result of the *Hund's rules*[8] a_2 is found to be negative. Hund's rules, which are true for LS-coupling, are as follows: For any electron configuration, out of all the terms, (1) a term with the highest multiplicity (i.e., the highest s_t-value) will lie deepest; and (2) of these terms the one with the highest l_t-value will lie deepest.

For the sp-configuration $l_1 = 0$, $l_2 = 1$, and hence $l_t = 1$. From Eq. (11.23), $\Delta E_2 = 0$, which is always true whenever one of the two electrons is in the s-state. For the pd-configuration, $l_1 = 1$; $l_2 = 2$, and hence $l_t = 3, 2, 1$. From Eq. (11.23), the corresponding values of ΔE_2 are $2a_2$, $-a_2$, and $-3a_2$, respectively. Remembering that a_2 is negative, the splittings are shown in Fig. 11.9.

The only term left to be calculated is $\Delta E_3 + \Delta E_4$ given by Eq. (11.24). Because the terms that we are concerned with here are spin-orbit couplings, the coefficients a_3 and a_4 are both positive. Thus, knowing l_1, s_1, l_2, s_2, s_t, l_t, and j_t, one can calculate A and hence $\Delta E_3 + \Delta E_4$. The splitting due to spin-orbit interaction is superimposed on the already split levels due to Coulomb interactions as shown in Fig. 11.9. The simple rules for such splittings will now be discussed.

C. The Landé Interval Rule[7]

The expression for the spin-orbit contribution to the fine structure can be derived from Eq. (10.24). If the LS-coupling is assumed to be true, according to the Landé interval rule energy separation between adjacent levels in a given multiplet (for a fixed value of s_t and l_t) are proportional to the larger of the j_t-values. Thus for example, for the triplet ${}^3P_0$, ${}^3P_1$, ${}^3P_2$ the ratio of the intervals between ${}^3P_0 - {}^3P_1$ and ${}^3P_1 - {}^3P_2$ is 1:2. Similarly for ${}^3D_1$, ${}^3D_2$, ${}^3D_3$, the intervals are 2:3, and so on. This rule can be derived in a very simple manner as follows.

Consider a triplet with total quantum numbers j, $j + 1$, and $j + 2$. According to Eq. (11.24), the fine-structure splitting due to spin-orbit coupling are

$$(\Delta E_3 + \Delta E_4)_j = \frac{1}{2} A[j(j + 1) - l(l + 1) - s(s + 1)]$$

$$(\Delta E_3 + \Delta E_4)_{j+1} = \frac{1}{2} A[(j + 1)(j + 2) - l(l + 1) - s(s + 1)] \quad \textbf{(11.28)}$$

$$(\Delta E_3 + \Delta E_4)_{j+2} = \frac{1}{2} A[(j + 2)(j + 3) - l(l + 1) - s(s + 1)]$$

From Eqs. (11.28) we may write

$$(\Delta E)_{j+1 \to j} = (\Delta E_3 + \Delta E_4)_{j+1} - (\Delta E_3 + \Delta E_4)_j$$

$$= \frac{1}{2} A[(j + 1)(j + 2) - j(j + 1)] \quad \textbf{(11.29)}$$

$$= A(j + 1)$$

Similarly

$$(\Delta E)_{j+2 \to j+1} = A(j + 2) \quad \textbf{(11.30)}$$

Dividing Eq. (11.29) by Eq. (11.30), we get

$$\frac{(\Delta E)_{j+1 \to j}}{(\Delta E)_{j+2 \to j+1}} = \frac{j+1}{j+2} \tag{11.31}$$

which is the Landé interval rule. Thus for the triplet $^3P_{0,1,2}$, $j = 0$, and the ratio is $1:2$. For the triplet $^3F_{2,3,4}$, $j = 2$, and the ratio is $3:4$, and so on. These results are depicted in Fig. 11.10; and, specifically, these rules were used in Fig. 11.9 as well. These theoretical results are found to be in close agreement with the experimentally determined ratios.

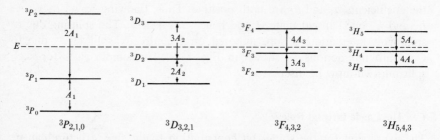

FIG. 11.10. *Illustration of the Landé interval rule: the ratios of the intervals in a given multiplet are proportional to the larger of the j values.*

4. SPECTRA OF TWO-VALENCE-ELECTRON ATOMS

The last three sections have presented enough material so that the reader should have no difficulty in understanding the spectra of not only two-valence-electron atoms but also for atoms of more than two valence electrons. We shall go through the discussions by taking Ca $(Z = 20)$ as an example of a typical alkaline earth metal; while a mention will be made how the changes take place with increasing Z. He $(Z = 2)$, although not an alkaline earths is considered to be the first member of the two-valence electron group.

We shall divide our discussion of the spectra of alkaline earth metals under the following headings.

A.   General Characteristics and the Energy-Level Diagrams
B.   Penetrating and Nonpenetrating Orbits of Two-Valence-Electron Atoms
C.   Observed Transitions and Triplet Fine-Structure
D.   Selection and Intensity Rules

A. General Characteristics and the Energy-Level Diagrams

The elements that have two-valence-electron atoms are He, Be, Mg, Ca, Zn, Sr, Cd, Ba, and Hg. Table 11.6 shows the electron configurations for these atoms in the normal states. As is evident, the electrons form closed shells and subshells. The last two electrons in each of these atoms are in the s-state, and thus the normal states consist of two equivalent s-electrons, which are responsible for the optical spectra of these atoms. By looking at the configurations, one can easily tell the states that will result when the atoms are excited. Because there are two optical electrons each with a spin of $\frac{1}{2}$, i.e., $s_1 = \frac{1}{2}$ and $s_2 = \frac{1}{2}$, the resultant spin $s_t = s_1 + s_2$ can have two values, $s_t = 0$ or 1. The value $s_t = 0$ corresponds to singlet states, while $s_t = 1$ corresponds to triplet states. Thus the energy levels of all two-valence-electron atoms will be singlets and triplets. In order to understand which of the levels will be excited, we shall investigate the energy-level diagram of calcium as a typical example.

TABLE 11.6

ELECTRON CONFIGURATIONS FOR THE ALKALINE
EARTHS IN NORMAL STATES

Element	Configuration					
	K	L	M	N	O	P
$_2$He	$1s^2$					
$_4$Be	$1s^2$	$2s^2$				
$_{12}$Mg	$1s^2$	$2s^22p^6$	$3s^2$			
$_{20}$Ca	$1s^2$	$2s^22p^6$	$3s^23p^6$	$4s^2$		
$_{30}$Zn	$1s^2$	$2s^22p^6$	$3s^23p^63d^{10}$	$4s^2$		
$_{38}$Sr	$1s^2$	$2s^22p^6$	$3s^23p^63d^{10}$	$4s^24p^6$	$5s^2$	
$_{48}$Cd	$1s^2$	$2s^22p^6$	$3s^23p^63d^{10}$	$4s^24p^64d^{10}$	$5s^2$	
$_{56}$Ba	$1s^2$	$2s^22p^6$	$3s^23p^63d^{10}$	$4s^24p^64d^{10}$	$5s^25p^6$	$6s^2$
$_{80}$Hg	$1s^2$	$2s^22p^6$	$3s^23p^63d^{10}$	$4s^24p^64d^{10}4f^{14}$	$5s^25p^65d^{10}$	$6s^2$

The ground state of calcium is $4s^2$, which may also be written as $4s4s$. Out of the two states, $^1S_0$ and $^3S_1$, that can be formed with these two equivalent electrons, $^3S_1$ is not permitted by the Pauli exclusion principle, and this exception is a special case whenever we have two equivalent s-electrons. In looking for excited states, we shall assume that one of the electrons always remains in $4s$. This assumption is true because most of the series observed do satisfy this condition. Thus different possible configurations for the S excited states are $4s5s$, $4s6s$, $4s7s$, . . . , $4s\infty s$, or in general, $4sns$, where $n = 5, 6, . . . , \infty$. The excited states resulting from the configurations $4sns$ are $^1S_0$ and $^3S_1$ states, as shown in Fig. 11.11. $^3S_1$ levels are degenerate and its triplet nature is revealed under the influence of a magnetic field. The P-states are obtained from the configurations of the type $4snp$ where $n = 4, 5, 6, . . . , \infty$, and the resulting states are singlets $^1P_1$ and the triplet states $^3P_2$, $^3P_1$, $^3P_0$ (or $^3P_{2,1,0}$). The configuration resulting from d-electrons are of the form $4snd$ where $n = 3, 4, 5, 6, . . . , \infty$. Note that we have taken $n = 3$ because $3d$ is not filled, as is shown in Table 11.6. The states resulting from $4snd$ are the singlet states $^1D_2$ and the triplet states $^3D_{3,2,1}$. Similarly, the configurations of the type $4snf$ where $n = 4, 5, 6, . . . , \infty$, result in the singlet states $^1F_3$ and the triplet states $^3F_{4,3,2}$. A complete energy-level diagram

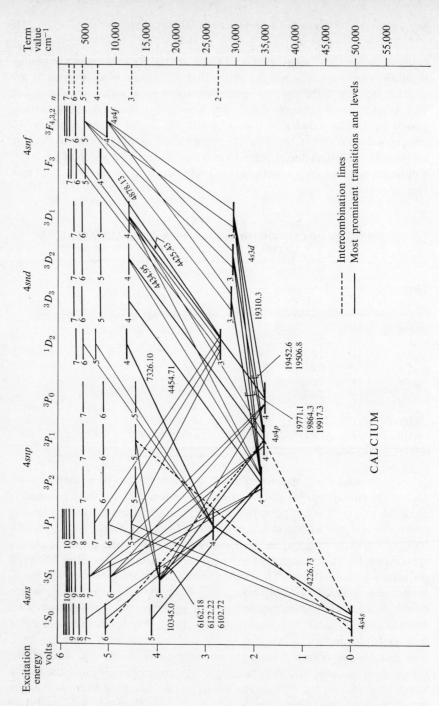

FIG. 11.11. *Energy-level diagram of neutral calcium showing four chief singlet and triplet series. Most prominent lines are shown as solid lines, while the intercombination lines are broken lines. Horizontal broken lines are levels of hydrogen.*

is shown in Fig. 11.11. The different states may be written in a summarized form as $4sns\ ^1S_0$, $4sns\ ^3S_1$; $4snp\ ^1P_1$, $4snp\ ^3P_{2,1,0}$; $4snd\ ^1D_2$, $4snd\ ^3D_{3,2,1}$; and $4snf\ ^1F_3$, $4snf\ ^3F_{4,3,2}$, etc.

From Fig. 11.11 one may make the following observations about the energy levels.

1. For a given l, the triplet levels lie deeper than the corresponding singlet levels. This is in accord with the theoretical prediction of the strong spin-spin coupling model, as explained in Sec. 3, and as shown in Fig. 11.9.
2. For a given n, it is quite clear from Fig. 11.11 that the staes with lower l values lie deeper. This is explained by means of penetrating and nonpenetrating orbits as discussed below.

A few triplets resulting from two-valence electron atoms are shown in Fig. 11.12.

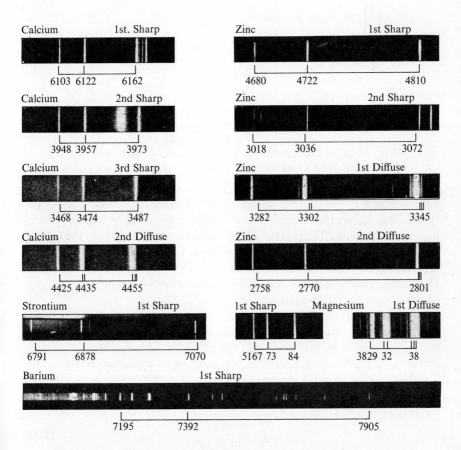

Fig. 11.12. *Photographs of triplets from two-valence electron atoms.* [*By Dr. A. S. King from White, H. E.,* Introduction to Atomic Spectra, *p. 174. New York: McGraw-Hill Book Company, 1934.*]

B. Penetrating and Nonpenetrating Orbits of Electrons for Two-Valence[10] Electron Atoms

Exactly as in the case of the sodium atom, we can draw a picture of penetrating and nonpenetrating electrons in the case of the neutral calcium atom. A neutral calcium atom consists of 20 electrons. Of these, the 18 surrounding the nucleus form a core, while the other two electrons may be found occasionally inside the core, or outside the core, as was shown in Fig. 10.10(c). Such a quantum-mechanical picture is shown in Fig. 11.13 where $4\pi r^2 \psi^* \psi$ has been

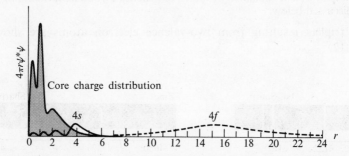

FIG. 11.13.   *Quantum mechanical model of the neutral calcium atom. The shaded area represents the charge-density distribution for the 18 electrons that form the calcium core. The plots of the two valence electrons with configuration 4s4f are also shown. [Printed with permission from White, H. E.,* Introduction to Atom Spectra, *p. 178. New York: McGraw-Hill Book Company, 1934.]*

plotted versus r, the electron-nuclear distance in units of Bohr radius. The shaded area shows the charge-density distribution for the 18 electrons forming the calcium core. The plots of the two valence electrons, one in the 4s-state and the other in the 4f, i.e., the configuration 4s4f, is also shown. An equivalent classical orbital picture for the configuration 4s4f is shown in Fig. 11.14. From these two figures it is quite obvious that the 4s-electron is much more penetrating than the 4f-electron.

The penetration of the electron into the atomic core leads to the deviation of the term value from those of the hydrogen atom, and this deviation may be expressed by two methods: (1) either by introducing the quantum defect, μ, or (2) by using a screening constant, σ, as explained below.

The general term for the hydrogen atom, $T = RZ^2/n^2$, may be modified for the calcium atom by introducing the quantum defect μ, and hence the terms for calcium are given by

$$T = \frac{RZ_0^2}{(n - \mu)^2} \tag{11.32}$$

where Z_0 is the effective nuclear field as seen by the electron when it is well outside the core. For nonpenetrating orbits μ is equal to zero (or almost equal to zero) while the value of μ increases with increasing penetration and is largest for the s-orbits, the most penetrating of orbits. In terms of the screening constant, σ, the terms of the calcium may be written as

$$T = \frac{R(Z - \sigma)^2}{n^2} \tag{11.33}$$

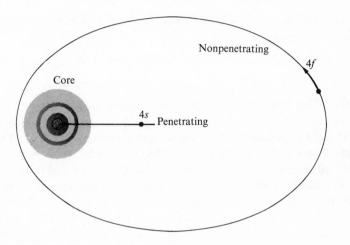

FIG. 11.14.   *The classical orbital model of the neutral calcium atom.*

For nonpenetrating orbits, as well as for hydrogen, $(Z - \sigma) = 1$, the value of $(Z - \sigma)$ increases with decreasing l and decreasing n. For a given n and large l-values, the orbits are almost nonpenetrating. Similarly, for a given l, as n increases $(Z - \sigma) \rightarrow 1$. All these facts are clearly visible from the energy-level diagram of calcium in Fig. 11.11 if one compares the deviation of the terms from the hydrogen-levels shown by horizontal dotted lines. From Fig. 11.11 it is also obvious that for the configurations $4s4f$, the F-levels almost coincide with the hydrogen levels, and hence for the most part f-electrons are nonpenetrating and their orbits do not penetrate the core. As a matter of fact, they are even well outside the s-orbits. All the other electrons such as $4sns$, $4snp$, $4snd$ are penetrating.

C. Observed Transitions and Triplet Fine-Structure

The spectra of two-valence-electron atoms show singlets and triplets, as in Fig. 11.11. Once again the spectra observed may be classified into four different series, i.e., sharp, principal, diffuse, and fundamental series.

     sharp series

    (1) singlet $n^1S_0 \rightarrow 4^1P_0$, where $n = 5, 6, 7, \ldots$

    (2) triplet $n^3S_1 \rightarrow 4^3P_1$, where $n = 5, 6, 7, 8, \ldots$

principal series

(1) singlet $n^1P_1 \rightarrow 4^1S_0$, where $n = 4, 5, 6, 7, \ldots$

(2) triplet $n^3P_{2,1,0} \rightarrow 5^3S_1$, where $n = 5, 6, 7, 8, \ldots$ (11.34)

diffuse series

(1) singlet $n\ ^1D_2 \rightarrow 4^1P_1$, where $n = 4, 5, 6, \ldots$

(2) triplet $n\ ^3D_{3,2,1} \rightarrow 4^3P_{2,1,0}$, where $n = 3, 4, 5, 6, \ldots$

fundamental series

(1) singlet $n\ ^1F_3 \rightarrow 3\ ^1D_2$, where $n = 4, 5, 6, \ldots$

(2) triplet $n\ ^3F_{4,3,2} \rightarrow 3\ ^3D_{3,2,1}$, where $n = 4, 5, 6, \ldots$

Not all the transitions resulting from these series are actually observed. Some of the transitions are forbidden by the selection rules (see Part D below). Some of the allowed transitions are shown in Fig. 11.11. The most prominent and strong transitions are shown by solid lines. As one might note, usually there are no transitions between the singlet and triplets, or vice versa, i.e., the transitions originating at singlet levels terminate at singlet levels; and those originating at triplet levels terminate at triplet levels, so that $\Delta s_t = 0$ (and $\Delta l_t = \pm 1$). But there are a few transitions that go against this general rule. For example, three such transitions are shown in Fig. 11.11 by the dotted lines. Two of these start from the triplet levels and end at a singlet 4^1S_0, while the third one starts from a 6^1S_0 and ends at 4^3P_1. Such lines are called *intercombination lines*. There are some transitions that result from (or terminate on) high levels and do not belong to these series; such lines are called *combination lines*.

Keeping in mind the selection rules and the triplet fine-structure of the levels, a close observation of the series reveals the following:

1. In the case of the sharp series, each member consists of three lines with equal separations.
2. In the case of the principal series, each member consists of three lines with unequal separations.
3. In the case of the diffuse and fundamental series, each member of either of the two series consists of six lines, three of which are usually strong and the other three are weak.

From the observed fine structure of the spectra, one can usually deduce the following conclusions about the separation between the triplet levels, i.e., the term intervals:

1. ^3P intervals are wider than the ^3D, and ^3D intervals are wider than ^3F intervals, as illustrated in Fig. 11.15.
2. With increasing n, the given series triplet-intervals converge rapidly as they reach a single common limit. This is also illustrated in Fig. 11.15.
3. The corresponding triplet intervals increase with increasing atomic number. This may be observed from the photographs of the triplets in Fig. 11.12.

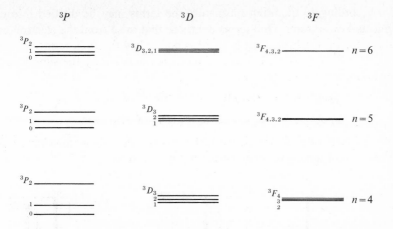

FIG. 11.15.   *The relative separations in the triplet fine-structure of the first three members of the three chief term-series* ^3P, ^3D, *and* ^3F.

D.   Selection Rules and Intensity Rules[11,12]

(i) *Selection Rules.* Without considering any terms resulting from different configurations and coupling schemes, the selection rules depending upon the individual l-values must be obeyed. Thus in the case of a single electron jump

$$\begin{cases} \Delta l_1 = \pm 1 \\ \Delta l_2 = 0 \end{cases} \quad \text{or} \quad \begin{cases} \Delta l_1 = 0 \\ \Delta l_2 = \pm 1 \end{cases} \tag{11.35}$$

For obtaining different terms from various configurations, further restrictions must be imposed depending upon the type of coupling. The transitions that do not follow either of the following two sets of selection rules corresponding to the two coupling schemes imply that the corresponding terms in the transition do not arise from either of the two coupling schemes.

For LS-coupling the selection rules are

$$\Delta s_t = 0$$
$$\Delta l_t = 0, \pm 1 \tag{11.36}$$
$$\Delta j_t = 0, \pm 1 \ (0 \to 0 \ \text{forbidden})$$

These selection rules are used in drawing the transitions of Fig. 11.11 and Fig. 11.16.

For the *jj*-coupling the selection rules are

$$\begin{cases} \Delta j_1 = 0 \\ \Delta j_2 = 0, \pm 1 \end{cases} \quad \text{or} \quad \begin{cases} \Delta j_1 = 0, \pm 1 \\ \Delta j_2 = 0 \end{cases} \tag{11.37}$$

$$\Delta j_t = 0, \pm 1 \ (0 \to 0 \ \text{forbidden})$$

According to quantum mechanics the terms may be divided into odd terms and even terms. Odd terms are those that arise from the electron configurations in which the sum $(l_1 + l_2)$ is odd, while the even terms are those for which $(l_1 + l_2)$ is even. The odd terms are denoted by the superscript o. For example:

$$pd(l_1 + l_2 = 3, \text{ odd}) \quad {}^1P_1^o \, {}^1D_2^o \, {}^1F_3^o \, {}^3P_{2,1,0}^o \, {}^3D_{3,2,1}^o \, {}^3F_{4,3,2}^o$$

$$pp(l_1 + l_2 = 2, \text{ even}) \quad {}^1S_0 \, {}^1P_1 \, {}^1D_1, \, {}^3S_1 \, {}^3P_{2,1,0} \, {}^3D_{3,2,1}$$

The selection rules for an individual l require that transitions occur only when the odd terms combine with even, or vice versa.

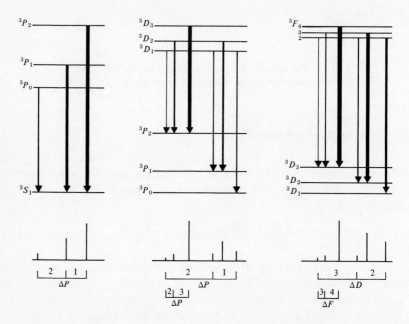

FIG. 11.16. *Some triplet-singlet and triplet-triplet transitions that illustrate selection rules and intensity rules.*

(ii) *Intensity Rules.* The sum rules used for the intensities of the doublets in alkali atoms as discussed in Chapter X can be extended to the relative intensities of the triplet fine-structure of the alkaline earths atoms in the case of LS-coupling. According to these sum rules

1. The sum of the intensities of all lines of a multiplet that start from the same initial level is proportional to the quantum weight, $2j + 1$, of the initial level.
2. The sum of the intensities of all lines of a multiplet that end on the same final level is proportional to the quantum weight, $2j + 1$, of the final level.

These rules are illustrated in Fig. 11.16 for the transitions between $^3D_{3,2,1}$ and $^3P_{2,1,0}$.

More accurate results for intensities have been derived by quantum-mechanical methods[13].

5. THE EXCITATION OF BOTH OF THE VALENCE ELECTRONS AND COMPLEX SPECTRA

The spectra of two valence electron atoms, those of alkaline earths beryllium, magnesium, calcium, strontium, and barium discussed in the previous section, results from the excitation of one of the two valence electrons, while the other electron remains in the ground state. As a matter of fact many more prominent lines are observed that cannot be classified into one of the four chief series of singlets and triplets: sharp, principal, diffuse, and fundamental. The detailed investigation of these prominent lines was made by Russell and Saunders[15] who were able to account for the complex spectra by assuming that both the valence electrons are excited.

A. Triad of Triplet-Multiplets

In the spectra of Ca, Sr, and Ba, three prominent groups of lines forming a triad of triplet-multiplets are observed. In the case of calcium three such great triplet-multiplets are shown in Fig. 11.17, one in the red region and the other two in the green. As is obvious from the frequency and intensity plot, each multiplet consists of three relatively strong lines and three or four fainter

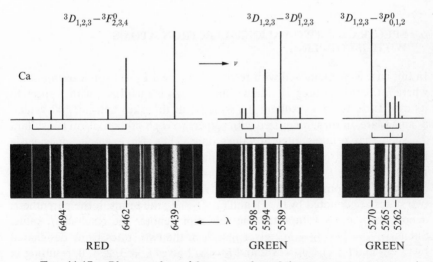

FIG. 11.17.   *Photographs and frequency plots of three prominent groups of lines forming the great calcium triad of triplet-multiplets, one in the red region and the other two in the green region of the spectrum.* [*Printed with permission from White, H. E.*, Introduction to Atomic Spectra, *p. 180. New York: McGraw-Hill Book Company, 1934.*]

lines. These three multiplets start from the triplet levels $^3P_{0,1,2}$, $^3D_{1,2,3}$, and $^3F_{2,3,4}$, all ending on the $^3D_{1,2,3}$ levels of the diffuse series, i.e., $^3D_{1,2,3} - {}^3P_{0,1,2}$, $^3D_{1,2,3} - {}^3D_{1,2,3}$, and $^3F_{2,3,4} - {}^3D_{1,2,3}$. The terms from which these transitions start do not belong to the four chief series; they result from the excitation of both of the valence electrons.

B. Anomalous Multiplets

Russell and Saunders also observed a series of anomalous multiplets in the ultraviolet region of the calcium spectrum. These series usually consist of running terms with a negative series limit; in other words, the limit of these terms lies above the limit of the chief S, P, D, and F series. The explanation of this lies in the fact that the atom contains enough energy to ionize, but still it is neutral because it contains all its electrons. The total energy though more than the ionization energy (for one electron removal) is divided between the two electrons, each one of which is excited to the higher state as suggested by Bohr and Wentzel[16]. For example, the series of ^3P terms found by Russell and Saunders results from one electron in the $3d$ state, while the other occupies the states $3d$, $4d$, $5d$, etc. The second electron finally takes the $n \to \infty$ value, leaving the first electron in the $3d$-state, which determines the series limit.

The above reasoning leads to the complete explanation of the anomalous multiplets and complex spectra observed not only in Ca but in other elements as well.

6. SPECTRA OF TWO-VALENCE-ELECTRON ATOMS WITH jj-COUPLING

In this case S_1 is quantized with respect to its own L_1 to form a resultant J_1, where j_1 takes half-integral values. Similarly, S_2 is quantized with respect to its own L_2 to form a resultant J_2, where j_2 again takes half-integral values. J_1 and J_2 are, in turn, quantized with respect to each other to form a resultant J_t, such that j_t takes integral values only. Thus, for example, consider a two-valence-electron atom with a configuration pd. For this case $l_1 = 1$, $s_1 = 1/2$, giving $j_1 = 1/2$, $3/2$; and $l_2 = 2$, $s_2 = 1/2$, giving $j_2 = 3/2$, $5/2$. Now $j_1 = 1/2$ combines with $j_2 = 3/2$, resulting in $j_t = 1$ and 2; and these two states are denoted by $(\frac{1}{2}, \frac{3}{2})_1$ and $(\frac{1}{2}, \frac{3}{2})_2$, i.e., the terms in the parenthesis denote the j_1 and j_2 values and the subscript denotes the resultant j_t value. Similarly $j_1 = 1/2$, $j_2 = 5/2$ gives $j_t = 2$, 3, the two states being designated by $(\frac{1}{2}, \frac{5}{2})_2$ and $(\frac{1}{2}, \frac{5}{2})_3$. $j_1 = 3/2$ and $j_2 = 3/2$ gives $j_t = 3$, 2, 1, 0, resulting in four states $(\frac{3}{2}, \frac{3}{2})_{3,2,1,0}$. $j_1 = 3/2$, $j_2 = 5/2$ gives $(\frac{3}{2}, \frac{5}{2})_{4,3,2,1}$ corresponding to $j_t = 4$, 3, 2, 1. If along with the term designation, we want to write the electron configuration also, we do so by writing the configuration immediately preceding the notation for state value, e.g., $4p3d(3/2, 5/2)_4$.

In heavier atoms (high Z) the spin-orbit interactions become much larger than the residual Coulomb interaction[17]. It is this dominance of the spin-orbit coupling that results in the coupling of spin and orbital angular-momenta of each optical electron separately, resulting in separate j's values, and hence *jj*-coupling. As an example of two-valence-electron atomic systems, consider elements in the carbon group, i.e., carbon, silicon, germanium, tin, and lead. Figure 11.18 shows the normal and the first excited states in this group of elements. $2p^2$ and $2p3s$, the normal and the first-excited state configuration of carbon show a perfect LS-coupling; while $6p^2$ and $6s7p$, the normal and the first-excited state configuration of lead are a perfect example of *jj*-coupling. Silicon, germanium, and tin show a gradual transition from LS-coupling to *jj*-coupling. We may point out that the number of levels obtained is the same from both types of couplings.

In Fig. 11.18 as we move from carbon towards lead, the Landé interval rule is obeyed with decreasing accuracy. The reasons are obvious because of the change in the type of coupling from LS to *jj*, and hence the interval rule must be modified. This can be done if we remember that in *jj*-coupling it is assumed that the interaction between the spin of each electron and its own orbit is greater than the interaction between the two spins and two orbits, respectively. Thus in Eq. (11.12), ΔE_3 and ΔE_4 are much larger than ΔE_1 and ΔE_2; while ΔE_5 and ΔE_6 are still negligible. Proceeding exactly in the same fashion as for the LS-coupling, and remembering that *jj*-coupling is stronger than LS-coupling, we get

$$\Delta E_3 = \frac{1}{2} a_3 [j_1(j_1 + 1) - l_1(l_1 + 1) - s_1(s_1 + 1)] \tag{11.38}$$

$$\Delta E_4 = \frac{1}{2} a_4 [j_2(j_2 + 1) - l_2(l_2 + 1) - s_2(s_2 + 1)] \tag{11.39}$$

and

$$\Delta E_1 = a_1 S_1 S_2 \cos(\mathbf{S}_1, \mathbf{S}_2) = a_1 S_1 S_2 \cos(\mathbf{S}_1, \mathbf{J}_1) \cos(\mathbf{J}_1, \mathbf{J}_2) \cos(\mathbf{J}_2, \mathbf{S}_2) \tag{11.40}$$

$$\Delta E_2 = a_2 L_1 L_2 \cos(\mathbf{L}_1, \mathbf{L}_2) = a_2 L_1 L_2 \cos(\mathbf{L}_1, \mathbf{J}_1) \cos(\mathbf{J}_1, \mathbf{J}_2) \cos(\mathbf{J}_2, \mathbf{L}_2) \tag{11.41}$$

which by using the law of cosines may be written as

$$\Delta E_1 + \Delta E_2 = \frac{1}{2} A [j_t(j_t + 1) - j_1(j_1 + 1) - j_2(j_2 + 1)] \tag{11.42}$$

where

$$A = a_1 b_1 + a_2 b_2 \tag{11.43}$$

and

$$b_1 = \frac{S_1^2 + J_1^2 - L_1^2}{2 J_1^2} \cdot \frac{S_2^2 + J_2^2 - L_2^2}{2 J_2^2} \tag{11.44}$$

$$b_2 = \frac{L_1^2 + J_1^2 - S_1^2}{2 J_1^2} \cdot \frac{L_2^2 + J_2^2 - S_2^2}{2 J_2^2} \tag{11.45}$$

Thus different energy level separation in *jj*-coupling may be calculated from

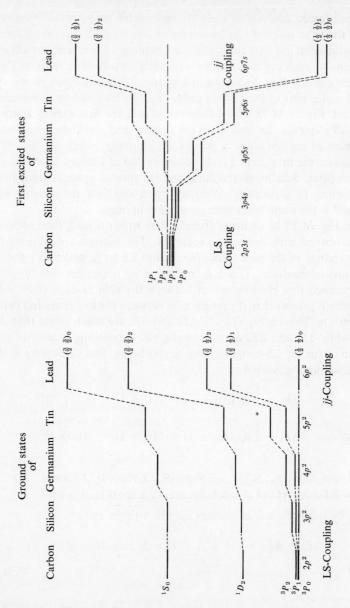

FIG. 11.18. *The normal and first-excited states in the carbon group of elements illustrating the transition from LS- to jj-coupling.* [*Printed with permission from White, H. E.,* Introduction to Atomic Spectra, *p. 200. New York: McGraw-Hill Book Company, 1934.*]

$$\Delta E = \Delta E_1 + \Delta E_2 + \Delta E_3 + \Delta E_4 \qquad (11.46)$$

where different quantities are given by the Eqs. (11.38) through (11.45). For example, if $l_1 = 1$, $s_1 = 1/2$, and $l_2 = 0$, $s_2 = 1/2$; we get $\Delta E_3 = a_3/2$, $-a_3$ and $\Delta E_4 = 0$; while $\Delta E_1 + \Delta E_2 = -5a_1/12$, $+3a_1/12$, and $-a_1/12$ and $+3a_1/12$. The four states $(\frac{3}{2}, \frac{1}{2})_{1,2}$, $(\frac{1}{2}, \frac{1}{2})_{0,1}$ are shown in Fig. 11.19 for the case of Sn.

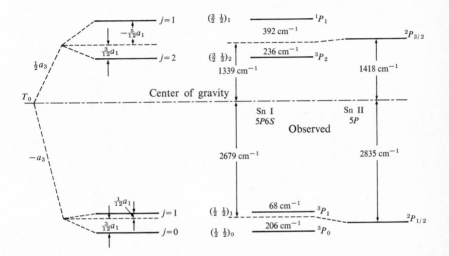

FIG. 11.19.   *The interaction energies between two valence electrons for the four states $(\frac{3}{2}, \frac{1}{2})_{1,2}$, $(\frac{1}{2}, \frac{1}{2})_{0,1}$ of tin. [Printed with permission from White, H. E.*, Introduction to Atomic Spectra, *p. 198. New York: McGraw-Hill Book Company, 1934.]*

7.   TWO-VALENCE-ELECTRON ATOMS IN AN EXTERNAL MAGNETIC FIELD

The magnetic effects on an atom that has two valence electrons can be divided into the following three different categories depending upon the strength of the magnetic field:

1. The Zeeman effect, which takes place when the magnetic field is *weak*.
2. The Paschen-Back effect, which takes place when the magnetic field is *strong*.
3. The complete Paschen-Back effect, which takes place when the magnetic field is *very strong*.

Making use of the vector model of the atom, it is easy to extend the methods of calculating the effects of a magnetic field on single-valence-electron atoms to the case of two-valence-electron atoms. Of course we are concerned with four vectors, L_1, S_1, L_2, S_2, instead of two, and this makes the situation more difficult. In order to find the effect of the magnetic fields, one has to know the total magnetic moment of the atom, and the Landé g-factor. The values of these two quantities will depend upon the type of coupling. In LS-coupling, the two spin vectors precess rapidly around their resultant S_t; the two orbital vectors precess rapidly around their resultant L_t; L_t and S_t in turn precess slowly around their common resultant J_t, while the precession of J_t around H is very slow. The magnetic quantum numbers to be used in this case, as shown in Fig. 11.20 are m_{s_t}, m_{l_t}, and m_{j_t}. Similarly,

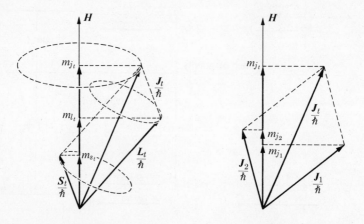

FIG. 11.20. *The magnetic quantum number m_{s_t}, m_{l_t}, and m_{j_t} to be used in the case of LS-coupling.*

FIG. 11.21. *The magnetic quantum numbers m_{j_1}, m_{j_2}, and m_{j_t} to be used in the case of jj-coupling.*

in the case of *jj*-coupling, L_1, S_1 precess rapidly around their resultant J_1; L_2, S_2 precess rapidly around their resultant J_2; J_1 and J_2 precess slowly around their resultant J_t; while the precession of J_t around H is very slow. The magnetic quantum numbers to be used in this case, as shown in Fig. 11.21, are m_{j_1}, m_{j_2}, and m_{j_t}.

A. The Total Magnetic Moment and the Landé g-Factor for Two-Valence-Electron Atoms[18]

We shall calculate these quantities for the case of LS-coupling. The individual magnetic moments corresponding to L_1, L_2, S_1, and S_2 are

$$\mu_{l_1} = 1 \cdot \sqrt{l_1(l_1 + 1)}\, \hbar \cdot \left(\frac{e}{2mc}\right) = L_1 \frac{e}{2mc}$$

$$\mu_{s_1} = 2 \cdot \sqrt{s_1(s_1 + 1)}\, \hbar \cdot \left(\frac{e}{2mc}\right) = 2S_1 \frac{e}{2mc}$$

(11.47)

$$\mu_{l_2} = 1 \cdot \sqrt{l_2(l_2 + 1)}\, \hbar \cdot \left(\frac{e}{2mc}\right) = L_2 \frac{e}{2mc}$$

$$\mu_{s_2} = 2 \cdot \sqrt{s_2(s_2 + 1)}\, \hbar \cdot \left(\frac{e}{2mc}\right) = 2S_2 \frac{e}{2mc}$$

(11.47)

The way these individual magnetic moments are added together to give a resultant μ_{j_t} and g-factors depends upon the type of coupling. In the case of LS-coupling, $\mathbf{S}_1$ and $\mathbf{S}_2$ are coupled strongly to form a resultant $\mathbf{S}_t$, the total μ_{s_t} will be the vector sum of the projections of μ_{s_1} and μ_{s_2} along $\mathbf{S}_t$, i.e.,

$$\mu_{s_t} = [S_1 \cos(\mathbf{S}_1, \mathbf{S}_t) + S_2 \cos(\mathbf{S}_2, \mathbf{S}_t)] \cdot 2\frac{e}{2mc} = 2S_t \frac{e}{2mc} \quad \text{(11.48)}$$

Similarly, for the two L's we get

$$\mu_{l_t} = [L_1 \cos(\mathbf{L}_1, \mathbf{L}_t) + L_2 \cos(\mathbf{L}_2, \mathbf{L}_t)] \frac{e}{2mc} = L_t \frac{e}{2mc} \quad \text{(11.49)}$$

The vector addition of μ_{l_t} and μ_{s_t} along $\mathbf{J}_t$ results in the total magnetic moment μ_{j_t}, i.e.,

$$\mu_{j_t} = \mu_{l_t} \cos(\mathbf{L}_t, \mathbf{J}_t) + \mu_{s_t} \cos(\mathbf{S}_t, \mathbf{J}_t)$$

$$= [L_t \cos(\mathbf{L}_t, \mathbf{J}_t) + 2S_t \cos(\mathbf{S}_t, \mathbf{J}_t)] \frac{e}{2mc}$$

(11.50)

or in terms of the Bohr magneton,

$$\mu_{j_t} = [L_t \cos(\mathbf{L}_t, \mathbf{J}_t) + 2S_t \cos(\mathbf{S}_t, \mathbf{J}_t)]\mu_B/\hbar \quad \text{(11.51)}$$

Substituting for

$$\cos(\mathbf{L}_t, \mathbf{J}_t) = \frac{J_t^2 + L_t^2 - S_t^2}{2L_t J_t}$$

and

$$\cos(\mathbf{S}_t, \mathbf{J}_t) = \frac{J_t^2 + S_t^2 - L_t^2}{2S_t J_t} \quad \text{(11.52)}$$

into Eq. (11.51); rearranging and replacing L_t^2 by $l_t(l_t + 1)\hbar^2$, S_t^2 by $s_t(s_t + 1)\hbar^2$ and j_t^2 by $j_t(j_t + 1)\hbar^2$; we get

$$\mu_{j_t} = \left[1 + \frac{j_t(j_t + 1) + s_t(s_t + 1) - l_t(l_t + 1)}{2j_t(j_t + 1)}\right]\sqrt{j_t(j_t + 1)}\, \mu_B \quad \text{(11.53)}$$

Also μ_{j_t} may be written as

$$\mu_{j_t} = gJ_t \mu_B/\hbar = g\sqrt{j_t(j_t + 1)}\, \mu_B \quad \text{(11.54)}$$

where g, by comparing Eqs. (11.53) and (11.54), is

$$g = 1 + \frac{j_t(j_t + 1) + s_t(s_t + 1) - l_t(l_t + 1)}{2j_t(j_t + 1)} \quad \text{(11.55)}$$

This Landé g-factor is identical to the one obtained in the case of a single-valence-electron atom except $\sqrt{j_t(j_t + 1)}$ replaces $\sqrt{j(j + 1)}$, $\sqrt{s_t(s_t + 1)}$ replaces $\sqrt{s(s + 1)}$, and $\sqrt{l_t(l_t + 1)}$ replaces $\sqrt{l(l + 1)}$.

Following a similar procedure, we obtain the following expression for g in the case of jj-coupling.

$$g = g_1 \frac{j_t(j_t + 1) + j_1(j_1 + 1) - j_2(j_2 + 1)}{2j_t(j_t + 1)}$$

$$+ g_2 \frac{j_t(j_t + 1) + j_2(j_2 + 1) - j_1(j_1 + 1)}{2j_t(j_t + 1)} \qquad (11.56)$$

where g_1 and g_2 are the g-factors for the two valence electrons, respectively.

B. The Zeeman Effect[19]

As long as the external applied field is weak, the LS-coupling remains intact, which means $\mathbf{L}_t$ and $\mathbf{S}_t$ precess slowly about $\mathbf{J}_t$, and $\mathbf{J}_t$ precesses even more slowly around $\mathbf{H}$, i.e., j_t is a valid quantum number. The projection of $\mathbf{J}_t$ on $\mathbf{H}$ is $M_{j_t} = m_j \hbar$, i.e.,

$$M_{j_t} = m_j \hbar = J_t \cos(\mathbf{J}_t, \mathbf{H}) = \sqrt{j_t(j_t + 1)}\, \hbar \cos(\mathbf{J}_t, \mathbf{H}) \qquad (11.57)$$

where m_{j_t} can take the value

$$m_{j_t} = j_t, (j_t - 1), \ldots, 1, 0, -1, \ldots, -(j_t - 1), -j_t \qquad (11.58)$$

The change in energy due to the precession of $\mathbf{J}_t$ around $\mathbf{H}$ caused by the external field is

$$\Delta E = \mu_{j_t} \cdot \mathbf{H} = \mu_{j_t} H \cos(\mathbf{J}_t, \mathbf{H}) \qquad (11.59a)$$

Substituting for μ_{j_t} from Eq. (11.54), we get

$$\Delta E = gHJ_t \mu_B \cos(\mathbf{J}_t, \mathbf{H})/\hbar$$

using Eq. (11.57) and $\mu_B = eh/4\pi mc$, we get

$$\Delta E = m_{j_t} \cdot g \cdot H \frac{eh}{4\pi mc} \qquad (11.59b)$$

Thus if the initial energy of the level is E_0 and the total quantum number j_t, the new $(2j_t + 1)$ energy levels are given by

$$E = E_0 + \Delta E = E_0 + m_{j_t} \cdot g \cdot H \frac{eh}{4\pi mc} \qquad (11.60)$$

In order to express energy in terms of wave numbers, we divide by hc, and we get

$$T = T_0 - \Delta T = T_0 - m_{j_t} \cdot g \cdot \mathsf{L} \ \text{cm}^{-1} \qquad (11.61)$$

where we have used Lorentz unit $\mathsf{L} = eH/(4\pi mc^2)$.

Knowing l_t, s_t, and j_t, we find g from Eq. (11.55), m_{j_t} from Eq. (11.58), and find the position of the energy levels in a magnetic field from Eq. (11.60) or Eq. (11.61).

Working with two-valence-electron atoms produces the following pecular-iar situations: We are dealing with $s_t = 0$ and $s_t = 1$, corresponding to the singlet and triplet levels. The transitions between singlets for which $s_t = 0$

lead to the normal Zeeman effect, while the transitions between the triplet levels for which $s_t = 1$ lead to more complex Zeeman patterns. As an example, consider the Zeeman patterns of the transitions $^1P_0 \rightarrow {}^1S_0$ and $^3P_{2,1,0} \rightarrow {}^3S_1$. The energy and the transitions may be calculated exactly as in Chapter X for one-valence electron atoms. The transitions observed in a magnetic field are shown in Fig. 11.22 and follow the same selection rules as for single-valence-electron atoms:

$$\Delta m_{j_t} = 0, \pm 1 \qquad (11.62)$$

and

$$\text{Viewed} \perp \text{to } H \begin{cases} \Delta m_{j_t} = 0; & \text{plane polarized } \| \text{ to } H; \quad p \\ \Delta m_{j_t} = \pm 1; & \text{plane polarized } \perp \text{ to } H; \quad s \end{cases} \qquad (11.63)$$

$$\text{Viewed} \| \text{to } H \begin{cases} \Delta m_{j_t} = 0; & \text{forbidden} \qquad\qquad\; p \\ \Delta m_{j_t} = \pm 1; & \text{circularly polarized}; \quad\; s \end{cases} \qquad (11.64)$$

The relative intensities may be calculated by using the sum rules and are shown in Fig. 11.22 with the actually observed intensities of the transitions.

Similar calculations can be made in the case of jj-coupling. Usually, the g-factors are quite different in the two cases of LS-coupling and jj-coupling, and hence the resulting Zeeman patterns are also different. Comparing the actually observed patterns with the calculated ones, one can decide about the type of coupling.

C. The Paschen-Back Effect[20]

In the case of a weak magnetic field the atom as a whole is quantized, i.e., j_t and m_{j_t} are valid quantum numbers. But as the field is increased and becomes stronger, the precession of $\mathbf{J}_t$ around $\mathbf{H}$ becomes faster, which means that the interaction between $\mathbf{J}_t$ and $\mathbf{H}$ increases. This leads to the eventual breakdown of the coupling between $\mathbf{L}_t$ and $\mathbf{S}_t$ in the case of LS-coupling, or between $\mathbf{J}_1$ and $\mathbf{J}_2$ in the case of jj-coupling. Figure 11.23 illustrates the precession of $\mathbf{L}_t$ and $\mathbf{S}_t$ independently around $\mathbf{H}$ in the case of LS-coupling and their projections lead to the new magnetic quantum numbers m_{l_t} and m_{s_t}. Similarly, in the case of jj-coupling the precession of $\mathbf{J}_1$ and $\mathbf{J}_2$ independently around $\mathbf{H}$ and their projections lead to the new magnetic quantum numbers m_{j_1} and m_{j_2}.

The calculations of energy shift $-\Delta E_H$ ($= hc \, \Delta T_H$) are exactly the same as in the case of one-valence electron atoms discussed in Chapter X except there is an additional small correction term due to spin-orbit coupling which is given by

$$-\Delta T_{L_t \cdot S_t} = A \cdot m_{l_t} \cdot m_{s_t} \qquad (11.65)$$

We add $-\Delta T_H$ and $-\Delta T_{L_t \cdot S_t}$ to the undisplaced line T_0, and obtain the term values of the level in the strong magnetic field as (for LS-coupling)

$$T = T_0 - (m_{l_t} + 2m_{s_t}) \cdot L - A \cdot m_{l_t} m_{s_t} \qquad (11.66)$$

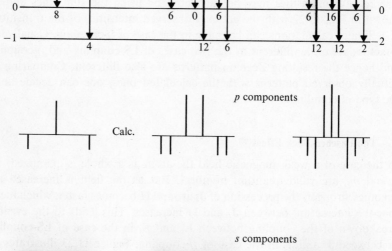

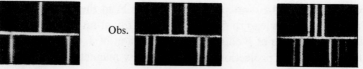

FIG. 11.22. *Calculated and observed Zeeman patterns of a principal series triplet* $^3S_1 \rightarrow {}^3P_{0,1,2}$. [*Printed with permission from White, H. E.*, Introduction to Atomic Spectra, *p. 220. New York: McGraw-Hill Book Company, 1934.*]

The allowed transitions may be drawn by making use of the selection rules

$$\Delta m_{s_t} = 0$$

and

$$\Delta m_{l_t} = \begin{cases} 0 \text{ for } \pi(p) \text{ component} \\ \pm 1 \text{ for } \sigma(s) \text{ component} \end{cases} \qquad \textbf{(11.67)}$$

Similarly in the case of jj-coupling the term value in a strong magnetic field is given by

$$T = T_0 - (g_1 m_{j_1} + g_2 m_{j_2}) \cdot \mathbf{L} - A \cdot m_{j_1} m_{j_2} \qquad (11.68)$$

The selection rules for the observed transitions in the case of jj-coupling are the following

$$\left. \begin{array}{l} \Delta m_{j_1} = 0 \\[2ex] \Delta m_{j_2} = \begin{cases} 0 \text{ for } p\text{-component} \\ \pm 1 \text{ for } s\text{-component} \end{cases} \end{array} \right\} \text{ or } \left\{ \begin{array}{l} \Delta m_{j_1} = \begin{cases} 0 \text{ for } p\text{-component} \\ \pm 1 \text{ for } s\text{-component} \end{cases} \\[2ex] \Delta m_{j_2} = 0 \end{array} \right. \qquad (11.69)$$

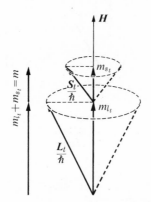

FIG. 11.23.   *The precession of L_t and S_t independently around H in the case of LS-coupling, and their projections, leading to new magnetic quantum numbers.*

D.   The Complete Paschen-Back Effect[21]

We have already seen that the effect of increasing the field from weak to strong led to the breakdown of the LS-coupling or the jj-coupling. If the field is made even stronger, eventually the coupling between $\mathbf{L}_1$, $\mathbf{L}_2$ and $\mathbf{S}_1$, $\mathbf{S}_2$, which form $\mathbf{L}_t$ and $\mathbf{S}_t$, respectively, in LS-coupling, also breaks down; while in the case of jj-coupling, the coupling between $\mathbf{L}_1$, $\mathbf{S}_1$ and $\mathbf{L}_2$, $\mathbf{S}_2$, which form $\mathbf{J}_1$ and $\mathbf{J}_2$, respectively, also breaks down. In the presence of a very strong external magnetic field, all the four vectors, $\mathbf{L}_1$, $\mathbf{S}_1$, $\mathbf{L}_2$, and $\mathbf{S}_2$, precess independently along the direction of the applied $\mathbf{H}$, irrespective of the type of coupling as shown in Fig. 11.24. This is called the complete Paschen-Back effect.

In the case of a weak magnetic field, j_t and m_{j_t} were valid quantum numbers. In a strong magnetic field l_t, m_{l_t} and s_t, m_{s_t} or j_1, m_{j_1} and j_2, m_{j_2} were valid quantum numbers. In the presence of a very strong magnetic field the quantum numbers to be used are l_1, l_2, s_1, s_2, and the corresponding magnetic

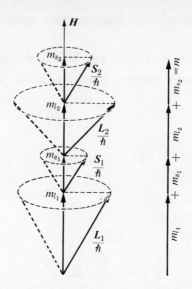

FIG. 11.24. *In a very strong magnetic field, the four vectors* L_1, S_1, L_2, *and* S_2 *precess independently around* H, *irrespective of the type of coupling. This is the complete Paschen-Back effect.*

quantum numbers m_{l_1}, m_{l_2}, m_{s_1}, m_{s_2}, respectively, represent the projections and are given by the relations

$$m_{l_1} = \frac{L_1}{\hbar} \cos(\mathbf{L_1}, \mathbf{H}) = 0, \pm 1, \pm 2, \ldots, \pm l_1$$

$$m_{l_2} = \frac{L_2}{\hbar} \cos(\mathbf{L_2}, \mathbf{H}) = 0, \pm 1, \pm 2, \ldots, \pm l_2$$

$$m_{s_1} = \frac{S_1}{\hbar} \cos(\mathbf{S_1}, \mathbf{H}) = \pm \frac{1}{2} \qquad \text{(11.70)}$$

$$m_{s_2} = \frac{S_2}{\hbar} \cos(\mathbf{S_2}, \mathbf{H}) = \pm \frac{1}{2}$$

The corresponding changes in the energy are given by

$$\Delta E_{l_1} = m_{l_1} \frac{eh}{4\pi mc} H, \qquad \Delta E_{l_2} = m_{l_2} \frac{eh}{4\pi mc} H$$

$$\Delta E_{s_1} = 2m_{s_1} \frac{eh}{4\pi mc} H, \qquad \Delta E_{s_2} = 2m_{s_2} \frac{eh}{4\pi mc} H \qquad \text{(11.71)}$$

Thus the total change in energy expressed in cm^{-1} and Lorentz units,

$$-\Delta T = (m_{l_1} + m_{l_2} + 2m_{s_1} + 2m_{s_2}) \cdot \mathbf{L} \qquad \text{(11.72)}$$

Different combinations of m_{l_1}, m_{l_2}, m_{s_1}, and m_{s_2} lead to different states. After correcting for the spin-orbit coupling terms, the energy of any level is given by

$$T = T_0 - (m_{l_1} + m_{l_2} + 2m_{s_1} + 2m_{s_2}) \cdot \mathbf{L} - a_1 m_{s_1} m_{s_2}$$
$$- a_2 m_{l_1} m_{l_2} - a_3 m_{l_1} m_{s_1} - a_4 m_{l_2} m_{s_2} \quad \textbf{(11.73)}$$

After calculating the levels from different states, the transitions are governed by the selection rules

$$\Delta m_{s_1} = \Delta m_{s_2} = 0$$

$$\Delta m_{l_2} = \begin{cases} 0 \text{ for } p\text{-components} \\ \pm 1 \text{ for } s\text{-components} \end{cases} \quad \text{or} \quad \begin{cases} \Delta m_{l_2} = 0 \\ \Delta m_{l_1} = \begin{cases} 0 \text{ for } p\text{-components} \\ \pm 1 \text{ for } s\text{-components} \end{cases} \end{cases} \quad \textbf{(11.74)}$$

A very strong magnetic field is required to observe a complete Paschen-Back effect. As an example, Fig. 11.25 shows how splitting takes place as the

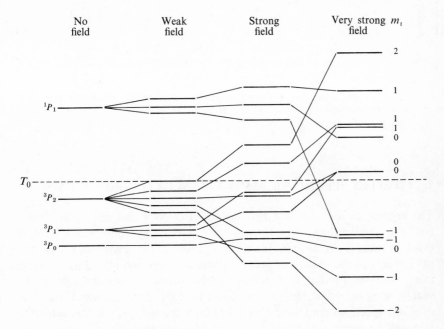

FIG. 11.25.   *Illustration of the changes in the splitting for the sp-electron configuration that take place as the strength of the field is changed from zero to a very high value.*

strength of the field is changed from zero to a very high value reaching the complete Paschen-Back effect. The corresponding transitions are shown in Fig. 11.26. It may be noted, once the splitting takes place in a weak field, changing the strength of the field does not change the number of levels; it only changes the relative separations. Similarly, the number of levels and the transitions in the case of LS-coupling are the same as in *jj*-coupling except that the relative separations are different in the two cases.

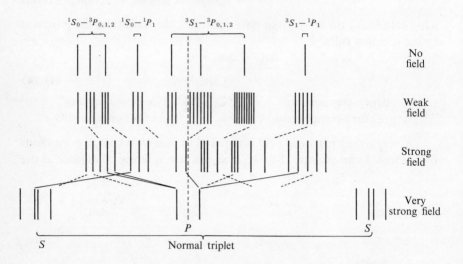

FIG. 11.26. *Illustration of the changes in the number of lines observed for the transition sp → ss as the strength of the magnetic field is changed from zero to a very high value.*

8. COMPLEX SPECTRA OF MANY-VALENCE-ELECTRON ATOMS[22,23]

The arguments for one- and two-valence-electron atoms can be easily extended to predict the spectra of many-valence-electron atoms, which we shall briefly discuss in this section. It was known long before 1920 that the spectra of elements of the middle of periodic table are very complex. For example, iron, rhodium, iridium, and others had hundreds of lines throughout the visible, ultraviolet, and infrared regions. In 1901, Snyder showed that the rhodium spectrum contained about 470 lines grouped together in an array of equal frequency differences. These complex spectra were assumed to consist of a number of triplet series, but it was shown by Sommerfeld that the grouping of lines in a complex spectrum arises from multiple energy levels.

It is shown that in addition to singlet, doublet, and triplet levels there are, in general, multiplet levels consisting of equally spaced four, five, six, seven, or even eight levels, called quartet, quintent, sextet, septet, and octet levels, respectively. The origin of these was discussed in detail in Sec. 2 of this chapter. With the help of the previous discussion and two laws given on the following page, it is easy to analyze the complex spectrum.

A.　The Displacement Law

This was first stated by Kossell and Sommerfeld[24] as the energy levels and spectrum of any neutral atom of atomic number, Z, are very similar to the energy levels and spectrum of the ionized atom with atomic number $(Z + 1)$ succeeding in the periodic table.

B.　Alternation of Law of Multiplicities[25]

According to this law the spectral terms arising from successive elements in the periodic table alternate between odd and even multiplicities. Table 11.7, illustrates the alternation law of multiplicities for the elements in the first long period. Also shown are the multiplicities of the singly ionized elements in the first long period, illustrating the displacement law. The spectra of the elements in the first long period shown in Fig. 11.27 also illustrates the alternation law of multiplicities.

9.　THE STARK EFFECT[26-28]

So far we have discussed the splitting of spectral lines in a magnetic field. The next question that arises is what happens when the source emitting the radiation is placed in an electric field? The splitting of the spectral lines takes place in an electric field as well, and this phenomenon is called the *Stark effect*. Even though the effect of the magnetic field was discovered by Zeeman as early as 1897, it was not until 1913 that Stark[29] showed that every line of the Balmer series of hydrogen is split into a number of components under the influence of a strong electric field of $\sim$100,000 volts/cm. The observation of the splitting of spectral lines in an electric field was dependent on the availability of very-high-potential gradients along a discharge tube.

　　The splitting in an electric field is due to the splitting of the terms, but the relationships are not quite as simple as in the Zeeman effect. The Stark effect, therefore, is not of much interest in spectroscopy, although it plays an important part in the theories of the formation of molecules from atoms, the broadening of spectral lines, and the investigations of dielectric constants. It is interesting to note that Epstein[30] and Schwarzschild[31] successfully applied Bohr theory to the treatment of the hydrogen atom in an electric field, and the later development of quantum mechanics by Schrödinger[32] and the Dirac theory of the electron[33] have not altered the original results.

　　Without going into the details of the theory, the interaction energy of a hydrogen-like atom in an electric field may be written as

$$\Delta T = A\varepsilon + B\varepsilon^2 + C\varepsilon^2 + \ldots \tag{11.75}$$

where ΔT gives the shift in the energy levels (in terms of wave numbers) of an atom from the field-free states to the states in an external electric field, ε.

TABLE 11.7
ILLUSTRATION OF THE ALTERNATION LAW OF MULTIPLICITIES FOR THE ELEMENTS IN THE FIRST LONG PERIOD

1, 2, 3, 4, 5, 6, 7, 8 stand for singlet, doublet, triplet, quartet, quintet, sextet, septet, and octet, respectively

K	Ca	Sc	Ti	V	Cr	Mn	Fe	Co	Ni	Cu	Zn	Ga	Ge
	1		1		1		1		1		1		1
2		2		2		2		2		2		2	
	3		3		3		3		3		3		3
		4		4		4		4		4			
			5		5		5		5				
				6		6		6					
					7		7						
						8							
Ca+	Sc+	Ti+	V+	Cr+	Mn+	Fe+	Co+	Ni+	Cu+	Zn+	Ga+	Ge+	As+

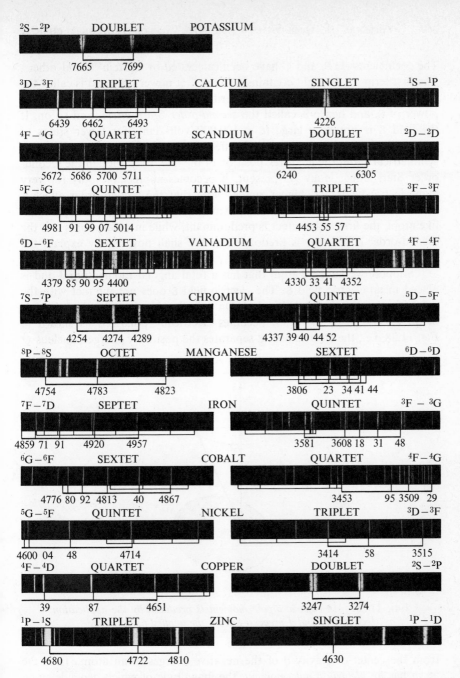

FIG. 11.27. *The spectra of the elements in the first long period. The alternation law of multiplicities is clearly demonstrated. Photographs were taken using a 15-ft. Rowland grating and mounting.* [*Printed with permission from White, H. E.,* Introduction to Atomic Spectra, *p. 250. New York: McGraw-Hill Book Company, 1934.*]

The coefficients A, B, and C have been calculated by Epstein[30] and others. The first term on the right contains ε to the first power only and is called the *first-order Stark effect*. The second term on the right contains the second power of ε, and hence is called the *second-order Stark effect*, and so on. If the field ε is not very large ($\varepsilon < 100{,}000$ volts/cm), for lower states of hydrogen only the first-order Stark effect is observed, and the splitting is symmetrical about the field-free position of the line. Even though the second-order Stark effect is always present, it becomes appreciable only for very high electric fields and higher states. Note that the second-order effect is unidirectional and hence results in unsymmetrical splitting. In the hydrogen-like atom, the first-order effect is predominant, while in other atoms it is the second-order effect that is predominant. We shall now briefly explain the interaction that leads to splitting.

Suppose we have an atom that has a total angular momentum **J** and is placed in an electric field ε. The electric field ε does not interact with the magnetic moment associated with **J**. On the other hand, under the influence of an electric field, the atom becomes electrically polarized as shown in Fig. 11.28, i.e., the electric field ε separates the positively charged nucleus Q

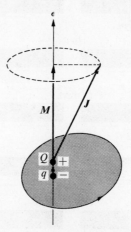

FIG. 11.28. *An electric dipole moment is produced by the application of an electric field and J precesses about the applied field.*

from the center-of-gravity q of the negative charges in an atom. Thus the atom has an *electric dipole-moment*, the magnitude of which depends upon the field strength and the orientation of the angular momentum vector, **J**.

As in the case of a magnetic field, the atom seeks a direction of minimum energy and hence results in the precession of **J** about ε such that the projection **M** of **J** on ε is constant as shown in Fig. 11.28, and $M = +J, J - 1,$ ..., $-J$. The energy shift in this case is equal to the product of the electric dipole-moment and the field strength ε. Because the electric dipole-moment is proportional to ε also, the splitting is proportional to the square of the field strength. This proportionality has an important consequence, i.e., the term *components differing only in sign of M*, $+M$ and $-M$, have the same energy shift. Thus the angular momentum vector **J** is space quantized except that the energy shift for $\pm M$ is the same. This means that the number of term components in an external electric field are $j + \frac{1}{2}$ if j is half-integral, and $j + 1$ if j is integral.

In order to illustrate the above points we consider the following two examples. Figure 11.29 shows the Stark effect of the D-lines of sodium. Field-

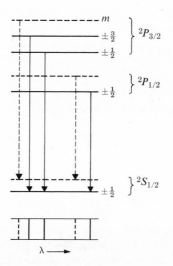

FIG. 11.29.   *Stark effect of the D-lines of sodium, Field-free levels and the transitions are shown by dotted lines while the continuous lines are levels and transitions in an external magnetic field.*

free levels and the transitions are shown by dotted lines while continuous lines are levels and transitions are in the presence of an external electric field.

Figure 11.30 shows the Stark-effect splitting of the helium line $\lambda = 4388 \text{ Å}$. In this photograph the field increases from top to bottom. The asymmetrical nature of splitting in the electric field is quite obvious from this illustration.

If the external electric field is very large, the velocity of precession about the direction of ε becomes very large and eventually leads to the breakdown in the LS-coupling as in the Paschen-Back effect. Thus in a strong electric field j and m are replaced by m_l and m_s, such that $m_l = l, l - 1, \ldots, 0$, and $m_s = +s, s - 1, \ldots, -s$. Note that when $m_l = 0$, m_s does not have different energies. Thus in a strong electric field, we observe effects similar to a strong magnetic field.

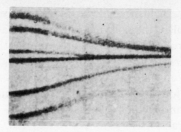

FIG. 11.30. *Stark effect splitting of the helium line* λ = *4388 Å. The field increases from top to bottom.* [*From: J. S. Foster,* J. Frank. Inst., *209, 585,* (*1930*).]

PROBLEMS

1. What are the values of s_t, l_t, j_t and S, L, J for the following terms: $^1S_0$, $^3P_2$, $^1P_1$, $^1D_2$, $^5D_1$, $^3F_4$?

2. What are the values of s_t, l_t, j_t and S_t, L_t, J_t for the terms $^3P_2$, $^6F_{9/2}$, $^2S_{1/2}$, $^2D_{5/2}$, and $^4P_{3/2}$?

3. Calculate the angle between the orbital and total angular-momenta of the state $^3F_4$.

4. What are the term values for each of the following configurations: $4d5p$, $2s3p$, and $3s3p3d$?

5. Write the terms corresponding to the configuration $3d^2$. What will be the possible ground state and the first-excited state?

6. Write the terms for the following configurations (a) nd^2, (b) $ndn'd$, (c) $npnd$ (d) $np^2n's$. What is the lowest energy state in each case?

7. Write the terms for the following configurations (a) np^3, (b) np^2nd, and (c) nd^3.

8. Calculate the possible term values for two equivalent d-electrons according to (a) the LS-coupling scheme and (b) the jj-coupling scheme. What is the possible ground state in each case?

9. For the electron configuration $npnd$, what are the possible term values considering jj-coupling. What is the ground state in this case?

10. With the help of the energy-level diagram for Ca given in the text, calculate the first two-lowest resonance potentials.

11. If electrons of 3.20-eV energy are used in exciting calcium atoms, what possible transitions will be emitted in calcium?

12. Write the electron configuration of Mg (Z = 12), and draw an approximate energy-level diagram and the possible transitions assuming that only one electron is excited. The first few terms are $^1S_0$, $^3P_0$, $^3P_1$, $^3P_2$, $^1P_1$, $^3S_1$, $^1S_0$, and $^1D_2$ with wave numbers (in cm^{-1}) 61,672.1; 39,821.3; 39,801.4; 39,760.5; 26,620.7; 20,474.5; 18,169.0; and 15,268.9, respectively. Identify these terms with different configurations, and calculate the wavelengths of possible transitions.

13. Consider the energy levels of helium-like atoms. Assume that one electron in

the ground state fully screens one nuclear charge. If the other electron is in the excited state, the energies of different levels are given by

$$E_n = -RhcZ^2 - Rhc \frac{(Z-1)^2}{n^2}$$

Show that the accuracy of this expression increases with increasing n.

14. Find the ground-state terms of the following atoms according to the Pauli principle: He, Li, Be, N, and O. What are the ground states of N and O if we make use of the Hund rule? Which values do you think are correct for N and O?

15. Draw the Zeeman-effect levels and the transitions for the following transitions in calcium: (a) $^1D \rightarrow {}^1P$, and (b) $^3D \rightarrow {}^3P$; both transitions in a weak field and then in a strong field.

16. Draw the Zeeman-effect levels and the transitions for the following transitions in calcium: (a) $^1F \rightarrow {}^1D$, and (b) $^3F \rightarrow {}^3D$.

17. Calculate the Landé g-factor for the states 4^1P_1 and 4^1S_0. Draw the possible Zeeman levels and the resulting transitions. If the wavelength of transition $4^4P_1 \rightarrow 4^1S_0$ is 4227 Å, calculate the separation of energy levels and the wavelengths of the transitions in the Zeeman effect. The applied magnetic field is 1.0 weber/m^2.

18. The wavelength of the transition $4^1D_2 \rightarrow 4^1P_1$ in calcium is 7326.1 Å. If this is placed in a magnetic field of 1.2 weber/m^2, calculate (a) the separations between the Zeeman levels and (b) the wavelengths of the allowed transitions.

19. Why does the normal Zeeman effect occur only in even-valence electron atoms? Demonstrate this with the help of two examples.

20. Referring to Fig. 11.25, draw the possible transitions for (a) no field, (b) weak field, (c) strong field, and (d) very strong field.

REFERENCES

1. Russell, H. N., and F. A. Saunders, *Astrophys. J.*, **61**, 38, (1925).

2. White, H. E., *Introduction to Atomic Spectra*, Chap. XII, New York: McGraw-Hill Book Company, 1934.

3. Gordon, W., *Zeit. fur Physik*, **48**, 11, (1929); also Dirac, P. A. M., *Proc. Roy. Soc.*, **A117**, 610, (1927), and **A118**, 351, (1928).

4. Heisenberg, W., and P. Jordon, *Zeit. fur Physik*, **37**, 263, (1926).

5. Pauli, W., *Zeit. fur Physik*, **31**, 765, (1925).

6. Landé, A., *Zeit. fur Physik*, **5**, 231, (1921).

7. Landé, A., *Zeit. fur Physik*, **15**, 189, (1923), and **19**, 112, (1923).

8. Hund, F., *Linienspektren*, p. 124, (1924).

9. Heisenberg, *Zeit. fur Physik*, **38**, 411, (1926), **39**, 499, (1926), and **41**, 239, (1926).

10. Hartree, D. R., *Proc. Camb. Phil. Soc.*, **25**, 225, (1929).

11. Tralli, N., and F. R. Pomilla, *Atomic Theory*, p. 253, New York: McGraw-Hill Book Company, 1969.

12. Sommerfeld, A., and H. Honl, *Sitz-ber. Berl. Akad. Wiss.*, **9**, 141, (1925); also Kronig, R. De L., *Zeit. fur Physik*, **31**, 885 (1925), and **33**, 261, (1925).
13. Dirac, P. A. M., *Proc. Roy. Soc.*, **A111**, 281, (1926).
14. Einstein, A., *Vehr. d. Deutschen Phys. Ges.*, **18**, 318, (1916); also *Zeit. fur Physik*, **18**, 121, (1917).
15. Russell, H. N., and F. A. Saunders, *Astrophys. J.*, **61**, 38, (1925).
16. Bohr, N., and G. Wentzel, *Zeit. fur Physik*, **24**, 106, (1923).
17. Heisenberg, *Zeit. fur Physik*, **41**, 239, (1926).
18. White, H. E., *Introduction to Atomic Spectra*, Chap. XIII. New York: McGraw-Hill Book Company, 1934.
19. Back, E., and A. Landé, *Zeeman effect und Multiplettstruktur*, Berlin: Springer, 1925.
20. Paschen, F., and E. Back, *Ann. Physik*, **39**, 897, (1912), and **40**, 960, (1913); also Darwin, K., *Proc. Roy. Soc.*, **A118**, 264, (1928).
21. Pauli, W., *Zeit. fur Physik*, **16**, 155, (1923), and **31**, 765, (1925).
22. White, H. E., *Introduction to Atomic Spectra*, Chap. XIV, McGraw-Hill Book Company, 1934.
23. Gieseler, H., *Ann. Physik*, **69**, 147, (1922); also Catalan, M. A., *Phil. Trans. Roy. Soc.*, **A223**, 127, (1922).
24. Kossell, W., and A. Sommerfeld, *Verh. d. Deutsch. Phys. Ges.*, **21**, 240, (1919).
25. White, H. E., *Introduction to Atomic Spectra*, p. 249, McGraw-Hill Book Company, 1934.
26. White, H. E., *Introduction to Atomic Spectra*, Chap. XX. New York: McGraw-Hill Book Company, 1934.
27. Herzberg, G., *Atomic Spectra and Atomic Structure*, p. 114. New York: Dover Publications, Inc., 1944.
28. Minkowski, R. in H. Geiger and K. Scheel, *Handbuch der Physik*, **31**, 389, (1929).
29. Stark, J., *Berl. Akad. Wiss.*, **40**, 932, (1913); *Ann. Physik*, **43**, 965, (1919).
30. Epstein, P. S., *Ann. Physik*, **50**, 489, (1916); *Zeit. fur Physik*, **17**, 148, (1916).
31. Schwarzschild, K., *Sitz-ber. Berl. Akad. Wiss.*, p. 548, (1916).
32. Schrödinger, E., *Ann. Physik*, **80**, 437, (1926).
33. Schlapp, R., *Proc. Roy. Soc.*, **A119**, 313, (1928).

SUGGESTIONS FOR FURTHER READING

1. White, H. E., *Introduction to Atomic Spectra*, Chaps. XI, XII, XIII, XIV, and XV. New York: McGraw-Hill Book Company, 1934.
2. Eisberg, R. M., *Fundamentals of Modern Physics*, Chap. 13. New York: John Wiley & Sons, Inc., 1961.
3. Herzberg, G., *Atomic Spectra and Atomic Structure*, Chap. IV. New York: Dover Publications, Inc., 1944.
4. Slater, J. C., *Quantum Theory of Matter*, 2nd ed., New York: McGraw-Hill Book Company, 1968.

5. Shore, B. W., and D. H. Menzel, *Principles of Atomic Spectra*, New York: John Wiley & Sons, Inc., 1968.

6. Condon, E. U., and G. H. Shortley, *The Theory of Atomic Spectra*, New York: Cambridge Univ. Press, 1963.

7. Green, A. E. S., and P. J. Wyatt, *Atomic and Space Physics*, Reading, Mass.: Addison-Wesley Publishing Company, Inc., 1965.

XII

Characteristic X-Ray Spectra
and the Periodic Table

1. INTRODUCTION

In Chapter X we discussed the electron configuration of different elements
and the Pauli Exclusion principle, which governs the positioning of electrons
in shells and subshells of the atom. The most appropriate topic of discussion
after that is usually the classification of elements in the periodic table;
Chapter XI, however, dealt with atomic spectra. In this chapter we shall
discuss the periodic table, but first we must become familiar with the characteristic x-ray spectra emitted by the elements, because the spectra is related to
the classification of elements in the table.

2. PRODUCTION AND PROPERTIES OF X-RAY
AND OPTICAL SPECTRA

There are many ways by which (a) optical spectra, (b) continuous x-ray
spectra, and (c) characteristic x-ray spectra are related. For example, the
electron configuration notations used in optical spectra and characteristic
x-ray spectra are similar, but the two spectra are in altogether different
energy ranges, and the spectra never appear simultaneously. As we shall see,
the fundamental processes by which optical and characteristic x-ray spectra
are produced are the same even though the energy differences are very large.
On the other hand, continuous x-ray spectra and characteristic x-ray spectra

commonly appear in the same energy range, but the mechanism by which they are produced is different. The wavelengths of optical spectra are in the visible region, i.e., $\sim$4000 Å to 6000 Å, while the continuous and characteristic x-ray spectra constitute a wavelength range between 0.1 Å and 10 Å.

An atom is usually in the normal, or ground, state which is the lowest energy state of the atom. In x-ray notation, the $n = 1$ shell is called the K-shell and contains 2 electrons; the $n = 2$ shell is called the L-shell and contains 8 electrons, while M, N, and O shells corresponding to $n = 3$, 4, and 5 contain 18, 32, and 50 electrons, respectively. Figure 12.1 and Fig. 12.2 are the two

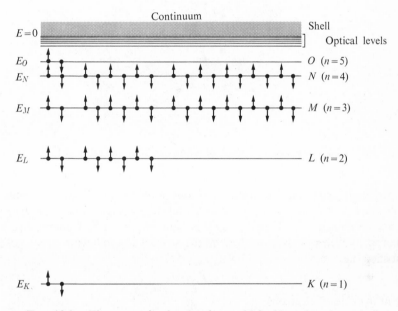

Fig. 12.1.   *The energy levels of cadmium (Cd). Note that the optical levels are near the continuum, while the other levels, K, L, M, N, and O, are the x-ray levels.*

representations of energy levels of Cd ($Z = 48$). The binding energies of the electrons in the lighter atoms, in which only the K- and L- shells may be filled, are very small and are of the order of a few electron volts. For heavier atoms the binding energies of the K- or L-electrons are very large and are usually of the order of a few keV. On the other hand, the binding energies of the outermost electrons in these heavy atoms are small, $\sim$ a few eV. The very high-binding energies of the electrons in the innermost shells are due to the very strong electric field of the nucleus acting on these electrons.

The excitation, or ionization, of these atoms is usually produced by bombarding them with fast-moving electrons or photons. In Chapter VIII, we discussed the Franck and Hertz experiment in which accelerated electrons

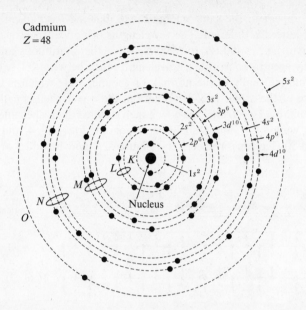

Fig. 12.2. *Shells and subshells of electrons. Cadmium ($Z = 48$).*

experienced elastic and inelastic collisions with the atom. In an inelastic collision the electron changes from its initial state where its binding energy is E_i to the excited state of energy E_f. The same thing can be accomplished by photons, which may be absorbed by the atom if the following condition is satisfied, i.e.,

$$hv \geqslant E_i - E_f \tag{12.1}$$

or in the case of electrons

$$\frac{1}{2} m_e v^2 \geqslant E_i - E_f \tag{12.2}$$

If an atom is to be completely ionized, with E_I as the ionization energy of the atom,

$$hv \geqslant E_I \tag{12.3}$$

or

$$\frac{1}{2} m_e v^2 \geqslant E_I \tag{12.4}$$

The surplus energy in the collisions appears in the form of kinetic energy.

Optical spectra are produced by the excitation of the valence, or optical, electrons—the electrons in the outermost orbit. Both in heavy as well as in light atoms, the binding energies of valence electrons are of the order of a few eV. Thus to produce optical spectra the colliding particles or photons need not have energies of more than a few eV. But suppose one wanted to remove an electron from the K-shell of a heavy element, such as shown in Fig. 12.2; the binding energy of that electron is of the order of 10^3 eV, and, of course, excitation by removing a K-electron requires the bombarding electrons (or photons) to have comparable energies. Thus when producing continuous x-ray spectra by bombarding heavy targets by fast-moving bombarding electrons, it is possible that these fast electrons may also remove K or L electrons from the atoms of the target. Now suppose a K-electron has been removed from its shell, leaving the atom in an excited state. And if the L-, M-, or N-shell are filled, depending upon the incident electron energy the K-electron will go either to an excited state or leave the atom completely. Once a vacancy has been created in the K-shell, an electron from the L- or M-shell will jump to occupy this "space," resulting in the emission of a photon, the energy of which is given by

$$h\nu_{K_\alpha} = E_K - E_L$$
$$h\nu_{K_\beta} = E_K - E_M$$

where E_K, E_L, and E_M are the binding energies of the electrons in those respective shells, and $h\nu_{K_\alpha}$ and $h\nu_{K_\beta}$ are the energies of the photons produced when the electrons jump from the L- to the K-shell and from the M- to the K-shell, respectively. Similarly, M- and L-shell vacancies will be filled by transitions from higher-energy states. Because the binding energies of electrons differ in different atoms, the corresponding photon energies will differ with different atoms, independent of the incident electron energies. The photons thus emitted are called *the characteristic lines*. Whenever continuous x-ray spectra are being produced, the characteristic lines appear superimposed on the continuous x-ray spectrum. The end-point of the continuous x-ray spectra changes with changing accelerating voltages of the bombarding electrons, but the positions of the characteristic lines remain the same so long as the same target is being used. This is clearly shown in Fig. 12.3 where the continuous and the characteristic x-ray spectra are shown at two different operating voltages.

When the incident, or bombarding, electron is of low energy, the K-electron may not be removed but an electron of another shell may be. For any characteristic line of frequency ν to be produced the following condition must be true:

$$K_e \left(= \frac{1}{2} m_e v^2 \right) \geqslant h\nu \geqslant hc/\lambda \qquad (12.5)$$

Table 12.1 summarizes the properties of optical spectra and characteristic and continuous x-ray spectra.

Resonance radiation. Resonance radiation is the process in which an atom absorbs a photon of a given energy and then emits a photon of the same energy. This will happen most often when the incident photon has enough energy to excite the atom to its first-excited state because, in the process of de-excitation, there is no alternative but to emit a photon of the same energy.

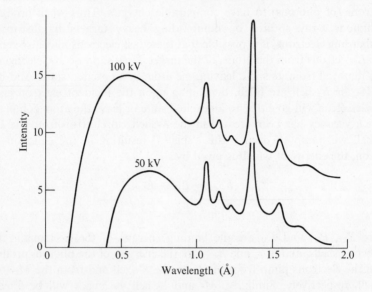

FIG. 12.3. *Typical x-ray spectra at two different voltages. Note that the positions of the characteristic lines, the peaks, remain the same, while the end-point of the continuous spectrum is a function of the voltage.*

Fluorescence radiation. Fluorescence radiation is the process in which an atom absorbs a single photon and then quickly emits two or more photons, while decaying to the ground state.

3. THE CHARACTERISTIC X-RAY SPECTRA

In this section we shall investigate the properties of the characteristic x-ray spectra, x-ray energy-level diagrams, and selection rules. According to Fig. 12.2, to remove one of the electrons in the K-level we must supply enough energy for that electron to be raised to the continuum, or to one of the optical levels near the continuum because in the case of heavy atoms other levels such as L, M, and N are already filled. Because the K-electrons are the most tightly bound, the energy of the incident electron or photon that will excite the K-electron must be very high. In addition the incident electron must come close enough to the bound electron to overcome the repulsing potential energy between the two. In general, the probability of knocking out electrons is small, but in heavy atoms the probability is much larger for the inner shell electrons than it is for the outer shell electrons. For example, as shown in

Fig. 12.2, the electrons in the N- or O-shells are spread over much larger orbits as compared to the electrons in the K- or L-shells, and thus the incident electron, if it has high enough energy, has a greater chance of interacting with the K- or L-electron than any other.

TABLE 12.1

PROPERTIES OF OPTICAL AND X-RAY SPECTRA

Optical spectra	Characteristic, or line, x-ray spectra	Continuous x-ray spectra
1. Produced by removing, or exciting, valence electrons.	Produced by removing electrons from inner shells of heavy atoms.	Produced by slowing down fast electrons in heavy atoms.
2. Consists of discrete, or line, spectra.	Consists of discrete, or line, spectra.	Consists of continuous spectra.
3. Occurs in the visible region with: (a) λ between 4000 Å to $\sim$6000 Å (b) energy between $\sim$0.1 eV to 10 eV	Occurs in the x-ray region with: (a) λ between $\sim$0.1 Å to $\sim$10 Å (b) energy between $\sim$1 keV to $\sim$50 keV	Occurs in the x-ray region with: (a) λ between $\sim$0.1 Å to $\sim$10 Å (b) energy between $\sim$1 keV to $\sim$50 keV
4. The wavelengths of the discrete lines depend upon the nature of the atoms being excited.	The wavelengths of the discrete lines depend upon the nature of the target elements.	The shape of the continuous spectrum depends only upon the energy of the incident electrons and not on the nature of the target.
5. A line of given frequency appears only if the exciting energy, K, is $> h\nu$.	A line of given frequency appears only if the exciting energy, K, is $> h\nu$.	The cut-off frequency, ν_0, depends upon the kinetic energy, $K = h\nu_0$.
6. Line intensity increases with increasing K.	Line intensity increases with increasing K as $I \propto (K - h\nu)^{1.5}$.	The fraction of the incident electron-energy converted into x-rays is $\propto ZK$.
7. There are abrupt changes in spectra from element to element.	Spectra vary smoothly from element to element.	No dependence of ν_0 on element.

Unlike the optical case where the zero level of the energy is that of the ionized atom, in x-ray spectroscopy the zero energy-level is taken as that of the ground state of the neutral atom. Thus in Fig. 12.4, $E = 0$ represents the ground state of the neutral atom. Let E_K be the energy needed to remove the K-electron. If the K-electron is now removed by supplying energy E_K, the atom now has excess energy equal to E_K. Similarly if one of the electrons from, say, the L-, M-, or N-shell is removed, the atom will have an excess energy (positive) of E_L, E_M, or E_N, respectively. Thus the energy levels corresponding to the removal of an electron of a specific shell from the atom are represented by the x-ray energy-level diagram of the atom, as shown in Fig. 12.4.

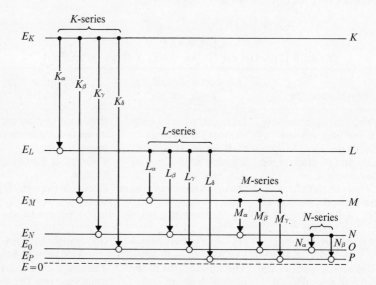

FIG. 12.4. *A simplified x-ray energy-level diagram of an atom. Note that E = 0 corresponds to the ground state. Also shown are the transitions corresponding to the K-, L-, M-, and N-series.*

We shall now describe the mechanism of characteristic x-ray transitions. Assume that one of the K-electrons has been removed, leaving the atom with an excess energy of E_K, which means that the atom is in the K-level, as in Fig. 12.4. In order to fill the vacancy created in the K-shell, an electron from one of the other shells, say, the L-shell, will jump to occupy the vacancy. Because the L-electron is less tightly bound than the K-electron, the increase in the binding energy when the L-electron goes to the K-shell is given out in the form of a photon, i.e., K_α x-ray. If ν_{K_α} is the frequency of the photon emitted, then $h\nu_{K_\alpha} = E_K - E_L$, as shown in Fig. 12.4. Instead of saying that the electron moves from the E_L-level to E_K-level, we may say that a hole, or vacancy, that was created when the K-electron was removed moves from the K-shell to the L-shell, accompanied by photon emission. On the other hand, if the hole moves to the E_M-level, while the electron moves from the E_M-level to fill the vacancy in the K-shell, a photon of frequency ν_{K_β}, given by $h\nu_{K_\beta} = E_K - E_M$, is emitted. Thus the hole keeps moving to lower energy levels until it is filled by a free electron. The photons or the characteristic x-rays that are emitted when the holes created in the K-shell of different atoms move to lower energy states like L, M, N, etc., are said to form the K-series. Mathematically, the frequencies of the x-ray K-series shown in Fig. 12.4 are given by

$$h \, \nu_{K_\alpha} = E_K - E_L$$

$$K\text{-series} \qquad h \, \nu_{K_\beta} = E_K - E_M \qquad\qquad (12.6)$$

$$h \, \nu_{K_\gamma} = E_K - E_N$$

$$\dots \dots \dots \dots \dots$$

Similarly, if the electrons are removed from the L-shells, (or if the L-electrons have moved to K-shells, thus leaving holes in the L-shells), the holes created in the L-levels will move towards lower energy states like M, N, O, ..., and photons of frequencies ν_{L_α}, ν_{L_β}, ν_{L_γ}, ... will be emitted. These photons are said to form the L-series shown in Fig. 12.4 and described by the following relations:

$$h \, \nu_{L_\alpha} = E_L - E_M$$

$$L\text{-series} \qquad h \, \nu_{L_\beta} = E_L - E_N \qquad\qquad (12.7)$$

$$h \, \nu_{L_\gamma} = E_L - E_O$$

$$\dots \dots \dots \dots \dots$$

In the same manner we may define the M-series and N-series, etc. We may point out that the probability that the hole in the K-shell will jump to the M-shell is much greater than the probability that it will jump to the N-shell, and so on.

In drawing the x-ray energy level diagram, shown in Fig. 12.4, we assumed that all the electrons in any one level have the same energy, i.e., no fine structure corresponding to different l for a given n. But this is not true. In a manner similar to optical spectra, we must calculate the number of possible states available, except in this case the states we are looking for correspond to a missing electron, i.e., we are looking for the possible states of a hole. From the symmetry properties, the state of a hole in an otherwise filled shell is the same as that of a single electron in an otherwise completely empty shell. Hence, a hole is designated by the quantum numbers n, l, and j, and for a hole in the K-level there is only one state available, designated by $n = 1, l = 0$, and $j = \frac{1}{2}$, as shown in Fig. 12.5. For a hole in the L-level there are three possible states available to the hole, denoted by (a) $n = 2, l = 0$, $j = \frac{1}{2}$; (b) $n = 2, l = 1, j = \frac{1}{2}$; and (c) $n = 2, l = 1, j = \frac{3}{2}$. Three possible states corresponding to these three sets of quantum numbers are named L_I, L_II, and L_III, respectively, and are shown in Fig. 12.5. Similarly for a hole in the M-level the number of possible states available is five, denoted by M_I, M_II, M_III, M_IV, and M_V, also shown in Fig. 12.5.

Note that in the x-ray energy-level diagram the ordering of the levels with respect to the quantum numbers, n, l, j, is reverse to that of the energy-level diagram of the optical spectra. This is understandable because in x-ray spectra, we are talking of the energy-level diagram of a hole, while in optical spectra we are concerned with the levels of a single electron; hence the reverse order.

Once again, from the symmetrical nature of the problem, the selection rules governing the transitions, i.e., jumping of the hole from one level to another, are the same as that in the case of an electron in optical spectra. Thus

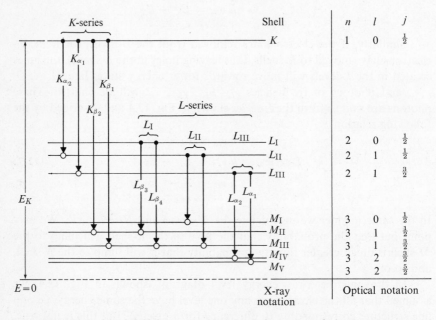

FIG. 12.5. *A detailed x-ray energy-level diagram and the transitions showing the x-ray as well as optical notations.*

the selection rules that govern the transitions shown in Fig. 12.5 are, in general, the following:

$$\Delta l = \pm 1$$

$$j = 0 \text{ or } \pm 1 \qquad (12.8)$$

$$0 \overset{\text{no}}{\to} 0$$

and there is no restriction on the value of n. The transitions for $\Delta n = 0$, like L_{I} to L_{II}, and L_{I} to L_{III}, are very weak and have not been observed with certainty.

As an example, Fig. 12.6 shows the x-ray energy-level diagram of uranium. Also shown are the possible transitions determined by the selection rules given by Eq. (12.8). Because we have more than one line of the type K_α, they are denoted by K_{α_1} and K_{α_2}. These two lines are denoted as α_1 and α_2 under the K-series in Fig. 12.6. Similarly we have K_{β_1}, K_{β_2}; K_{γ_1}, K_{γ_2}; and K_{δ_1} and K_{δ_2}. Related notation is used for the transitions starting from the L_{I}, L_{II}, and L_{III} levels resulting in the L-series, and so on. We shall not go any further into this complicated notation.

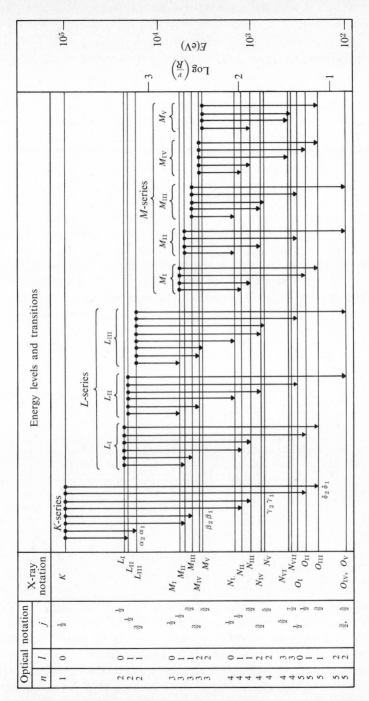

Fig. 12.6. *X-ray energy-level diagram for uranium ($Z = 92$) showing
the transitions allowed by the selection rules ($\Delta l = \pm 1$ and $\Delta j = 0, \pm 1$).*

4. THE MOSELEY LAW AND ATOMIC STRUCTURE

The importance of the investigation of the characteristic x-ray radiation lies in the fact that the wavelengths (or frequencies) of the spectra vary smoothly as we move from one element to another in the periodic table. This is unlike the optical spectra, in which the changes from element to element are abrupt.

The regularities in the characteristic x-ray spectra were first observed by Moseley[1,2] in 1913 and 1914 when he made a systematic study of the K x-ray radiation from the elements Ca, Ti, V, Cr, Mn, Fe, Co, Ni, Cu, and Zn with $Z = $ 20, 22, 23, 24, 25, 26, 27, 28, 29, and 30, respectively. The elements were used as targets in an x-ray tube, and the radiation emitted was analyzed by means of a potassium ferrocyanide single-crystal diffraction spectrometer. A photographic plate was used for recording the spectrum. Because of the poor resolution of the spectrometer, the lines K_{α_1} and K_{α_2} were observed as a single K_α line; similarly K_{β_1} and K_{β_2} lines were observed as a single K_β line. Figure 12.7 shows an arrangement of the elements versus

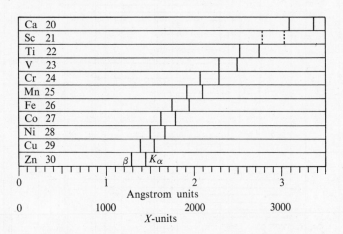

FIG. 12.7.   *Wavelengths of K-series x-ray lines for different elements.* [*After Moseley.*]

wavelengths of K x-rays. It is quite obvious that the wavelengths decrease with increasing Z. While Moseley was engaged in this work, Rutherford, who established the nuclear model of the atom, and Bohr, who introduced the Bohr model of the hydrogen atom, both were led to the conclusion that the atomic number, Z, was a more fundamental quantity than the atomic weight. Moseley plotted the square root of the frequency of K-radiation versus Z and found it to be a straight line as shown in Fig. 12.8. This figure also shows a plot of the square root of the frequency of K-radiation versus the atomic weight. It is clear from this figure that $\sqrt{\nu_{K\alpha}}$ versus Z gives a perfect fit. The

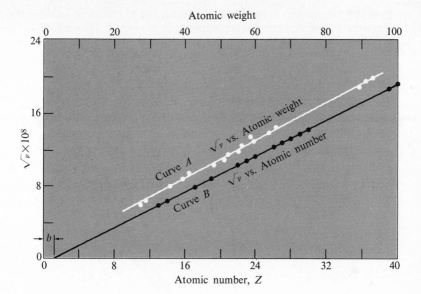

FIG. 12.8.   *Curve A is the plot of the square root of frequency, $\sqrt{\nu}$, versus atomic weight. Curve B showing the plot of the square root of frequency, $\sqrt{\nu}$, versus atomic number, Z, is Moseley's law. [From Richtmyer, F. K., E. H. Kennard, and T. Lauritsen,* Introduction to Modern Physics, *5th ed. New York: McGraw-Hill Book Company, 1955.]*

plot of $\sqrt{\nu}$ versus Z for a given series is known as the Moseley law, and Moseley expressed this mathematically for the K_α-line as

$$\sqrt{\nu_{K_\alpha}} \propto Z$$

$$\nu_{K_\alpha} = \frac{3}{4} cR(Z - 1)^2$$

(12.9)

where ν_{K_α} is the frequency of the K_α line, R is the Rydberg constant, and c is the velocity of light. By substituting the values of c and R, the curve in Fig. 12.8 is given by

$$\nu = 0.248 \times 10^{16}(Z - 1)^2$$

(12.10)

The importance of the Moseley law as expressed by Eq. (12.9) and shown graphically in Fig. 12.8 led to the following important conclusions:

(a) It was obvious that elements in the periodic table should be arranged according to the increasing atomic number, Z, and not the atomic weight as had previously been done. Hence Z was the most important and more fundamental quantity in discussing the structure of the atoms of different elements.

(b) Many discrepancies in the arrangement of the elements in the periodic table could be accounted for. For example, the atomic weight of cobalt ($Z = 27$) is 58.9 and that of nickel ($Z = 28$) is 58.7. Before Moseley's discovery, the elements were arranged according to increasing atomic weights and nickel preceded cobalt. But from Fig. 12.7 and Fig. 12.8, it is clear that these two elements should be arranged according to increasing Z. Thus, nickel follows cobalt.

(c) "Missing" elements could be predicted and arranged properly in the periodic table. For example, scandanium, Sc, which was not known in 1913, was assumed to exist with $Z = 21$, shown by dotted lines in Fig. 12.7.

A continuation of Moseley's work using spectrometers of improved resolution led to the discovery of many additional characteristic x-ray series. K_α and K_β were, of course, found to be close doublets, represented by K_{α_1}, K_{α_2}; and K_{β_1}, K_{β_2}. The Moseley law for these four lines is shown graphically in Fig. 12.9. The L-series, which are of much longer wavelengths, were

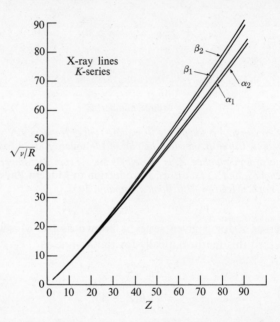

FIG. 12.9.   *The Moseley law for the four K-series components, K_{α_1}, K_{α_2}, K_{β_1}, and K_{β_2} of x-ray lines. [Printed with permission from White, H. E.,* Introduction to Atomic Spectra. *New York: McGraw-Hill Book Company, 1934.]*

discovered by Barkla[3]. The photographs of the L-series, with their fine structure, for several elements is shown in Fig. 12.10. M-radiation was discovered in 1916 by Siegbahn[4] in the heavier elements, while in 1922 Dolejsek[5] discovered N-radiation. The wavelengths of M- and N-radiations are much longer than the K- and L-radiations. In general the hard x-rays (K-series) extend from $\sim$0.01 Å to 1 Å, the soft x-rays (L-series) vary from $\sim$1 to 10 Å, while the very soft x-rays (M- and N-series) vary from $\sim$10 Å to 100 Å. The x-ray wavelengths are usually expressed in x-units, where

$$1 \ X.U. = 1 \times 10^{-3} \ \text{Å} \qquad \textbf{(12.11)}$$

The wavelength of a given component of a series decreases with increasing Z, and it is possible that wavelengths of the N-series of the heavier elements may be in the same region as the L-series of the light elements, and so on. It is the investigation of these radiations that gives us the details of the shell structure of different atoms.

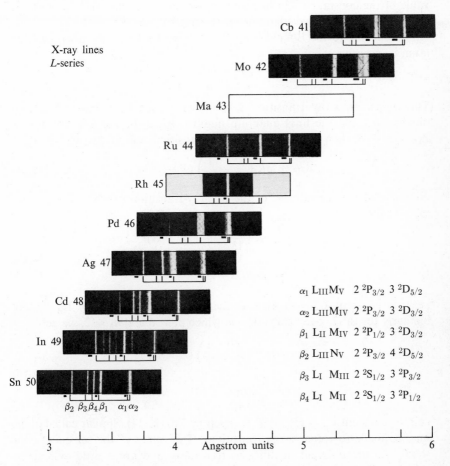

FIG. 12.10.   *Photographs of L-series x-rays with their fine structure for several elements.* [*After Richtmyer.*]

The mathematical form of the Moseley law given by Eq. (12.9) for the K_α-line was obtained by making a fit to the experimental points. A similar expression for the L-series (ignoring the fine structure) was found to be of the form

$$\nu_L = \frac{5}{36} cR(Z - 7.4)^2 \tag{12.12}$$

As a matter of fact, Eqs. (12.9) and (12.12) may be generalized, and for any series we may write

$$\nu = C_n(Z - S)^2 \tag{12.13}$$

where C_n and S are constants. A justification for the form of Eq. (12.13) is easily seen by considering the Bohr theory, which leads us to the correct value of the constant C_n in different transitions. The constant S, called the *screening constant*, is calculated from Hartree's theory[6].

According to the Bohr theory, the energy of a level in a hydrogen-like atom is given by

$$T = \frac{cRZ_{\text{eff}}}{n^2}$$

Thus when an x-ray transition takes place between the initial quantum number, n_i, and the final quantum number, n_f, while the effective charge $Z_{\text{eff}} = Z - S$, then the frequency of the transition is given by

$$\nu = cR \left(\frac{1}{n_f^2} - \frac{1}{n_i^2} \right) (Z - S)^2 \tag{12.14}$$

Now consider a special case of the K x-ray-transition in which $n_i = 2$ and $n_f = 1$; therefore

$$\nu_K = cR \left(\frac{1}{1^2} - \frac{1}{2^2} \right) (Z - S)^2$$
$$= \frac{3}{4} cR(Z - S)^2 \tag{12.15}$$

i.e., the constant $C_n = (3/4)cR$ is the same as that given by Eq. (12.9). Similarly for the L x-ray-transition in which $n_i = 3$ and $n_f = 2$, we get

$$\nu_L = cR \left(\frac{1}{2^2} - \frac{1}{3^2} \right) (Z - S)^2$$
$$= \frac{5}{36} cR(Z - S)^2 \tag{12.16}$$

i.e., the constant $C_n = (5/36)cR$ as given by Eq. (12.12). Similar calculations may be made for other x-ray transitions. The values of the screening constants[7] S are different in different transitions and are a little difficult to calculate. But some idea of such calculations may be obtained in simple cases. For example, in the case of K x-ray radiation when an electron from the L-shell is ready to jump to the K-shell vacancy, the effective charge seen by this electron is the $+Ze$ charge on the nucleus and $-1e$ charge of the electron in the K-shell. Thus the net effective charge seen by the electron is $+(Z - 1)e$ instead of $+Ze$. This is true because the K-shell is so close to the nucleus. Hence the value of S in Eq. (12.15) is 1, i.e.,

$$\nu_K = \frac{3}{4} cR(Z - 1)^2 \tag{12.17}$$

which is Moseley's law given by Eq. (12.9). Such calculations in other cases are difficult. For example, in the case of a transition from the M-shell to the L-shell, even though there are nine electrons as seen by the electron in the M-shell, the effective charge instead of $+(Z - 9)e$ is $+(Z - 7.4)e$. This is because the L-shell electrons are not as close to the nucleus as are the K-shell electrons, as can be seen in Fig. 12.1. Thus in Eq. (12.16), $S = 7.4$. The values of the screening constants for different transitions may be calculated from experimentally measured wavelengths. But instead, theoretical calculations (Hartree theory) have been made that coincide with the experimental results. From these, one can obtain the information about the shell structure or the probability density (and charge density) of the electrons around the nucleus, particularly in medium and heavy nuclei.

5. THE MEASUREMENT AND ABSORPTION OF X-RAYS

There are many different processes by which x-rays, or photons, interact with matter and lose their energies. However, the law of absorption, which we shall discuss here, is independent of the process by which the energy is lost.

A. Absorption Coefficient[8]

Consider a monoenergetic beam of x-rays passing through a material. It is found that the change in intensity, ΔI, is (a) directly proportional to the incident intensity, I, and (b) directly proportional to the thickness, Δx, of the material, i.e.,

$$\Delta I \propto I \, \Delta x$$

or

$$\Delta I = -\mu I \, \Delta x \qquad (12.18)$$

where μ is the proportionality constant and is known as the *absorption coefficient*. For a given material, μ differs for photons of different energies. The negative sign in Eq. (12.18) indicates that the intensity decreases with increasing thickness. Thus for a homogeneous radiation, μ is constant, and from Eq. (12.18) we get, by imposing the condition that $I = I_0$ when $x = 0$, and integrating

$$I = I_0 e^{-\mu x} \qquad (12.19)$$

where I is the intensity of the beam after the beam of initial intensity, I_0, has crossed a thickness x of the material. We may also write

$$I = h\nu\phi \qquad (12.20)$$

Where $h\nu$ is the energy of each photon, and ϕ, the flux, is the number of photons crossing a unit area in a unit time. Combining Eq. (12.19) and Eq. (12.20)

$$\phi = \phi_0 e^{-\mu x} \qquad (12.21)$$

where ϕ_0 is the initial flux. Note that I denotes the energy flux (or intensity), and ϕ is the number flux; μ is also called the *linear absorption-coefficient*, and is a function of photon energy and the absorber.

In addition to the linear absorption coefficient, μ, other coefficients that are commonly used are *mass absorption-coefficient*, μ_m; *atomic absorption-coefficient*, $_a\mu$; and the *electronic absorption-coefficient*, $_e\mu$. These four coefficients are related in the following way:

$$_a\mu = A \,_e\mu = \frac{\rho N_A}{A} \,_a\mu = \frac{\rho N_A Z}{A} \,_e\mu$$

$$\mu_m = \frac{\mu}{\rho} = \frac{N_A \,_a\mu}{A} = \frac{N_A Z}{A} \,_e\mu$$

(12.22)

where Z is the atomic number, A is the atomic weight, ρ is the density in gm/cm³, and N_A is Avogadro's number. Because μx is a dimensionless quantity, if x is expressed in cm, μ will be in cm⁻¹. Accordingly, for the mass absorption-coefficient, μ_m, x is expressed in gm/cm², and μ_m in cm²/gm. Similarly, if x is expressed in atom/cm² or electron/cm², $_a\mu$ and $_e\mu$ are expressed as cm²/atom and cm²/electron, respectively.

The *half-thickness*, $x_{1/2}$, is a characteristic of the absorber and is defined as the thickness that reduces the incident beam-intensity to one-half of its initial value, i.e.,

$$\frac{I}{I_0} = \frac{1}{2} = \exp\left(-\mu x_{1/2}\right)$$

or

$$x_{1/2} = \frac{ln2}{\mu} = \frac{0.693}{\mu} = \frac{0.693}{\rho\mu_m}$$

(12.23)

B. Interactions of Photons with Matter

There are several different processes by which photons interact with matter and lose their energy. The three main processes and the energy range in which they are dominant are the photoelectric effect (P. E.), $\sim$0.01 MeV to 0.5 MeV; Compton effect (C. E.), or scattering, $\sim$0.1 MeV to 10 MeV; and pair production (P. P.) for energies $\geqslant$ 1.02 MeV. We have already explained the photoelectric and Compton effects; pair production is the process in which an incident photon with energy greater than 1.02 MeV disappears in the Coulomb field of the nucleus producing an electron and positron pair. Pair production satisfies the energy condition

$$h\nu = 2m_0c^2 + K^+ + K^-$$

(12.24)

where $2m_0c^2$ is the sum of the rest masses of the electron and the positron, and K^- and K^+ are the kinetic energies, respectively. The recoil energy of the nucleus is small and has been neglected. If we are dealing with x-rays of energies less than 1.02 MeV, which usually is the case with the characteristic x-rays, pair-production may be neglected. In general, we may write the change in intensity as

$$\Delta I = (\Delta I)_{\text{P. E.}} + (\Delta I)_{\text{C.E.}} + (\Delta I)_{\text{P.P.}}$$
$$= -(\mu_\tau + \mu_\sigma + \mu_K)I\,\Delta x \tag{12.25}$$

Thus we may write

$$\mu = \mu_\tau + \mu_\sigma + \mu_K \tag{12.26}$$

Other processes contribute to the photon energy loss but do so to a much smaller extent than the above three processes are[8]: These processes are (i) Rayleight scattering, (ii) Thomson scattering, (iii) Nuclear photo-electric effect, (iv) nuclear resonance scattering and (v) elastic nuclear potential scattering.

C. Experimental Measurements

There are two different types of experiments that we shall discuss here: (1) the measurement of absorption coefficients and their variation with energy or wavelength of x-rays, and (2) the magnetic spectrograph method for investigating x-ray energy levels of atoms.

An experimental arrangement for measuring the absorption coefficient and for studying the x-ray absorption spectrum of an element is shown in Fig. 12.11. A continuous narrow beam of x-rays is obtained from the x-ray

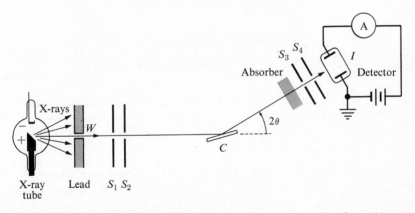

FIG. 12.11.   *An experimental arrangement for measuring the absorption coefficient and x-ray absorption spectrum.*

tube and the arrangement of the slits S_1 and S_2. The intensity of the diffracted beam from the crystal, C, is detected by the ionization chamber, I, and measured by the current-measuring device A. The energy or wavelength of the x-rays diffracted at an angle θ may be calculated from the Bragg condition

$$2d \sin \theta = n\lambda \tag{12.27}$$

By keeping the angle θ fixed and changing the thickness, x, of the absorber, one can measure the intensity, I, as a function of x. The plot of I versus x follows the exponential law as stated by Eq. (12.19). By using the definition of half-thickness $x_{1/2} = 0.693/\mu$, one can calculate μ from such a plot.

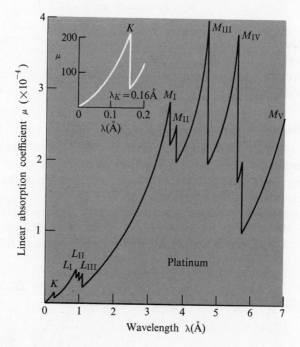

FIG. 12.12. *The plot of linear absorption coefficient, μ, versus wavelength, λ. [From Thomas H. Osgood, et. al.,* Atoms, Radiation & Nuclei, *3rd ed. New York: John Wiley & Sons, Inc., 1955.]*

From the plot of μ versus λ in Fig. 12.12, we see that whenever the incident x-ray energy is equal to the binding energy of an electron in a particular shell, the absorption coefficient increases by a very large amount. As soon as the energy of the x-ray is more or less than the binding energy of the electron, the absorption coefficient decreases. These sudden changes (or peaks) in μ are called the absorption edges and are useful in investigating the shell structures of different elements. From Fig. 12.12 we see that in platinum there is only one shell corresponding to K, while L and M have 3 and 5 subshells, respectively.

Another method of investigating the x-ray-energy levels of an atom is to utilize the photoelectric effect. Suppose a photon of energy $h\nu$ is incident on a thin foil. If the binding energy of the emitted electron is I_B and its kinetic energy $\frac{1}{2}mv^2$, then

$$\frac{1}{2} mv^2 = h\nu - I_B \qquad (12.28)$$

Electrons emitted from different shells will have differing velocities because the binding energies I_B are not the same. Thus if one measures the velocities (and hence the kinetic energies) of these photoelectrons, one can find the energies of the shells and the subshells, i.e., one can find the x-ray energy levels of an atom.

The experimental arrangement for measuring the velocities of the photoelectrons is shown in Fig. 12.13. This is the Robinson magnetic spectro-

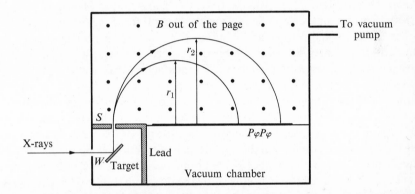

Fig. 12.13.   *An experimental arrangement, Robinson's magnetic spectrograph, for measuring the velocities of photoelectrons.*

graph. A narrow beam of monoenergetic x-rays, which may be the K_α-line of some known target, passes through a thin window, W, and strikes the target in an evacuated chamber. The photoelectrons emitted are deflected into a semicircle under the influence of a uniform magnetic field and are received on the photographic plate, PP. By measuring the radius r and using the relation

$$Hev = \frac{mv^2}{r} \qquad (12.29)$$

we get the velocity to be

$$v = Hr \cdot \frac{e}{m} \qquad (12.30)$$

The x-ray energy levels obtained by this method are in agreement with the measurements made by using the x-ray absorption method.

6. THE PERIODIC TABLE[9,10]

We have seen in the previous chapters the usefulness of the Pauli exclusion principle in assigning quantum states to electrons in multi-electron atoms. The resulting atomic shells and subshells lead to periodic variations in the physical and chemical properties, as we shall discuss in detail in this section. The periodic variations in the properties of the naturally occurring elements had been observed long before the formulation of the Pauli principle. The occurrence of elements with similar physical and chemical properties at regular intervals is called the *periodic law;* while the tabular arrangement of these elements showing recurrence of properties is called the *periodic table.*

The first elementary form of the periodic table of elements was given by J. A. R. Newland (England, 1837–1898), who introduced the law of octaves. Later, Dmitri Mendeléyev (Russia, 1834–1907), and Lothar Meyer (Germany, 1830–1895) set up the periodic table in the general form as it is known today. First the elements were arranged, using the order of increasing valence as the criterion. Later the elements were arranged in the order of increasing atomic weights, which was found to be satisfactory except for some minor discrepancies. Eventually the order was rearranged to that of increasing atomic number, Z, which is equal to the number of electrons in an element. This arrangement, coupled with the quantum states of the electrons, results in the currently accepted periodic table, as shown in Table 12.2. In each box, at the top, is the atomic number of the element, followed by the symbol of the element. Below the symbol is the atomic weight of the element (in amu up to second decimal place), followed by the quantum states of the outermost electrons in the last one or two subshells. The table is divided into groups and periods, explained below.

A. Classification into Groups and Periods

The elements with similar chemical and physical properties are said to form a *group.* There are eight groups and these are shown in vertical columns in Table 12.2. Group I consists of hydrogen (H) and the alkali metals (Li, Na, K, Rb, Cs, and Fr) all of which have valences of +1; all are chemically very active. Group VII consists of the halogens (F, Cl, Br, I, and At) all of which have valences of −1; all very active nonmetals. Finally, Group VIII consists of rare gases (He, Ne, Ar, Kr, Xe, and Rn) all of which have 0 valences; all are chemically very inert.

The horizontal rows in Table 12.2 are called *periods.* The properties of the elements at the two extremes (left and right) of a period are drastically different, with a steady transition from element to element between the two extremes. At the beginning of a period, the elements are active metals, followed by less active metals, weakly active metals, very inactive metals near the end of a period, and finally the period is closed by an inert gas. In a given group the properties of the elements do not change much with changing

TABLE 12.2

Group →	I	II											III	IV	V	VI	VII	VIII
1s (Period 1)	H 1 1.00 $1s^1$																	He 2 4.00 $1s^2$
2s / 2p (Period 2)	Li 3 6.94 $2s^1$	Be 4 9.01 $2s^2$											B 5 10.81 $2p^1$	C 6 12.01 $2p^2$	N 7 14.01 $2p^3$	O 8 16.00 $2p^4$	F 9 19.00 $2p^5$	Ne 10 20.18 $2p^6$
3s / 3p (Period 3)	Na 11 22.99 $3s^1$	Mg 12 24.31 $3s^2$											Al 13 26.98 $3p^1$	Si 14 28.09 $3p^2$	P 15 30.98 $3p^3$	S 16 32.07 $3p^4$	Cl 17 35.46 $3p^5$	Ar 18 39.94 $3p^6$
4s / 3d / 4p (Period 4)	K 19 39.10 $4s^1$	Ca 20 40.08 $4s^2$	Sc 21 44.96 $3d^1$	Ti 22 47.90 $3d^2$	V 23 50.94 $3d^3$	Cr 24 52.00 $4s^1 3d^5$	Mn 25 54.9 $4s^2 3d^5$	Fe 26 55.85 $4s^2 3d^6$	Co 27 58.93 $4s^2 3d^7$	Ni 28 58.71 $4s^2 3d^8$	Cu 29 63.54 $4s^1 3d^{10}$	Zn 30 65.37 $4s^2 3d^{10}$	Ga 31 69.72 $4p^1$	Ge 32 72.59 $4p^2$	As 33 74.92 $4p^3$	Se 34 78.96 $4p^4$	Br 35 79.91 $4p^5$	Kr 36 83.8 $4p^6$
5s / 4d / 5p (Period 5)	Rb 37 85.47 $5s^1$	Sr 38 87.66 $5s^2$	Y 39 88.91 $5s^2 4d^1$	Zr 40 91.22 $5s^2 4d^2$	Nb 41 92.91 $5s^1 4d^4$	Mo 42 95.94 $5s^1 4d^5$	Tc 43 (99) $5s^2 4d^5$	Ru 44 101.1 $5s^1 4d^7$	Rh 45 102.91 $5s^1 4d^8$	Pd 46 106.4 $5s^0 4d^{10}$	Ag 47 107.87 $5s^1 4d^{10}$	Cd 48 112.40 $5s^2 4d^{10}$	In 49 114.82 $5p^1$	Sn 50 118.69 $5p^2$	Sb 51 121.75 $5p^3$	Te 52 127.60 $5p^4$	I 53 126.90 $5p^5$	Xe 54 131.30 $5p^6$
6s / 5d / 6p (Period 6)	Cs 55 132.91 $6s^1$	Ba 56 137.34 $6s^2$	57–71 *	Hf 72 178.49 $6s^2 5d^2$	Ta 73 180.95 $6s^2 5d^3$	W 74 183.85 $6s^2 5d^4$	Re 75 186.2 $6s^2 5d^5$	Os 76 190.2 $6s^2 5d^6$	Ir 77 192.2 $6s^2 5d^7$	Pt 78 195.09 $6s^1 5d^9$	Au 79 197.0 $6s^1 5d^{10}$	Hg 80 200.59 $6s^2 5d^{10}$	Tl 81 204.37 $6p^1$	Pb 82 207.19 $6p^2$	Bi 83 208.98 $6p^3$	Po 84 (210) $6p^4$	At 85 (210) $6p^5$	Rn 86 222 $6p^6$
7s / 6d (Period 7)	Fr 87 (223) $7s^1$	Ra 88 226.05 $7s^2$	89–103 †															

4f — Lanthanides:

														VI	VII
La 57 138.91 $6s^2 5d^1$	Ce 58 140.12 $5d^1 5f^1$	Pr 59 140.91 $5d^0 4f^3$	Nd 60 144.24 $5d^0 4f^4$	Pm 61 (145)	Sm 62 150.35 $5d^0 4f^6$	Eu 63 152.0 $5d^0 4f^7$	Gd 64 157.25 $5d^1 4f^7$	Tb 65 158.92 $5d^1 4f^8$	Dy 66 162.50	Ho 67 164.92	Er 68 167.26	Tm 69 168.93 $5d^0 4f^{13}$	Yb 70 173.04 $5d^0 4f^{14}$	Lu 71 174.97 $5d^1 4f^{14}$	

5f — Actinides:

Ac 89 227 $7s^2 6d^1$	Th 90 232.04 $6d^2 5f^0$	Pa 91 231	U 92 238.03 $5d^1 5f^3$	Np 93 (237)	Pu 94 (242)	Am 95 (243) $6d^0 5f^7$	Cm 96 (247)	Bk 97 (249)	Cf 98 (251)	Es 99 (254)	Fm 100 (253)	Md 101 (256)	No 102 (254)	Lw 103 (257)

* Lanthanides (rare earths).
† Actinides.

atomic number (or atomic weight); but in a given period the properties of the adjacent elements change rapidly with atomic number (or atomic weight).

Referring to Table 12.2, in the first period there are two elements, $_1$H and $_2$He. $_1$H appears in Group I because its properties are similar to the rest of the elements in this group, while $_2$He is placed in Group VIII because He behaves as inert gases do in many respects. For example, as in inert gases, the first excited state of $_2$He is far away from its ground state. Following H and He, there are eight elements in the second period. These are $_3$Li, $_4$Be, $_5$B, $_6$C, $_7$N, $_8$O, $_9$F, and $_{10}$Ne. This is followed by a third period, again consisting of eight elements $_{11}$Na, $_{12}$Mg, $_{13}$Al, $_{14}$Si, $_{15}$P, $_{16}$S, $_{17}$Cl, and $_{18}$A, with properties of Na similar to Li, Mg similar to Be, Al similar to B, and so on.

The fourth period starts with $_{19}$K and $_{20}$Ca, but the next ten elements $_{21}$Sc, $_{22}$Ti, $_{23}$V, $_{24}$Cr, $_{25}$Mn, $_{26}$Fe, $_{27}$Co, $_{28}$Ni, $_{29}$Cu, and $_{30}$Zn do not show any resemblance to the elements in other periods under different groups. These elements appearing between Group II and Group III are called the transition elements, and thus form the first transition group. These elements are metals and show close chemical resemblance to one another. The fourth period is then completed with $_{31}$Ga, $_{32}$Ge, $_{33}$As, $_{34}$Se, $_{35}$Br, and $_{36}$Kr, which are part of Groups III, IV, V, VI, VII, and VIII, respectively.

The fifth period is opened with $_{37}$Rb and $_{38}$Sr starting with Groups I and II, followed by another set of ten transition elements, the second transition group, starting with $_{39}$Y and closing at $_{48}$Cd; while $_{49}$In, $_{50}$Sn, $_{51}$Sb, $_{52}$Te, $_{53}$I, and $_{54}$Xe finish the fifth period.

The sixth period starts with $_{55}$Cs and $_{56}$Ba occupying places in Groups I and II. The period contains fifteen elements starting with $_{57}$La and closing with $_{71}$Lu, which are the lanthanides, or rare-earth elements, and resemble each other so closely that it is hard to distinguish between them chemically. To make things complicated the rare-earth elements are followed by a third group of transition elements from $_{72}$Hf to $_{80}$Hg. The sixth period finishes with elements $_{18}$Tl to $_{86}$Rn.

The seventh period starts with $_{87}$Fr and $_{88}$Ra and is followed by another long group of fifteen elements starting with $_{89}$Ac and closing with $_{103}$Lw; these fifteen elements are the actinides.

Naturally occurring elements have Z values ranging from $Z = 1$ for hydrogen to $Z = 92$ for uranium—with three exceptions $Z = 61$, 85, and 87, which have been produced artificially. Elements with atomic numbers $Z = 93$ to 103 (or even higher) have been produced artificially and are mostly unstable. The actinides with $Z > 92$ are the transuranic elements.

In summary, the elements are arranged into seven periods, eight groups, three transition series, the lanthanides, and the actinides.

B.   Shells, Subshells, and the Pauli Exclusion Principle

In order to understand the variations and the resemblances between the physical and chemical properties of different elements in the periodic table, we must investigate the structure of complex atoms. The two basic rules for determining the arrangement of the electrons in multi-electron atoms are: (i) No two electrons in an atom can exist in the same quantum state, as stated by the Pauli exclusion principle; and (ii) A system of particles, an atom consisting of electrons in this case, will be stable when its total energy is a minimum.

As discussed earlier, in Chapter X, any quantum state of an electron can be denoted by a set of four quantum numbers, n, l, m_l, and m_s. The electrons having the same value of n are said to be in the same shell; while those electrons having the same value of l are said to be in the same subshell. For any value of n, l can have any one of the values $0, 1, 2, \ldots, n - 1$, while for any value of l, m_l can have any one of the $(2l + 1)$ values, i.e., l, $(l - 1)$, $\ldots, 1, 0, -1, \ldots, -l$. For a given m_l, m_s can take on two values: $+\frac{1}{2}$ or $-\frac{1}{2}$. As explained before, in any subshell there are $2(2l + 1)$ different possible states and in any shell there are

$$\sum_{l=0}^{n-1} 2(2l + 1) = 2n^2 \qquad (12.31)$$

different possible states. Thus there are

$$2, 8, 18, 32, 50, \ldots$$

electrons in shells corresponding to

$$n = 1, 2, 3, 4, 5, \ldots$$

Denoting the orbital quantum numbers, $0, 1, 2, 3, 4, \ldots$ by the letters $s, p, d, f, g, \ldots$, the filling of the shells and subshells by the electrons in any atom will take place in the following sequence

$$1s^2; \; 2s^2 2p^6; \; 3s^2 3p^6 3d^{10}; \; 4s^2 4p^6 4d^{10} 4f^{14}; \; \ldots \qquad (12.32)$$

and we should have $2, 8, 18, 32, 50, \ldots$ elements in the successive rows, but this is not true as we shall explain.

In complex, or multi-electron, atoms, electrons not only interact with the nuclear charge, they also interact with one another. Calculations can be carried out by assuming that each electron moves in a constant mean force-field. This mean field is the result of the nuclear charge and the electron shielding. The electrons that have the same total quantum number, n, are, on the average, the same distance from the nucleus, and hence each such electron is shielded from the nucleus by the intervening electrons to the same degree. Thus all electrons in the same shell have approximately the same energies. To a lesser extent the electron's energy depends upon the value of l as well. For a given n, i.e., in a given shell, the large-l-value electrons have more circular distribution and do not penetrate into the core; they are shielded more from the nucleus as compared to the low-l-value electrons, which have more elliptical paths and do penetrate the core. This leads to the conclusion that electrons of higher angular momentum possess more energy than electrons of lower angular momentum. This results in the overlapping of the sublevels of more than one main level.

In assigning quantum states to electrons in complex atoms, the electrons are placed in different levels in such a way that the total energy of the atom is a minimum. This can be achieved by using Hartree-theory calculations[6]. Such calculations are tedious for multi-electron atoms, and one must depend instead upon experimentally measured values from optical, as well as x-ray spectroscopy. The general rule is: For a given n value, the subshell with the lowest l value has the lowest energy; while for a given l value, the subshell with the lowest n value has the lowest energy. Such considerations lead to the rearrangement in the sequence of the levels. This new sequence is shown in Table 12.3. Note that the 3d-level has more energy than the 4s, and similarly the 4d has more than the 5s, 5d more than 6s, and 4f more than 6s, ...

TABLE 12.3
THE ORDER IN WHICH THE OUTER SUBSHELLS ARE FILLED

	State designation nl	Maximum capacity $2(2l + 1)$
Lowest negative energy ⟶	1s	2
	2s	2
	2p	6
Increasing	3s	2
energy	3p	6
	4s	2
↓	3d	10
	4p	6
	5s	2
	4d	10
	5p	6
	6s	2
	4f	14
	5d	10
	6p	6
	7s	2

This rearrangement in the levels explains the periodic table as well as many characteristics of different elements. There will be certain unexpected deviations. Table 12.3 shows the electron configurations and the ground states of the elements from $Z = 1$ to $Z = 103$ with their corresponding names and symbols. Note that the correct configuration of a system is one that results in the minimum energy of the system.

C. Characteristics of Elements in Different Groups

The chemical properties of the elements can be explained in relation to their electron configurations.

(i) *The Alkali Metals.* (Group I) Even though H is not an alkali metal, it is placed in this group because its electron configuration is similar to those of the alkali metals. For all the elements in this group there is a single electron outside the closed shell. In the ground state this electron is always in the S-subshell resulting in the valence of $+1$. The single electron is very loosely bound, which means that it can be easily removed, changing the neutral atom to a singly-charged positive ion. That the binding energy of the s electron in alkali metals is small can be seen from Fig. 12.14, where ionization energy

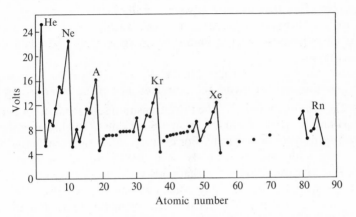

FIG. 12.14. *A plot of the ionization potential versus atomic number, Z. The periodic atomic structure is evident from this figure.*

versus Z is plotted. This low ionization energy also accounts for the great chemical activity of the alkali metals. Because of their electron configurations, the alkali metals may be regarded as hydrogen-like atoms, which means their optical spectra is similar.

(ii) *The Alkaline-Earth Elements.* (Group II) These elements each have two s-electrons outside a closed p-subshell, which results in a valence of $+2$. When singly ionized, the alkaline-earth elements behave like alkali metals.

(iii) *The Halogens.* (Group VII) The atoms of these elements lack one electron to complete a p-subshell, and hence have a valence of -1. The halogens are chemically very active because they are always seeking an electron to close the p-shell. This is just opposite to the alkali metals, which are always trying to lose one electron. Thus halogens easily combine with alkali metals to form compounds like NaCl and NaBr.

(iv) *The Rare Gases.* (Group VIII) Except for $_2$He, the atoms of all the elements in this group have electron configurations with closed p-shells. The elements have completely filled subshells, resulting in spherically symmetric charge distributions, and hence do not produce any net external electric and magnetic fields. Because the total angular momentum is zero, the total magnetic moment of the atom is also zero. The chemical inertness of these gases is explained not only by the fact that the electrons form completely closed subshells but also from other considerations. There is a large energy difference between the filled p-subshell and the next empty s-sublevel. To cause the excitation of rare gas atoms, therefore, high excitation energies are needed. This same reasoning can be applied to $_2$He also, even though the closed subshell is s and not p. The filled $1s^2$-sublevel of $_2$He is separated from the next $2s$-sublevel by a large energy difference, and hence $_2$He is a true noble gas. Another proof that the rare gases are really inert can be seen from the plot of ionization potential versus Z as shown in Fig. 12.14. As is obvious, the inert gases have the highest ionization energies, while the alkali metals have the lowest.

We shall not discuss Groups III, IV, V, and VI because their characteristics are easily deduced from the characteristics of the other groups.

(v) *The Transition Series.* The three transition series that occur between Groups II and V, and in periods 4, 5, and 6 are due to the filling of the $3d$-, $4d$-, and $5d$-subshells, respectively. For example, after the completion of the ground state with configuration $4s^2$, the $3d$-sublevel starts filling, thus initiating the first transition series that ends with the closing of the $3d$-level at Zn, for which $Z = 30$. We may point out that the actual configuration does not obey the order given in Table 12.3 or in Eq. 12.32. For example, according to this table, the $4s$-sublevel always has less energy than the $3d$-sublevel, while in Cr and Cu, instead of having the configurations $4s^23d^4$ and $4s^23d^9$, the actual configurations are $4s^13d^5$ and $4s^13d^{10}$, respectively. Similar conditions occur in other transition series as well as in rare-earth elements. This is so much the case for Pd that there is no electron in the $5s$-sublevel while there are 10 in the $4d$-sublevel; the configuration of Pd is $5s^04d^{10}$. All this means is that the energy differences between $3d$ and $4s$, $4d$ and $5s$, and $5d$ and $6s$ are small and vary from element to element. The same situation occurs in the lanthanides and the actinides.

The chemical activity of the elements of the transition series are due to the outer s-electrons, while the electrons in the incomplete d-subshells give rise to a total magnetic moment that is *not zero.* Therefore, many of the elements in the transition series are either paramagnetic (weakly magnetic) or ferromagnetic (strongly magnetic).

The origin of these magnetic properties can be explained with the help of Hund's rule, according to which whenever possible, electrons in an atom try to remain unpaired, i.e., they have parallel spins. Thus, for example, five of the six electrons in the $3d$-sublevels of iron have parallel spins. Because each unpaired spin has a spin magnetic-moment, iron, with five unpaired spins, has a large resultant magnetic moment and hence is ferromagnetic. The magnetism of cobalt and nickel can be similarly explained.

(vi) *The Rare-Earth Elements, or Lanthanides.* As shown in the periodic table the rare-earth elements are those corresponding to the filling of the 4f-subshell. The 4f-subshell lies deep in the 6s-subshell. The 6s-subshell is completely filled in these elements. The 4f-subshell electrons are completely shielded from the outside by the 6s-electrons. Thus, the chemical properties of rare-earth elements are due to the 6s-electrons, and hence the rare-earth elements are almost indistinguishable one from the other.

(vii) *Actinides.* These elements are the result of the filling of the 5f-subshell inside the already completely filled 7s-subshell. Most of the elements in this group are unstable, particularly the nuclei of the elements with $Z > 92$, the transuranic elements. It is the instability of the heavier nuclei that prevents the formation of heavier atoms.

PROBLEMS

1. The longest wavelength that may be used to produce resonance radiation in mercury is 2536 Å. Calculate the first-excitation potential of mercury.

2. Calculate the minimum kinetic energy of an electron that collides with a sodium atom to produce (a) the first resonance line, and (b) all the possible fluorescence radiation.

3. Calculate the minimum kinetic energy of an electron that collides with a hydrogen atom to produce (a) the first resonance line, and (b) all the possible fluorescence radiation.

4. Suppose we want to produce a complete x-ray fluorescence of mercury, for which $Z = 80$, by bombarding with characteristic x-rays. Why is it necessary for these characteristic x-rays to originate from a material with $Z > 80$?

5. Calculate the wavelength, frequency, and energy of the K_α-line in silver ($Z = 47$). What is the fractional decrease in the mass of silver because of the emission of the K_α x-ray?

6. Consider the emission of the K_α-line from uranium ($Z = 92$). (a) What is the speed with which the uranium atom recoils after emitting a K_α-photon? (b) Calculate the ratio of the kinetic energy of the recoiling atom to the energy of the emitted K_α-photon.

7. If the vapors of sodium are bombarded with electrons that have been accelerated through a potential difference of 2.11 volts, the sodium D-lines are observed. Taking the mean wavelength of the sodium D-lines to be 5893 Å, calculate the ratio of h/e. Compare this value with the value obtained in Prob. 12.8.

8. In order to produce a K x-ray series from tungsten, the critical voltage is 69.5 kilovolts. The measured value of the K-absorption edge in tungsten is 0.178 Å. From this data calculate the value of h/e.

9. The wavelength of the K_α-lines emitted from certain elements are as follows:

$$\text{Mg } (Z = 12): 9.87 \text{ Å}; \quad \text{Co } (Z = 27): 1.79 \text{ Å}$$
$$\text{S } \ \ (Z = 16): 5.36 \text{ Å}; \quad \text{Cu } (Z = 29): 1.54 \text{ Å}$$
$$\text{Ca } (Z = 20): 3.35 \text{ Å}; \quad \text{Rb } (Z = 37): 0.93 \text{ Å}$$
$$\text{Cr } (Z = 24): 2.29 \text{ Å}; \quad \text{W } \ (Z = 74): 0.21 \text{ Å}$$

Make a plot of the square root of the K_α-line frequency versus Z, and calculate the values of A and S in the expression

$$\sqrt{\nu} = A(Z - S)$$

Compare these values with those given in the text.

10. Draw an x-ray energy-level diagram for calcium $(Z = 20)$. Calculate the minimum energy that the incident electrons must have to produce a K_α-series.

11. How many K, L, and M absorption edges does one expect to find in the following: (a) magnesium, (b) cobalt, (c) tungsten, and (d) uranium?

12. Suppose copper is being used as a target in an x-ray tube for producing a continuous x-ray spectrum. What should be the operating voltage of this tube so that the K-radiation from copper corresponding to wavelength 1.54 Å will be emitted?

13. The K-absorption edge in copper corresponds to 1.377 Å, while the wavelength of the K x-ray emitted is 1.54 Å. Why in this case, and in general, is the wavelength that corresponds to the K-absorption edge slightly smaller than the corresponding K x-ray radiation?

14. The wavelength of the K-absorption edge for copper is 1.377 Å; the critical voltage for the emission of the K-lines from copper is 9 kilovolts. Calculate the value of h/e from this data.

15. Calculate the critical voltage required for the characteristic K-series of tungsten if the K-absorption edge of tungsten is 0.178 Å.

16. What should be the minimum energy of a beam of x-ray photons so as to produce the L and M fluorescent spectral series of bismuth? For bismuth the L_I absorption edge occurs at 0.756 Å.

17. What should be the minimum energy of a beam of photons so as to produce the L and M fluorescent spectral series of tungsten? For tungsten the L_I absorption edge occurs at 1.02 Å.

18. Calculate the energy difference between the $1s$- and $2p$-shells in cobalt $(Z = 27)$ provided the wavelength of the K_α radiation in cobalt is 1.785 Å. Compare this value with the energy difference between the $1s$- and $2p$-shells of sodium, and explain why the difference in cobalt is larger than it is in sodium. How do these values compare with that of hydrogen?

19. What is the ratio of the slopes obtained by plotting $\sqrt{\nu}$ versus Z for K_α-frequencies and for K_β-frequencies?

20. Show that after the K-electron has been emitted, the K-shell possesses an angular momentum equal to $\sqrt{\frac{1}{2}(\frac{1}{2} + 1)}\,\hbar$ and a magnetic moment of $\sqrt{3}$ Bohr magnetons.

21. What is the angular momentum and the magnetic moment of the L-shell if (a) one electron, (b) two electrons, or (c) three electrons have been removed from the L-shell?

22. By making a plot of $\sqrt{\nu}$ versus Z for the following elements, determine the value of the screening constant.

Element	Z	λ(Å)
zirconium	40	6.057
ruthenium	44	4.843
lanthanum	57	2.669
samarium	62	2.206
tantalum	73	1.530
platinum	78	1.322
bismuth	83	1.153
uranium	92	0.921

With the help of the above plot identify the elements that have lines of wavelengths 3.601 Å and 1.791 Å.

23. Calculate the attenuation of an x-ray beam after it has passed through a thickness of material equivalent to (a) two half-value thicknesses, (b) four half-value thicknesses, and (c) six half-value thicknesses.

24. The mass-absorption coefficient of aluminum for x-rays of certain energy is 0.25 cm²/gm. (a) Calculate the half-thickness of aluminum for these x-rays. (b) What thickness of aluminum is needed to attenuate these x-rays by 90%?

25. The mass absorption coefficient of iron for x-rays of a certain wavelength is 0.48 cm²/gm. (a) Calculate the half-thickness of iron for these x-rays. (b) Calculate the thickness required to reduce the intensity to $1/100$.

26. The K_{α}-line of uranium has a wavelength of 0.0126 Å. A silver foil placed in a magnetic spectrograph is bombarded with these x-rays. The magnetic field applied is 400 gauss. (a) What are the kinetic energies of the K-, L-, and M-electrons ejected from silver? (b) What are the velocities of the ejected electrons? (c) What are the radii of these electrons? (Use relativistic equations.)

27. What electrons will be ejected if a uranium foil is bombarded with K x-rays of silver (wavelength 0.558 Å)? If the uranium foil is in the magnetic spectrograph, calculate the velocities and the radii of these ejected electrons. The magnetic field applied is 300 gauss. What are the values of the magnetic rigidity ($=$ Hr) for the M-electrons?

28. Two beams of x-rays pass through a material of thickness t having mass absorption coefficients μ_1 and μ_2 for the two beams, respectively. If the intensities of these two beams of x-rays are reduced in the ratio of 4:1, show that

$$t = \frac{ln4}{\mu_1 - \mu_2}$$

29. Usually there is considerable variation in the ionization energies in consecutive sequences of elements, but the ionization energies of elements with $Z = 20$ through $Z = 29$ are all nearly equal. Explain why.

30. How do you explain the variations according to the periodic table of different elements of (a) ionization potential, (b) characteristic x-ray spectra, and (c) melting point?

REFERENCES

1. Moseley, H. G. J., *Phil. Mag.*, **26**, 1024, (1913).
2. Moseley, H. G. J., *Phil. Mag.*, **27**, 703, (1914).

3. Barkla, C. G., and C. A. Sadler, *Phil. Mag.*, **17**, 739, (1909).

4. Siegbahn, M., *Verh. d. Deutsch Phys. Ges.*, **18**, 278, (1916); *Compt. Rend.*, **18**, 162, 787, (1916).

5. Dolejsek, V., *Zeit. fur Physik*, **10**, 129, 236, (1922).

6. Hartree, D. R., *Proc. Camb. Phil. Soc.*, **24**, 89, 111, (1928).

7. Sommerfeld, A., *Atombau and Spektrallinien*, 4th ed. Wieweg, F., *Braunschweig*, 1922. Pauling, L., *Zeit. fur Physik*, **40**, 344, (1926).

8. Arya, A. P., *Fundamentals of Nuclear Physics*, Chap. IX. Sec. 2. Boston, Mass.: Allyn & Bacon, Inc., 1966.

9. McLennan, J. S., A. B. McLay, and H. G. Smith, *Proc. Roy. Soc.*, **A112**, (1926).

10. Dushman, S., *Chem. Rev.*, **5**, 109, (1928).

SUGGESTIONS FOR FURTHER READING

1. White, H. E., *Introduction to Atomic Spectra*, Chap. XVI. New York: McGraw-Hill Book Company, 1934.

2. Richtmyer, F. K., E. H. Kennard, and T. Lauritsen, *Introduction to Modern Physics*, 5th ed., Chap. 8. New York: McGraw-Hill Book Company, 1955.

3. Eisberg, E. M., *Fundamentals of Modern Physics*, Chap. 14. New York: John Wiley & Sons, Inc., 1961.

4. Herzberg, G., *Atomic Spectra & Atomic Structure*, Chap. III. New York: Dover Publications, Inc., 1944.

5. Condon, E. U., and G. H. Shortley, *The Theory of Atomic Spectra*, New York: Cambridge Univ. Press, 1963.

6. Green, A. E. S., and P. J. Wyatt, *Atomic and Space Physics*, Reading, Mass.: Addison-Wesley Publishing Company, Inc., 1965.

XIII

Hyperfine Structure
and Line Broadening

1. DISCOVERY OF HYPERFINE STRUCTURE

By the close of the nineteenth century, A. A. Michelson[1], C. Fabry and
A. Perot[2], and O. Lummer and E. Gehrcke[3] had developed instruments of
very high resolution for observing spectra. The investigation of spectral lines
of the elements revealed that each line that appeared to be a singlet using a
spectroscope of medium resolution was found to constitute a group of very
closely-spaced lines. The separation between these components is about three
orders smaller than the separation between the fine structure lines. This new
structure is called the *hyperfine structure* (denoted by *hfs*) and was first
observed by Michelson[1] in 1891. (The hyperfine structure is observed without the application of any external field and should not be confused with the
Zeeman or Paschen-Back effects.) The discovery of hyperfine structure was
confirmed by Janicki[4] in 1909 and by Wali-Mohammed[5] in 1914 both of
whom observed and reported the hyperfine structure of spectral lines from a
large number of elements.

At first it was thought that the hyperfine structure was due to the
existence of different isotopes of the same chemical element. Later, however,
it was found that elements that have only one isotope, i.e., are monoisotopic,
also exhibited this structure.

The correct explanation was first suggested by Pauli[6] and, independently, by Russell[7]. According to Pauli, each nucleus has associated with it

some magnetic dipole moment and an associated angular momentum. The electrons orbiting about the nucleus produce a magnetic field at the nucleus. The interaction between the magnetic dipole-moment and the magnetic field leads to the splitting of a given atomic level into different energies; hence many spectral lines are observed. Thus we may conclude that there are two different types of hyperfine structure.

1. The structure due to the existence of different isotopes of the same chemical element is the *isotope effect*.
2. The structure due to the nuclear mechanical and magnetic dipole-moments is the *hyperfine structure*.

In addition to the magnetic dipole-moment of the nucleus, the higher moments, say, the electric quadrupole moment, can also interact, but such effects are very small and cause little shift in energy levels. In addition to the shift in energy levels caused by the isotopes, very small shifts are caused by the differences in nuclear size and charge distribution. Before discussing the details of the *hfs* we shall give a few examples of the isotope effect and the hyperfine structure.

Isotope-structure   Tungsten   λ5225

FIG. 13.1. *Photograph taken with a high-resolution instrument, the Fabry-Perot etalon, illustrating the isotope structure as observed in tungsten with mass numbers A = 182, 184, and 186.* [*Taken from Grace, More, MacMillan, and White; printed with permission from White, H. E.,* Introduction to Atomic Spectra, *p. 253. New York: McGraw-Hill Book Company, 1934.*]

Figure 13.1[8] shows the isotope effect resulting in the splitting of a line in the element tungsten. Tungsten has five isotopes of mass numbers $A = 180$, 182, 183, 184, and 186, with relative abundances of 0.14%, 26.41%, 14.4%, 30.6%, and 28.41%, respectively. Of these five, only three isotopes, with $A = 182$, 184, and 186 are shown in the structure in Fig. 13.1 because the other two isotopes have low abundances. Thus a single line of wavelength $\lambda = 5225$ Å is shown split into three lines. The photograph was taken with an interferometer, called the Fabry-Perot etalon, in which the pattern of three lines is repeated several times because of the multiple-beam method used in this instrument. Figure 13.2 shows a hyperfine structure of a tantalum line of wavelength $\lambda = 5997$ Å, obtained with the same interferometer. Note that tantalum is monoisotopic, and the seven-component pattern obtained is due to the interaction of the nuclear moment, not the isotope effect.

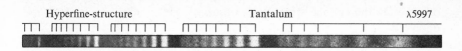

FIG. 13.2. *Photograph taken with a high-resolution instrument, the Fabry-Perot etalon, illustrating the hyperfine structure of a tantalum line.* [*Taken from Grace, More, MacMillan, and White; printed with permission from White, H. E.,* Introduction to Atomic Spectra, *p. 253. New York: McGraw-Hill Book Company, 1934.*]

Figure 13.3[9] shows the photographs of the hyperfine structure pattern of a number of lines arising from the rare-earth element praseodymium. This type of pattern, the flag pattern, is one of the most common, in which each line contains several components, the intensity and interval gradually decreasing towards the shorter or longer wavelengths, as shown. These photographs taken at Mount Wilson by White[9] are in the fourth order of 75 ft. spectrograph.

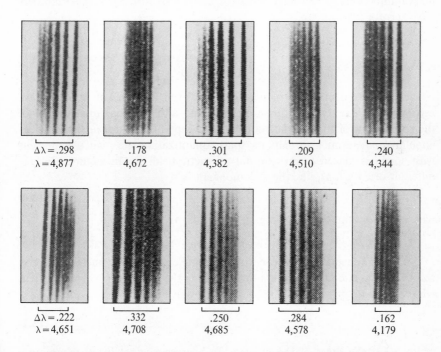

| $\Delta\lambda = .298$ | .178 | .301 | .209 | .240 |
| $\lambda = 4,877$ | 4,672 | 4,382 | 4,510 | 4,344 |

| $\Delta\lambda = .222$ | .332 | .250 | .284 | .162 |
| $\lambda = 4,651$ | 4,708 | 4,685 | 4,578 | 4,179 |

FIG. 13.3. *Photographs illustrating the hyperfine structure of many of the lines in praseodymium, taken in the fourth order of the 75-ft spectrograph on Mt. Wilson.* [*Printed with permission from White, H. E.,* Introduction to Atomic Spectra, *p. 252. New York: McGraw-Hill Book Company, 1934.*]

We may note that in some elements, the *hfs* alone is observed, while in others only the isotope structure is observed; yet in some others both are observed.

2. HYPERFINE STRUCTURE DUE TO THE MAGNETIC-DIPOLE INTERACTION

Observations of the *hfs* by Back of the spectral lines of bismuth led Goudsmit[10] to introduce a new quantum vector, associated with the nucleus, in order to further explain the *hfs*. It is assumed that a nucleus, like an electron, has a mechanical angular-momentum. The magnitude of this nuclear angular momentum vector, I, according to wave mechanics, is given by

$$I = |\mathbf{I}| = \sqrt{i(i+1)}\,\hbar \qquad \text{where} \qquad \hbar = h/2\pi \qquad (13.1)$$

i is usually called nuclear spin, even though it is actually the sum of the nuclear orbital angular-momentum and the intrinsic spin angular-momentum. The experimental evidence indicates the following rule: Nuclei with odd mass-numbers have half-integral spins, and those with even mass-numbers have zero or integral spins, i.e.,

$$\text{for odd } A, \; i = \frac{1}{2}, \frac{3}{2}, \frac{5}{2}, \frac{7}{2}, \ldots$$
$$\text{for even } A, \; i = 0, 1, 2, 3, 4, \ldots \qquad (13.2)$$

Nuclei with even numbers of neutrons *and* even numbers of protons have zero spin. i is a typical quantum number, and the maximum value of the component of the angular momentum in any direction is $i\hbar$. The nuclear angular-momentum also exhibits space quantization, i.e., when a nucleus with spin i is placed in an external magnetic field, it can assume $(2i + 1)$ different orientations, i.e., the Z component is

$$I_z = m_i \hbar \qquad (13.3)$$

where m_i can take the following values as shown in Fig. 13.4.

$$m_i = i, (i - 1), \ldots, 1, 0, -1, \ldots, -(i - 1), -i \qquad (13.4)$$

As in the case of an electron, the revolving charge of the nucleus will give rise to a magnetic moment, μ_I, oriented along the spin axis (I) of the nucleus which, in analogy with Eq. (10.48), may be written as

$$\mu_i = \frac{e}{2Mc}\mathbf{I} \qquad (13.5)$$

where M is the mass of the nucleus. In a more general form, assuming a magnetic moment arising from a single proton, we may write, according to Eq. (10.50),

$$\frac{\mu_i/\mu_N}{\mathbf{I}/\hbar} = g_i \qquad (13.6)$$

or

$$\mu_i = g_i\sqrt{i(i+1)}\mu_N \tag{13.7}$$

where g_i is the nuclear g-factor; and μ_N is called the *nuclear magneton* and is $1/1836$ times the Bohr magneton, i.e.,

$$\mu_N = \frac{e\hbar}{2m_p c} = \frac{\mu_b}{1836} = 5.05 \times 10^{-24} \frac{\text{ergs}}{\text{gauss}} \tag{13.8}$$

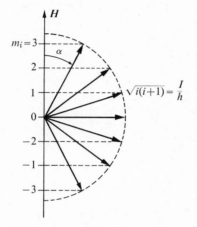

FIG. 13.4. *The space quantization of* **I**. *Components of* **I** *along the direction* **H** *can take only those values for which* $m_i = \sqrt{i(i+1)} \cos \alpha = i,$ $i-1, \ldots, 0, \ldots, -(i-1), -i.$

where m_p is the mass of the proton. The *nuclear gyromagnetic-ratio*, γ_i is the ratio of the nuclear magnetic-moment to the angular momentum

$$\gamma_i = \frac{\mu_i}{\sqrt{i(i+1)}\hbar} = \frac{g_i\sqrt{i(i+1)}\dfrac{e\hbar}{2m_p c}}{\sqrt{i(i+1)}\hbar}$$

or

$$\gamma_i = g_i \frac{e}{2m_p c} \tag{13.9}$$

g_i cannot be calculated because of the lack of the knowledge of this type of coupling. The experiments reveal that $g_i \sim 1$ in most cases.

The nuclear magnetic moment μ_i given by Eq. (13.6) or (13.7) interacts with the magnetic field $\mathbf{H}_e$ produced by the atomic electron at the nucleus as shown in Fig. 13.5. The interaction results in a shift of the energy levels of the atom, which consists of the electrons and the nucleus, by an amount

$$\Delta E = -\boldsymbol{\mu}_i \cdot \mathbf{H}_e \tag{13.10}$$

The direction of H_e is opposite to that of J, the total angular-momentum of the atom, because of the negative charge of the electron. Hence

$$\Delta E = -\mu_i H_e \cos \theta \qquad (13.11)$$

where θ is the angle between μ_I and H_e. We may rewrite Eq. (13.11), as

$$\Delta E = \mu_i H_e \cos (I, J) = \mu_i H_e \frac{I \cdot J}{\sqrt{i(i+1)}\hbar \sqrt{j(j+1)}\hbar} \qquad (13.12)$$

Note that the negative sign in Eq. (13.11) cancels, with J being opposite to H_e. Thus the different values of $I \cdot J$, which are quantized, lead to the splitting of a level of given J.

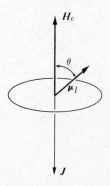

FIG. 13.5. *The interaction of the nuclear magnetic moment, μ_i, with the magnetic field, H_e, produced at the nucleus by the atomic electron.*

The result of the above interaction is that the vector I adds to vector J giving rise to the grand total angular-momentum vector, F, as shown in Fig. 13.6, i.e.,

$$F = J + I \qquad (13.13)$$

Also, like J, L, and S, F has a magnitude given by

$$F = \sqrt{f(f+1)}\,\hbar \qquad (13.14)$$

where f is a quantum number having integer or half-integer values differing by unity, such that $(j + i) \geq f \geq |j - i|$. Thus in an atom consisting of a nucleus with spin I and an electron with total angular momentum J, the energy level corresponding to J is then split into sublevels having all possible values of F, i.e.,

$$|J - I| \leqslant F \leqslant |J + I| \qquad (13.15)$$

Thus F has $(2i + 1)$ values if $i < j$; and $(2j + 1)$ values if $j < i$. As a matter of fact the nuclear spin is determined by counting the number of lines.

F is space-quantized with its z components

$$F_z = m_f \hbar \tag{13.16}$$

where m_f has the following $(2f + 1)$ values,

$$m_f = f, (f = 1), \ldots, 1, 0, -1, \ldots, -(f - 1), -f \tag{13.17}$$

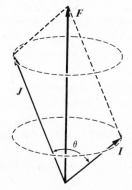

FIG. 13.6. *Vector model illustrating the result of the interaction between the nuclear moment and the electron moment. The addition of the vector I to the vector J results in the grand total angular-momentum vector F.*

Using Eq. (13.13) and Fig. 13.6, we can get the value of $\mathbf{I} \cdot \mathbf{J}$ to be used in Eq. (13.2) for the calculation of ΔE. Using the cosine law

$$F^2 = I^2 + J^2 + 2IJ \cos(\mathbf{I}, \mathbf{J}) \tag{13.18}$$

or

$$\cos(\mathbf{I}, \mathbf{J}) = \frac{f(f + 1) - i(i + 1) - j(j + 1)}{2\sqrt{i(i + 1)}\sqrt{j(j + 1)}} \tag{13.19}$$

Combining Eq. (13.19) with Eq. (13.12), we get

$$\Delta E_{\mathbf{I} \cdot \mathbf{J}} = \frac{1}{2} A[f(f + 1) - i(i + 1) - j(j + 1)] \tag{13.20}$$

where A is a constant given by

$$A = \frac{\mu_i}{\sqrt{i(i + 1)}} \frac{\langle H_e \rangle_{\mathrm{av}}}{\sqrt{j(j + 1)}} \tag{13.21}$$

where $\langle H_e \rangle_{\mathrm{av}}$ is the average value of the magnetic field produced at the nucleus by the electron. The value $\langle H_e \rangle_{\mathrm{av}}$ will be calculated in the next section; it varies from 10^5 to 10^7 gauss for different atoms. For the purpose of calculating the relative magnitude of separation in the *hfs* it is not necessary to know the value of A. Note that no splitting of the energy levels can occur if either $i = 0$ or $j = 0$, because ΔE will be equal to zero from Eq. (13.20).

In order to find the possible transitions between different hyperfine levels, we must know the selection rules for f. The selection rules for f in the *hfs* are the same as those for j in fine structure, i.e.,

$$\Delta f = 0, \pm 1 \qquad (13.22)$$

while transitions from $0 \rightarrow 0$ are forbidden.

The *hfs* of the level is called *normal* when the smallest f value lies the deepest, while it is called *inverted* if the largest f value lies the deepest. The normal *hfs* corresponds to the positive value of A in Eq. (13.21), while the inverted corresponds to the negative value of A. Both negative and positive values of A can arise from the same element and, in some cases, even in the same multiple term.

Let us now consider some examples of the hfs. Consider an atomic transition from a $^3P_1$ level to a $^3S_0$ level. Let us assume that the nuclear spin is 1/2. For the $^3P_1$ level, $j = 1$, $i = 1/2$, we get $f = 3/2$ or $1/2$. The relative displacements of the levels $f = 3/2$ and $1/2$ from the undisplaced level $j = 1$ is found from Eq. (13.20) to be $A/2$ and $-A$, respectively as shown in Fig. 13.7(a). For the $^1S_0$ level, $j = 0$, $i = 1/2$, therefore, $f = 1/2$, and from Eq.

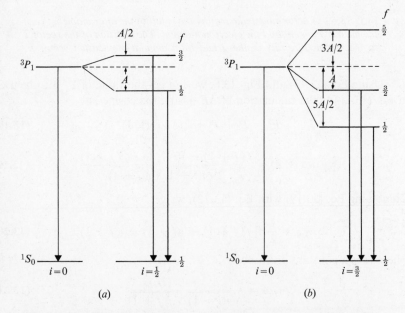

FIG. 13.7. *Hyperfine structure splitting of the atomic energy levels $^3P_1$ and $^1S_0$ for the nuclear spin (a) $i = \frac{1}{2}$, and (b) $i = \frac{3}{2}$. The possible allowed transitions between the hyperfine structure components are also shown.*

(13.20), $\Delta E = 0$. Similarly, if we assumed that the nuclear spin were 3/2 instead of 1/2, we see the $^3P_1$ and $^1S_0$ levels split as shown in Fig. 13.7(b). Using the selection rules given in Eq. (13.22), we may draw the allowed *hfs* transitions, those shown in Fig. 13.7. One fine structure transition is replaced by two in case (a), and three in case (b).

Let us now consider the splitting of a fine structure level $^2D_{5/2}$, assuming the nuclear spin to be 9/2. Thus, $i = 9/2$ and $j = 5/2$. This results in the following allowed values:

$$f = 7, 6, 5, 4, 3, 2$$

The values of f are denoted as subscripts to the left of the term designation, as for example $^2_7D_{5/2}$, $^2_6D_{5/2}$. Using Eq. (13.20), we get the following values of the displacements from the original fine-structure level $^2D_{5/2}$ shown dotted in Fig. 13.8, corresponding to the values of $f = 7, 6, 5, 4, 3, 2$,

$$+\frac{45}{4}A, \frac{17}{4}A, -\frac{7}{4}A, -\frac{27}{4}A, -\frac{43}{4}A, \text{ and } -\frac{55}{4}A$$

while the differences between these levels are given by

$$7A, 6A, 5A, 4A, \text{ and } 3A$$

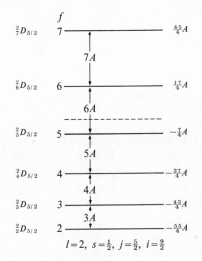

FIG. 13.8.   *The interval rule for hyperfine structure in the case of a* $^2D_{5/2}$ *level for* $i = \frac{9}{2}$.

as shown in Fig. 13.8. From these values we note that the differences are proportional to the larger of the f values. Thus these differences could be derived directly from Eq. (13.20) by first substituting $f + 1$, and then f. This results in the following expression for the differences

$$\Delta E_{\text{dif}} = A(f + 1) \tag{13.23}$$

which is the Landé interval rule and has been experimentally verified in many cases. For example in bismuth for the $^2D_{5/2}$ level where $i = 9/2$, the frequency differences are found to be

$$\Delta\nu = 0.563, 0.491, 0.385, 0.312, \text{ and } 0.256 \text{ cm}^{-1}$$

which are very closely in the ratios of

$$7 : 6 : 5 : 4 : 3$$

In order to find the relative intensities of different transitions we must know the type of coupling. It is found that in nearly all the *hfs* there is the ideal coupling between I and J, similar to LS-coupling. Hence the intensity rules given for LS-coupling are directly applicable to *hfs* if we replace the electron spin resultant S by the nuclear spin I, the orbital resultant L by the electron resultant J, and the electron resultant J by the grand total resultant F. The complete derivation of *hfs* intensity rules is given by Hill[11].

Let us now consider the *hfs* pattern for one of the two resonance lines of manganese, an intercombination line, $\lambda = 5394$ Å, starting from $^8P_{7/2}$ and terminating at $^6S_{5/2}$, the electron configuration of the two states being $3d^54s4p$ and $3d^54s4s$ with $j = 5/2$ and $7/2$, respectively. The value of the nuclear spin is $i = 5/2$. Thus for $j = 5/2$ and $i = 5/2$, $f = 0, 1, 2, 3, 4, 5$; and for $j = 7/2$, $i = 5/2$, $f = 1, 2, 3, 4, 5, 6$, as shown in Fig. 13.9. By using the selection rules we can draw the allowed transitions shown in the figure. The theoretically calculated values of the intensities are shown at the bottom.

3. NUCLEAR MAGNETIC-DIPOLE INTERACTION WITH ONE-VALENCE ELECTRON ATOMS

So far we have been able to predict the relative spacing of hyperfine structure levels by making use of Eq. (13.20). In order to calculate the absolute separations we must know the value of the constant A in Eq. (13.20). Calculations of the interaction energy between a single electron and a nucleus (with a mechanical and magnetic moments) have been made by Fermi[12], Hargreaves[13], Breit[14], Goudsmit[15], and Casmir[16]. We shall follow the semi-classical treatment similar to the one given in Sec. 9 of Chapter X for the fine-structure splitting (spin-orbit interaction), including the proper quantum mechanical modifications. Modifications will have to be made especially for the case of s-electrons where the following treatment is not applicable.

We may divide the interaction of a single electron with the nucleus into (A) the interaction of the electron orbital angular momentum, **L**, with the nuclear angular momentum, **I**, and (B) the interaction of the electron spin angular momentum, **S**, with the nuclear angular momentum, **I**.

A. Electron Orbital Motion and Nuclear Motion

According to classical theory, the electric field at the nucleus produced by the orbiting electron at a distance r is

$$E = \frac{e}{r^3}\mathbf{r} \qquad (13.24)$$

while the magnetic field at the nucleus due to the orbital motion of the electron is

$$\mathbf{H}_e = \frac{\mathbf{E} \times \mathbf{v}}{c} \qquad (13.25)$$

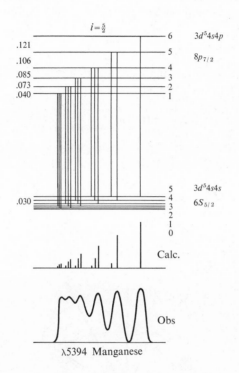

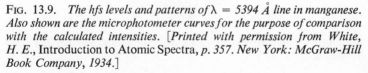

λ5394 Manganese

FIG. 13.9. *The hfs levels and patterns of* λ = 5394 Å *line in manganese. Also shown are the microphotometer curves for the purpose of comparison with the calculated intensities. [Printed with permission from White, H. E.,* Introduction to Atomic Spectra, *p. 357. New York: McGraw-Hill Book Company, 1934.]*

where **v** is the velocity of the electron around the nucleus. According to Bohr's relation

$$2\pi m\mathbf{r} \times \mathbf{v} = \mathbf{L} \qquad (13.26)$$

from which we can substitute the value of **v** into Eq. (13.25), yielding the magnetic field $\mathbf{H}_e$ to be

$$\mathbf{H}_e = \frac{e}{mc}\mathbf{L}\left(\frac{1}{r^3}\right) \qquad (13.27)$$

where $L = \sqrt{l(l + 1)}\hbar$, and e and m are the mass and charge, respectively, of the orbiting electron. Because in any orbit, the electron-nucleus distance r is not a constant, we must use an averaged value of $(1/r^3)$. Because of the presence of the magnetic field $\mathbf{H}_e$ at the nucleus, the nucleus with a mechanical moment $\mathbf{I}(I = \sqrt{i(i + 1)}\hbar)$ and a magnetic moment $\boldsymbol{\mu}_i$ displays Larmor precession around the field, $\mathbf{H}_e$, with an angular velocity ω_L. According to Eq. (10.63), ω_L is given by the product of the field strength $\mathbf{H}_e$ and the ratio between the magnetic and the mechanical moments. According to Eq. (13.9)

$$\frac{\mu_i}{\sqrt{i(i + 1)}\hbar} = g_i \frac{e}{2m_pc} \tag{13.28}$$

i.e., we are assuming that μ_i and I are due to a single spinning proton. Thus the precessional angular frequency ω_L is given by

$$\omega_L = g_i \frac{e}{2m_pc} H_e = g_i \frac{e}{2m_pc} \frac{e}{mc} L \left\langle\frac{1}{r^3}\right\rangle_{\text{av}} \tag{13.29}$$

The interaction energy is given by the product of ω_L and the projection of $\mathbf{I}$ on $\mathbf{L}$, or by using the relation $\Delta E = -\boldsymbol{\mu}_i \cdot \mathbf{H}_e$, i.e.,

$$\Delta E_{\mathbf{I}\cdot\mathbf{L}} = g_i \frac{e}{2m_pc} \frac{e}{mc} L \left\langle\frac{1}{r^3}\right\rangle_{\text{av}} I \langle\cos(\mathbf{I}, \mathbf{L})\rangle_{\text{av}} \tag{13.30}$$

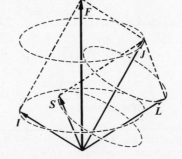

FIG. 13.10.   *Precession of vectors **L** and **S** around **J**, and that of **J** and **I** around **F**.*

As shown in Fig. 13.10, it is because of $\mathbf{L}$ precessing around $\mathbf{J}$, and $\mathbf{J}$ and $\mathbf{I}$ precessing around their resultant $\mathbf{F}$, that we must use the average value of the cosine. Because of the very slow precession of $\mathbf{J}$ and $\mathbf{I}$ around $\mathbf{F}$, as compared to the precession of $\mathbf{L}$ around $\mathbf{J}$, it is possible to project $\mathbf{L}$ on $\mathbf{J}$, and $\mathbf{J}$ on $\mathbf{I}$, and thus get the following value for the average cosine,

$$\langle\cos(\mathbf{I}, \mathbf{L})\rangle_{\text{av}} = \cos(\mathbf{I}, \mathbf{J})\cos(\mathbf{L}, \mathbf{J}) \tag{13.31}$$

Substituting this in Eq. (13.30) yields the interaction energy between $\mathbf{I}$ and $\mathbf{L}$,

$$\Delta E_{\text{I}\cdot\text{L}} = g_i \frac{e}{2m_pc} \frac{e}{mc} L \left\langle \frac{1}{r^3} \right\rangle_{\text{av}} I \cos (\textbf{I}, \textbf{J}) \cos (\textbf{L}, \textbf{J}) \tag{13.32}$$

Before evaluating the cosines, we shall calculate the interaction of the electron spin momentum **S** with **I**.

B. Electron Spin and Nuclear Motion

Let μ_I and μ_S be the magnetic moments corresponding to **I** and **S**, respectively, placed at a distance r apart. Once again according to classical electromagnetic theory the mutual energy of two magnetic dipoles is given by[17]

$$\Delta E_{\text{I}\cdot\text{S}} = \frac{\mu_I \cdot \mu_S}{r^3} - 3 \frac{(\mu_r \cdot \textbf{r})(\mu_S \cdot \textbf{r})}{r^5} \tag{13.33a}$$

$$\Delta E_{\text{I}\cdot\text{S}} = \frac{\mu_I \mu_S}{r^3} \left[\cos (\mu_I, \mu_S) - 3 \cos (\mu_I, \textbf{r}) \cos (\mu_S, \textbf{r}) \right] \tag{13.33b}$$

The average value of the term in brackets in Eq. (13.33b), evaluated by making use of direction cosines[18], is given by

$$-\frac{1}{2} \cos (\textbf{I}, \textbf{J}) \cos (\textbf{J}, \textbf{S}) - 3 \cos (\textbf{J}, \textbf{L}) \cos (\textbf{S}, \textbf{L})$$

Substitution of this along with the values of μ_I and μ_S given by

$$\mu_i = g_i \frac{e}{2m_pc} I \quad \text{and} \quad \mu_s = -2 \frac{e}{2mc} S$$

into Eq. (13.33b), we get the following expression for $\Delta E_{\text{I,S}}$

$$\Delta E_{\text{I}\cdot\text{S}} = g_i \frac{e}{2m_pc} I 2 \frac{e}{2mc} S \left\langle \frac{1}{r^3} \right\rangle_{\text{av}} \frac{1}{2} \cos (\textbf{I}, \textbf{J}) \cos (\textbf{J}, \textbf{S}) - 3 \cos (\textbf{J}, \textbf{L}) \cos (\textbf{S}, \textbf{L})$$

$$\tag{13.34}$$

Thus, combining Eqs. (13.32) and (13.34), we get the following expression for the total nuclear magnetic dipole-interaction with the orbit and spin of the one-valence electron atom.

$$\Delta E_{\text{I}\cdot\text{J}} = \Delta E_{\text{I}\cdot\text{L}} + \Delta E_{\text{I}\cdot\text{S}} = g_i \frac{e}{2m_pc} \frac{e}{mc} L \left\langle \frac{1}{r^3} \right\rangle_{\text{av}} I \cos (\textbf{I}, \textbf{J}) \cos (\textbf{L}, \textbf{J})$$

$$+ g_i \frac{e}{2m_pc} I 2 \frac{e}{2mc} S \left\langle \frac{1}{r^3} \right\rangle_{\text{av}} \frac{1}{2} \cos (\textbf{I}, \textbf{J}) \cos (\textbf{J}, \textbf{S}) - 3 \cos (\textbf{J}, \textbf{L}) \cos (\textbf{S}, \textbf{L})$$

$$\tag{13.35}$$

Substituting for $m_p = 1836\, m$, and using the cosine law for evaluating cos **(I, J)**, i.e.,

$$f(f+1)\hbar^2 = i(i+1)\hbar^2 + j(j+1)\hbar^2 + 2\sqrt{i(i+1)}\sqrt{j(j+1)}\hbar^2 \cos (\textbf{I}, \textbf{J})$$

we obtain

$$\Delta E_{\text{I}\cdot\text{J}} = AIJ \cos (\textbf{I}, \textbf{J}) = \frac{1}{2} A \left[f(f+1) - i(i+1) - j(j+1) \right] \tag{13.36}$$

where A is a constant given by

$$A = \frac{g_i}{1836} \frac{e^2 h^2}{8\pi^2 m^2 c^2} \left\langle \frac{1}{r^3} \right\rangle_{av} \left[\frac{L}{J} \cos (\mathbf{L}, \mathbf{J}) + \frac{S}{2J} \cos (\mathbf{S}, \mathbf{J}) - \frac{3S}{2J} \cos (\mathbf{J}, \mathbf{L}) \right.$$

$$\left. \times \cos (\mathbf{S}, \mathbf{L}) \right] \quad \textbf{(13.37)}$$

Because for a given spectral line, s, l, and j are fixed, so is A, i.e., A is a constant as mentioned in Eq. (13.20), and hence leads to the Landé interval rule.

Substituting the value of $\langle 1/r^3 \rangle_{av}$ from Eq. (10.80), and replacing the term in square brackets by L^2/J^2 as shown by Fermi[12], Hargreaves[13], Breit[14], and Goudsmit[15], we obtain the following expression for A

$$A = \frac{g_i}{1836} \frac{Rhc\alpha^2 Z^3}{n^3 \left(l + \frac{1}{2} \right) j(j + 1)} \quad \textbf{(13.38a)}$$

or to get A in terms of cm^{-1}, we divide by hc, i.e.,

$$A' = \frac{A}{hc} = \frac{g_i}{1836} \frac{R\alpha^2 Z^3}{n^3 \left(l + \frac{1}{2} \right) j(j + 1)} \quad \textbf{(13.38b)}$$

where R is the Rydberg constant, and α is the fine structure constant. If the nuclear g-factor, g_i, is positive, A will be positive, resulting in the normal *hfs* term; and if g_i is negative, A will be negative, resulting in the inverted *hfs* term.

4. ELECTRIC QUADRUPOLE-INTERACTION AND HYPERFINE STRUCTURE

Although in many instances the energy separation between the components of the *hfs* are given by Eq. (13.20), there are many situations where the separations do not follow this rule. For example, Fig. 13.11 shows the *hfs* of the 2537 Å line of mercury. As shown there are three components of the 2537 Å line that are due to Hg^{201}, and the separations between these components do not agree with the interval rule predicted by Eq. (13.20), which is derived from the interaction of the nuclear dipole-moment and the magnetic field produced by the orbiting electron. These deviations are due to the interaction of atomic electrons with the electric quadrupole-moment of the nucleus.

Assume a nucleus containing discrete charges, q_i, located at the origin of the XYZ coordinate system. The charges q_i are located at distances r_i from the origin, and the atomic electrons produce a potential $V(r_i)$ at r_i where the charge is q_i. The energy resulting from this interaction is

$$E = \sum_i q_i V(x_i, y_i, z_i) \quad \textbf{(13.39)}$$

If we expand $V(r)$ in a Taylor series about the origin, we obtain

$$E = V_0 \sum_i q_i$$

$$+ \left(\frac{\partial V}{\partial x}\right)_0 \sum_i q x_i + \left(\frac{\partial V}{\partial y}\right)_0 \sum_i q_i y_i + \left(\frac{\partial V}{\partial z}\right)_0 \sum_i q_i z_i$$

$$+ \frac{1}{2}\left(\frac{\partial^2 V}{\partial x^2}\right)_0 \sum_i q_i x_i^2 + \frac{1}{2}\left(\frac{\partial^2 V}{\partial y^2}\right)_0 \sum_i q_i y_i^2 + \frac{1}{2}\left(\frac{\partial^2 V}{\partial z^2}\right)_0 \sum_i q_i z_i^2 \qquad (13.40)$$

$$+ \left(\frac{\partial^2 V}{\partial xy}\right)_0 \sum_i q_i x_i y_i + \left(\frac{\partial^2 V}{\partial xz}\right)_0 \sum_i q_i x_i z_i + \left(\frac{\partial^2 V}{\partial yz}\right)_0 \sum_i q_i y_i z_i + \ldots$$

The quantity

$$\sum_i q_i$$

is called the *electric monopole-moment;* the three quantities defined as

$$p_x = \sum_i q_i x_i \, ; \, p_y = \sum_i q_i y_i \, ; \, p_z = \sum_i q_i z_i \qquad (13.41)$$

are the three components of *electric dipole-moment*, while the six quantities

$$p_{xx} = \sum_i q_i x_i^2 \, ; \, p_{yy} = \sum_i q_i y_i^2 \, , \, p_{zz} = \sum_i q_i z_i^2$$

$$p_{xy} = \sum_i q_i x_i y_i \, , \, p_{xz} = \sum_i q_i x_i z_i \, , \, p_{yz} = \sum_i q_i y_i z_i \qquad (13.42)$$

are the components of *electric quadrupole-moments*.

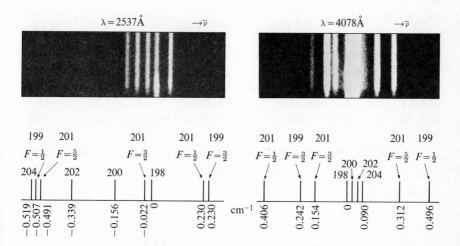

FIG. 13.11   *The hyperfine structure of the 2537 Å line and 4078 Å line of mercury. The Hg^{198} component is shown longer in the spectrogram, while the three components due to Hg^{201} do not follow the interval rule.* [*From* Melissinos, A. C., Experiments in Modern Physics, *New York: Academic Press, 1966.*]

Assuming the charge to be completely spherically symmetric, all the components in Eq. (13.40) will vanish, and the interaction energy will be zero. If the nuclear charge distribution has an axial symmetry about the Z axis, i.e., the charge distribution has the shape of an ellipsoid of rotation, then all components of the dipole moments are zero, i.e., $p_x = p_y = p_z = 0$. Three of the six components of the quadrupole moments are zero, i.e., $p_{xy} = p_{yz} = p_{zz} = 0$; while the other three components p_{xx}, $p_{yy}(= p_{xx})$, and p_{zz} are not zero. Hence contribution to the interaction energy is due only to the electric quadrupole moment (neglecting the higher terms) and may be written as

$$\Delta E_Q = \frac{1}{2}\left(\frac{\partial^2 V}{\partial x^2}\right)_0 p_{xx} + \frac{1}{2}\left(\frac{\partial^2 V}{\partial y^2}\right)_0 p_{yy} + \frac{1}{2}\left(\frac{\partial^2 V}{\partial z^2}\right)_0 p_{zz}$$

Using $p_{xx} = p_{yy}$, and from Laplace's theorem,

$$\left(\frac{\partial^2 V}{\partial x^2}\right)_0 + \left(\frac{\partial^2 V}{\partial y^2}\right)_0 + \left(\frac{\partial^2 V}{\partial z^2}\right)_0 = 0$$

we get

$$\Delta E_Q = \frac{1}{2}(p_{zz} - p_{xx})\left(\frac{\partial^2 V}{\partial z^2}\right)_0 = \frac{1}{4} Q \left(\frac{\partial^2 V}{\partial z^2}\right)_0 \tag{13.43}$$

where

$$Q = 2(p_{zz} - p_{xx}) \tag{13.44}$$

is called the electric quadrupole moment, and may be expressed as

$$Q = 2p_{zz} - p_{xx} - p_{yy} = \sum_i q_i(2z_i^2 - x_i^2 - y_i^2) = \sum e(3z_i^2 - r_i^2) \tag{13.45}$$

or for a continuous charge distribution

$$Q = \int \rho(3z_i^2 - r^2)\, dv \tag{13.46}$$

where ρ is the nuclear charge density and the integration is taken over the volume of the nucleus. Note that if $p_{zz} > p_{xx}$ or $2z^2 > (x^2 + y^2)$, $Q > 0$, (positive), and the charge distribution is prolate ellipsoidal with major axis along Z about the Z axis. If $p_{zz} < p_{xx}$, or $2z^2 < (x^2 + y^2)$, $Q < 0$, (negative), and the charge distribution is oblate (ellipsoidal with major axis) perpendicular to Z.

In order to make Eq. (13.46) quantum-mechanical, we can replace $\rho(r)$ by

$$\rho(r) = e\psi^*(r)\psi(r) \tag{13.47}$$

Combining Eqs. (13.43), (13.46), and (13.47), making the quantum-mechanical calculations yields the following expression for the energy shift of an F-sublevel[19]

$$\Delta E_Q = B \frac{\frac{3}{4} c(c + 1) - i(i + 1)j(j + 1)}{2i(2i - 1)j(2j - 1)} \tag{13.48}$$

where B is the quadrupole interaction constant given by

$$B = eQ \left\langle \left(\frac{\partial^2 V}{\partial z^2}\right)_0 \right\rangle_{av} \tag{13.49}$$

where $\langle(\partial^2 V/\partial z^2)_0\rangle_{av}$ is the average value of the gradient of the electric field of the electrons at the nucleus; Z is along the **J** vector about which the potential and the field are symmetric, while c is the magnetic dipole spacing given by

$$c = f(f+1) - i(i+1) - j(j+1)$$

Also if $i = 0$ or $\frac{1}{2}$, $Q = 0$; and if $j = 0$ or $\frac{1}{2}$, B must be zero; therefore, $\Delta E_Q \neq 0$ only if $i > 1$ and $j > 1$.

Thus to get the total energy shift, ΔE, for any *hfs* level, E_Q given by Eq. (13.48) must be added to $E_{\text{I·J}}$ given by Eq. (13.20); i.e.,

$$\Delta E = \Delta E_{\text{I·J}} + \Delta E_Q$$

which is the sum of the magnetic dipole interaction energy and the electric quadrupole interaction energy

$$\Delta E = \frac{1}{2}Af(f+1) - i(i+1) - j(j+1)$$
$$+ B\frac{\frac{3}{4}c(c+1) - i(i+1)j(j+1)}{2i(i-1)j(2j-1)} \tag{13.50}$$

In general ΔE_Q is small, but when it is not, it becomes important. In order to detect contribution from ΔE_Q, very precise measurement of *hfs* are needed that are difficult to get by means of optical spectroscopy. Unless specified, we shall not consider the effect of ΔE_Q in the rest of this chapter.

5. EFFECT OF AN EXTERNAL MAGNETIC FIELD ON HYPERFINE STRUCTURE

Effects similar to the anomalous Zeeman and Paschen-Back effects observed in the fine structure are also observed in the case of the *hfs* in the presence of external magnetic fields. In a very weak magnetic field (weaker than the one applied in the case of the anomalous Zeeman effect in fine structure) the *hfs* lines each break up into symmetrical patterns similar to the anomalous patterns of the fine structure in a weak field. This is the Zeeman effect of *hfs*. The condition for the very weak field is required so as not to break the coupling between **J** and **I**. If the magnetic field is increased to the degree in which it is classified as a weak magnetic field (the same as in the case of the anomalous Zeeman effect in fine structure) the coupling between **I** and **J** breaks down and the *Back-Goudsmit effect* in *hfs* is observed. The Back-Goudsmit effect is similar to the Paschen-Back effect in fine structure. We may point out that the separation between different components of any *hfs* level in a magnetic field is very small, and the limited resolution of optical instruments make these observations very difficult.

The first observation of the effect of a magnetic field on *hfs* were made in bismuth by Back and Goudsmit[20] in 1928. They showed that all the derivations and formulas for the anomalous Zeeman effect and the Paschen-Back effect could be carried over to *hfs* if we replace

$$S, L, J, g_s, g_l, g_j, m_s, m_l, \text{ and } m_j$$

by

$$I, J, F, g_i, g_j, g_f, m_i, m_j, \text{ and } m_f \tag{13.51}$$

respectively. Without going into any detail, we shall briefly explain the Zeeman and Back-Goudsmit effects in *hfs*.

A. Zeeman Effect in Hyperfine Structure

In the presence of a very weak magnetic field, **H**, the coupling between **I** and **J** resulting in **F** is as shown in Fig. 13.12. The magnetic moments associated with the mechanical moments **J** and **I** are, respectively,

$$\mu_j = g_j \frac{e}{2mc} \mathbf{J}, \qquad \text{and} \qquad \mu_i = g_i \frac{e}{2m_p c} \mathbf{I} \tag{13.52}$$

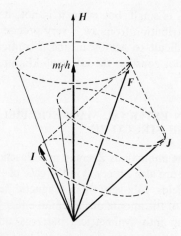

Fig. 13.12. *Vector model of an atom with a nuclear spin showing the precession of F around a very weak magnetic field* **H**.

The resultant magnetic moment is obtained by adding the parallel components along **F**, while the perpendicular components cancel out; (note that μ_i and **I** are parallel),

$$\mu_f = \mu_i \cos (\mathbf{J}, \mathbf{F}) - \mu_i \cos (\mathbf{I}, \mathbf{F}) \tag{13.53}$$

substituting for μ_j and μ_i, and $m_p = 1836\, m$, we get

$$\mu_f = \left[g_j \sqrt{j(j + 1)} \cos (\mathbf{J}, \mathbf{F}) - \frac{g_i}{1836} \sqrt{i(i + 1)} \cos (\mathbf{I}, \mathbf{F}) \right] \frac{eh}{4\pi mc} \tag{13.54}$$

or

$$\mu_f = g_f \sqrt{f(f+1)} \frac{eh}{4\pi mc} = g_f F \frac{e}{2mc} \qquad (13.55)$$

where

$$g_f F = g_j J \cos (\mathbf{J}, \mathbf{F}) - \frac{g_i}{1836} I \cos (\mathbf{I}, \mathbf{F}) \qquad (13.56)$$

and using the cosine law we may write

$$g_f = g_j \frac{f(f+1) + j(j+1) - i(i+1)}{2f(f+1)} - \frac{g_i}{1836} \frac{f(f+1) + i(i+1) - j(j+1)}{2f(f+1)} \qquad (13.57)$$

Because $g_i/1836$ is very small as compared to g_j, (i.e., g_i is smaller by a factor of $1/1000$ as compared to g_j), we may neglect the second term and write

$$g_f = g_j \frac{f(f+1) + j(j+1) - i(i+1)}{2f(f+1)} \qquad (13.58)$$

Going back to Eq. (13.55), in the presence of a magnetic field $\mathbf{H}$, the change in energy ΔE is given by

$$\Delta E = -\boldsymbol{\mu}_i \cdot \mathbf{H} = g_f F \frac{e}{2mc} H \cos (\mathbf{F}, \mathbf{H}) \qquad (13.59)$$

But

$$F \cos (\mathbf{F}, \mathbf{H}) = m_f \hbar \qquad (13.60)$$

Therefore,

$$\Delta E = g_f m_f \hbar H \frac{e}{2mc}$$

$$= g_f m_f H \frac{eh}{4\pi mc} \qquad (13.61)$$

where

$$m_f = f, (f-1), \dots, 1, 0, -1, \dots, -f \qquad (13.62)$$

Dividing both sides of Eq. (13.61) by hc, we get energy change in terms of wave numbers, i.e.,

$$-\Delta T_F = g_f m_f \frac{He}{4\pi mc^2} \text{ cm}^{-1} = g_f \cdot m_f \cdot L \text{cm}^{-1} \qquad (13.63)$$

As an example of the Zeeman effect in hfs, Fig. 13.13 shows this for the case of the transition $7p^2$, $P_{3/2} \rightarrow 7s^2$, $S_{1/2}$ in a doubly ionized thallium atom for which the nuclear spin, i, equals $\frac{1}{2}$. As in the case of fine structure, the selection rules for hfs are

$$\Delta m_f = 0, \pm 1 \qquad (13.64)$$

where 0 corresponds to p-components and ± 1 to s-components.

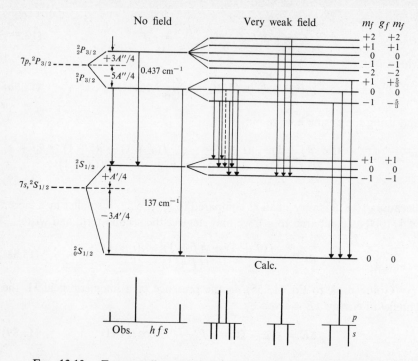

Fɪɢ. 13.13. *Zeeman effect of hfs, in a very weak magnetic field, of the transition $7p^2P_{3/2} \rightarrow 7s^2S_{1/2}$ in a doubly-ionized thallium atom for which the nuclear spin $i = \frac{1}{2}$.* [*From White, H. E.,* Introduction to Atomic Spectra, *p. 375. New York: McGraw-Hill Book Company, 1934.*]

B. Back-Goudsmit Effect in Hyperfine Structure

In the presence of a weak magnetic field (note that a weak field in the case of fine structure is a strong field for *hfs*) the coupling between **J** and **I** breaks and each precesses independently around **H** as shown in Fig. 13.14. The total magnetic interaction energy is made up of the energies due (i) to the interaction between **I** and **H**, (ii) to the interaction between **J** and **H**, and (iii) to the interaction between **I** and **J**. Carrying out the calculations in the same way as we did in Sec. 14 of Chapter X, for the Paschen-Back effect, we get the following:

$$\text{(i)} \quad \Delta E_{\mathbf{I \cdot H}} = -g_i J \frac{e}{2mc} H \cos(\mathbf{I, H}) = -g_i m_i \frac{eh}{4\pi mc} H \qquad \textbf{(13.65)}$$

$$\text{(ii)} \quad \Delta E_{\mathbf{J \cdot H}} = g_j J \frac{e}{2mc} H \cos(\mathbf{J, H}) = g_j m_j \frac{eh}{4\pi mc} H \qquad \textbf{(13.66)}$$

$$\text{(iii)} \quad \Delta E_{\mathbf{I \cdot J}} = AIJ \langle \cos(\mathbf{I, J}) \rangle_{\text{av}} = AI \cos(\mathbf{I, H}) J \cos(\mathbf{J, H})$$
$$= A' m_i m_j \qquad \textbf{(13.67)}$$

Adding these three equations together, we get the total energy change to be

$$\Delta E = (-g_i m_i + g_j m_j) \frac{eh}{4\pi mc} H + A' m_i m_j \qquad (13.68)$$

Expressing this in terms of wave numbers (dividing by hc)

$$-\Delta T = (-g_i m_i + g_j m_j) \frac{eH}{4\pi mc^2} + A_0 m_i m_j$$

$$= (-g_i m_i + g_j m_j)\mathsf{L} + A_0 m_i m_j \qquad (13.69)$$

(Note that g_i should be replaced by $g_i/1836$ to be consistent.)

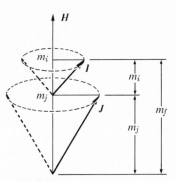

FIG. 13.14. *Independent precession of the electron vector, J, and of the nuclear vector, I, in a weak magnetic field, H, results in the Back-Goudsmit effect.*

The Back-Goudsmit effect in one of the resonance lines of thallium $\lambda = 5349$ Å, $6p, {}^2P_{3/2} \to 7s, {}^2S_{1/2}$ as obtained by Wulff[21,22] is shown in Fig. 13.15. The selection rules for such transitions are

$$\Delta m_i = 0$$

$$\Delta m_j = 0, \pm 1 \qquad (13.70)$$

Once again in Δm_j, 0 corresponds to p-components while ± 1 corresponds to s-components.

6. ISOTOPE STRUCTURE

Isotope structure and *hfs* are usually exhibited simultaneously. Only those elements that are monoisotopic will exhibit *hfs* and no isotope structure. On the other hand, those elements for which the nuclear spin, I, and hence nuclear magnetic moment, μ_i, is zero will exhibit isotope structure and no *hfs*. Because for even-even nuclei, nuclei with an even number of protons and an even number of neutrons, the nuclear spin is zero, it will be possible to observe the isotope structure alone for those elements whose isotopes are even-even.

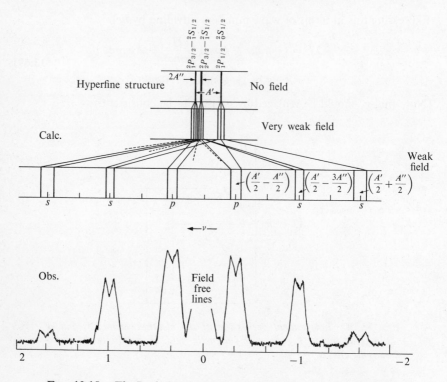

FIG. 13.15. *The Back-Goudsmit effect in one of the resonance lines of a thallium hfs pattern* $\lambda = 5349\ \mathring{A}$, $6p$, $^2P_{3/2} \rightarrow 7s$, $^2S_{1/2}$. *Note the changes that occur from* no field *to* very weak field *to* weak field: (a) *calculated (after White), and (b) observed (after Wulff).*

A.   Isotope Shift

Isotope shift is the result of two different contributions: (i) the finite mass of the nucleus, and (ii) the finite size of the nucleus.

The isotope shift resulting from the finite mass of the nucleus is significant in the case of light elements, while the isotope shift resulting from the finite size of the nucleus is significant in the case of heavy elements.

(i) *Finite Mass of the Nucleus.*   Consider a hydrogen-like atom with a nucleus of mass M. The energy levels of such an atom are given by

$$E_n = -\frac{hcZ^2R_M}{n^2} \tag{13.71}$$

where R_M is the Rydberg constant given by

$$R_M = \frac{M}{M + m} R_\infty \qquad (13.72)$$

and m is the mass of the electron, $R_\infty = 1.097 \times 10^{-3}$ Å^{-1} is the Rydberg constant if the nucleus is assumed to have an infinite mass.

If a given element has two or more isotopes, R_M will differ for each isotope. For such cases there will be two Rydberg constants and hence

$$R_{M_1} - R_{M_2} = \frac{m(M_1 - M_2)}{(M_1 + m)(M_2 + m)} R_\infty \qquad (13.73)$$

or

$$\Delta R = \frac{m\Delta M}{M_1 M_2} R_\infty \simeq \frac{m}{m_p} \frac{\Delta A}{A^2} R_\infty \qquad (13.74)$$

Thus for a given quantum number n, the difference in energy of the same level in two isotopes is obtained by combining Eq. (13.74) with Eq. (13.71) as

$$\Delta E_n = E_n(M_1) - E_n(M_2)$$

or

$$\Delta E_n \simeq \frac{hcZ^2}{n^2} \frac{m}{m_p} \frac{\Delta A}{A^2} \qquad (13.75)$$

ΔA is small and m is small as compared to m_p, hence the energy difference is very small. Note that the contribution from the finite mass-effect decreases as $1/A^2$ and hence the isotope shift for light elements is due mainly to this effect. We may point out that it is not possible to measure the absolute magnitude of the isotope shift of an energy level; only the differences between the isotope shifts of a level from one isotope to another isotope are measured. For example, consider a transition from a level n_i to n_f in an element with two isotopes denoted by 1 and 2. Therefore,

$$h\nu_1 = h\nu_0 + [\Delta E_{n_i}(1) - \Delta E_{n_f}(1)] \qquad (13.76a)$$

$$h\nu_2 = h\nu_0 + [\Delta E_{n_i}(2) - \Delta E_{n_f}(2)] \qquad (13.76b)$$

The transitions are schematically demonstrated in Fig. 13.16, and, as is obvious, one measures the difference $h\nu_1 - h\nu_2$, not the absolute values.

(ii) *Finite Size of the Nucleus.* The nucleus of an atom is not a point nucleus, it has a finite size, and has been shown[23] that its radius, R, may be expressed in terms of a mass number, A, as

$$R = r_0 A^{1/3} \qquad (13.77)$$

where $r_0 = 1.2 \times 10^{-13}$ cm. Because of the finite size, the Coulomb potential near the nucleus does not change as $1/r$; it changes as shown in Fig. 13.17. Because of the difference in the mass numbers of two isotopes, the difference in the radii, ΔR, between them leads to the following energy shift[24–26] between them

$$\Delta E_n \simeq \frac{hcZ^2 R_\infty}{n^2} F(Z, R) \frac{\Delta R}{R} \qquad (13.78)$$

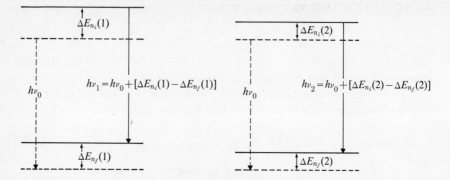

FIG. 13.16. *The initial and final energy-level states of two different isotopes of mass numbers A and (A + 1). The broken lines represent the levels without isotope shift of atomic spectral lines.*

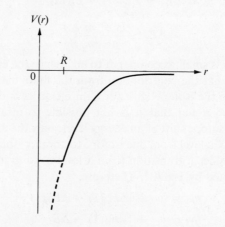

FIG. 13.17. *Coulomb potential of the nucleus, assuming the nucleus to have a finite size with radius* $R = r_0 A^{1/3}$.

where $F(Z, R)$ is some function of Z and R. Note that ΔR is negligible for isotopes of light elements but it becomes appreciable for heavy elements-

B. Isotope Shift and Hyperfine Structure Combined

The combined effects of the two will be observed whenever an element consists of two or more isotopes and when the nuclear spin of one or more of these isotopes is other than zero. An excellent example is that of mercury isotopes that has been analyzed by Schüler, Westmeyer, and Jones[27] for the transition

$$6s6p, \; {}^3P_2 \rightarrow 6s6d, \; {}^3D_1$$

of $\lambda = 3662$ Å, as demonstrated in Fig. 13.18. Of the seven isotopes of mercury with mass numbers 196, 198, 199, 200, 201, 202, and 204, five with even mass numbers have $i = 0$, $\mu_i = 0$. For Hg[199], $i = \frac{1}{2}$, $g_i \cong 1.1$, and for Hg[201], $i = 3/2$, $g_i \cong -0.41$. In Fig. 13.18, heavy lines are due to even isotopes, light ones are due to isotope 201, and dotted lines are due to 199. Note the number of components that have resulted by considering the *hfs* of isotopes.

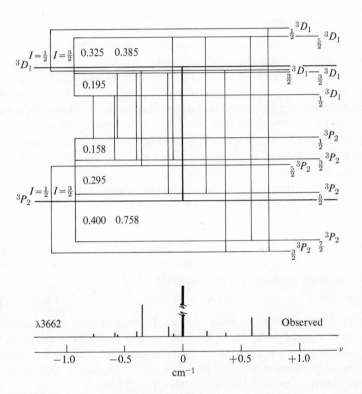

FIG. 13.18. *Isotope shift and hyperfine structure combined, shown diagrammatically for the case of mercury isotopes as observed in the transition $6s6p$, $^3P_2 \rightarrow 6s6d$, $^3D_1$; $\lambda = 3662$ Å. (After Schüler, Westmeyer, and Jones.)*

7. THE WIDTH OF SPECTRAL LINES[28, 29]

Each component of a spectrum line has a finite width. In order to resolve the components even when using a spectroscope of the highest possible resolution requires that the width of each component must be less than the separation between the components. We may point out that the width of a spectral line arises because of the finite widths of the levels between which the transition is taking place.

The purpose of this section is to investigate briefly the causes of broadening of the lines, which may be divided into A, the natural width; and B, the external effects, which may be further subdivided into the following: (i) Doppler broadening, (ii) pressure, or collision, broadening, (iii) external fields (and Stark effect), and (iv) self-absorption.

A. The Natural Width

Even if we could remove all possible external effects of line broadening, there is still a certain minimum width, the natural width, of a line and hence a natural width of a level. According to quantum mechanics, energy levels of a system should not be thought of as discrete levels but as a continuous distribution with very high probabilities wherever the levels are observed, and zero probability everywhere else. The transitions between these levels do not give rise to infinitely sharp spectral lines. The width of these levels, and hence of the transitions may be explained as a result of Heisenberg's uncertainty principle. According to this principle, if the energy measurement of a level is carried out in a time interval Δt, an energy uncertainty of the level by an amount ΔE will exist that is given by

$$\Delta E \, \Delta t \sim \hbar \qquad (13.79)$$

Let us consider that at time $t = 0$, there are N_0 atoms in an excited state. As the time goes on, the atoms in the excited state decay to another state according to an exponential law (see Prob. 13.9).

$$N_t = N_0 e^{-t/\tau} \qquad (13.80)$$

where N_t is the number of atoms left in the excited state of the atom after time t, and τ is the mean lifetime of the excited state of the atom. Now the energy of any level is determined by measuring the transition energy, and this measurement must be made within the mean lifetime of the excited level. This implies that $\Delta t \sim \tau$, and hence from Eq. (13.79)

$$\Delta E \sim \hbar/\tau \qquad (13.81)$$

Usually ΔE is replaced by Γ, the width of an energy level, and Eq. (13.81) is written as

$$\Gamma \sim \hbar/\tau \qquad (13.82)$$

The energy width ΔE (or Γ) may be expressed as a frequency range $\Delta \nu$ given, because $E = h\nu$, by

$$\Gamma = \Delta E = h\Delta \nu \sim \hbar/\tau$$

or

$$\Delta \nu = \frac{\Gamma}{h} = \frac{1}{2\pi\tau} \qquad (13.83)$$

Thus the transition emitted will have frequency between ν and $(\nu + \Delta \nu)$, i.e., the natural width of a spectrum line is $\Delta\nu$, given by Eq. (13.83). If there is no transition from a level, it means the mean lifetime, τ, of a level is infinite, and hence from Eq. (13.83) $\Gamma = 0$, and also $\Delta\nu = 0$. But if there are transitions from these levels, τ is finite and hence $\Gamma \neq 0$ and also $\Delta\nu \neq 0$. We may point out that because for the ground state of any system τ is infinite, the ground-state level is infinitely sharp, i.e., its width is zero.

The existence of a finite width associated with each discrete energy level is not a new phenomena caused by quantum mechanics. On the contrary, the same thing happens in classical theory. For example, consider an electrical circuit containing inductance and capacitance, only, connected to a source of variable frequency. It is known that this circuit will draw power from the source only if the resonance frequency, ν_0, of the circuit is equal to the frequency of the source. In actual practice there is no circuit without an appreciable resistance. Hence the circuit will accept power $P(\nu)$ not only at ν_0 but at other source frequencies as well, given by the relation

$$P(\nu) \propto \frac{1}{(\nu - \nu_0)^2 + (\Delta\nu/2)^2} \tag{13.84}$$

The plot of $P(\nu)$ versus ν is the resonance curve; $\Delta\nu$ is the full width at half-maximum as shown in Fig. 13.19, and is a function of the resistance of the

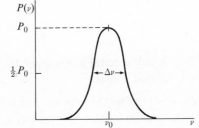

FIG. 13.19. $P(\nu)$ versus ν, i.e., the plot of the resonance curve; $\Delta\nu$ is the full-width at half-maximum.

circuit. Full-width at half-maximum is defined as the interval between the two points on the resonance curve where the intensities are half of the maximum value at ν_0. After the circuit has been in operation, if we suddenly switch off the source, the energy content of the circuit will decrease with time according to the following

$$E_t = E_0 e^{-t/\tau} \tag{13.85}$$

where E_0 is the energy content of the circuit at $t = 0$, and E_t is the energy content of the circuit at a later time, t, while τ is given by

$$\tau = \frac{1}{2\pi\Delta\nu} \tag{13.86}$$

Now let us assume that an atom in the ground state is constantly exposed to a source of electromagnetic radiation of all frequencies. If the energy of the excited state differ from the ground state by $h\nu_0$, according to quantum mechanics the transition rate $P(h\nu)$ is given by

$$P(h\nu) \propto \frac{1}{(h\nu - h\nu_0)^2 + (h\,\Delta\nu/2)^2} \qquad (13.87)$$

where $h\Delta\nu$ is the full-width at half-maximum denoted by Γ. This leads to the following definition of the mean lifetime, τ, of the excited state

$$\tau = \frac{1}{2\pi h\Delta\nu} = \frac{\hbar}{\Gamma} \qquad (13.88)$$

Defining $E = h\nu$, $E_0 = h\nu_0$, we may write Eq. (13.87) as

$$P(h\nu) \propto \frac{1}{(E - E_0)^2 + (\Gamma/2)^2} \qquad (13.89)$$

The plot of this equation is just like the one shown in Fig. 13.19. Furthermore, the excited state decays according to the same law as for the electrical circuit given by Eq. (13.85), which is similar to Eq. (13.80).

A typical natural width of a spectrum line, say of the sodium-yellow line, is ~ 0.0001 Å, which is very small compared to the broadening due to external effects. On the other hand, the natural widths of x-ray levels are much greater than optical levels.

B. The External Effects

The actual observed width of any spectral line is much larger than the natural width because of several external effects:

(i) *Doppler Broadening*[30]. The Doppler effect is a classical phenomena and is applied easily to the atomic system without any quantum-mechanical modifications. If the atoms emitting electromagnetic radiation were at rest, there would be no Doppler effect. But due to their thermal energies, atoms or molecules in a gas move in random directions with velocities given by Maxwellian distribution. Due to the velocity of an atom, its transition frequency is Doppler-shifted. But due to the random motion, there is a net broadening of the line with no apparent shift of its central maximum. This Doppler broadening (a) increases with increasing temperature, and (b) decreases with increasing atomic number. The full width at half-maximum is[28]

$$\Delta\nu_d = 1.67 \frac{\nu_0}{c} \sqrt{\frac{2RT}{M}} \qquad (13.90)$$

where R is the universal gas constant, T is the absolute temperature, and M is the molecular weight.

As an example, for the sodium D-line of wavelength 5890 Å, at a temperature of 500° K, $\Delta\lambda_d \simeq 0.02$ Å (note that $\Delta\nu/\nu = \Delta\lambda/\lambda$). Note that this is large enough to mask all the hyperfine structure. This broadening can be decreased by cooling the source, say, with liquid air.

(ii) *Pressure, or Collision, Broadening.* The natural width of a level calculated in Part A is true only if the pressure in the source vapor is low. If the pressure is too high, the emitting atoms will collide more frequently with other atoms, and the time, Δt, between the collisions becomes smaller than the lifetime, τ, of the excited state. This means that it is not possible to make an undisturbed measurement for a time comparable to τ, and it may be in time $(\tau + \Delta t)$, $(\tau + 2\Delta t)$, or more. This results in the broadening of the line more than the natural width. In order to minimize this effect the pressure of the vapor in the discharge tube is kept below 1 mm of mercury.

(iii) *External Fields.* Without going into the details of this subject, we may point out that electric fields are produced when atoms are ionized in an arc; a variable electric field is produced as ions approach or recede from one another. If we can calculate the average electric field thus produced, we can estimate *Stark splitting* and hence Stark broadening of the lines, which in this case is of the same order of magnitude as Doppler broadening. Magnetic fields also produce broadening of the lines.

(iv) *Self-absorption.* Other effects such as the self-absorption, in which the resonance line produced at the center of the source is absorbed by the source as it travels outward in the source causes the broadening. The absorption is proportional to the source length and the absorption cross-section.

8. THE MÖSSBAUER EFFECT[31,32,33]

The recoilless emission and absorption of γ-rays is the Mössbauer effect. The phenomenon, discovered by R. Mössbauer in 1958, is of great importance in the investigations of hyperfine structure, in nuclear physics, and in solid-state physics. As we shall show, it is possible, by using the Mössbauer effect, to measure an energy difference of 1 part in 10^{13}.

Assume a photon of energy $h\nu$ is emitted from a certain atom when it changes its state from E to E_0 $(E > E_0)$ where E is the energy of the excited state and E_0 that of the ground state. Now if the photons of the same energy, $h\nu$, are incident on these atoms, the atoms will absorb this radiation and will be raised from the ground state E_0 to the excited state E. These two processes are called *resonance emission* and *resonance absorption*, respectively. That such a process is possible was first experimentally verified by R. W. Wood in 1904. A well collimated beam of sodium light containing D-lines of wavelength 5890 Å and 5896 Å is incident on a cell containing sodium vapor. Sodium atoms absorb this radiation (resonance absorption) and then in the process of resonance emission, light of the same wavelength is emitted in all directions with equal probability. The detection of sodium D-lines at right angles to the incident beam verifies this.

We shall now apply the laws of conservation of linear momentum and energy and show that this resonance process is not possible if we are considering high energy gamma rays emitted by the nuclei. Suppose a system, an atom or a nucleus, is in the excited state E, emits a gamma ray of energy $h\nu$ and is left in the ground state with energy E_0. The conservation of energy requires

$$E - E_0 = h\nu + E_K \tag{13.91}$$

where E_K is the recoil energy of the system. Because the system was at rest before emission, its momentum was zero. After emission, the photon momentum is $h\nu/c$, and in order to conserve linear momentum, the recoiling system must satisfy the relation

$$MV = \frac{h\nu}{c} \tag{13.92}$$

where M and V are the mass and the recoil velocity of the system, respectively. Therefore, the kinetic energy carried away by the recoiling system is

$$E_K = \tfrac{1}{2}MV^2 = \frac{(MV)^2}{2M} = \frac{(h\nu/c)^2}{2M} = \frac{h^2\nu^2}{2Mc^2} \tag{13.93}$$

Therefore, Eq. (13.91) takes the form

$$E - E_0 = h\nu + \frac{h^2\nu^2}{2Mc^2} \tag{13.94}$$

From this equation it is obvious that the energy of the photon, $h\nu$, is less than the transition energy, $E - E_0$, by an amount $h^2\nu^2/2Mc^2$. Similarly, if the ground state E_0 is to be raised to a level E by resonance absorption of photons, an additional energy $E_K(= h^2\nu^2/2Mc^2)$ is required for the recoil of the system in order to conserve momentum. These processes are illustrated in Fig. 13.20.

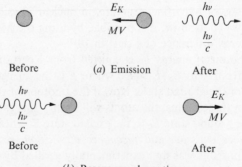

FIG. 13.20.   *The recoil of the nucleus is due to momentum conservation in (a) the emission, and, (b) the resonance-absorption, of nuclear gamma rays.*

Thus if photons of energy $h\nu$ are used to excite the energy level, E, the energy of the photons will be less than the energy required to cause resonance absorption (or excitation) by an amount ΔE_R given by

$$\Delta E_R = \frac{h^2\nu^2}{2Mc^2} + \frac{h^2\nu^2}{2Mc^2} = \frac{h^2\nu^2}{Mc^2} \qquad (13.95)$$

If the excited level, E, were sharp with no width, i.e., $\Delta E = 0$ (which means that from the uncertainty principle the lifetime $\tau = \hbar/\Delta E$ would be infinite), it will not be possible to cause resonance absorption of photons of energy $h\nu - \Delta E_R$. But the width of the level is not zero and if ΔE_R, the energy loss in recoil, is less than ΔE, the level width, resonance absorption is possible as demonstrated in Fig. 13.21(a). On the other hand, if ΔE_R is greater than ΔE, no resonance absorption will be possible as shown in Fig. 13.21(b).

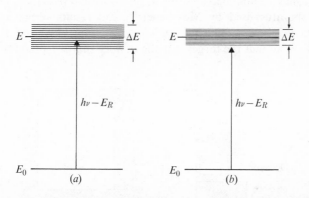

FIG. 13.21. *Depending upon the level width, ΔE, the photon energy $(h\nu - E_R)$ may or may not be enough to cause resonance absorption. (a) $\Delta E_R < \Delta E$, and, (b) $\Delta E_R > \Delta E$.*

In the case of atomic systems, the width of the levels are much more than the energy taken by the recoiling atoms, i.e., usually $\Delta E/\Delta E_R \approx 10^3$. This implies that resonance absorption of radiation is possible in atomic systems as shown in Fig. 13.21(a). On the other hand, if we are considering a nuclear system that is emitting gamma rays, the ratio $\Delta E/\Delta E_R \approx 10^{-3}$ and hence the resonance absorption of gamma rays is not possible, as shown in Fig. 13.21(b). Nuclear resonance-absorption can be achieved only if the lost recoil energy is restored. The difficulty of restoring the recoil energy has been overcome by using either the Doppler effect or the Mössbauer effect.

Using the Doppler effect[34-36], the source is placed on the tip of a high speed rotor. The Doppler effect will increase the frequency of emitted radiation. If the speed of the rotor is such that the condition

$$E_\gamma \left(\frac{v}{c}\right) = \frac{E_\gamma^2}{Mc^2} \qquad (13.96)$$

is satisfied, it will be possible to observe resonance scattering with photons of energy E_γ. This method has been demonstrated by P. Moon and W. Davey[34,35]. Doppler broadening[36] has also been achieved by heating the source to temperatures of the order of 1200° C.

Using the Mössbauer effect[33], the need to supply the recoil energy is eliminated. The gamma-emitting nucleus is incorporated into a crystal lattice, and the recoil energy is shared by the whole lattice, not only the nucleus. Such a condition is usually achieved by placing the source, which forms a part of the crystal, at low temperature. Under such circumstances, the energy loss by the recoil is negligible because the recoiling mass, M, which is now the mass of the crystal, is very large. Similarly, the target, which is the same material as the source, is made a part of the lattice at low temperature. Resonance absorption is possible now by using photons emitted by the source. A resonance curve may be obtained by using a small variable-velocity of the source.

The apparatus used by Mössbauer[38] and results obtained for Ir^{191} which emits 129 keV gamma rays as shown in Fig. 13.22 and Fig. 13.23, respectively. Note that the target is made of very thin Ir ($\sim$0.0001 in.).

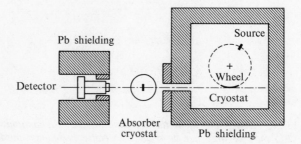

FIG. 13.22. *The experimental arrangement used by Mössbauer. Both the source and the absorber are inside the cryostat. The source is mounted on the wheel, which may be rotated in either direction with variable velocity.* [*From: R. L. Mössbauer,* Natur Wiss, *45, 538, (1958).*]

As another example, Fig. 13.24 shows the resonance curve obtained for the Mössbauer effect of Fe^{57}. The source used for this is Co^{57}, which decays to Fe^{57}, with emission of 14.4 keV gamma rays. The target was an enriched thin Fe^{57} absorber. As is clear from Fig. 13.24(a), in addition to the zero velocity peak, there appear many subsidiary peaks. These peaks are due to the hyperfine structure splitting of the nuclear energy levels of Fe^{57}. In iron, there is a strong magnetic field at the site of the nuclei. The magnetic field results in the splitting of the nuclear energy levels, i.e., results in the Zeeman effect for the nucleus. Figure 13.24(b) shows the schematic splitting of the 14.4 keV level (which has a nuclear spin of 3/2) and the ground state of Fe^{57}, (which has a nuclear spin of 1/2). Thus as shown in Fig. 13.24(a), the 14.4

keV line has six hyperfine structure components. As is clear, we can use the Mössbauer effect for the investigation of the hyperfine structure because of the availability of such precise measurements. As mentioned earlier the energy differences of the order of 1 part in 10^{13} (corresponding to a velocity of $v \approx 0.006$ mm/sec) may be measured easily.

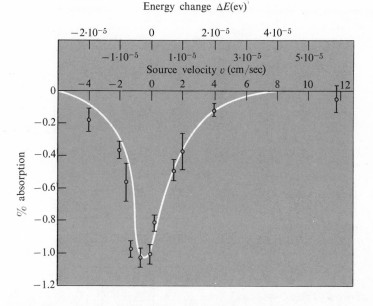

FIG. 13.23.   *Recoilless resonance-absorption of 129-keV gamma radiation of* Ir^{191}*. The effect of the motion of the source on resonant absorption at 88° K is shown. The half-width at half-maximum absorption is*

$$2\Gamma = (9.2 \pm 1.2)10^{-6} \ eV$$

[*From: R. L. Mössbauer,* Natur Wiss, *45, 538, (1958).*]

PROBLEMS

1. Show all the necessary steps leading to the derivation of Eq. (13.68).

2. Na^{23} has a nuclear spin of 3/2 (i.e., $i = 3/2$). Using this value of the nuclear spin, draw the hyperfine structure of sodium D-lines. Making use of the selection rules, draw all the possible transitions.

3. If the orbital motion of an electron results in a magnetic field at the center of the nucleus of the order of 10^6 gauss, calculate the amount of splitting in the case of hyperfine structure of sodium D-lines. The nuclear spin of sodium is 3/2, while the nuclear g-factor is 1.4.

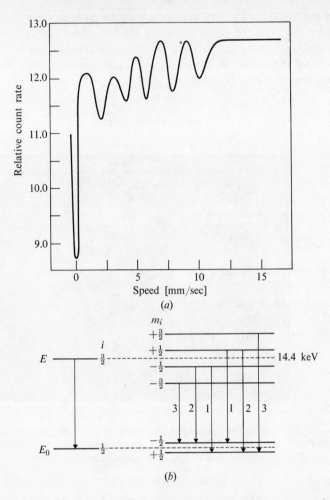

Fig. 13.24.   *Nuclear hyperfine structure in* Fe^{57} (a) *as measured by using the Mössbauer Method.* [*From: Hanna, et al.*] (b) *The energy level diagram.*

4. Show that the interaction energy of two s-electrons with a nuclear moment is given by (using jj-coupling)

$$a\frac{j_t(j_t + 1) - s_1(s_1 + 1) - s_2(s_2 + 1)}{2j_t(j_t + 1)}$$

where a is a constant.

5. Consider the transition $^2S_{1/2} \rightarrow {}^2P_{3/2}$, and assume that the nuclear spin is 1/2. Show the possible nuclear Zeeman levels and the resulting transitions in the hyperfine structure.

6. Show the Back-Goudsmit effect in the hyperfine structure of sodium D-lines considered in Prob. 13.4.

7. Show the Back-Goudsmit effect in the hyperfine structure considered in Prob. 13.5.

8. Rubidium is a mixture of two stable isotopes, Rb^{85} and Rb^{87}. The nuclear spins of these are 5/2 and 3/2, respectively, while their g-factors are 0.5 and 1.9, respectively. Show the Zeeman effect (very weak field) and the Back-Goudsmit effect (weak field) in this hyperfine structure.

9. If the number of atoms, ΔN, decaying in an interval dt is directly proportional to dt and the number of atoms N present in the excited level, show that the number of atoms, N, remaining at any time t is given by

$$N = N_0 e^{-t/\tau}$$

where $1/\tau$ is a constant. What is the physical significance of τ?

REFERENCES

1. Michelson, A. A., *Phil. Mag.*, **31**, 338, (1891).

2. Fabry, C., and A. Perot, *Ann. Chim. et Phys.* (7), **12**, 459, (1897).

3. Lummer, O., and E. Gehrcke, *Ann. Physik*, **10**, 457, (1903).

4. Janicki, L., *Ann. Physik*, **29**, 833, (1909).

5. Wali-Mohammed, Ch., *Astrophys. J.*, **39**, 185, (1914).

6. Pauli, W., *Naturwiss.*, **12**, 741, (1924).

7. Russell, H. N., W. F. Meggers, and K. Burns, *J. Opt. Soc. Amer.*, **14**, 449, (1927).

8. White, H. E., *Introduction to Atomic Spectra*, p. 353. New York: McGraw-Hill Book Company, 1934.

9. White, H. E., *Introduction to Atomic Spectra*, p. 352. New York: McGraw-Hill Book Company, 1934.

10. Goudsmit, S., and E. Back, *Zeit. fur Physik*, **43**, 321, (1927), and **47**, 174, (1928).

11. Hill, E. L., *Proc. Nat. Acad. Sci.*, **15**, 779, (1929).

12. Fermi, E., *Zeit. fur Physik*, **60**, 320, (1930).

13. Hargreaves, J., *Proc. Roy. Soc.*, **A127**, 141, (1930).

14. Breit, G., *Phys. Rev.*, **37**, 51, (1931).

15. Goudsmit, S. A., *Phys. Rev.*, **37**, 663, (1931): also Pauling, L., and S. A. Goudsmit, *The Structure of Line Spectra*, p. 204. New York: McGraw-Hill Book Company, 1930.

16. Casimir, H. B. G., p. 208 in L. Pauling and S. A. Goudsmit, *The Structure of Line Spectra*. New York: McGraw-Hill Book Company, 1930.

17. Panofsky, W. K. H., and M. Phillips, *Classical Electricity and Magnetism*, p. 16. Reading, Mass.: Addison-Wesley Publishing Co., Inc., 1955.

18. Pauling, L., and S. A. Goudsmit, *The Structure of Line Spectra*, p. 206. New York: McGraw-Hill Book Company, 1930.

19. Casimir, H., *Physica*, **7**, 169, (1940), also H. Casimir, *On the Interaction Between Atomic Nuclei and Electrons*, reprinted by W. H. Freeman, San Francisco (1963).

20. Back, E., and S. A. Goudsmit, *Zeit. fur Physik*, **47**, 174, (1928).

21. Wulff, J., *Zeit. fur Physik*, **69**, 74, (1931).

22. Green, J. B., and J. Wulff, *Phys. Rev.*, **38**, 2176, (1931), and **38**, 2186, (1931).

23. Arya, A. P., *Fundamentals of Nuclear Physics*, Chap. VI. Boston, Mass.: Allyn and Bacon, Inc., 1966.

24. Breit, G., *Phys. Rev.*, **42**, 348, (1933).

25. Rosenthal, J. E., and G. Breit, *Phys. Rev.*, **41**, 459, (1932).

26. Racah, G., *Nature*, **129**, 723, (1932).

27. Schüler, H., and J. E. Keyston, *Zeit. fur Physik*, **72**, 423, (1931); also Schüler, H., and E. G. Jones, **74**, 631, (1932), and **77**, 801, (1932).

28. White, H. E., *Introduction to Atomic Spectra*, Chap. XXI. New York: McGraw-Hill Book Company, 1934.

29. Weisskopf, V., *Zeit. fur Physik*, **34**, 1, (1933); also Max Born, *Optik*, pp. 421–455, Berlin: J. Springer, 1933.

30. Kopfermann, H., and R. Ladenburg, *Zeit. fur Physik*, **48**, 26, (1928).

31. Mössbauer, R. L., *Zeit fur Physik*, **151**, 124, (1958).

32. Boyle, A. J. F., and H. E. Hall, *Rep. Prog. Phys.*, **25**, 441, (1962).

33. Mössbauer, R. L., *Naturwiss.*, **45**, 538, (1958); *Z. Naturforsch*, **149**, 211, (1959); *Zeit. fur Physik*, **151**, 124, (1958).

34. Moon, P. B., *Proc. Phys. Soc.*, **A-64**, 76, (1961).

35. Davy, W. G., and P. B. Moon, *Proc. Phys. Soc.*, **A-66**, 956, (1953).

36. Frich, O. R., *Prog. Nucl. Phys.*, **7**, (1959).

SUGGESTIONS FOR FURTHER READING

1. White, H. E., *Introduction to Atomic Spectra*, Chaps. XVIII and XXI. New York: McGraw-Hill Book Company, 1934.

2. Herzberg, G., *Atomic Spectra & Atomic Structure*, Chap. V. New York: Dover Publications, Inc., 1944.

3. Melissinos, A. C., *Experiments in Modern Physics*, Chaps. 7 and 8. New York: Academic Press, 1966.

4. Ramsey, N. F., *Nuclear Moments*, New York: John Wiley & Sons, 1953; also *Experimental Nuclear Physics*. Ed. by E. Segrè. Vol. 1, p. 395. New York: John Wiley & Sons, Inc., 1963.

5. Kopfermann, H., *Nuclear Moments*, New York: Academic Press, 1958.

6. Wertheim, G. K., *Mössbauer Effect: Principles and Applications*. New York: Academic Press, 1964.

XIV

Structure and Spectra of Molecules

1. INTRODUCTION

Identical or nonidentical atoms combine to form stable systems, molecules. Because the structure of matter is very closely related to the structure of the molecules, we shall investigate molecular structure. There are many questions that must be answered: What is a molecule? How do atoms combine to form a molecule? What type of forces hold atoms together in a molecule?

The advent of quantum theory led to a satisfactory explanation of many different aspects of atomic structure and spectra. The same is not true for molecules. Even though quantum theory has explained many aspects of molecular structure that could not be answered satisfactorily by classical theory, mathematical analysis of the theoretical predictions are far from being complete. Because molecules consist of two, and usually many more, atoms, the problem is that of solving the Schrödinger wave equation for a many-body system. Usually the solutions of such many-body systems are attempted by combining statistical mechanics with the Schrödinger wave equation. The complexity of the mathematical analysis does not permit one to make quantitative predictions, but the qualitative predictions of the theories have shown reasonable agreement with experiments.

Another important question is: When a molecule is formed, do the atoms retain their individualities? There are three different lines of thought that make up the answer. First, one may treat a molecule as if only the motion of electrons in the outermost shells is affected; thus one may say that molecular interaction is the result of the interaction between the outermost electrons. The second view is that in the formation of a molecule, atoms lose their individualities completely; in other words, a molecule is a stable configuration consisting of different nuclei and electrons. The third view, which is more practical, is to take an intermediate position of the above two extremes; this seems to be a good approximation in analyzing molecular structure.

Because of the complexity of the problem involved in molecular structure and because of the limitations of this text, it will not be possible to go into complete detail. The purpose of this chapter is to introduce the reader to the problems of molecular structure and molecular spectra. Most of the chapter will be devoted to the simplest of all the molecules, i.e., the diatomic molecules. Of course an occasional reference will be made to polyatomic molecules as well.

A molecular system will be stable if its mass (or equivalent energy) is less than the sum of the masses (or equivalent energies) of the atoms from which the molecule is formed. The amount of energy equivalent to the difference in the masses is the binding energy that holds different constituents of the molecule in a stable configuration. Thus in order to break a stable molecule into its constituent parts, we will have to supply energy from an external source equivalent to the binding energy. The attractive forces that hold together the two atoms of diatomic molecules may be caused by two extremely different types of bonds: (A) the covalent bond and (B) the ionic bond.

A. The Covalent Bond[1]

A covalent bond is said to be responsible for the formation of a stable diatomic molecule if the attractive force between the two atoms results from the sharing of one or two pairs of electrons by both the atoms. These electrons spend more time between the atoms than anywhere else, thereby producing an attractive force. Figure 14.1 shows pure covalent bonding in the

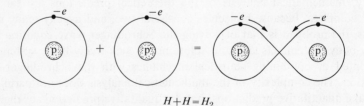

$$H + H = H_2$$

Fig. 14.1. *Covalent bonding in the formation of a hydrogen molecule. The two electrons, shared by both the protons, spend most of their time between the protons.*

simplest of the molecules, the hydrogen molecule, H_2. As is obvious from the figure, both the electrons are shared by the two protons. Covalent bonding is also referred to as *homopolar binding*[2].

B. The Ionic Bond

In this case one or more electrons transfer from one atom to another, thereby producing positive and negative ions. These ions in turn attract each other and form a stable diatomic molecule. Ionic binding is also known as *hetero-polar binding*. Figure 14.2 illustrates a simple example of a formation of an

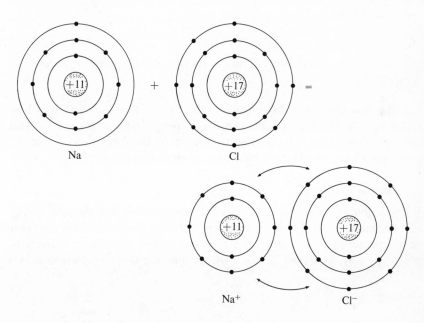

Na + Cl ⟶ Na⁺ + Cl⁻ ⟶ NaCl

Fɪɢ. 14.2.   *Ionic bonding in the formation of a sodium chloride molecule.*

ionic diatomic molecule, NaCl. The Na atom transfers its electron to the Cl atom thereby producing Na^+ and Cl^-. These two ions attract each other forming a stable diatomic molecule, NaCl.

Usually both types participate to some extent in the formation of any molecule. In the following, we shall discuss in some detail the above two types of bonding.

2. THE HYDROGEN MOLECULAR ION[3]

The simplest of all the molecular systems is H_2^+, the hydrogen molecular ion. It consists of two protons and an electron, the electron binding the two protons. The formation of the H_2^+ molecule may be written as $H + H^+ \rightarrow H_2^+$, i.e., a hydrogen atom (H) captures a proton (H^+) forming a hydrogen molecular ion (H_2^+). Once the H_2^+ molecule is formed, as shown in Fig. 14.3, it is not possible to distinguish the hydrogen atom from the proton. We may say that the electron is shared by both the protons and moves in the electric field of the two protons, which are separated by a distance r.

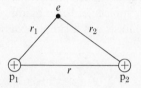

FIG. 14.3.   *Two protons and an electron forming a hydrogen molecular ion, H_2^+.*

We shall divide our discussion into three parts. First we shall show how the sharing of an electron leads to a lower energy and a stable system. This will be followed by a qualitative discussion of the formation of the H_2^+ molecule. Finally, we shall calculate the ground-state energy of H_2^+.

A.   Electron Sharing in H_2^+

Without going into mathematical detail[4], we can show that the total energy of a system when an electron is shared by both the protons is lower than that of a separate hydrogen atom and a proton. When an electron belongs to proton p_1 only, as shown in Fig. 14.4, we may say that the electron is in a

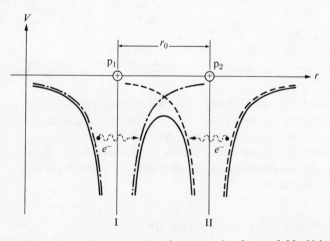

FIG. 14.4.   *Potential energy of an electron in the electric field of* (a) p_1, *a proton alone, denoted by* $\_ \_ . \_ . \_$; (b) p_2, *a proton alone, denoted by* $\_ \_ \_ \_ \_$; *and* (c) *both protons, p_1 and p_2, denoted by heavy lines.*

potential well, I. Similarly, when the electron belongs to only proton p_2, we say that the electron is in the potential well II. When the electron is shared by both protons, the potential is represented by the solid lines. Though classically the electron cannot go from well I to well II, quantum mechanically we know that the electron can penetrate the barrier and go from I to II, and vice versa. When this happens, we say that the electron is shared by both protons.

The frequency of the barrier crossing is a function of the distance between the protons. If this distance is, say, 1 Å, the electron may be going from one proton to the other about once every 10^{-15} sec. Because such small intervals are hard to detect, we may say that the electron belongs to both the protons. This is stated by saying that there is equal probability of finding the electron in the vicinity of either proton. On the other hand, if the distance between the two protons is on the order of 10 Å, the exchange of the electron between the two protons may take place only once every second. Thus in this case it will be possible to associate the electron with one or the other proton, and hence there is no sharing. In terms of wave functions, we may say that sharing takes place when the wave functions overlap. Because the effective radius of the $1s$ wave function of the hydrogen atom is 0.53 Å, the sharing takes place when $r \leqslant 2(0.53)$, i.e., $r \sim 1$ Å.

Furthermore, when an electron is in the hydrogen atom, it is confined to a certain distance (in a circle of radius $\sim$0.53 Å) and has a certain binding energy (-13.58 eV). Now if this confinement distance is increased, according to the uncertainty principle, its momentum and hence its energy will decrease. This is precisely what happens when the electron is shared by both the protons. The electron is less confined, i.e., the distance over which it moves is larger, and hence its kinetic energy is less, thereby leading to a stable H_2^+ molecular system.

B. Formation of the H_2^+ Molecule

Making use of the hydrogen atom wave-function we shall discuss the formation of the H_2^+ molecule. The potential energy, E_p, of the system, consisting of two protons and an electron, as shown in Fig. 14.3, may be written as

$$E_p = \frac{e^2}{4\pi\epsilon_0} \left(-\frac{1}{r_1} - \frac{1}{r_2} + \frac{1}{r} \right) \qquad (14.1)$$

where the first two terms in the parentheses give the attractive potential energy between the electron and the two protons, and the third term gives the repulsive potential energy between the two protons. Knowing E_p, if we know the wave function, ψ, of the system, we can solve the Schrödinger wave equation and determine the possible energy states in which the system may exist. Assuming the protons to be at rest, the Schrödinger wave equation of the system is

$$\left[-\frac{\hbar^2}{2m}\nabla^2 + \frac{e^2}{4\pi\epsilon_0}\left(-\frac{1}{r_1}-\frac{1}{r_2}+\frac{1}{r}\right)\right]\psi = E\psi \tag{14.2}$$

or

$$H\psi = E\psi \tag{14.3}$$

where the first term in Eq. (14.2) is the kinetic energy of the electron. Solving this equation is a very complicated task[5]. But much can be learned without actually solving it, as we shall see below.

Let us assume that the electron is orbiting proton p_1, forming a hydrogen atom in the ground state $1s$, while the proton p_2 is far away such that $r_2 \gg r_1$ and $r \gg r_1$. In this case Eq. (14.2) reduces to a typical Schrödinger wave equation for a hydrogen atom, and the wave function for the system in Fig. 14.5(a) may be written as[6] (see Chapter IX)

$$\psi_1 \approx \frac{1}{\sqrt{\pi}\, a_0^{3/2}} e^{-r_1/a_0} \tag{14.4}$$

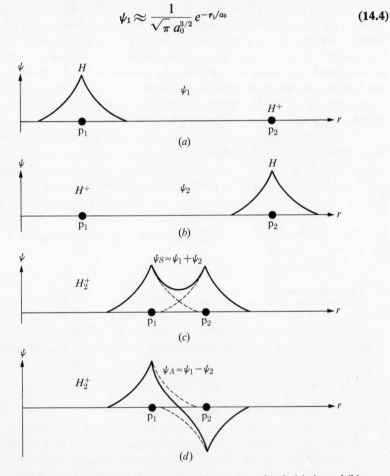

FIG. 14.5.   *The linear combination of the atomic orbitals* (a) ψ_1 *and* (b) ψ_2 *(1s wave functions of hydrogen atoms) to form molecular orbitals of* H_2^+, *(c)* ψ_{even} *(=* ψ_S*), and* (d) ψ_{odd} *(=* ψ_A*).*

where a_0 is the first Bohr-orbit radius. Similarly, if the electron is orbiting proton p_2 and proton p_1 is far away as shown in Fig. 14.5(b), the wave function of the system is again like that of the $1s$ hydrogen atom given by

$$\psi_2 \approx \frac{1}{\sqrt{\pi}\, a_0^{3/2}}\, e^{-r_2/a_0} \qquad (14.5)$$

Now we start decreasing the distance between the two protons. The wave function of the electron is disturbed by the approaching proton which tries to pull the electron away from the other proton. From Fig. 14.4 we see that the electron potential in the H_2^+ molecule is symmetric, and hence the probability distribution of the electron must have the same symmetry; in this case symmetry means that exchanging 1 and 2 does not change the wave function or potential. Thus the wave function and hence the electron distribution must have pronounced peaks around each proton, where the potential energy is less. The wave functions of the H_2^+ may be formed by linear combinations of the two wave functions shown in Fig. 14.5(a) and (b). Two possible wave functions that will satisfy the symmetry condition may be formed. These are

$$\psi_{\text{even}}\,(=\psi_S) \approx (\psi_1 + \psi_2) \qquad (14.6)$$

and

$$\psi_{\text{odd}}\,(=\psi_A) \approx (\psi_1 - \psi_2) \qquad (14.7)$$

where ψ_S is a symmetric wave function, and ψ_A is an antisymmetric wave function. The plot of ψ_S is shown in Fig. 14.5(c), and that of ψ_A is shown in Fig. 14.5(d). The individual wave functions of the atoms, like ψ_1 and ψ_2, are called *atomic orbitals*. The wave functions ψ_S and ψ_A, resulting from the linear combination of atomic orbitals, are called *molecular orbitals*, or MO. The theory of forming the molecular orbitals[7] is the *linear combination of atomic orbitals*, or LCAO. Also the wave function ψ_{even} is denoted by $\sigma_g 1s$ and ψ_{odd} by $\sigma_u 1s$, as we shall explain later.

Figure 14.6 shows the plots of the probability-density distributions for the two states ψ_S (or $\sigma_g 1s$) and ψ_A (or $\sigma_u 1s$) in different forms. Without going into mathematical detail we shall explain that the energies of these two states are different[8] and that ψ_S is a bonding wave function while ψ_A is an antibonding wave function. When the electron is between the two protons, it pulls the protons together, and the electrostatic attraction offsets the repulsion. On the other hand, if the electron is on either side, it helps to pull the protons apart. Thus the electron between the two protons works as a bonding force, or "cement," for producing a stable configuration. From the probability density plots in Fig. 14.6, we see that the electron in the ψ_S state spends more time between the protons as compared to the electron in the ψ_A state. As a matter of fact $|\psi_A|^2$ is almost zero between the two protons because of the node in the ψ_A wave function. From this we may conclude that the H_2^+ system is more strongly bound in the ψ_S state. In other words, the state ψ_S (or $\sigma_g 1s$) has a lower energy than the ψ_A (or $\sigma_u 1s$) state.

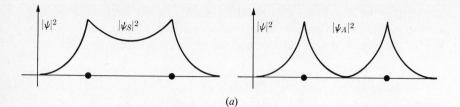

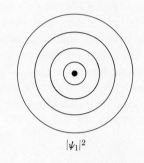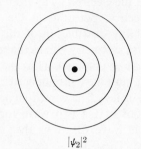

(b)

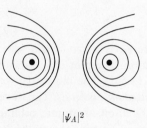

(c)

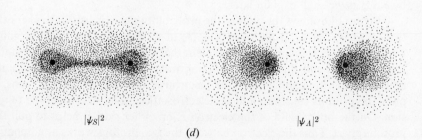

(d)

FIG. 14.6. (a) *Plots of the probability density distributions corresponding to ψ_S and ψ_A along the line joining the two protons.* (b) *Plots of $|\psi_1|^2$ and $|\psi_2|^2$ in the form of contour lines.* (c) *Plots of probability density of the electron in the form of contour lines in the plane containing the two protons.* (d) *Same as* (c) *except that the density of the points, the shading, indicates the relative probability of finding the electron.*

540

Now we shall investigate the variation of binding energy versus separation distance between the two protons. When the two protons are separated by a large distance, i.e., $r \to \infty$, the electron belongs only to one proton, and hence the binding energy of the system is that of the hydrogen atom, i.e., -13.58 eV. When $r = 0$, i.e., H_2^+ becomes He^+ and the binding energy is Z^2 times the binding energy of the hydrogen atom, i.e., $= 4(-13.58 \text{ eV}) = -54.32$ eV. Between $r = 0$ and $r = \infty$, the energy of the electron changes between -54.32 eV and -13.58 eV as shown in Fig. 14.7, curve I[9]. But as the two protons are brought closer, the Coulomb repulsion increases and is given by

$$V_p = \frac{e^2}{4\pi\epsilon_0 r} \tag{14.8}$$

The plot of this is given by curve II in Fig. 14.8. Thus the net binding energy of the H_2^+ molecule in the ψ_S state is obtained by the addition of curves I and II, which is shown as curve III. As is obvious the maximum binding

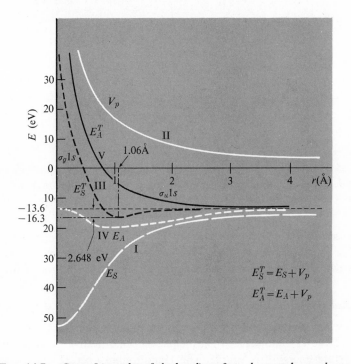

FIG. 14.7. *Curve I is a plot of the bonding of an electron due to the two protons, as a function of distance between them. Curve II is a plot of V_p, the repulsion between the two protons. Curve III is curve I plus curve II, i.e., $E_S^T = E_S + V_p$. Curve IV is the plot of the bonding of the electron resulting from the state ψ_A. Curve V is curve IV plus curve II, i.e., $E_A^T = E_A + V_p$. Because there is no minimum in the E_A^T curve, this state does not correspond to a stable configuration.*

energy occurs when $r = 1.06$ Å. The separation distance corresponding to the most stable position (for maximum binding energy) is called the *equilibrium distance*, r_0. The binding energy of the H_2^+ molecule is $-16.228 - (-13.58) = -2.648$ eV for the equilibrium distance $r_0 = 1.06$ Å. A similar procedure can be used for calculating the binding energy as a function of the proton separation distance for the ψ_A state. The results are shown in Fig. 14.7. Curve IV is the plot of bonding energy E_A of the electron resulting from the state ψ_A. As is obvious there is no minimum in the resultant curve for E_A^T (total), and hence the ψ_A (or $\sigma_u 1s$) state is not stable, or not bound.

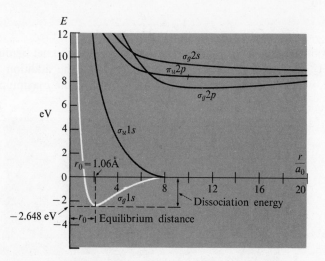

FIG. 14.8.   *Plots of electron potential energies in the H_2^+ molecule in different states. The equilibrium distance r_0 is 1.06 Å, while the dissociation energy is -2.648 eV.*

Figure 14.8 shows in addition to the ground-state electron potential-energy of the H_2^+ molecule, the potential energies of some excited states[10]. Also shown is the ground state binding energy and the equilibrium distance r_0.

C.   Calculation of the Ground-State Energy of H_2^+

So far we have limited our discussion to the qualitative nature of the binding energy of the H_2^+ molecule. In principle the quantitative evaluation of the ground-state energy[4] is simple. The Hamiltonian operator of the moving electron and the two protons at rest in the H_2^+ molecule, from Eq. (14.2), is given by

$$H = -\frac{\hbar^2}{2m} \nabla^2 + \frac{e^2}{4\pi\epsilon_0} \left(-\frac{1}{r_1} - \frac{1}{r_2} + \frac{1}{r} \right) \qquad (14.9)$$

where the first term on the right is the kinetic energy of the electron and the last three are the potential energy terms. Thus the average energy of the electron in H_2^+ is

$$E = \frac{\int \psi^* H \psi \, d\tau}{\int \psi^* \psi \, d\tau} \tag{14.10}$$

where ψ is either ψ_S or ψ_A given by Eqs. (14.6) and (14.7), i.e.,

$$\psi = \psi_S \approx (\psi_1 + \psi_2) \tag{14.11}$$

or

$$\psi = \psi_A \approx (\psi_1 - \psi_2) \tag{14.12}$$

Using the hydrogen atom $1s$-state wave function for ψ_1 and ψ_2, we can evaluate approximately the ground state energy[11,12] from Eq. (14.10). There is a reasonable agreement between theory and experiment.

3. COVALENT DIATOMIC MOLECULES[1]

A simple example of a diatomic molecule having covalent bonding is that of the H_2 molecule, a homonuclear molecule. The H_2 molecule, consisting of two protons and two electrons, is shown in Fig. 14.9. The total electrical potential energy of such a system is

$$V_T = \frac{e^2}{4\pi\epsilon_0} \left(-\frac{1}{r_{11}} - \frac{1}{r_{12}} - \frac{1}{r_{21}} - \frac{1}{r_{22}} + \frac{1}{r_e} + \frac{1}{r_p} \right) \tag{14.13}$$

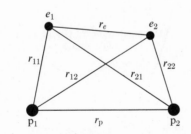

FIG. 14.9. *The hydrogen molecule, H_2.*

The first two terms on the right correspond to the interaction of proton p_1 with the two electrons; the third and fourth terms, that of the interaction of proton p_2 with the two electrons; the fifth term, the interaction between the two electrons; and the sixth term, that between the two protons. Thus the problem is to solve the Schrödinger wave equation. Because there are two electrons in the H_2 molecule, as compared to one electron in the H_2^+ molecule, the problem is much more complicated, yet simple enough so that it can be analyzed in great detail without actually solving the Schrödinger equation. We may point out that the formation of the H_2 molecule, by bringing two neutral hydrogen atoms together, cannot be explained by means of classical theories. Only by the use of the Schrödinger equation and the Pauli exclusion principle can the binding in the H_2 molecule be explained.

When the two hydrogen atoms are separated at a distance greater than 0.51 Å (the radius of the first Bohr-orbit), each electron is easily identified with its own nucleus. But when these atoms are brought closer, there is absolutely no way of identifying which electron is associated with which nucleus. According to the Pauli exclusion principle, both electrons in the H_2 molecule can be in the same orbital state ψ_{nlm_l} provided that their spins are antiparallel. We will expect that because there are two electrons, the binding energy of the H_2 molecule is twice that of the H_2^+ molecule, which has only one electron, i.e., $2(-2.648 \text{ eV}) = -5.296$ eV for H_2, and -2.648 eV for H_2^+. But the measured dissociation energy for the H_2 molecule is -4.476 eV. This difference is possible to explain by noting that the H_2 molecule differs from the H_2^+ in one important aspect. In the H_2 molecule, the Coulomb repulsion between the two electrons, which is absent in the H_2^+ molecule, reduces the binding energies. Similar considerations lead to the conclusion that the equilibrium distance, r_0, (or bond length) in H_2 is 0.74 Å, which is somewhat larger than that one obtains from wave functions of H_2^+. The results of the study of H_2^+ molecules can be extended further to say that as in the case of H_2^+, the symmetric state, ψ_S, of H_2 is stable, while the antisymmetric state, ψ_A, of H_2 is unstable. Figure 14.10 shows the variation

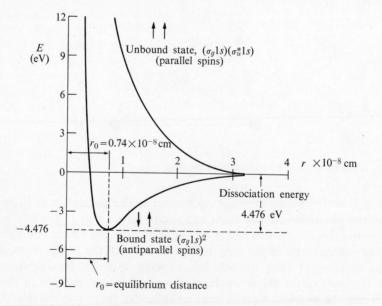

FIG. 14.10. *The variation of energy, E, as a function of the internuclear-separation distance, r, for bonding and antibonding states in H_2.*

of the energy of the system of two hydrogen atoms as a function of the separation distance between them[13]. As is obvious, the H_2 system with antiparallel electron spins is stable, while parallel electron spins lead to an unstable system. Remembering that the configuration of the electron in the stable (or bonding) state is denoted by $\sigma_g 1s$, while in the unstable (or antibonding) state it is denoted by $\sigma_u^* 1s$, the electron configuration of the H_2 molecule in the stable state is $(\sigma_g 1s)^2$ while in the unstable state it is $(\sigma_g 1s)(\sigma_u^* 1s)$. In general, we may say that molecular binding occurs when two electrons with opposite spins spend most of the time in the region between the two combining atoms.

There seems to be some discrepancy in the above conclusions when we say that the system with the symmetric wave function, ψ_S, is stable while the antisymmetric state, ψ_A, is unstable. According to the Pauli principle, the total wave function of a stable system must be antisymmetric. The apparent controversy is removed when we say that the total wave function of the system is not ψ only but a product of the spatial wave function, ψ, and a spin wave function, χ. Denoting the total wave function by $\Phi(x, y, z, s)$, we may write

$$\Phi(x, y, z, s) = \psi(x, y, z)\chi(s) \qquad (14.14)$$

According to Pauli, it is Φ that should be antisymmetric. This may be achieved by the following two combinations. Either

$$\Phi_A = \psi_A \chi_S \qquad (14.15)$$

or

$$\Phi_A = \psi_S \chi_A \qquad (14.16)$$

χ_S means a symmetric spin wave function, which is the case when the spins of two electrons are parallel ($\uparrow\uparrow$), because interchanging the two electrons will not change the sign of χ. On the other hand χ_A stands for the two electrons with antiparallel spins ($\uparrow\downarrow$), which results in a change of sign in χ if the two electrons are interchanged, and thus χ_A is antisymmetric. Hence both the configurations given by Eqs. (14.15) and (14.16) are possible and correspond to the antibonding and bonding states, respectively, in the H_2 molecule. We may point out that it is the application of the Pauli exclusion principle that leads to the difference in the energies of the two states.

We may now give some consideration to the type of forces that hold the H_2 molecule together. The energy responsible for such binding is called *exchange energy*[14], which is strictly a quantum-mechanical phenomenon without any classical analog. The exchange implied here is that of the spins of the two indistinguishable electrons. In the case of the H_2 molecule in the bonding state with the electrons having antiparallel spins, an electron spin pointing up ($\uparrow$) may suddenly change to a spin pointing down ($\downarrow$), while the other electron spin pointing down ($\downarrow$) simultaneously changes to a spin pointing up ($\uparrow$), i.e., the two electrons $\uparrow\downarrow$ change to $\downarrow\uparrow$. This exchange of spins results in a contribution to the binding of the H_2 molecule. The two antialigned electrons can be found simultaneously in between the two protons, which results in attractive forces for each electron with both protons.

The electron configurations, dissociation energies, and bond lengths of some diatomic molecules will be given later.

4. IONIC DIATOMIC MOLECULES[2]

Diatomic molecules, such as NaCl, HI, CO, and KCl, consist of two different nuclei. Such molecules are called *heteronuclear*, the formation of which is the result of heteropolar or ionic, binding, as we shall explain in this section. We may point out that molecular bonding may range from purely covalent, as in the case of H_2, where both the electrons are equally shared by both protons, to the purely ionic bonding as in the case of the NaCl. The formation of the NaCl molecule is the result of the shifting of an electron from a sodium atom to the chlorine atom; thus Na^+ and Cl^- ions are formed that attract electrostatically to form a stable NaCl molecule. In this process there is no electron sharing at all. The NaCl molecule is typical of the way ionic diatomic molecules are formed.

Atoms with completely filled electron subshells form the most stable electron configurations. Atoms with incomplete outer subshells tend to gain or lose electrons in order to attain stable configurations. Thus if two atoms are brought together and one gains an electron, becoming an electronegative ion, and the other loses an electron, becoming an electropositive ion, the resulting ions of opposite polarities will attract each other. If the attraction exceeds the Coulomb repulsion between the ions, a stable ionic molecular system will be formed. We shall illustrate this by discussing in detail the formation of the NaCl molecule.

The sodium atom $_{11}Na$, consisting of 11 electrons, belongs to the alkali-metal group, the first group of the periodic table, and has the electron configuration $1s^2 2s^2 2p^6 3s^1$. The single 3s-electron is very weakly bound and can be removed by adding energy in the amount of 5.1 eV, which will ionize the atom, leaving a charge of $+1e$. This may be represented as

$$Na + 5.1\ eV = Na^+ + e^- \qquad (14.17)$$

Because alkali metals easily lose electrons to form positive ions, they are said to be *electropositive*.

The chlorine atom $_{17}Cl$, consisting of 17 electrons, belongs to the seventh group of the periodic table, and has the electron configuration $1s^2 2s^2 2p^6 3s^2 3p^5$. As is obvious, the neutral chlorine atom lacks one electron to complete the 3p-subshell and form a tightly bound system. Thus when a chlorine atom captures an electron, Cl^- is formed, and energy in the amount of 3.8 eV is given out. This may be represented as

$$Cl + e^- = Cl^- + 3.6\ eV \qquad (14.18)$$

The Cl⁻ ion formed is said to be *electronegative* and has an *electron-affinity energy* of 3.6 eV. (Similar remarks apply to the halogens in general.)

Combining Eqs. (14.17) and (14.18) gives

$$Na + Cl + 1.5 \text{ eV} = Na^+ + Cl^- \tag{14.19}$$

which states that if 1.5 eV energy is supplied to neutral Na and Cl atoms, Na^+ and Cl^- ions will be formed as illustrated in Fig. 14.11. Of course, it is assumed that Na^+ and Cl^- are separated by a large distance so that they do not interact.

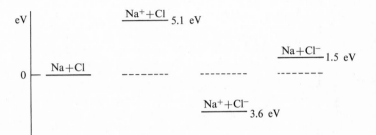

FIG. 14.11. *Energy differences of sodium and chlorine atoms and ions.*

Let us now bring Na^+ and Cl^- closer, say, to a separation distance of 4 Å. Electrostatic attraction will take place and the amount of energy given out will be equal to the potential energy between $+e$ and $-e$ separated by a distance of 4 Å, i.e.,

$$V = -\frac{1}{4\pi\epsilon_0}\left(\frac{e^2}{r}\right) = -9 \times 10^9 \text{ n-m}^2/\text{coul}^2 \times \frac{(1.6 \times 10^{-19} \text{ coul})^2}{4 \times 10^{-10} \text{ m}} \tag{14.20}$$

$$= -3.6 \text{ eV}$$

Thus at a distance of 4 Å, Eq. (14.19) takes the form

$$Na + Cl + 1.5 \text{ eV} = \overset{\longleftarrow 4\text{ Å} \longrightarrow}{(Na^+ + Cl^-)} + 3.6 \text{ eV}$$

which is the same as

$$Na + Cl = \overset{\longleftarrow 4\text{ Å} \longrightarrow}{(Na^+ + Cl^-)} + 2.1 \text{ eV} \tag{14.21}$$

Because the net result at a distance of 4 Å between the Na^+ and Cl^- ions is attraction, an amount of energy 2.1 eV is emitted, thus resulting in a stable system, i.e., the NaCl molecule. Figure 14.12 shows the variation in energy as a function of the separation distance. The equilibrium distance in the NaCl molecule is 2.51 Å, corresponding to the minimum in energy, while the dissociation energy is -3.58 eV. If the two ions are brought closer than the equilibrium distance, r_0, the repulsion between the two nuclei and the electronic shells exceeds the ionic attraction, as shown in Fig. 14.12. (Note that

NaCl molecules exist as independent units only in the gaseous state and not in the crystal form.) If the separation $r = \infty$, $V = -1.42$ eV, as shown in Fig. 14.12, and there is no attraction.

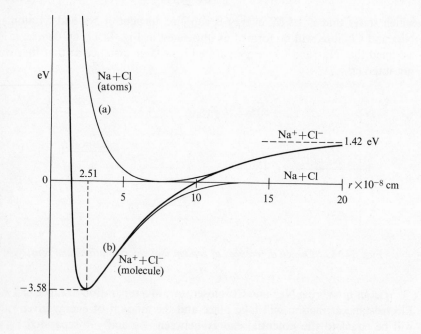

FIG. 14.12. *The variation of potential energy with separation distance for the systems* (a) *Na and Cl atoms, and* (b) *Na^+ and Cl^- ions.*

In the case of covalent bonding, as in H_2, the electrons are shared equally by both the nuclei, and hence the charge distribution is symmetric. In the case of ionic molecules, because of the transfer of electrons, the resulting charge distribution is uneven, i.e., unsymmetric, and the molecule is polarized. Because of the unsymmetric charge distribution, ionic molecules have electric dipole moments associated with them. Table 14.1 lists some covalent and ionic molecules together with their bond lengths, dissociation energies, and electric dipole-moments (if any).

Because of the unsymmetric charge distribution, the molecular orbital (or wave function) of a heteronuclear diatomic molecule (ionic molecule) cannot be expressed by the wave function of the type given in Eqs. (14.6) and (14.7) for the covalent molecule. If ψ_A and ψ_B are the atomic wave functions of the electrons associated with the atoms A and B in the diatomic molecule, the molecular orbital ψ is given by

$$\psi = \psi_A + \lambda\psi_B \qquad (14.22)$$

TABLE 14.1

BOND LENGTHS, DISSOCIATION ENERGIES, AND ELECTRIC
DIPOLE MOMENTS OF SOME DIATOMIC MOLECULES

Molecules	Bond lengths r_0 in Å	Dissociation energies in eV	Electric dipole moments in debyes (D)*
A. Covalent			
H_2	0.74	4.48	0
N_2	1.09	7.37	0
O_2	1.21	5.08	0
NO	1.15	5.3	0.15
HI	1.61	3.06	0.38
B. Ionic			
HCl	1.27	4.43	1.07
NaCl	2.51	3.58	8.5
KCl	2.79	4.92	8.0
KI	3.23	3.0	9.24
CsCl	3.06	3.76	9.97

* $1\ D = 3.3 \times 10^{-30}$ m-coul.

The value of λ is such that it gives the correct energy of the system. By changing the value of λ, the charge distribution may be enhanced in the desired region.

5. CONFIGURATIONS AND THEORIES OF MOLECULAR BONDING[11,14,15,16]

So far we have been considering only the two simplest molecular systems involving covalent and the ionic bonding. In this section we shall extend these to more complicated systems. Before investigating different theories of molecular structure, we must realize that whenever we work with more than one electron in a system we must impose the Pauli exclusion principle, and must take into account the spin as well as the orbital motion of electrons in the molecule. Hence we shall briefly introduce the notation used in the electron configuration of the molecules.

It is clear from our previous discussion that in any linear molecule (or diatomic molecule) electrons do not move in a central field of force. This implies that the angular momentum, L, of an electron does not remain constant during its motion. But the resultant force acting on the electron always passes through the line joining the nuclei in the linear molecule. This is illustrated in Fig. 14.13(a) in the case of a diatomic molecule. The line joining the nuclei is denoted as the Z axis, and hence the fact that the resultant force, **F**, passes through the Z axis implies that it is an *axial force*. The torque acting on the electron with respect to 0 will be perpendicular to the Z axis, and therefore the component of the angular momentum, **L**, parallel to the Z axis, denoted by L_Z, will be constant as shown in Fig.

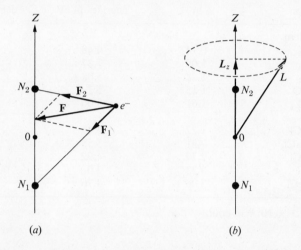

(a)   (b)

Fɪɢ. 14.13.   (a) *The resultant force acting on an electron always passes through the line joining the nuclei as shown.* (b) *The orbital angular-momentum of an electron in a diatomic molecule.*

14.13(b). Thus if l is the orbital quantum number of the electron, $L = \sqrt{l(l+1)}\,\hbar$ and $L_Z = m_l\hbar$, where $m_l = 0, \pm1, \pm2, \pm3, \ldots$. The sign of m_l determines the sense of rotation, clockwise or counterclockwise, about the Z axis. Because the energy of the electron is independent of the sense of rotation, in order to specify the state of the electron we need to give only the magnitude of m_l, which is denoted by λ, i.e., $\lambda = |m_l|$. Designations of different angular-momentum states is given in Table 14.2; also shown is the designation for the multielectron molecular systems.

TABLE 14.2
DESIGNATION OF ANGULAR-MOMENTUM STATES

For a single electron			For more than one electron		
m_l	$\lambda = |m_l|$	Symbol	$m_{l_t} = \sum\limits_i m_{li}$	$\Lambda = |m_{l_t}|$	Symbol
0	0	σ	0	0	Σ
±1	1	π	±1	1	Π
±2	2	δ	±2	2	Δ
±3	3	ϕ	±3	3	Φ

The state σ has only one m_l value while all other states, π, δ, ϕ, $\ldots$, have two values of m_l, and hence except for the σ state all states are doubly degenerate. In the σ state we can have two electrons, one spin pointing up and one spin pointing down, corresponding to $m_s = +\frac{1}{2}$ and $m_s = -\frac{1}{2}$. We can have four electrons in all the other states, π, δ, ϕ, $\ldots$; i.e., each of the two degenerate states having two electron spins, one pointing up ($m_s = +\frac{1}{2}$) and one pointing down ($m_s = -\frac{1}{2}$). A notation used for describing the molecular orbital states of the electron is λnl where nl describes the atomic orbitals from which the molecular orbit λ has been formed by a linear combination. Each of the molecular states such as σnl, πnl, and δnl corresponds to a different energy. The orbital states of the homonuclear molecules described by the even-wave function, ψ_{even}, are called g-states (g standing for *gerade*, a German word meaning even); and the orbital states described by the odd-wave function, ψ_{odd}, are called u-states (u standing for *ungerade*, a German word meaning odd). Thus this explains the notation σ_g, σ_u, $\ldots$, used earlier. Similar meaning holds for π_g, π_u, δ_g, δ_u, etc. (As usual * indicates excited state.) Table 14.3 gives the electron configuration of some homonuclear diatomic molecules using this notation.

We are now in a position to discuss the electronic structure of molecules from a theoretical point of view. Two different methods, which have been discussed to some extent already, commonly employed are: (A) valence-bonding, and (B) molecular orbitals. In the valence-bonding approach, a molecule is assumed to consist of individual atoms that are held together by localized covalent bonds. In the molecular-orbital approach, a molecule is an entity by itself consisting of nuclei and electrons, with no room for individual identity of the atoms. In valence-bonding the orbitals belong to the individual atoms, while in molecular orbitals method the orbitals belong to the molecule. Usually the calculations carried on by either method are very complex and the results in both the cases are the same, with some minor exceptions.

A. The Valence-Bond Method

A covalent bond by which two atoms are supposed to be held together, consists of two electrons with antiparallel spins. The electrons are contributed one from each atom and spend more time, on the average, between the atoms. Each shared pair of electrons is represented graphically by a dash or two dots between the atoms held by the bond. For example, H_2 bonded by one pair of electrons, O_2 bonded by two pairs of electrons, and N_2 by three pairs of electrons are represented, respectively, by

$$H{-}H \qquad O{=}O \qquad N{\equiv}N$$

or

$$H:H \qquad O::O \qquad N:::N$$

Thus, in order to form a bond between two atoms, each atom must have

TABLE 14.3

ELECTRONIC CONFIGURATION OF SOME HOMONUCLEAR DIATOMIC MOLECULES

Molecule	Configuration								Ground state	Dissociation energy (eV)	Bond length (Å)
	$1s$ σ_g	$1s$ σ_u^*	$2s$ σ_g	$2s$ σ_u^*	$2p$ π_u	$2p$ σ_g	$2p$ π_g^*	$2p$ σ_u^*			
hydrogen-ion H_2^+	↑								$^2\Sigma_g$	2.6	1.06
hydrogen H_2	↑↓								$^1\Sigma_g$	4.5	0.74
helium-ion He_2^+	↑↓	↑							$^2\Sigma_u$	3.1	1.08
helium He_2	↑↓	↑↓							$^1\Sigma_g$	unstable	—
lithium Li_2	↑↓	↑↓	↑↓						$^1\Sigma_g$	1.03	2.67
beryllium Be_2	↑↓	↑↓	↑↓	↑↓					$^1\Sigma_g$	unstable	—
boron B_2	↑↓	↑↓	↑↓	↑↓	↑ ↑				$^3\Sigma_g$	3.0	1.59
carbon C_2	↑↓	↑↓	↑↓	↑↓	↑↓ ↑↓				$^1\Sigma_g$	6.5	1.3
nitrogen N_2	↑↓	↑↓	↑↓	↑↓	↑↓ ↑↓	↑↓			$^1\Sigma_g$	7.37	1.09
oxygen O_2	↑↓	↑↓	↑↓	↑↓	↑↓ ↑↓	↑↓	↑ ↑		$^3\Sigma_g$	5.1	1.21
fluorine F_2	↑↓	↑↓	↑↓	↑↓	↑↓ ↑↓	↑↓	↑↓ ↑↓		$^1\Sigma_g$	2.8	1.44
neon Ne_2	↑↓	↑↓	↑↓	↑↓	↑↓ ↑↓	↑↓	↑↓ ↑↓	↑↓	$^1\Sigma_g$	unstable	—

at least one unpaired electron so that it can combine (antiparallel) with the unpaired electron of the other atom. Because in a closed subshell of an atom there are as many electrons with spins up as there are with spins down, there is no unpaired electron; hence such atoms do not form molecules. In an unfilled subshell, according to Hund's rule, there are as many electrons as possible with spins parallel. Thus in an s-subshell corresponding to $l = 0$, $m_l = 0$, there is only one s-orbital available for bonding. For a p-subshell, $l = 1$, and there are three p-orbitals corresponding to $m_l = 1, 0, -1$. Similarly for a d-subshell the maximum number of orbitals available is five, corresponding to $m_l = 2, 1, 0, -1, -2$. As an example, the number of unpaired electrons in the atoms of the first two periods of the periodic table are shown in Table 14.4; bond energies are also shown. As is obvious from

TABLE 14.4

STRUCTURE AND NUMBER OF UNPAIRED ELECTRONS
OF SOME DIATOMIC MOLECULES ACCORDING
TO THE VALENCE-BOND APPROACH

Element (Z)	Atomic configuration	Atomic orbitals					Unpaired electrons	Molecular structure
		$1s$	$2s$	$2p_x$	$2p_y$	$2p_z$		
H (1)	$1s$	↑	—	—	—	—	1	H—H
He (2)	$1s^2$	↑↓	—	—	—	—	0	unstable
Li (3)	$1s^22s$	↑↓	↑	—	—	—	1	Li—Li
Be (4)	$1s^22s^2$	↑↓	↑↓	—	—	—	0	unstable
B (5)	$1s^22s^22p$	↑↓	↑↓	↑	—	—	1	B—B
C (6)	$1s^22s^22p^2$	↑↓	↑↓	↑	↑	—	2	C=C
N (7)	$1s^22s^22p^3$	↑↓	↑↓	↑	↑	↑	3	N≡N
O (8)	$1s^22s^22p^4$	↑↓	↑↓	↑↓	↑	↑	2	O=O
F (9)	$1s^22s^22p^5$	↑↓	↑↓	↑↓	↑↓	↑	1	F—F
Ne (10)	$1s^22s^22p^6$	↑↓	↑↓	↑↓	↑↓	↑↓	0	unstable

the table, He ($Z = 2$) and Ne ($Z = 10$) do not have any unpaired electrons, and hence do not form molecules. Oxygen, with the configuration $1s^22s^22p^4$, has only two unpaired electrons available for forming two bonds; while fluorine $1s^22s^22p^5$ has only one unpaired electron.

One of the major assumptions of the valence-bond approach is that each bond formation is independent of the other bonds present. This assumption is very well justified, that molecules with a single bond have a bond energy between 1 and 3 eV; molecules with two bonds have bond energies $\sim$6 eV, while triply bonded molecules have bond energies $\sim$10 eV. We say that molecular forces saturate.

Of course, this approach is not without some shortcomings. As is obvious, any molecule formed will have zero net spin and hence zero net magnetic-moment. i.e., the molecules will be diamagnetic. On the contrary both O_2 and B_2 show paramagnetism. This and other discrepancies are accounted for by the molecular-orbital approach.

B. The Molecular-Orbital Method

According to this method, as explained in the case of H_2^+, atomic orbitals combine to form a molecular orbital. In order to understand how two atoms bond to form a molecule, it is obvious that we must know the variation of the electron probability distribution in space corresponding to each angular momentum state. The procedure for obtaining molecular orbitals is as follows: We consider two atoms separated by a large distance and picture the atomic orbitals associated with each atom. The technique of this method lies in guessing the form of the molecular orbital resulting from the linear combination of the atomic orbitals, ψ_1 and ψ_2, as the two atoms are brought together. We made use of this technique in constructing molecular orbitals of H_2^+ as shown in Fig. 14.6. The advantages of this method is the fact that it is not limited to diatomic molecules—it may extend to polyatomic molecules—and that it gives some physical picture of the situation.

Figure 14.14 illustrates the formation of molecular orbitals (wave functions) resulting from the linear combinations of different atomic orbitals. (Only the angular distributions of the wave functions, $\Theta\Phi$, are shown.) Figure 14.14(a) shows how two s atomic wave functions, ψ_1 and ψ_2, that are spherically symmetric may combine to yield $\psi_1 + \psi_2$ and $\psi_1 - \psi_2$, corresponding to the states denoted by σ_g and σ_u, respectively. (Note that the line joining the two nuclei is the Z axis, while σ corresponds to $\lambda = 0$.) Figure 14.14(b) shows two possible combinations of two p_z atomic orbitals, while Fig. 14.14(c) shows two possible combinations of two p_x or two p_y atomic orbitals. Furthermore, all these orbitals are modulated by the radial part $R(r)$ of the wave function ψ. The notation used for the molecular orbitals is the one already explained, i.e., $\lambda = 0, 1, 2, 3, \ldots$ stands for $\sigma, \pi, \delta, \ldots$, respectively; * in the superscript indicates an unbound state, g for even, or symmetric, wave function, and u for the odd, or antisymmetric, wave function. In the formation of a molecule, when the two atoms are brought together, their orbitals start overlapping. This overlapping may either *increase* the electron probability density between the atoms, a situation that corresponds to a *bonding molecular orbital*, while a *decrease* corresponds to an *antibonding molecular orbital*, as illustrated in Fig. 14.14.

Our next aim is to get some idea of the relative energies of the various molecular orbitals. This can be achieved by making a drawing of the type shown in Fig. 14.15. Consider the two atoms of a molecule under two extreme conditions corresponding to nuclear separation $r = 0$ and $r = \infty$. When $r = 0$, the molecule reduces to an atom. Make a plot of the energy levels of the combined atom for $r = 0$ on one side, and the energy levels of the separated atoms (in the homonuclear case) corresponding to $r = \infty$, on

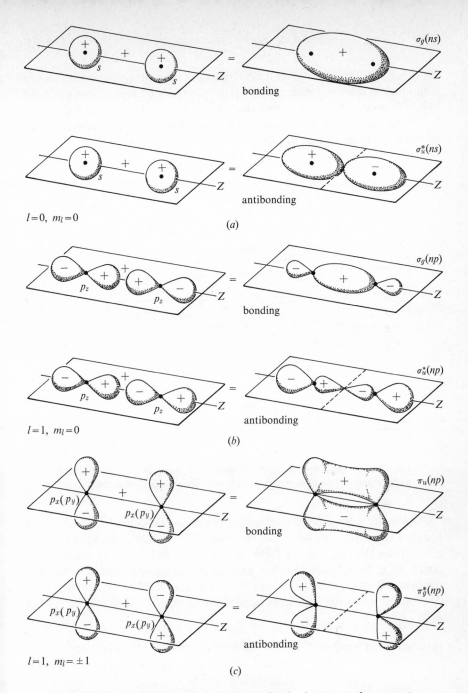

FIG. 14.14. *Formation of molecular orbitals from* s *and* p *atomic orbitals in homonuclear diatomic molecules.* (a) *The possible molecular orbitals from two* s *atomic orbitals.* (b) *The possible molecular orbitals from two* p_z *atomic orbitals.* (c) *The possible molecular orbitals from two* p_x *or two* p_y *atomic orbitals.* [*Reprinted by special permission from Alonso-Finn,* Fundamental University Physics, *vol. III, 1968, Addison-Wesley, Reading, Mass.*]

the other side. In order to conserve the symmetry or antisymmetry of the homonuclear diatomic molecule, we join the separated atomic levels and the united atomic levels of the same character. This is illustrated in Fig. 14.15. It is obvious that the order of levels in a particular molecule is determined by the nuclear separation distance, r.

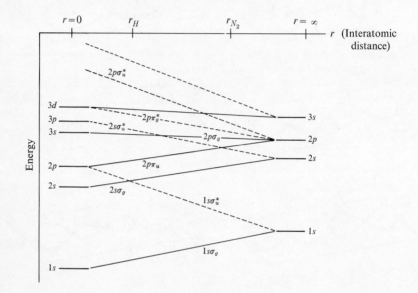

FIG. 14.15. *Relative energies of molecular orbitals as a function of nuclear separation distance, r, in diatomic homonuclear molecules.*

As in the valence-bond method, for the molecular-orbital method a bond between two atoms is due to two electrons. The molecular stability is determined from the fact whether these electrons lead to bonding or antibonding states. It is found that bonding and antibonding have almost equal but opposite effect on molecular stability. Thus the stability of a molecule is determined by the net number of bonds in its molecule, which may be defined as

$$\text{net number of bonds} = \frac{1}{2} \text{(the number of electrons in the bonding orbitals} - \text{the number of electrons in the antibonding orbitals)} \qquad (14.23)$$

Table 14.5 shows the electron configuration of molecules in the molecular-orbital approach. As we see, we get the same number of bonds as before, but the formation of B_2 and O_2 molecules leads to two unpaired electrons in each case. This is because $2p_x\pi_u$ and $2p_y\pi_u$ have the same energy, and so of the two available electrons, one goes into each orbit. The unpairing of

TABLE 14.5

ELECTRON CONFIGURATION OF SOME HOMONUCLEAR DIATOMIC MOLECULES
ACCORDING TO THE MOLECULAR-ORBITAL APPROACH

Molecule	Molecular configuration										Net number of bonds	Molecular structure
	$1s$		$2s$		$2p_x$		$2p_y$		$2p_z$			
	g	u	g	u	g	u	g	u	g	u		
H_2	σ^2										1	H—H
He_2	σ^2	σ^{*2}									0	unstable
Li_2	σ^2	σ^{*2}	σ^2								1	Li—Li
Be_2	σ^2	σ^{*2}	σ^2	σ^{*2}							0	unstable
B_2	σ^2	σ^{*2}	σ^2	σ^{*2}	π		π				1	B—B
C_2	σ^2	σ^{*2}	σ^2	σ^{*2}	π^2		π^2				2	C=C
N_2	σ^2	σ^{*2}	σ^2	σ^{*2}	π^2		π^2		σ^2		3	N≡N
O_2	σ^2	σ^{*2}	σ^2	σ^{*2}	π^2	π^*	π^2	π^*	σ^2		2	O=O
F_2	σ^2	σ^{*2}	σ^2	σ^{*2}	π^2	π^{*2}	π^2	π^{*2}	σ^2		1	F—F
Ne_2	σ^2	σ^{*2}	σ^2	σ^{*2}	π^2	π^{*2}	π^2	π^{*2}	σ^2	σ^{*2}	0	unstable

electrons in B_2 and O_2 explained the observed paramagnetism in these two cases.

So far we have been talking about the molecular orbitals of homonuclear diatomic molecules. It is easy to extend these methods of obtaining molecular orbitals in the case of heteronuclear diatomic molecules. In heteronuclear molecules, the characteristics of the combining atomic orbitals may be altogether different. For example, in the case of the HF (hydrogen fluoride) molecule, the $1s$ atomic orbital of the H atom combines with the $2p_z$ orbital of the F atom, each containing one electron. As shown in Fig. 14.16 there

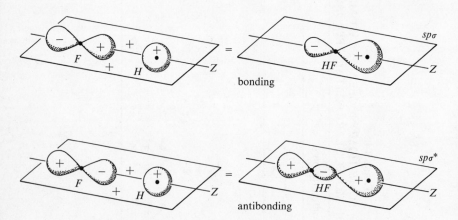

FIG. 14.16. *Is orbital of H, and $2p_z$ orbital of F, combine to form bonding and antibonding molecular orbitals in HF.*

are two possible combinations of $1s$ and $2p_z$, resulting in a bonding molecular orbital, $sp\sigma$, and an antibonding molecular orbital, $sp\sigma^*$. Once again the $sp\sigma$ molecular orbital is occupied by two electrons, meaning thereby that the HF molecule is held by a single bond.

6. POLYATOMIC AND CONJUGATED MOLECULES[17,18]

The basic principle in the formation of polyatomic molecules is that *bonding is favored whenever the sharing electrons spend most of their time between two joining atoms.* In terms of wave functions we may state this by saying that bonding is favored if the atomic orbitals of the atoms forming the molecular orbital are concentrated between the two atoms. The degree of overlapping of the orbitals (or wave functions) determines the strength of the bond. This is the so called principle of *maximum overlapping* of atomic wave functions in forming molecular orbitals.

Another factor that must be taken into consideration whenever we are dealing with more than two atoms is the geometric arrangement of the electrons and the nuclei, i.e., molecular symmetry has to be taken into consideration. We shall see the application of these points in considering the structure of different molecules, which may be conveniently divided into the following two types: (A) simple $sp\sigma$ bonding, and (B) hybrid orbitals.

A.   Simple $sp\sigma$ Bonding[19]

The capability of three p atomic orbitals to combine with s atomic orbitals to form molecular orbitals, as shown in Fig. 14.16 in the case of the HF molecule, helps in understanding the structure of polyatomic molecules.

Let us consider the structure of the H_2O molecule first. We might be tempted to say that the structure of the H_2O molecule is linear, i.e., H—O—H, but as we shall see it is not true. The oxygen atom, consisting of eight electrons, has a configuration of $1s^2 2s^2 2p^4$. Except for the last two electrons in the L-shell, the other six are paired off and to a first approximation may be ignored. The last two electrons, as seen from Table 14.4, must be parallel and in different p-states. We may assume that one electron is somewhere along the X axis while the other along the Y axis, i.e., in the states p_x and p_y, respectively, as shown in Fig. 14.17. (Note that the other two

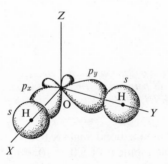

FIG. 14.17.   *Electronic distribution and structure of the H_2O molecule.* [*Reprinted by special permission from Alonso-Finn,* Fundamental University Physics, *vol. III, 1968, Addison-Wesley, Reading, Mass.*]

p-electrons are paired off along the Z axis.) The two H atoms, each with one $1s$-electron, have formed bonds with the oxygen atom in such a way that there is a maximum overlapping of the wave functions. This is achieved by placing the $1s$-electron of H along the X and Y axes as shown in Fig. 14.17. This gives a sp-type bonding. Thus we have an H_2O molecule with a right-angle shape in the form

$$O—H$$
$$|$$
$$H$$

(14.24)

The angle between the two O—H bonds is not 90° but slightly greater, i.e., 104.5°, because of the Coulomb repulsion between the two hydrogen atoms. That this larger angle is due to the Coulomb repulsion is verified from molecules such as H_2Se and H_2S where H atoms are separated by larger distances from the large atoms Se and S so that there is less Coulomb repulsion, resulting in 90° and 92° bond angles, respectively.

The presence of the H atoms in H_2O deforms, or polarizes, the motion of the p-electrons in the O atom, i.e., the centers of mass of the negative and the positive charges do not coincide. This in turn leads to a net electric dipole moment of the order of 6.2×10^{-30} mC (meter coulomb) for the H_2O molecule along the line bisecting the bond angle.

Let us consider the NH_3 molecule. Three unpaired p-electron orbitals of N, occupying states $2p_x, 2p_y, 2p_z$, combine with each $1s$ orbital of hydrogen forming $sp\sigma$ bonds, resulting in the pyramidal shape of the ammonia molecule, with the N atom at one vertex and the H atoms at the base vertices, as shown in Fig. 14.18. Instead of 90°, the bond angles are 107.3°, as in the case

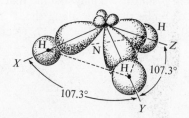

FIG. 14.18. *Electronic distribution and structure of the NH_3 molecule. [Reprinted by special permission from Alonso-Finn*, Fundamental University Physics, *vol. III, 1968, Addison-Wesley, Reading, Mass.]*

of the H_2O molecule where the bond angle is 104.5°. The molecule is polarized with a net electric dipole moment of 5.0×10^{-30} mC directed along the axis of the pyramid. The dipole moments for linear or coplanar molecules are zero.

B. Hybrid Orbitals[20]

The ideas of simple $sp\sigma$-bonding cannot be applied to the formation of molecules of the form CH_4. A carbon atom has two electrons in the $1s$-state, and one each in the $2p_x$ and $2p_y$ states. Thus we would expect carbon to form molecules of the type CH_2 with a bond angle of 90°. But this is not so. Carbon does form stable CH_4 (methane) molecules, and we must theoretically justify such a structure. It is possible to explain this by the technique called *hybridization of wave functions*, which generates new wave functions by the combination of atomic wave functions as explained below.

In carbon, the $2s$-state lies very close to the p-state. For example, in the excited state of carbon there is one electron in the $2s$-state and three electrons are one each in the $2p_x$, $2p_y$, and $2p_z$ states. The linear combinations of these four orbitals corresponding to s, p_x, p_y, and p_z result in the following new wave functions given by

$$\psi_1 = \frac{1}{2}[\psi_s + \psi_{p_x} + \psi_{p_y} + \psi_{p_z}]$$

$$\psi_2 = \frac{1}{2}[\psi_s + \psi_{p_x} - \psi_{p_y} - \psi_{p_z}]$$

$$\psi_3 = \frac{1}{2}[\psi_s - \psi_{p_x} + \psi_{p_y} - \psi_{p_z}]$$

$$\psi_4 = \frac{1}{2}[\psi_s - \psi_{p_x} - \psi_{p_y} + \psi_{p_z}]$$

(14.24)

These new functions are called the hybrid wave functions. The formation of hybrid wave functions in C is shown in Fig. 14.19. The maxima of the

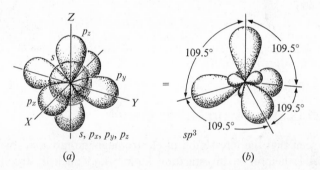

FIG. 14.19. *The sp^3 hybrid wave functions resulting from linear combinations of the orbitals of s, p_x, p_y, and p_z. (a) Before combination. (b) After combination. [Reprinted by special permission from Alonso-Finn, Fundamental University Physics, vol. III, 1968, Addison-Wesley, Reading, Mass.]*

hybrid wave functions are pronounced toward the vertices of a tetrahedron. The angles between the directions of these maxima are $109° 28'$. Note that the energies of all the hybrid wave functions thus formed are the same. Because hybrid wave functions are formed from s- and p-functions, which correspond to different angular-momentum states, the hybrid wave functions do not correspond to well-defined angular momentum states. This type of hybridization is denoted by sp^3. It readily explains not only the formation of CH_4 and C_2H_6 ($H_3C—CH_3$, methane) molecules as shown in Fig. 14.20, but also many others.

In addition to sp^3, we may have hybridization of the type sp^2 and sp in a manner similar to that of sp^3. Some examples of sp^2 and sp types are ethylene and acetylene, respectively. We could extend our discussion to other types of molecules, called *conjugate molecules*, such as C_4H_6 (butadiene), and *cyclic conjugate molecules*, such as C_6H_6 (benzene), and others.

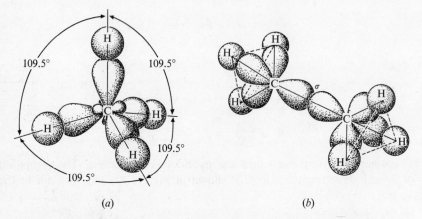

(a)   (b)

FIG. 14.20.   *Examples of localized sp^3 molecular orbitals in* (a) *methane, CH_4 and* (b) *ethane, C_2H_6.* [*Reprinted by special permission from Alonso-Finn,* Fundamental University Physics, *vol. III, 1968, Addison-Wesley, Reading, Mass.*]

7.   MOLECULAR ROTATIONAL SPECTRA[21]

We have seen that the interaction of electromagnetic radiations with atoms and nuclei is helpful in investigating atomic and nuclear structure. In a similar fashion, by analyzing electromagnetic radiations emitted by molecules, we may learn the nature of molecular structure.

The simplest motion that a diatomic molecule can execute as a whole is that of pure rotation about a center of mass, as shown in Fig. 14.21.

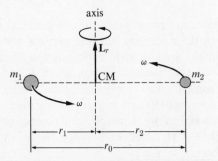

FIG. 14.21.   *Rotational motion of a diatomic molecule about its center of mass.*

Because the mass of the electron is negligible, we may consider only the masses m_1 and m_2 of the two nuclei. Let the masses m_1 and m_2 be located at distances r_1 and r_2, respectively, from the center of mass, and let r_0 be the distance between the two masses so that $r_0 = r_1 + r_2$. From the definition of center of mass

$$m_1 r_1 = m_2 r_2 \qquad (14.26)$$

The moment of inertia, I, of the molecule about an axis perpendicular to the line joining the two masses and passing through the center of mass, as shown in Fig. 14.21, is given by

$$I = \Sigma_i m_i r_i^2 = m_1 r_1^2 + m_2 r_2^2 \qquad (14.27)$$

Combining Eqs. (14.26) and (14.27), we get

$$I = \left(\frac{m_1 m_2}{m_1 + m_2}\right)(r_1 + r_2)^2 \qquad (14.28)$$

or

$$I = \mu r_0^2 \qquad (14.29)$$

where $\mu \; (= m_1 m_2 / m_1 + m_2)$ is the reduced mass of the molecule, and $r_0 = r_1 + r_2$. Equation (14.28) and Eq. (14.29) mean that the motion of two masses both rotating at the same angular frequency, ω, about the center of mass is equivalent to the rotation of a single particle of mass μ with angular frequency, ω, about an axis located a distance r_0 from μ. Note that because of the small size of the nuclei and negligible mass of the electrons, the moment of inertia along the interatomic axis is negligible.

The angular momentum L_r of the molecule is, therefore, given by

$$L_r = I\omega \qquad (14.30)$$

In Chapter IX we showed that the orbital angular-momentum, L, of an electron in the hydrogen atom is quantized and can have only the values

$$L = \sqrt{l(l + 1)}\, \hbar \qquad (14.31)$$

where $l = 0, 1, 2, 3, 4, \ldots$. Similarly, the angular momentum L_r of the molecule is quantized and is given by

$$L_r = \sqrt{K(K + 1)}\, \hbar \qquad (14.32)$$

where K is the *rotational quantum number* and can take the integral values $K = 0, 1, 2, 3, \ldots$.

We are now in a position to calculate the energies of the possible rotational levels. The total rotational energy, E_r, of a rotating molecule is thus given by

$$E_r = \frac{1}{2} I\omega^2 = \frac{(I\omega)^2}{2I} = \frac{L_r^2}{2I} \qquad (14.33)$$

Substituting the value of L_r from Eq. (14.32), we get

$$E_r = K(K + 1)\frac{\hbar^2}{2I} \qquad (14.34)$$

Thus the possible energy levels are obtained by substituting for K, resulting in $E_r = 0,\ 2(\hbar^2/2I),\ 6(\hbar^2/2I),\ 12(\hbar^2/2I),\ 20(\hbar^2/2I),\ 30(\hbar^2/2I),\ \dots$, for $K = 0, 1, 2, 3, 4, 5, \dots$, respectively, as shown in Fig. 14.22. Note that the rotational energy levels get farther apart as the energy increases with increasing value of the quantum number K.

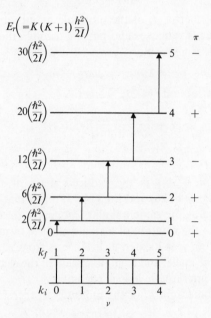

FIG. 14.22. *Rotational energy-level diagram and pure rotational absorption spectrum of a diatomic molecule.*

By making electromagnetic radiation incident on a sample of diatomic molecular gas, we can observe the absorption spectra of the molecules. The frequencies of such absorption lines resulting from molecular rotation may be calculated in a simple manner. Let us consider a transition between a lower rotational energy state, E_i, and the upper final rotational energy state, E_f. Such a transition will occur by the absorption of a photon of energy $h\nu$ given by

$$h\nu = E_f - E_i = [K_f(K_f + 1) - K_i(K_i + 1)]\frac{\hbar^2}{2I} \tag{14.35}$$

The selection rule for the rotational transition is

$$\Delta K = \pm 1 \tag{14.36}$$

This implies that the only possible transitions are those between adjacent levels. Thus if $K_i = K$, $K_f = K + 1$, and Eq. (14.35) takes the form

$$\nu = (K + 1)\frac{\hbar}{2\pi I} \tag{14.37}$$

Thus for $K = 0, 1, 2, 3, 4, \ldots, \nu = (\hbar/2\pi I), 2(\hbar/2\pi I), 3(\hbar/2\pi I), 4(\hbar/2\pi I),$ $5(\hbar/2\pi I), \ldots$, respectively, which implies that the rotational spectrum resulting from transitions from different possible levels are equally spaced lines as shown in Fig. 14.22, where the absorption spectrum of a typical diatomic molecule is shown. The frequencies of these lines fall in the far-infrared and microwave regions of the electromagnetic spectrum corresponding to a wavelength range from 10^{-3} cm to 10 cm.

It is usually easier, as we have implied above, to investigate the absorption spectra instead of emission spectra of diatomic molecules. Because for absorption spectra $\Delta K = +1$ (for emission $\Delta K = -1$), one would think that one could have only an absorption line corresponding to the transition $K_i = 0$ to $K_f = 1$ because the molecules may be all in the ground state corresponding to $K_i = 0$. But this is not true as we shall show. Corresponding to a wavelength, say 1 cm, the energy separation between the levels is

$$\Delta E = h\nu = \frac{hc}{\lambda} = \frac{6.6 \times 10^{-34} \times 10^8}{10^{-2}} \approx 2 \times 10^{-23} \text{ joule} \simeq 10^{-4} \text{ eV}$$

while at room temperature the molecules of a gas have kinetic energies on the order of

$$\text{KE} = \frac{3}{2} kT = \frac{3}{2} \times 1.4 \times 10^{-23} \times 300 \simeq 6 \times 10^{-21} \text{ joule} \simeq 4 \times 10^{-2} \text{ eV}$$

which is much larger than 10^{-4} eV (by a factor of 400) and implies that even at room temperature quite a substantial fraction of the molecules are in the higher rotational state, and hence transitions other than $K_i = 0$ to $K_f = 1$ are observed in the absorption spectra (or emission spectra).

In order to observe a pure rotational spectrum, the diatomic molecule must have a permanent electric dipole moment. The pure rotational emission spectrum results from the rotation of such an electric dipole, while the absorption spectrum results from the interaction of the incident photon with a permanent electric dipole. Because homopolar, or covalent, molecules do not have permanent electric dipole moments, they do not produce pure rotational spectra. On the other hand, the heteropolar, or ionic, molecules do have permanent electric dipole moments and hence exhibit pure rotational spectra. As an example, Fig. 14.23 shows a pure rotational absorption spectrum of HCl molecules[22] in the gaseous phase. The frequencies of the absorption peaks are given by Eq. (14.37) for $K = 1, 2, 3, 4, \ldots$.

By measuring the space between the rotational absorption lines for a particular type of molecule, we can find the moment of inertia, I, from Eq. (14.37). Because $I = \mu r_0^2$, if we know the atomic masses, we can find the reduced mass and hence the value of r_0, the bond length, between the nuclei of the two atoms in the molecule. Thus for an HCl molecule $r_0 = 1.3$ Å, and in a CO molecule $r_0 = 1.1$ Å.

In the case of triatomic molecules, the calculations are much more complicated, but one gets more information about the structure as well. For example, in the case of a nonlinear triatomic molecule one can find the bond length r_{01}, r_{02}, and the angle θ between them.

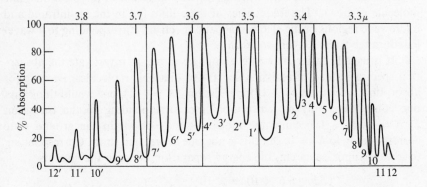

FIG. 14.23. *Pure rotational absorption spectrum resulting from HCl molecules in gaseous state.* [*Reprinted with permission: G. Herzberg, Molecular Spectra and Molecular Structure, New York: Van Nostrand, 1939.*]

8. MOLECULAR VIBRATIONAL SPECTRA[23]

So far we have been considering the rotation of the nuclei in the molecule about their center of mass, assuming that the nuclei do not vibrate about their equilibrium distance, r_0, which is fixed. But this is not true, and the two atoms in a diatomic molecule do vibrate, and the resulting displacement measured from r_0 is $(r - r_0)$ while the potential $V(r)$ between the atoms of a molecule changes as already shown in Fig. 14.8 and again reproduced in Fig. 14.24 as the unbroken line curve. The vibrations of such a diatomic molecule may be thought of as if the two atoms were joined by a spring, and the stretching and contracting of the spring results in the vibrations. Of course, in the diatomic molecule it is the chemical binding force, that behaves like a spring. Thus when the molecule absorbs a photon, the energy absorbed is converted to vibrational energy of the molecules. The molecular vibration absorption (or emission) spectra are observed in the infrared region, and covers a range starting from the end of the visible at about 7000 Å to the microwave region starting at 1000 microns, i.e., from 7×10^{-5} cm to 10^{-1} cm.

Before considering the case of a vibrating diatomic molecule, we shall review the classical example of a mass m tied to an "ideal" spring that obeys Hooke's law in the x direction about an equilibrium position x_0, as shown in Fig. 14.25. According to Hooke's law, the force is directly proportional to the displacement and is given by

$$F = -C(x - x_0) \qquad (14.38)$$

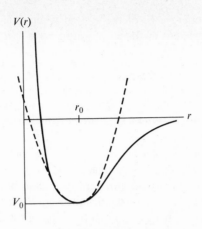

FIG. 14.24.   *Actual potential $V(r)$ between the two atoms of a diatomic molecule is represented by a continuous line; the broken line is the parabolic approximation of the actual potential.*

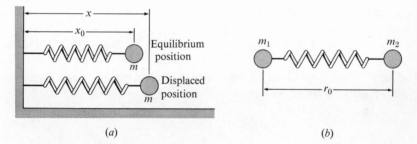

(a)   (b)

FIG. 14.25.   (a) *Vibrations of a mass, m, tied to an "ideal" spring obeying Hooke's law.* (b) *Equivalent diatomic molecule.*

where C is a force constant. Substituting $F = m(d^2x/dt^2)$, the equation of motion of mass m becomes

$$m\frac{d^2x}{dt^2} + C(x - x_0) = 0 \qquad (14.39)$$

which has a solution

$$x - x_0 = A \cos \sqrt{\frac{C}{m}}\, t \qquad (14.40)$$

where A is a constant. Thus the classical vibrational frequency is given by

$$\nu_c = \frac{\omega}{2\pi} = \frac{1}{2\pi} \sqrt{\frac{C}{m}} \qquad (14.41)$$

while the potential energy, V, of the system when m is at x (assuming the potential energy to be zero at the equilibrium x_0) is

$$V(x) = \int_{x_0}^{x} - F(x)\, dx = C \int_{x_0}^{x} (x - x_0)\, dx = \frac{1}{2} C(x - x_0)^2$$

i.e.,

$$V(x) = \frac{1}{2} C(x - x_0)^2 \qquad (14.42)$$

which is an equation of a parabola in which the potential energy $V(x)$ is proportional to the square of the displacement from the equilibrium.

Now we shall return to the problem of a diatomic molecule in which the atoms attract each other at large distances and repel each other at small distances. The potential energy $V(r)$ as a function of the separation distance r between the atoms is shown in Fig. 14.24. If we expand $V(r)$ in a Taylor's series around the equilibrium (minimum) position r_0, we get

$$V(r) = V(r_0) + (r - r_0)\left[\frac{dV(r)}{dr}\right]_{r=r_0} + \frac{1}{2}(r - r_0)^2 \left[\frac{d^2V(r)}{dr^2}\right]_{r=r_0} + \dots \quad (14.43)$$

For small displacements we can neglect the higher terms. Because $V(r)$ has zero slope at $r = r_0$, therefore, $[dV(r)/dr]_{r=r_0} = 0$. Hence

$$V(r) = V(r_0) + \frac{1}{2}(r - r_0)^2 \left[\frac{d^2V(r)}{dr^2}\right]_{r=r_0} \qquad (14.44)$$

The term $V(r_0)$ is a constant and may be taken to be zero. Denoting $\{[d^2V(r)]/dr^2\}_{r=r_0}$ by C, we get

$$V(r) = \frac{1}{2} C(r - r_0)^2 \qquad (14.45)$$

This parabolic approximation to the real potential is represented by the broken-line curve in Fig. 14.24. This is also similar to the classical potential given by Eq. (14.42). Thus, classically, one would expect the frequency of the diatomic molecule to be, according to Eq. (14.42) after replacing m by μ, the reduced mass,

$$\nu_c = \frac{1}{2\pi} \sqrt{\frac{C}{\mu}} = \frac{1}{2\pi} \sqrt{\frac{\left(\dfrac{d^2V(r)}{dr^2}\right)_{r=r_0}}{\mu}} \qquad (14.46)$$

We shall now start analyzing the problem from a quantum-mechanical point of view. This amounts to solving the Schrödinger wave equation for a particle moving under the influence of a parabolic potential $V(x) = \frac{1}{2}Cx^2$, i.e.,

$$-\frac{\hbar^2}{2\mu}\frac{d^2\psi}{dx^2} + \frac{1}{2} Cx^2 \psi = E\psi \qquad (14.47)$$

This is the familiar problem of the simple harmonic oscillator solved in

Sec. 6 of Chapter XIII. We showed by solving the Schrödinger wave equation that the total vibrational energy, E_v, of the oscillator is quantized and the allowed energy levels are given by

$$E_v = \left(v + \frac{1}{2} \right) \hbar\omega_0 \qquad\qquad (14.48)$$

where v, the *vibrational quantum number*, can take the values 0, 1, 2, 3, 4, . . . , and $\omega_0 = 2\pi\nu_0$ is the classical frequency $= \sqrt{C/\mu}$. There are two fundamental differences between the results of quantum mechanics and that of classical mechanics. According to quantum mechanics the energy levels are quantized while according to classical mechanics the simple harmonic oscillator can take any continuous range of energies. According to classical mechanics the minimum energy is zero and the oscillator may be at rest; while according to quantum mechanics from Eq. (14.48), the minimum energy is $\frac{1}{2}\hbar\omega_0$, as shown in Fig. 14.26. The existence of the minimum zero-

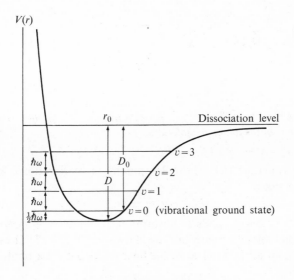

Fig. 14.26. *The vibrational-zero-point-energy, vibrational levels, and dissociation energy of a diatomic molecule.*

point-vibration-energy is consistent with the uncertainty principle, $\Delta x\, \Delta p_x \geqslant \hbar$. If the oscillator were at rest, both $x = 0$ and $p_x = 0$, which implies that both position and momentum are known with complete precision; this is not in accord with the uncertainty principle.

The minimum energy level $\frac{1}{2}\hbar\omega_0$ and other levels, which are equally spaced an amount $\hbar\omega_0$, according to Eq. (14.48) are shown in Fig. 14.26.

Because of the zero-point energy the dissociation energy D_0 of the diatomic molecule as illustrated in Fig. 14.26 is

$$D_0 = D - \frac{1}{2}\hbar\omega_0 \tag{14.49}$$

Thus corresponding to $v = 0, 1, 2, 3, 4, \ldots$, the energy levels are $\frac{1}{2}\hbar\omega_0, \frac{3}{2}\hbar\omega_0, \frac{5}{2}\hbar\omega_0, \frac{7}{2}\hbar\omega_0, \frac{9}{2}\hbar\omega_0, \ldots$, respectively, as shown in Fig. 14.27. The

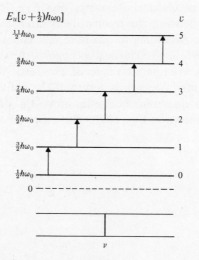

FIG. 14.27.   *Energy levels and possible transitions resulting from pure vibrations of the diatomic molecules.*

transitions, which are electric dipoles, among these vibrational levels follow the selection rules

$$\Delta v = \pm 1 \tag{14.50}$$

where $\Delta v = +1$ corresponds to absorption, while $\Delta v = -1$ corresponds to emission. The possible transitions are shown in Fig. 14.27. Thus the transition between an initial level E_i to the final level E_f gives a photon of energy

$$h\nu = E_f - E_i = \left(v_f + \frac{1}{2}\right)\hbar\omega_0 - \left(v_i + \frac{1}{2}\right)\hbar\omega_0 = (v_f - v_i)\hbar\omega_0 \tag{14.51}$$

According to the selection rule $(v_f - v_i)$ must be $+1$ for absorption (or -1 for emission) and hence

$$h\nu = E_f - E_i = \hbar\omega_0 \tag{14.52}$$

i.e., all the transitions have one single frequency as shown in Fig. 14.27, and it is the same as expected from the classical theory.

It may be pointed out that for a low degree of excitation, the potential is almost parabolic and the vibrational levels are equally spaced. But for higher degrees of excitation of vibrational levels, i.e., for high values of v, the potential is not truly parabolic, resulting in vibrational levels that are not equally spaced but are crowded together near the dissociation energies. In order to truly describe the potential, another term must be added to Eq. (14.45). This leads to the change in shape of the potential and the equilibrium distance, resulting in a change in the moment of inertia and hence the rotation. Such changes are said to have resulted from a rotational-vibrational interaction[24].

For vibrational transitions to occur, the diatomic molecule must have a permanent dipole moment. Thus polar molecules like HCl, which have permanent electric-dipole moments, exhibit pure vibrational spectra; homopolar molecules like H_2, N_2, etc., which do not have permanent electric dipole moments do not exhibit pure vibrational spectra.

We have already mentioned that the vibration spectra are observed in the near infrared and hence have energies 100 times larger than those of the rotational transition. Thus the total molecular energy, both due to rotation and vibration is given by

$$E_{vr} = E_v + E_r = \left(v + \frac{1}{2}\right)\hbar\omega_0 + K(K + 1)\frac{\hbar^2}{2I} \qquad (14.53)$$

where $\hbar/2I$ is $\sim 10^{-4}$ eV while $\hbar\omega_0 \sim 10^{-1}$ eV, which implies that corresponding to each vibration level there are many rotational levels. This means that each vibrational level has a fine structure and is replaced by a band of levels as shown in Fig. 14.28. The vibration-rotation spectrum results from the transitions between two vibrational levels as shown in Fig. 14.29. The selec-

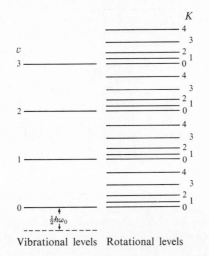

Vibrational levels   Rotational levels

FIG. 14.28. *Many rotational levels are excited corresponding to each vibrational level, resulting in the fine structure of vibrational levels.*

tion rules to be used in this case are $\Delta K = \pm 1$ and $\Delta v = \pm 1$. Combining Eqs. (14.52) and (14.27), we say the frequencies of these transitions are

$$hv = (E_{vr})_f - (E_{vr})_i$$

$$= \left[\left(v_f + \frac{1}{2} \right) \hbar\omega_0 + K_f(K_f + 1)\frac{\hbar^2}{2I} - \left(v_i + \frac{1}{2} \right) \hbar\omega_0 - K_i(K_i + 1)\frac{\hbar^2}{2I} \right]$$

(14.54)

Because $\Delta K = \pm 1$ and $\Delta v = \pm 1$, we get

$$v = v_0 + (K + 1)\frac{\hbar}{2\pi I},$$ (14.55)

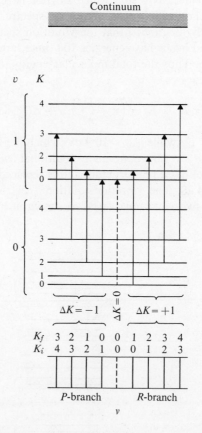

FIG. 14.29. *Vibration-rotation transitions from $v = 0$ to $v = 1$ in a diatomic molecule. $\Delta K = 0$ is not allowed, and hence the central line of frequency v_0 is missing.*

Thus the frequencies corresponding to different transitions are equally spaced with the separation $= \hbar/2\pi I$, on both sides of the central frequency v_0. Note that the central line of frequency ν_0 is missing because it is not allowed by the selection rule, i.e., $\Delta K = 0$ is forbidden. The transitions corresponding to $\Delta K = +1$ are called the R-branch of the spectrum; while the transitions corresponding to $\Delta K = -1$ are called the P-branch of the spectrum. As an example, the vibration-rotation absorption spectrum of HCl molecules[25] is shown in Fig. 14.30. Because chlorine has two isotopes corresponding to

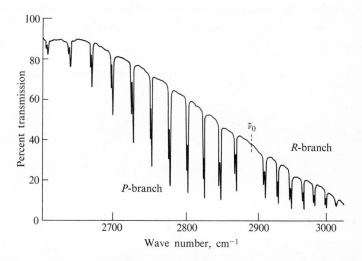

FIG. 14.30. *The vibration-rotation absorption spectrum of HCl molecules. The big dips are due to HCl^{35} molecules while the smaller dips are due to HCl^{37} molecules. Note the central missing line of frequency ν_0. The intensities were measured by the photometric method.* [*From M. Alonso and E. J. Finn,* Fundamental University Physics, *vol. III. Reading, Mass.: Addison-Wesley Publishing Co., Inc., 1968.*]

mass numbers 35 and 37, there are two different values for both ν_0 and I. Hence the spectra of molecules having different isotopes are slightly displaced. This is shown clearly in Fig. 14.30 for the case of HCl^{35} and HCl^{37}.

Before closing this section we shall extend our discussion a little further to the case of polyatomic molecules. If a molecule vibrates such that all the nuclei of its atoms vibrate with constant phase relations, the vibrations are said to be in the *normal mode*. Corresponding to each normal mode is a different frequency. Of course, in some cases because of the symmetry, some of the frequencies will be equal, i.e., we have degenerate states. The spectra of the polyatomic molecules is analyzed in terms of these normal modes of the respective molecules. As an example, Fig. 14.31(a) shows the normal modes of vibration of a linear triatomic molecule such as CO_2; Fig. 14.31(b) shows the normal modes of vibration of a planar triatomic (nonlinear) molecule such as H_2O. Note that in the case of the CO_2 molecule, only three longitudinal normal modes are shown, denoted by frequencies ω_1, ω_2, and ω_3.

The mode corresponding to ω_1 is spectroscopically inactive because the normal vibrations in this case do not induce an oscillating electric-dipole moment. Frequencies ω_2 and ω_3 are observed; these two modes do induce oscillating electric-dipole moments, which result in vibrational frequencies. As is obvious, the complete energy level diagrams of such molecules are very complicated.

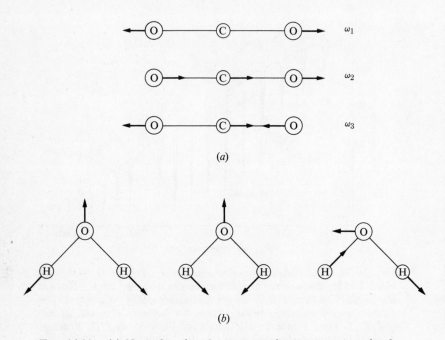

FIG. 14.31. (a) *Normal modes of a symmetric linear triatomic molecule such as CO_2*. (b) *Normal vibration modes of a planar triatomic molecule such as H_2O*.

9. ELECTRONIC TRANSITIONS IN MOLECULES

So far we have concerned ourselves with the rotation and vibration of the nuclei in molecules, assuming that no electronic excitations are taking place in the molecule. If the energy available for excitation is high enough, say from 1 eV to 10 eV, it is possible that the electronic structure of a molecule can change when an electron in the molecule changes its state. Because the rotational and vibrational transitions are much slower ($\sim 10^{-13}$ sec) as compared to the electronic transitions ($\sim 10^{-16}$ sec), we may assume that there is no change in the electronic state of a molecule during vibration or rotation, i.e., the electrons are able to follow the nuclei in the molecule. Once the molecule is electronically excited, the position and size of the potential-energy curve changes as well as the dissociation energy, D_0, and the equilibrium distance, r_0, between the nuclei. The change in r_0 changes the moment of inertia. Hence the vibrational and rotational energy levels of a molecule corresponding to the excited electronic state are different from those of the ground electronic state. Corresponding to a given electronic state there are many vibrational levels, and for a given vibrational state there are many rotational levels. These and the other features discussed above are illustrated in Fig. 14.32. Note that when an electron in a molecule jumps from one configuration to another, the radiation given out is in the visible or ultraviolet regions of the spectrum.

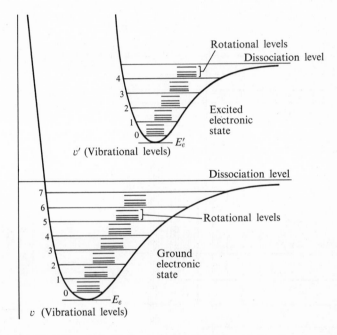

FIG. 14.32.   *Energy-level diagram showing some of the vibrational and rotational levels associated with two electronic states of a diatomic molecule.*

Let us see how we calculate the frequency of a transition when a molecule experiences an electronic transition. We may write the approximate energy of a molecule as

$$E = E_e + E_v + E_r = E_e + \left(v + \frac{1}{2}\right)\hbar\omega_0 + K(K + 1)\frac{\hbar^2}{2I} \quad (14.56)$$

where E_e is the electronic energy at the minimum of the potential energy curve. In an electronic transition, all three energies may change. As pointed out earlier, both I and ω_0 are, in general, different for different electronic states. The energy levels corresponding to Eq. (14.56) are shown in Fig. 14.33. The energy change in the electronic transition between these levels is

$$\Delta E = E' - E = \Delta E_e + \Delta E_v + \Delta E_r \qquad (14.57)$$

where the prime denotes the higher energy state, and where ΔE_e is the change in the electronic energy, given by the difference in the minima of the two

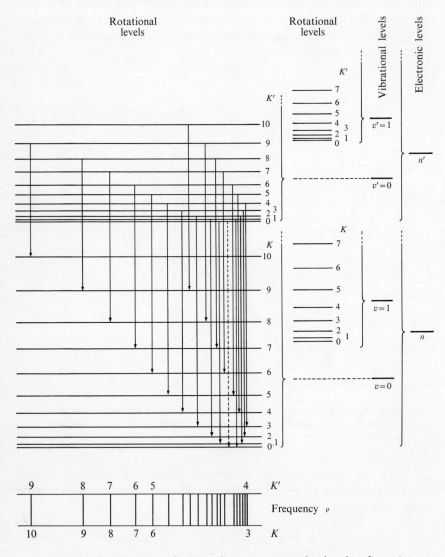

FIG. 14.33. *Rotation-vibration electronic energy-levels of a diatomic molecule showing how the transitions form a typical electronic-band and the lines converging to a "head" at the high-frequency limit.*

electronic states, as shown in Fig. 14.32; and ΔE_v and ΔE_r are the changes in vibrational and rotational energies, respectively. Therefore, the frequency of the transition in the electronic transition of a molecule may be written as

$$\nu = \frac{\Delta E}{h} = \nu_e + \frac{\Delta E_v}{h} + \frac{\Delta E_r}{h} = \nu_e + \left[\left(v' + \frac{1}{2}\right)\nu_0' - \left(v + \frac{1}{2}\right)\nu_0\right]$$
$$+ \left[K'(K+1)\frac{\hbar}{4\pi I'} - K(K+1)\frac{\hbar}{4\pi I}\right]$$

(14.58)

In order to find the possible transitions, we must know the selection rules for the rotational and vibrational levels. Considering electric-dipole transitions, the rotational selection rule is

$$\Delta K = 0, \pm 1 \quad \text{but not} \quad K' = 0 \text{ to } K = 0 \qquad (14.59)$$

It may be pointed out that $\Delta K = 0$ is allowed in this case because the electronic configuration of the molecule has changed during the transition. But the transition from $K' = 0$ to $K = 0$, shown by the dotted line in Fig. 14.33, is forbidden, because it does not satisfy the conservation of angular momentum, the radiation emitted or absorbed must carry one unit of angular momentum.

For the vibrational levels there is no restriction on the change in the value of the vibrational quantum number, v. The transitions in this case are drawn by using the *Franck-Condon principle*[26]. This is illustrated in Fig. 14.34, where if we draw vertical lines from P, Q, and R for $v = 5$, 3, and 2, respectively, these lines end up in the excited state at P', Q', R', respectively,

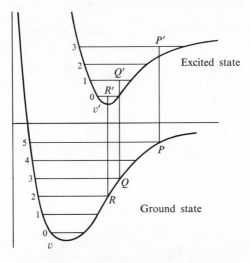

FIG. 14.34. *Electronic transitions in a diatomic molecule allowed by the Franck-London principle for vibrational states.*

corresponding to $v' = 3, 1, 0$. Thus the transitions are between $v' = 3$ to $v = 5$; $v' = 1$ to $v = 3$; and $v' = 0$ to $v = 2$.

The above selection rules, when applied to the electronic-vibration-rotational levels, result in transitions that are shown in Fig. 14.33. The electronic transitions give rise to closely packed lines converging to a "head" on one side of the band. This is called *rotational-vibrational-electronic spectra* of the molecules. Note that corresponding to a given electronic state there are many vibrational levels, and for each vibrational level there are many rotational levels. As a practical example, Fig. 14.35 shows bands in a portion of the molecular spectra of PN in the ultraviolet.

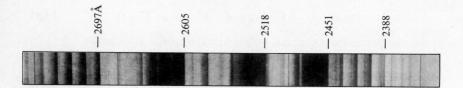

FIG. 14.35. *Typical diatomic molecular spectrum showing bands in the spectrum of the PN molecule in the ultraviolet region.* [*From Herzberg, G.,* Atomic Structure and Atomic Spectra. *New York: Dover Publications, Inc., 1944. Reprinted through permission of the publisher.*]

10. RAYLEIGH AND RAMAN SCATTERING[27]

When a beam of light of a given wavelength is incident on a sample of a liquid or a gas, it is expected, according to the classical theory, that the scattered light is of the same wavelength as the incident wavelength. This is called *coherent*, or *Rayleigh*, *scattering*. This type of scattering can be easily explained with the help of the diagram in Fig. 14.36. The incident light is

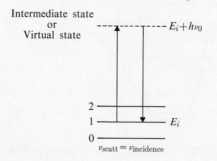

FIG. 14.36. *Rayleigh scattering.*

absorbed by one of the molecules in the ground state or excited state, which is then raised to an intermediate, or virtual, state shown as a broken line in Fig. 14.36. The excited molecule returns to its initial level and in this process emits radiation of the same wavelength as the incident radiation.

In 1928, Sir C. V. Raman, while investigating the scattering of light by liquids, in order to find an explanation for the blue of the sea and sky, found that when a beam of monochromatic light passed through a liquid like benzene or toluene, the scattered light, observed at an angle of 90° to the incident, was found to contain frequencies other than the frequency of the incident radiation. This is called *Raman scattering*. This effect had been predicted theoretically in 1923 by Smekal, but Raman was the first one to observe it experimentally.

The production of Raman lines can be explained simply if we assume Raman scattering to be a molecular process. Suppose the incident light of frequency ν_0 is absorbed by a molecule in the energy state E_i; the molecule will then be in the intermediate, or virtual, state with energy $E^* = E_i + h\nu_0$. The state E^* may now decay by emitting radiation of frequency ν and the molecule will then be in the energy state E_f (Fig. 14.37). Thus, from the conservation of energy,

$$h\nu_0 + E_i = E_f + h\nu$$

or

$$\nu = \nu_0 + \frac{E_i - E_f}{h} \qquad (14.60)$$

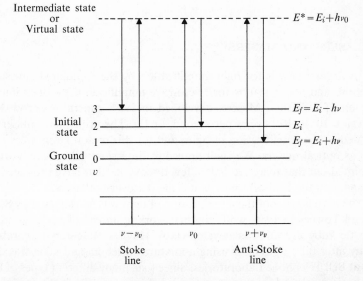

FIG. 14.37. *Raman scattering, involving monochromatic incident light and the vibrational states of molecules.*

If $E_i = E_f$, $v = v_0$ and hence there is no change in frequency. If $E_i < E_f$, then $v < v_0$ and these lines are called *Stokes lines*, and if $E_i > E_f$, then $v > v_0$ and these are called *anti-Stoke lines* as shown in Fig. 14.37. The levels shown in the figure are the molecular vibrational levels for which the selection rules are $\Delta v = \pm 1$. Thus the Stokes line will have frequency $v = v_0 - v_v$ while anti-Stokes lines will have $v = v_0 + v_v$ as shown in Fig. 14.37, where v_v is the vibrational frequency of the molecule.

All experimental evidence points to the fact that the Raman effect is a molecular phenomenon. Scattering from free molecules can result in three different types of Raman effect: (i) the rotational Raman effect, (ii) the vibrational Raman effect, and (iii) the electronic Raman effect.

Because the energies of rotational levels of the molecules are very small, the rotational Raman lines lie very close to the incident line. The selection rules in the case of rotational Raman lines are $\Delta K = 0$, ± 2. Under certain circumstances one can also observe a mixed rotational-vibrational effect. In addition to gas and liquid molecules, solids can exhibit another type of Raman effect in which the crystal lattice as a whole takes the place of the molecule.

The Raman effect has been used extensively for the investigation of the structure of molecules both in physics and chemistry. This includes molecular structure, crystal physics, nuclear physics for spin and statistics, inorganic chemistry for chemical constitution and valence bands, organic chemistry for identifying the presence or absence of certain bonds, physical chemistry for specific heat, electrolytic dissociation, hydrolysis, and many other problems.

11. LASERS AND MASERS[28-32]

The word *laser* stands for *l*ight *a*mplification by the *s*timulated *e*mission of *r*adiation, and *maser* stands for *m*icrowave *a*mplification by the *s*timulated emission of *r*adiation. Masers, developed in 1954, generate microwaves in the region 10^9 to 10^{11} cycles per second, or Hz. The principle of masers was extended to the amplification of light, and for this reason lasers were recognized as optical masers. We shall limit our discussion to lasers only. It may be pointed out that there are only a few discoveries that have produced such an impact on the field of optics as did the discovery of lasers.

The original idea of the amplification of light was investigated by Schawlow and Townes in 1958, while the first working model of the laser using a synthetic ruby crystal was developed by Hughes Research Laboratories. Shortly after this, a gas laser using a mixture of helium and neon was developed at Bell Telephone Laboratories. Since then many different types of lasers have been developed that produce light at frequencies from the far infrared to the ultraviolet regions.

A laser consists of an amplifying medium placed inside an optical resonator, or cavity. The amplification is caused by means of external excitations. This produces a standing wave in the cavity, and hence we may say that the laser is essentially an oscillator. In the case of a conventional light source, the luminous intensities correspond to temperatures of $\leqslant 10^4\ °K$. The output of a laser consists of an intense beam of highly monochromatic radiation with intensities corresponding to temperatures of 10^{20} to $10^{30}\ °K$. These highly intense beams are used in optical radar, long-distance communications, microwelding, and for many other purposes.

In order to understand the working of the laser, we must be familiar with stimulated emission and population inversion. For convenience we shall divide our discussion into the following parts:

A. Stimulated Emission and Population Inversion
B. Methods of Producing Population Inversion
C. Different Types of Lasers

A. Stimulated Emission and Population Inversion

Consider a system containing a large number of atoms in different, quantized states at temperature T. Furthermore, let us suppose that the state i has energy E_i and there are N_i atoms in this state, while the state j has energy E_j and there are N_j atoms in this state. Let a beam of photons of energy $h\nu$, where

$$\nu = (E_j - E_i)/h \qquad (14.61)$$

be incident on this system. The interaction between the photons and the atoms in the states i and j is described, according to Einstein (who introduced the concept of stimulated, or induced, emission in 1917), by three processes (Fig. 14.38).

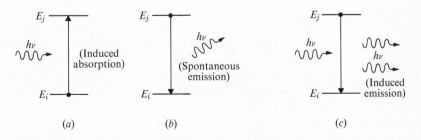

FIG. 14.38.   *Schematic illustration of* (a) *induced absorption,* (b) *spontaneous emission, and* (c) *induced emission.*

(i) *Induced Absorption.*   The atoms in state i absorb photons of energy $h\nu$ and remain in the excited state j (Fig. 14.38a). Let B_{ij} be the probability for this process. If the density of the photons is $u(\nu)$, the number of transitions from state i to state j per second, R_{ia}, will be

$$R_{ia} = N_i B_{ij} u(\nu) \tag{14.62}$$

(ii) *Spontaneous Emission.* The atoms in state j decay to state i by emitting photons of energy $h\nu = E_j - E_i$ (Fig. 14.38b). Let A_{ji} be a constant that describes the probability of spontaneous emission. Because there are N_j atoms in state j, the number of spontaneous transitions per second, R_{se}, will be given by

$$R_{se} = N_j A_{ji} \tag{14.63}$$

The radiation is emitted equally in all directions, i.e., it is incoherent radiation.

(iii) *Induced Emission.* The presence of photons of energy $h\nu = E_j - E_i$ also induce the atoms in the state j to emit photons in the direction of the incident photons (Fig. 14.38c), i.e., this is coherent radiation. The atoms then decay to the lower state i. Let us say B_{ji} is the constant that describes the probability of induced emission. Thus the rate of induced emission, R_{ie}, is given by

$$R_{ie} = N_j B_{ji} u(\nu) \tag{14.64}$$

The constant A_{ji}, B_{ij}, and B_{ji} are called Einstein coefficients.

Because the system at a given temperature is in equilibrium, the upward transitions per second must be equal to the downward transitions per second. Hence from Eqs. (14.62), (14.63), and (14.64), we get

$$R_{ia} = R_{se} + R_{ie}$$

or

$$N_i B_{ij} u(\nu) = N_j A_{ji} + N_j B_{ji} u(\nu) \tag{14.65}$$

Solving for $u(\nu)$, we obtain

$$u(\nu) = \frac{N_i A_{ji}}{N_i B_{ij} - N_j B_{ji}} \tag{14.66}$$

which may be rewritten as

$$u(\nu) = \frac{A_{ji}}{B_{ji}} \frac{1}{\left(\dfrac{B_{ij}}{B_{ji}}\right)\left(\dfrac{N_i}{N_j}\right)^{-1}} \tag{14.67}$$

From Boltzmann's statistics, if the system at temperature $T\,^\circ K$ contains N_0 atoms, then the number of atoms in states of energies E_i and E_j, when the system is in thermal equilibrium, are

$$N_i = N_0 e^{-E_i/kT} \tag{14.68}$$

and

$$N_j = N_0 e^{-E_i/kT} \tag{14.69}$$

Therefore,

$$\frac{N_i}{N_j} = e^{(E_i - E_i)/kT} = e^{h\nu/kT} \tag{14.70}$$

because we have already assumed that $h\nu = E_j - E_i$. Substituting for (N_i/N_j) from Eq. (14.70) into Eq. (14.67), we obtain

$$u(\nu) = \frac{A_{ji}}{B_{ji}} \frac{1}{\left(\dfrac{B_{ij}}{B_{ji}}\right)e^{h\nu/kT} - 1} \tag{14.71}$$

which is an expression for the energy density of photons of frequency ν in equilibrium at temperature T with atoms of energies E_i and E_j. In order for this expression to agree with the Planck radiation formula (see Eq. 4.59), i.e., $u(\nu) = (8\pi h\nu^3/c^3)[1/(e^{h\nu/kT} - 1)])$ the following relations must be true

$$\frac{A_{ji}}{B_{ji}} = \frac{8\pi h\nu^3}{c^3} \tag{14.72}$$

and

$$B_{ij} = B_{ji} \tag{14.73}$$

Thus if the atoms are in equilibrium with the thermal radiation at a temperature T, the ratio of the induced (or stimulated) emission rate to the spontaneous emission rate is given by combining the above expressions with Eqs. (14.64) and (14.63)

$$\frac{\text{induced emission rate}}{\text{spontaneous emission rate}} = \frac{R_{ie}}{R_{se}} = \frac{N_j B_{ji} u(\nu)}{N_j A_{ji}}$$

$$= \frac{B_{ji} u(\nu)}{A_{ji}} = \frac{1}{e^{h\nu/kT} - 1} \tag{14.74}$$

For an ordinary optical source of light for which T may be $\sim 10^3$ °K, the ratio R_{ie}/R_{se} is very small. Thus the visible region of the spectrum will be due to spontaneous transitions, while the induced emission rate will be almost negligible. But the spontaneous transitions occur in a random fashion and hence the visible radiation emitted is incoherent.

On the contrary, theory shows that induced radiation is emitted in the same direction as the primary, or incident, radiation that caused the induced transitions and that the emitted radiation has a definite phase relationship. Thus the induced emitted radiation is coherent with the incident radiation. The basic requirement for the working of a laser is for predominantly induced transitions. Not only is the emitted radiation in a laser highly coherent, but the spectral intensity of a laser source is much greater than the spectral intensity of an ordinary light source. The incident beam is said to be amplified after passing through such a medium.

It is possible to create a situation so that the induced emission rate predominates over the spontaneous emission rate. This is achieved by causing *population inversion* as we shall explain. According to the Boltzmann distribution given by Eq. (14.68), the plot of E versus N is as shown in Fig. 14.39(a). It is obvious that if $E_j > E_i$, then $N_j < N_i$ as shown in Fig. 14.39(a). On the other hand, if $E_j > E_i$, but also $N_j > N_i$ as shown in Fig. 14.39(b), the resulting situation is called *population inversion*. Because there are more atoms in the E_j state than in the E_i state, it is possible that if photons of energy $h\nu = E_j - E_i$ are incident on this system, the downward induced transition rate may far exceed the spontaneous rate. The population inversion may be achieved by many different ways.

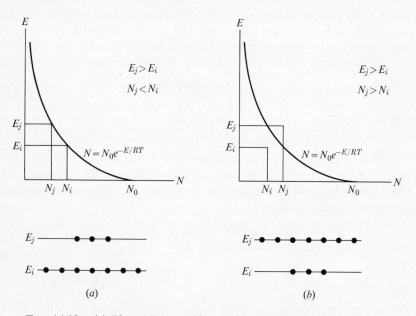

FIG. 14.39. (a) *Plot of E versus N according to Boltzmann distribution in which $N_j > N_i$ for $E_j > E_i$. (b) The case of population inversion in which $N_j < N_i$ for $E_j > E_i$.*

B. Methods of Producing Population Inversion

There are three methods commonly used for producing population inversion: (i) excitation by photons, or optical pumping; (ii) excitation by electrons; and (iii) excitation by inelastic atom-atom collisions. These three processes are illustrated in Fig. 14.40. The aim is to select a material, the atoms of which, when raised from the ground state E_0 to the excited state E_2, do not decay back to E_0, i.e., the transitions from E_2 to E_0 are forbidden by the selection rules. Instead the atoms in the excited E_2 decay to state E_1 by spontaneous emission, then from E_1 to E_0. If it so happens that the lifetime of E_1 is very long ($> 10^{-8}$ sec), i.e., it is a metastable state, the atoms reach the state E_1 at a much faster rate than they leave the state E_1. Eventually there will be more atoms in state E_1 than in E_0. This process, called *optical pumping*, is shown in Fig. 14.41(a). The resulting population inversion is shown in Fig. 14.41(b).

Once the population inversion is achieved, the state E_1 is exposed to a

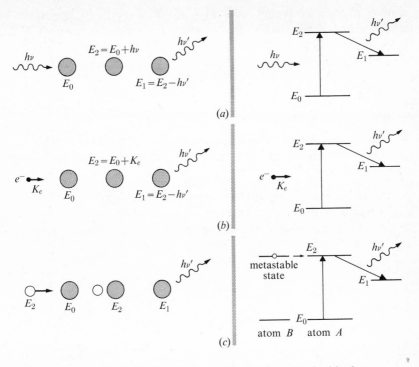

FIG. 14.40. *Methods of producing population inversion by* (a) *photons, optical pumping,* (b) *electrons, and* (c) *inelastic atom-atom collisions.*

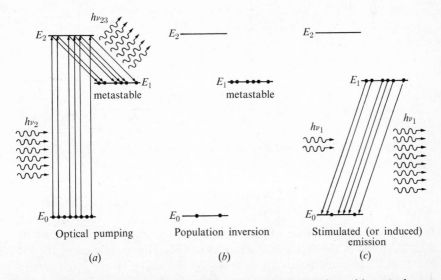

FIG. 14.41. *Schematic representation of working of laser* (a) *optical pumping,* (b) *population inversion, and* (c) *stimulated (or induced) emission.*

beam of photons of energy $h\nu_1 = E_1 - E_0$. This results in stimulated, or induced, emission as shown in Fig. 14.41(c). The result is a coherent, highly intense beam of photons of energy $h\nu_1$ in the direction of the incident beam, i.e., we have achieved *l*ight *a*mplification by *s*timulated *e*mission of *r*adiation (laser).

C. Different Types of Lasers

Most lasers are either gas lasers or optically pumped solid-state lasers. There are only a few liquid lasers. We shall limit our discussion to gas and solid-state lasers.

(i) *Gas Lasers.*   In order to understand the workings of a gas laser, consider a typical example: a helium-neon laser. The energy-level diagram of the mixture of He and Ne is shown in Fig. 14.42, while the actual experimental

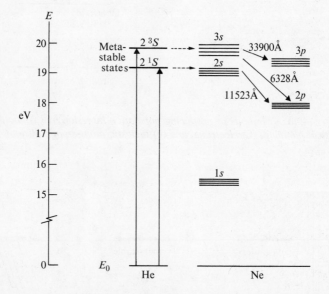

FIG. 14.42.   *Energy level diagram of a mixture of helium and neon used in a laser.*

arrangement is shown in Fig. 14.43. The most suitable ratio of the mixture of helium to neon is about 7 to 1 at a pressure of $\sim$1 torr. Referring to Fig. 14.42, the He atoms in the discharge tube are excited by collisions with electrons to the metastable states ^3S and ^1S. The population of the He atoms in these states builds up, because the transitions to the ground state are not allowed. As shown, the 2s and 3s levels of neon lie very close to the ^3S and ^1S levels of He. Therefore, in collisions between He and Ne atoms, the He atoms in the excited states lose their energy to the ground state Ne atoms, resulting in the excitation of the Ne atoms to the states $2s$ and $3s$, i.e.,

$$\text{He }(^3S) + \text{Ne (ground)} \rightarrow \text{He (ground)} + \text{Ne }(2s)$$
$$\text{He }(^1S) + \text{Ne (ground)} \rightarrow \text{He (ground)} + \text{Ne }(3s)$$

(14.75)

Thus, this results in the population inversion of Ne atoms. The following transitions, in addition to some other weaker transitions, in the Ne atoms are responsible for the laser action of the He-Ne mixture.

$$3s \rightarrow 2p \qquad 6328 \text{ Å}$$
$$2s \rightarrow 2p \qquad 11523 \text{ Å}$$
$$3s \rightarrow 3p \sim 33900 \text{ Å}$$

as shown in Fig. 14.42.

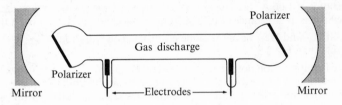

Fig. 14.43. *Typical experimental arrangement of a gas laser.*

Figure 14.43, representing the experimental arrangement, consists of a discharge tube with a He-Ne mixture. The discharge is maintained by direct current, alternating current, or by an electrodeless high-frequency source. The ends of the laser tube are equipped with Brewster end-windows so that the output of the laser is linearly polarized. The two spherical mirrors placed at both ends act as a surface of a cavity so that light from the discharge tube forms standing waves between these mirrors. The mirrors are coated with dielectric films (many layers) to obtain high reflectance in multiple reflections of the standing waves. A small hole in the mirror is made through which a coherent, highly intense visible beam passes. The color of the light depends on the mixture of gases used. There are several kinds of gas lasers[31,32] that are commercially available.

(ii) *Solid-State Laser.* A typical example of a solid-state laser is a ruby laser. Ruby consists of aluminium oxide (Al_2O_3) doped with $\sim 0.05\%$ chromium (Cr) atoms, which replace Al atoms. The laser action is due to the Cr atoms in Al_2O_3, the host material. The metastable state has a lifetime of 3×10^{-3} sec. In practice the ruby is made in the form of a cylinder and placed in a glass or crystal supporting material. The ends of the supporting material are optically ground and polished so as to form a cavity. The ruby crystal itself may be polished, or two external mirrors may be employed, without using the supporting material. The optical pumping is done by using an external source of light.

Many different types of solid-state lasers[29] have been developed for different uses.

PROBLEMS

1. Very often the dissociation energy is expressed in kcal/mole (kilocalorie/mole). Show that 1 eV $\simeq$ 23 kcal/mole.

2. The ionization energy of lithium is 5.39 eV. The equilibrium separation of the two nuclei in a Li_2 molecule is 2.67 Å. (a) Calculate the Coulomb repulsion energy of the Li^+ ions at the equilibrium distance. (b) Calculate the dissociation energy.

3. Calculate the potential energy of an electron in the hydrogen molecule-ion for the following two cases when the nuclei are separated by an equilibrium distance of 1.06 Å: (a) The electron is midway between the two nuclei. (b) The electron is at a distance of 0.53 Å from one nucleus and 1.59 Å from the other.

4. Both H_2^- and He_2^+ have the same electronic configuration. Why is He_2^+ more stable than H_2^-?

5. The first ionization potential of potassium is 4.34 volts, and the electron affinity of fluorine is 4.07 eV/electron. The equilibrium internuclear separation in a single KF molecule is 2.67 Å. The cohesive energy relative to the separated ions is 0.50 eV/molecule less than the Coulomb attractive energy. Calculate the energy needed to separate the KF molecule into neutral atoms.

6. Calculate the amount of energy released when $AlCl_3$ dissociates into neutral atoms. The equilibrium distance between the two nuclei of the molecule is 2.13 Å.

7. The electric dipole moment of the H_2O molecule is 6.2×10^{-30} m-C. (a) Find the dipole moment corresponding to each O—H bond. (b) If the O—H bond length is 0.96 Å, what fraction of the hydrogen electron has been transformed to the oxygen atom?

8. Explain why (a) linear molecules, and (b) coplaner molecules, do not have electric dipole moments.

9. Show that the angle between the directions of maxima in the hybrid wave-function of carbon is 109.5°.

10. Write the possible hybrid wave-functions for sp^2 and sp.

11. Write the electronic configuration of the molecules NO and N_2. How many bonds are present in each molecule? Which molecule is more stable?

12. Write the electron configuration of the molecules CO and CO_2. How many bonds are present in each molecule? Which molecule is more stable?

13. What are the electronic configurations of CO and CO^+? Which is more stable?

14. Write the electronic configuration and discuss the bond structure of the following molecules: (a) S_2, (b) Cl_2, (c) CN, and (d) HI.

15. Show that for very large rotational quantum numbers, the frequency of a photon resulting from a transition between the adjacent levels of a diatomic molecule is the same as the classical frequency of the rotation of the molecule about its center of mass. (This is the correspondence principle.)

16. The wave numbers of the lines observed in the rotational spectrum of a HCl molecule are 81, 105, 125, and 145. Calculate (a) the rotational inertia, and (b) the equilibrium distance.

17. The equilibrium distance between the nuclei of the H_2 molecule is 1.06 Å. Calculate (a) the energies (in eV) of the first three rotational levels, and (b) the wavelengths of the allowed transitions from these levels.

18. Calculate (a) the three lowest energy levels, and (b) the frequencies of the two lowest absorption lines, of a CsF molecule. The dissociation energy of the molecule is 5.5 eV while the equilibrium distance is 2.345 Å.

19. Consider the molecules HCl^{35} and HCl^{37}, and assume that they have the same equilibrium distance of 1.27 Å. Calculate (a) the first three rotational states of each molecule, and (b) the wavelengths of the photons absorbed in transitions among such energy levels.

20. In rotational motion it was assumed that the molecule is rigid. In an actual situation the bond length changes according to Hooke's law. The restoring force provides the centripetal force acting on the atoms as they rotate, i.e.,

$$k(r - r_0) = \mu \omega^2 r$$

Starting with this equation

$$E = \tfrac{1}{2} I \omega^2 + \tfrac{1}{2} k(r - r_0)^2$$

and using the quantization condition for the angular momentum, show that the rotational energy levels are given by

$$E_{\text{rot}} \approx \left[\frac{K(K+1)\hbar^2}{2\mu r_0^2} - \frac{K(K+1)^2 \hbar^4}{2\mu^2 r_0^6 k} \right]$$

21. Consider a polyatomic molecule with three principal moments of inertia I_x, I_y, and I_z, so that the total energy is given by

$$E = \frac{L_x^2}{2I_x} + \frac{L_y^2}{2I_y} + \frac{L_z^2}{2I_z}$$

such that $L = \sqrt{L_x^2 + L_y^2 + L_z^2} = \sqrt{K(K+1)}\,\hbar$, where $K = 0, 1, 2, 3, \ldots$. Suppose there is an axis of symmetry along the Z axis ($I_x = I_y$) such that $L_z = m\hbar$, where $m = 0, \pm 1, \pm 2, \ldots$. Show that the total energy for the state with quantum numbers K and m is given by

$$E_{K,m} = \frac{K(K+1)\hbar^2}{2I_x} + m^2 \hbar^2 \left(\frac{1}{2I_z} - \frac{1}{2I_x} \right)$$

Draw the energy levels for the two cases: (a) $I_z = 0.75 I_x$, and (b) $I_z = 1.25 I_x$.

22. Consider two masses M and m joined by a spring of elastic constant k. Show that when they are released on a frictionless surface, the masses will oscillate with a frequency $\nu = (1/2\pi)\sqrt{k/\mu}$ where μ is the reduced mass.

23. The HCl molecule shows a strong absorption line of wavelength $\lambda = 3.465$ microns. Calculate the force constant for the HCl bond. Also calculate the zero-point energy.

24. (a) Assuming the same force constants for the molecules H^1Cl^{35} and H^2Cl^{35}, calculate the ratio of the vibrational frequencies for the two molecules.

(b) Assuming the same force constants for the molecules H^1Cl^{35} and H^1Cl^{37}, calculate the ratio of the vibrational frequencies for the two molecules.

(c) Compare the results of (a) and (b).

25. If the force of the HCl^{35} molecule is 516 N/m, calculate the energies of the three lowest vibrational energy levels. Is it possible that this molecule will be excited to the first level at room temperature? What are the frequencies (or frequency) of the transitions?

26. The force constant of the HF molecule is 966 N/m. (a) Find the frequency of vibration. (b) What are the energies of the three lowest levels?

27. Assume that the force constants of H_2, D_2, and HD are the same. The H_2 molecule shows an absorption line at 2.3×10^{-4} cm. Calculate the vibration frequencies of D_2 and HD.

REFERENCES

1. Gray, H., *Electrons and Covalent Bonds*, New York: W. A. Benjamin, 1964.

2. Spic, J., *Chemical Binding and Structure*. New York: The Macmillan Co., 1964.

3. Pauling, L., *The Nature of the Chemical Bond*, p. 15. New York: Cornell Univ. Press, 1960.

4. Born, M., and J. R. Oppenheimer, *Ann. Physik*, **84**, 457, (1927).

5. Burrau, Ø., *Kgl. Danske Videnskab. Selskab.*, **7**, 1, (1927); also E. A. Hylleraas, *Zeit. fur Physik*, **71**, 739, (1931).

6. Wang, S. C., *Phys. Rev.*, **31**, 579, (1928); also Condon, E. U., *Proc. Nat. Acad. Sci.*, **13**, 466, (1927); also Heitler, W., and F. London, *Zeit. fur Physik*, **44**, 455, (1927).

7. Hund, F., *Zeit. fur Physik*, **40**, 742, **42**, 93, (1927); also R. S. Mulliken, *Phys. Rev.*, **32**, 186, (1928); also J. E. Lennard Jones, *Trans. Faraday Soc.*, **25**, 668, (1929).

8. Pauling, L., and D. M. Yost, *Proc. Nat. Acad. Sci.*, **18**, 414, (1932); also L. Pauling, *J.A.C.S.*, **54**, 3570, (1932).

9. Pauling, L., *Chem. Revs.*, **5**, 173, (1928).

10. Finkelstein, B. N., and G. E. Horowitz, *Zeit. fur Physik*, **48**, 118, (1928).

11. Slater, J. C., *Quantum Theory of Matter*, 2nd ed. Chaps. 20 and 21. New York: McGraw-Hill Book Company, 1968.

12. Slater, J. C., *Quantum Theory of Matter*, 2nd ed. p. 398, New York: McGraw-Hill Book Company, 1968.

13. Kolos, W., and C. C. J. Roothons, *Revs. Mod. Phys.*, **32**, 219, (1960).

14. Dixon, R. N., *Spectroscopy and Structure*, London: Methuen & Co., Ltd., 1965.

15. Pauling, L., *The Nature of the Chemical Bond*. Ithaca, New York: Cornell Univ. Press, 1960.

16. Stevenson, R., *Multiplet Structure of Atoms and Molecules*. Chap. 6. Philadelphia: W. B. Saunders Co., 1965.

17. Moskowitz, J. W., and M. C. Harrison, *J. Chem. Phys.*, **42**, 1726, (1965); also Slater, J. C., *Quantum Theory of Matter*, Chap. 29, 2nd ed., New York: McGraw-Hill Book Company, 1968.

18. Pauling, L., and J. Sherman, *J. Chem. Phys.*, **1**, 679, (1933).

19. Hall, G. G., and J. Lennard-Jones, *Proc. Roy. Soc.* (London), **A205**, 357, (1951).

20. Slater, J. C., *Phys. Rev.*, **37**, 481, (1931); also J. H. Van Vleck, *J. Chem. Phys.*, **1**, 177, 219, (1933), and **2**, 20, (1934).

21. King, G. C., *Spectroscopy and Molecular Structure*, New York: Holt, Rinehart and Winston, Inc., 1964.

22. Herzberg, G., *Spectra of Diatomic Molecules*. Princeton, N. J.: D. Van Nostrand Co., Inc., 1950.

23. Wilson, E. B., Jr., J. C. Decius, and P. C. Cross, *Molecular Vibrations*. New York: McGraw-Hill Book Company, 1955.

24. Allen, J. C., Jr., and P. C. Cross, *Molecular Vib-Rotors*. New York: John Wiley & Sons, Inc., 1963.

25. Herzberg, G., *Spectra of Diatomic Molecule*. Princeton, N. J.: D. Van Nostrand, 1950.

26. Dixon, R. N., *Spectroscopy and Structure*, Chap. 6. London: Methuen & Co., Ltd., 1965.

27. Herzberg, G., *Infrared and Raman Spectra*, New York: D. Van Nostrand Co., Inc., 1945.

28. Gordon, J. P., H. Z. Zeiger, and C. H. Townes, *Phys. Rev.*, **95**, 282, (1954).

29. Lengyel, B. A., *Introduction to Laser Physics*. New York: Wiley, 1966.

30. Javan, A., W. R. Bennet, Jr., and D. R. Herriott, *Phys. Rev. Letters*, **6**, 106, (1961).

31. Jensen, R. C., and G. R. Fowles, *Proc. IEEE*, **52**, 1350, (1964).

32. Silfvast, W. T., G. R. Fowles, and B. H. Hopkins, *Appl. Phys. Letters*, **8**, 318, (1966).

SUGGESTIONS FOR FURTHER READING

1. Herzberg, G., *Molecular Spectra and Molecular Structure*, Chaps. 2, 3, and 4. New York: D. Van Nostrand Co., Inc., 1950.

2. Slater, John C., *Quantum Theory of Matter*, 2nd ed., Chaps. 19–29. New York: McGraw-Hill Book Company, 1968.

3. Johnson, R. C., *An Introduction of Molecular Spectra*, London: Methuen & Co., Ltd., 1959.

4. Condon, E. U., "Electronic Structure of Molecules," Chap. 7, *Handbook of Physics*, New York: McGraw-Hill Book Company, 1958.

5. King, G. W., *Spectroscopy and Molecular Structure*, New York: Holt, Rinehart and Winston, Inc., 1964.

6. Allen, H. C., Jr., and P. C. Cross, *Molecular Vib-Rotors*, New York: John Wiley & Sons, 1963.

7. Pauling, L., *The Nature of the Chemical Bond*, 2nd ed., New York: Cornell Univ. Press, 1940.

8. Green, A. E. S., and P. J. Wyatt, *Atomic and Space Physics*, Chap. 7. Reading, Mass.: Addison-Wesley Publishing Co., Inc., 1965.

9. Stevenson, R., *Multiplet Structure of Atoms and Molecules*, Chap. 6. Philadelphia: W. B. Saunders Co., 1965.

10. Dixon, R. N., *Spectroscopy and Structure*, Chaps. 3–7. London: Methuen & Co., Ltd., 1965.

11. Herzberg, G., *Infrared and Raman Spectra*, Princeton, N. J.: D. Van Nostrand Co., Inc., 1945.

12. Wilson, E. B., Jr., J. C. Decius, and P. C. Cross, *Molecular Vibrations*, New York: McGraw-Hill Book Company, 1955.

13. Townes, C. H., and A. L. Schawlow, *Microwave Spectroscopy*, New York: McGraw-Hill Book Company, 1955.

14. Troup, G. J. F., *Masers and Lasers*, 2nd ed., London: Methuen & Co., Ltd., 1963.

15. Fowles, G. R., *Introduction to Modern Optics*, Chap. 8. New York: Holt, Rinehart and Winston, Inc., 1968.

XV

Structure and Theories of Solids

1. INTRODUCTION

The field of solid state physics has developed rapidly in the last thirty years and there have been so many interesting and important discoveries made that it will not be possible to do full justification here. Our study of solid state physics in this closing chapter will be an extension of the atomic and molecular structure to the structure of solids, and the application of quantum mechanics to the phenomena which involve a large number of atoms and molecules, i.e., solids.

Furthermore, solids may be divided into (a) crystalline solids, and (b) amorphous solids. A *crystalline solid* consists of a regular arrangement of atoms or group of atoms falling in a repeated three-dimensional pattern. The structure of solids exhibiting such regularity, or periodicity, constitutes a *crystal lattice*. An *amorphous* (without form) *solid* consists of atoms or molecules that are tightly bound to one another, but there is little geometric regularity or periodicity in the arrangement of the atoms within it. Because of the long-range ordering of atoms or molecules, the crystalline solids are better understood than amorphous solids. Our brief discussion in this chapter will be limited to a few aspects of the crystalline solids.

First of all, we shall investigate the types of bondings in the solids and the corresponding properties of these solids. This will be followed by a brief mention of the mechanical and thermal properties. Finally, a generous use of quantum mechanics will be made to investigate two important theories of solids—free electron theory of metals and quantum theory (zone theory and band theory) of solids with special emphasis on semiconductors.

2. TYPES OF SOLIDS AND THEIR PROPERTIES

We define *cohesive energy*, or *binding energy*, of a crystal as the amount of energy needed to separate the crystal into its constituent atoms, i.e., it is equal to the energy of the crystal in the ground state at absolute zero, minus the sum of the ground state energies of the isolated atoms. An ideal way to identify this crystal energy would be to write a Hamiltonian of all electrons and atoms or ions in the crystal and then find its expectation value. Such a procedure is tedious and in practice one uses more approximate methods for such calculations.

We can classify the crystalline solids into the following five categories according to the nature and strength of their bonding. But it must be kept in mind that the classification is very artificial, and many solids fall into intermediate categories.

A. *Ionic crystals* have binding energies of $\sim$5–10 eV per molecule; sodium chloride is an example.
B. *Valence crystals* have binding energies of $\sim$10 eV per molecule; diamond is an example.
C. *Hydrogen-bonded crystals* have binding energies of $\sim$0.5 eV per molecule; ice is an example.
D. *Molecular crystals* have binding energies up to 0.1 eV per molecule; methane is an example.
E. *Metallic-bonded crystals* have energies of $\sim$1–5 eV per molecule; sodium is an example.

A. Ionic Crystals[1,2]

An ionic crystal consists of a regular array of positive and negative ions as shown in Fig. 15.1 for the structure of a NaCl crystal which has a face-centered cubic (fcc) structure and Fig. 15.2 for the CsCl crystal which has a body-centered cubic (bcc) structure. The ionic bonds in crystals are very similar to ionic bonds in molecules. The bonds occur whenever atoms that lose electrons easily (elements of Group I) combine with atoms that have high electron affinities (elements of Group VII). In stable equilibrium, the attractive forces between oppositely charged ions exceed the repulsive forces between similar ions. If there were only net attractive forces the molecules would coalesce into a closely packed structure with no stable configuration. This collapse is prevented by the application of Pauli's exclusion principle that requires that when electron shells of different atoms overlap, additional electrons will be forced to occupy higher energy states, and, in addition, there is repulsion between the nuclei at short distances.

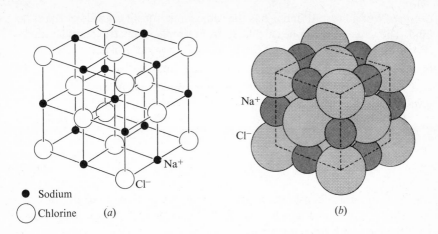

Sodium

Chlorine   (a)

(b)

FIG. 15.1.   *The face-centered cubic structure of a NaCl crystal:* (a) *geometrical arrangement, and* (b) *scale model.*

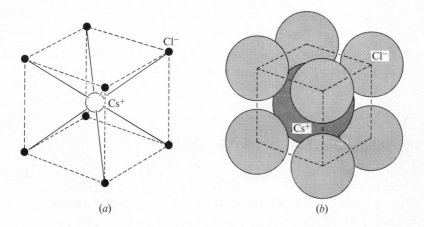

(a)

(b)

FIG. 15.2.   *The body-centered cubic structure of a CsCl crystal:* (a) *geometrical arrangement, and* (b) *scale model.*

The cohesive energy or the internal potential energy of an ionic crystal is the sum of the potential energies due to the two forces mentioned above. The total electrostatic potential-energy, V_{coul}, leading to a net attractive force, of any ion in the crystal due to the other ions surrounding it may be written as

$$V_{\text{coul}} = -\alpha \frac{e^2}{4\pi\epsilon_0 r} \qquad (15.1)$$

where r is the distance between two nearest opposite ions and α is *Madelung's* constant[3] of a crystal; and α has the same value for all crystals of the same kind. The value of α can be calculated from simple geometric considerations. (For example, in a NaCl crystal there are six Cl^- ions at a distance r from Na^+, then 12 Na^+ ions at a distance $\sqrt{2}r$ from the same Na^+ ion, next 8 Cl^- ions at a distance $\sqrt{3}r$ from the same Na^+ ion and so on. Adding these values gives the above equation.) The value of α lies between 1.6 and 1.8.

The repulsive force is given to a fair degree of accuracy by the following expression suggested by the German physicist, Max Born[4]:

$$V_{repul} = A \frac{e^2}{4\pi\epsilon_0 r^n} \tag{15.2}$$

where A and n are constants, n being much greater than 1, so that it leads to a short-range force which is negligible at large distances in comparison with the Coulomb ionic attraction.

Thus the total effective potential energy, E_p, is obtained by adding Eqs. (15.1) and (15.2), i.e.,

$$E_p = V_{coul} + V_{repul}$$
$$= -\frac{e^2}{4\pi\epsilon_0}\left(\frac{\alpha}{r} - \frac{A}{r^n}\right) \tag{15.3}$$

The plot of E_p versus r is as shown in Fig. 14.14 (Chap. XIV). Thus at the equilibrium distance, r_0, the potential energy is minimum and hence by definition $(dE_p/dr)_{r=r_0} = 0$ and it gives

$$A = \frac{\alpha}{n} r_0^{n-1} \tag{15.4}$$

Substituting this in Eq. (15.3), we get

$$E_p = -\alpha \frac{e^2}{4\pi\epsilon_0 r_0}\left[\frac{r_0}{r} - \frac{1}{n}\left(\frac{r_0}{r}\right)^n\right] \tag{15.5}$$

If we substitute $r = r_0$, we obtain the potential energy at the equilibrium distance to be

$$E_{p,r_0} = -\alpha \frac{e^2}{4\pi\epsilon_0 r_0}\left(1 - \frac{1}{n}\right) \tag{15.6}$$

For ionic crystals n is found to be ≈ 9.

Let us apply this equation to the case of a NaCl crystal for which $r_0 = 2.81$ Å, $\alpha = 1.7476$ and $n = 9$. The lattice energy, the energy needed to form a crystal from its ions (rather than atoms) is $E_{p,r_0} = -7.97$ eV/ion pair or -3.99 eV/ion. The energy needed to form Na^+ and Cl^- ions from Na and Cl atoms is 0.77 eV/ion and hence $E_{cohesive} = (-3.99 + 0.77)$ eV/atom $= -3.22$ eV/atom which agrees with the experimentally measured value of -3.28 eV per atom.

Because of the strength of the ionic bonds, most ionic crystals are hard, usually brittle, and have very high melting points. Because there are no free electrons, these crystals are poor conductors of heat and electricity. Since the ions with complete shells have all electrons paired off and hence have no magnetic moment; most ionic crystals are diamagnetic.

B. Covalent Crystals

The bonding in covalent crystals is similar to the bonding in covalent molecules. Each atom in a covalent bond contributes an electron, and such electrons are shared equally by both atoms in a bond. Because these electrons spend more time between the atoms than anywhere else, they give rise to a cohesive force in covalent crystals. In a manner similar to the case of an H_2 molecule, the atoms in covalent crystals are bound together by localized directional bonds, and the nature and the orientation of these directional bonds determines the type of crystal lattice.

A typical example of a covalent crystal is diamond with tetrahedral structure, as shown in Fig. 15.3. The tetrahedral structure is the result of the

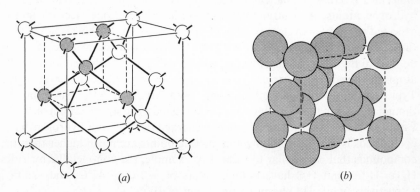

(a)   *(b)*

FIG. 15.3. *The tetrahedral structure of a diamond crystal:* (a) *geometrical arrangement, and* (b) *scale model.*

ability of each carbon atom to form covalent bonds with four other atoms. The four bonding electrons of each carbon atom are oriented by means of sp^3 hybrid wave functions given in Sec. 14.6. The length of each bond, or separation between two carbon atoms in a diamond crystal, is 1.54 Å. Other examples of pure covalent crystals are silicon, germanium, and silicon carbide.

As expected, the covalent bond is a very strong one. Cohesive energies of carbon in diamond and of SiC are 7.4 eV and 12.3 eV, respectively. The rigid electronic structure explains some of the common properties of covalent crystals, which are extremely hard and difficult to deform. Diamond is the hardest substance known, and SiC is the industrial abrasive Carborundum. Covalent crystals have high melting points and are insoluble in most liquids. Because there are no free electrons to carry energy, the covalent crystals are poor conductors of heat and electricity. Because the excitation energies of most covalent crystals are very high (for example, the electronic excitation energy of diamond is ~ 6 eV) compared with the thermal energies (~ 0.025 eV), the covalent crystals are normally in their ground states. Because the energies of the visible photons are between 0.8 and 3.1 eV, while the first excited electronic states are higher than this, many covalent crystals are transparent to visible light.

We may point out that it is not always possible to classify a given crystal as wholly ionic or wholly covalent. For example, AgCl (resembling NaCl structure) and CuCl (resembling diamond structure) both exhibit bonds of intermediate character.

C. Hydrogen-Bonded Crystals

Hydrogen-bonded crystals are very much like ionic crystals except (i) their bonding is very weak, and (ii) they are characterized by being strongly polar molecules (having permanent electric dipole moments) with one or more hydrogen atoms. A neutral hydrogen atom has only one electron and is expected to form a covalent bond with one other atom. But this is not always the case. Under certain circumstances the hydrogen atom appears to be bonded to two other atoms, forming what is called the hydrogen bond. Other atoms involved are electronegative such as oxygen, fluorine, or nitrogen. Typical examples of hydrogen-bond are H_2O, HF, and NH_3. These bonds, though weaker than ionic bonds or covalent bonds, are stronger than ordinary van der Waals bonds. The prominent characteristic of the hydrogen bond compounds is that their boiling and melting points are much higher than the compounds that are similar to these. For example, the non-metallic hydrides H_2Te, H_2Se, and H_2S have boiling points of $-2°C$, $-42°C$, and $-60°C$, respectively, while H_2O has a boiling point of $100°C$.

The reason for the formation of the hydrogen bond is the following: In hydrides, atoms are so electronegative that they attract the electrons from the hydrogen atom completely, leaving behind a bare proton with a positive charge. The positive hydrogen ion, the proton, being relatively small, may attract the negative end of the other molecule, forming chains of molecules, such as H_2F_2, H_3F_3, H_4F_4, etc., which may also be denoted as HF · HF, HF · HF · HF, HF · HF · HF · HF, etc.

An interesting example of such chains[5] is the case of ice, as shown in Fig. 15.4. Water molecules have a tetrahedral arrangement. Such an open structure explains why ice, or water in the solid phase, by comparison occupies a larger volume than water in the liquid phase, i.e., the density of ice is low. As ice melts, the big clusters of chains break into small clusters, thereby occupying less volume and increasing the density of water from 0°C to a maximum at 4°C.

The tetrahedral structure is accounted for by the existence of four pairs of electrons (six from oxygen and two from two hydrogen atoms) which occupy four sp^3 hybrid orbitals as shown in Fig. 15.5. Each H_2O molecule forms hydrogen bonds with four other H_2O molecules. In two of these bonds the central molecule provides the bridging protons, while the protons in the other two bonds are provided by the attached molecules. In the solid state these bonds are stable, forming large and stable clusters. In liquid state the hydrogen bonds between adjacent molecules are continually broken and reformed due to thermal agitation, but at any one instant, the molecules are in the form of definite clusters.

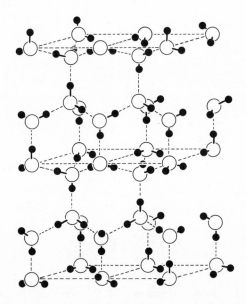

FIG. 15.4. *Water molecules in ice. Note that there is one proton along each oxygen-oxygen axis, close to one or the other of the two oxygen atoms.* [*From Pauling, L.,* The Nature of the Chemical Bond, *Ithaca, N. Y.: Cornell University Press, 1960.*]

D. Molecular Crystals

Molecular crystals are those substances whose molecules are not polar, i.e., the molecules do not have a permanent electric dipole moment. Because all the electrons in these molecules are paired off, no covalent bonds are possible between atoms of two different molecules. The inert gases, He, Ne, Ar, Kr, Xe, and Rn, the outer shells of which are complete, solidify as molecular solids. Other examples of molecular solids are Cl_2, I_2, CO_2, and CH_4, when found in solid state. The molecules in these solids retain their individualities and are bounded by intermolecular forces called van der Waals forces[6]. These forces, though very weak, are responsible for the condensation of gases into liquids, and the freezing of liquids into solids even in the absence of any ionic, covalent, or metallic bonding.

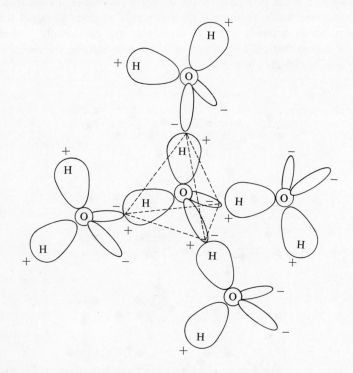

FIG. 15.5.   *Tetrahedral structure of H_2O molecules. The four pairs of electrons occupy the four sp^3 hybrid orbitals.*

Even though the molecules do not have permanent electric dipole moments, their electronic configuration at any instance will give rise to instantaneous electric dipole moments. Consider a polar molecule in the neighborhood of a molecule that does not have a permanent electric dipole moment. As illustrated in Fig. 15.6, the dipole molecule causes the rearrangement of the charges in the other molecule, resulting in an induced moment in the direction of the dipole molecule. It is the attraction between these two instantaneous electric dipoles of the molecules that is the basis of the van der Waals forces, and the magnitude of which is proportional to $1/r^7$. The magnitude of the van der Waals interaction potential energy is illustrated in Fig. 15.7 for inert gases. Thus van der Waals forces are effective only at short distances.

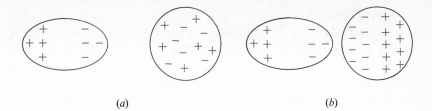

(a)   *(b)*

FIG. 15.6. *A polar molecule causes an induced moment in the nonpolar polarizable molecule leading to an attractive force between them* (a) *when far apart, and* (b) *when moved together.*

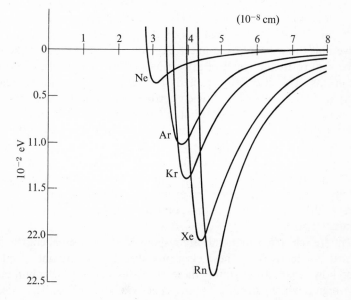

FIG. 15.7. *Plots of van der Waals interatomic potential-energy for inert gases.*

Because van der Waals forces are much weaker than ionic- and covalent-bond forces, molecular crystals have very low melting points and boiling points, and are easily deformable, i.e., they do not have much mechanical strength. Molecular crystals are not good conductors of heat and electricity. The cohesive energies are low, such as 0.1 eV/molecule in solid methane, which melts at $-183°C$, and 0.01 eV/molecule in solid hydrogen, which melts at $-259°C$. Also it may be pointed out that some of the properties of matter in bulk such as surface tension, friction, and viscosity are due to van der Waals forces.

E.   Metallic Crystals

Metallic solids have small ionization energies and are formed from atoms that have only a few weakly bound electrons in their outer shells. When atoms are brought together, each valence electron is, on the average, much closer to one molecule or another than it would be if it belonged to a single isolated atom. Thus the potential energy of an electron in a crystal is less than the potential energy of an electron in an atom. This decrease in the potential energy leads to the formation of the metallic bonds. Not all energy released is used in the formation of bonds in the crystal. Some of this energy is used in increasing the kinetic energy of the valence electrons. Thus the outermost electrons are easily set free using a part of the energy released when the crystal is formed. The free electrons in the crystal do not belong to any particular ion and move more or less freely throughout the crystal lattice. These free electrons are said to form an *electron gas*. A metal has a regular lattice of spherically symmetric positive ions that remain fixed in the electron gas. Thus the metallic bonding may be said to be the result of attraction between the positive ions and the electron gas. This attraction exceeds the repulsion between the electrons. Note that if the number of valence electrons per atom increases, the average kinetic energy also increases without any further decrease in the potential energy. This explains why metallic crystals are usually formed from the elements of the first three groups. The energy of the free electrons in the metal may have any value between 0 and certain maximum U_F, the *Fermi energy*. For example, in lithium $U_F = 4.72$ eV, while the average kinetic energy of free electrons is 2.8 eV. The formation of metallic bonds is going to be a subject of further discussion, hence at this point we shall merely summarize some of its characteristics.

The free electrons in metals are responsible for the excellent thermal and electrical conductivities. These electrons absorb any amount of energy no matter how small. In addition these electrons can absorb photons in the visible region which accounts for the opacity of the metals. The existence of free electrons also explains the light reflection coefficients of metals for electromagnetic waves, especially in the radio-frequency region. The metallic bonds are weaker than covalent ionic bonds but stronger than van der Waals bonds. For example, cohesive energies of lithium, copper, and lead are 1.6 eV/atom, 3.5 eV/atom, and 2.0 eV/atom, respectively.

Some solids are a mixture of more than one type, while others have different bondings under different conditions. An example of the former is graphite, and of the latter is tin. The structure of graphite lattice is shown in Fig. 15.8. The carbon atoms in a layer are bonded by covalent bonds, while the successive parallel layers are held together by weak van der Waals forces in a manner similar to molecular crystals. This explains why graphite is flaky and slippery.

In the case of tin below 13.2°C, tin is gray (hence the name "gray tin") and has a covalent structure similar to diamond. Above 13.2°C, it is "white tin," having a body-centered tetragonal structure.

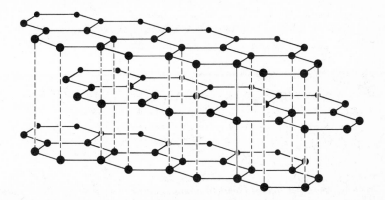

FIG. 15.8. *Structure of a graphite lattice: each layer consists of carbon atoms held by covalent bonding in a hexagonal array. The layers are held together by weak van der Waals forces.*

3. THEORY OF LATTICE VIBRATIONS[5,6,7]

Many physical properties of crystals can be explained by analyzing the lattice vibrations of the crystal. For example, investigating the dynamic mechanical properties of crystals amounts to finding the normal modes of vibrations of the atomic lattice, which is treated as an harmonic oscillator. Such oscillators may be excited by means of external sources; excitations by sound waves are helpful in measuring the acoustical properties. Vibrations of the lattice may be produced by internal energy as well, such as by heating the crystal. From these vibrations much can be learned about the thermal properties of solids, such as specific heat, thermal conductivity, thermal expansion etc.

In this section we shall briefly discuss the theory of lattice vibrations. For simplicity, we shall impose the following three conditions: (i) only one-dimensional lattice will be considered. The results obtained may be easily extended to three dimensions. (ii) We shall investigate only the normal modes of vibrations, i.e., the vibrations of the solid when no external forces are acting. (iii) In addition to the longitudinal waves, there are two types of transverse waves that can propagate in an isotropic medium. We shall limit ourselves to the longitudinal vibrations only.

Let us first investigate wave motion along a line of identical atoms, i.e., a linear monatomic lattice. In a crystal the waves are transmitted by the vibrations of atoms. To a first approximation let us assume that the force between any two atoms is proportional to their relative displacement from their equilibrium separation. Figure 15.9 shows a line of identical atoms, each

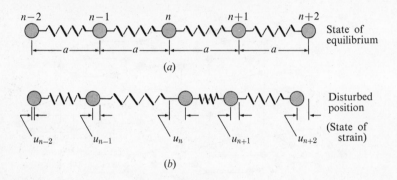

FIG. 15.9. *A line of identical atoms of lattice constant a in* (a) *a state of equilibrium, and* (b) *a disturbed position, or state of strain.*

of mass m, that are a distance a apart when in their equilibrium positions. Let u_n be the displacement of the nth atom from its equilibrium position. The resultant force, F_n, acting on the nth atom, assuming only the effects of its two nearest neighbors the $n - 1$ and $n + 1$ atoms, is given by

$$F_n = \beta(u_{n+1} - u_n) - \beta(u_n - u_{n-1}) \tag{15.7}$$

where β is an elastic constant. This equation may be written as

$$m \frac{d^2 u_n}{dt^2} = \beta(u_{n+1} - u_n) - \beta(u_n - u_{n-1}) \tag{15.8}$$

Though this is not a wave equation, there exist traveling-wave solutions in which the atoms vibrate with the same frequency. Such a wave solution is

$$u_n = A_0 e^{i(\omega t + kna)} \tag{15.9}$$

where k is the wave vector, n is an integer, and A_0 is the amplitude (identical for all atoms) which may be complex, but only the real part of the right side is taken. Substituting Eq. (15.9) into Eq. (15.8), and simplifying, we get

$$\omega = \pm \sqrt{\frac{4\beta}{m}} \sin \frac{ka}{2} \tag{15.10}$$

which is the dispersion relation, the relation between ω and k, for the linear lattice, and Eq. (15.10) gives the allowed frequencies in the lattice. The plot of the dispersion relation is shown in Fig. 15.10. Because ω is a periodic function of k with a period $2\pi/a$, there are many k-values that represent the same atomic displacement (or lattice waves). It is a usual practice to restrict k-values to lie within the range $-\pi/a < k < \pi/a$. This region is the *first Brillouin zone*. Note that inside the Brillouin zone for each value of ω there

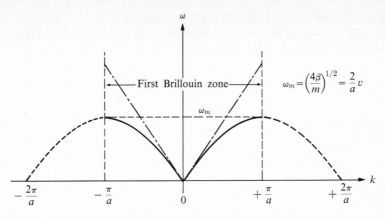

FIG. 15.10. *Dispersion curve for a linear monatomic lattice.*

are two values of k that are equal in magnitude but opposite in sign. These correspond to two waves moving in opposite directions, i.e., there is two-fold degeneracy. The maximum value of ω occurs at $k = \pi/a$. The existence of a maximum frequency means that there is an upper limit or cut off frequency for the elastic or acoustical waves in solids. This limit for most solids is $\sim 10^{15}$ Hz (cycles/sec) and is in the extreme ultrasonic frequencies. This maximum frequency for a given lattice is $\omega_m = 2v/a$. Hence only those waves are propagated for which $\omega < 2v/a$, i.e., the wavelengths shorter than $\lambda = 2a$ cannot be propagated down a linear lattice.

Let us now consider a linear diatomic lattice, i.e., a lattice with two types of atoms spaced equally at a distance a apart, as shown in Fig. 15.11. The

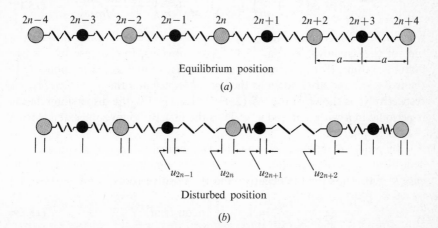

FIG. 15.11. *A linear diatomic lattice of lattice constant 2a in* (a) *a state of equilibrium, and* (b) *a disturbed position, or state of strain.*

alternate atoms have masses M and m such that $M > m$. The atoms with masses M are located at even sites, while the atoms with masses m are located at odd sites. By considering only the nearest neighbors we can analyze the problem in exactly the same way we did in the previous case except we get two equations for the two masses. These equations are

$$F_{2n} = M\frac{d^2u_{2n}}{dt^2} = \beta(u_{2n+1} - 2u_{2n} + u_{2n-1}) \tag{15.11}$$

and

$$F_{2n+1} = m\frac{d^2u_{2n+1}}{dt^2} = \beta(u_{2n+2} - 2u_{2n+1} + u_{2n}) \tag{15.12}$$

Once again there exist traveling-wave solutions of those equations of the type

$$u_{2n} = A_1 e^{i[\omega t + 2nka]} \tag{15.13}$$

and

$$u_{2n+1} = A_2 e^{i[\omega t + (2n+1)ka]} \tag{15.14}$$

Substituting these in Eqs. (15.11) and (15.12), respectively, and rearranging, we get

$$A_1(\omega^2 M - 2\beta) + A_2 2\beta \cos ka = 0 \tag{15.15}$$

$$A_1 2\beta \cos ka + A_2(\omega^2 m - 2\beta) = 0 \tag{15.16}$$

These two simultaneous equations have a non-trivial solution only if the determinant of the coefficients is zero, that is:

$$\begin{vmatrix} \omega^2 M - 2\beta & 2\beta \cos ka \\ 2\beta \cos ka & \omega^2 m - 2\beta \end{vmatrix} = 0 \tag{15.17}$$

which on solving gives

$$\omega^2 = \beta\left(\frac{1}{M} + \frac{1}{m}\right) \pm \beta\sqrt{\left(\frac{1}{M} + \frac{1}{m}\right)^2 - \frac{4\sin^2 ka}{Mm}} \tag{15.18}$$

which is the dispersion relation for the case of a linear diatomic lattice. The plot of this is shown in Fig. 15.12. As is obvious, in the case of a linear diatomic lattice, there are two sets of solutions, ω_+ and ω_-, corresponding to the two signs and are known as the *optical branch* and the *acoustical branch*, respectively, as shown in Fig. 15.12. From Eq. (15.18), the dispersion relation is periodic in k with a period π/a. Thus the first Brillouin zone extends from $-\pi/2a$ to $+\pi/2a$.

In order to understand why the two branches are called optical and acoustical, we shall calculate the ratio of the amplitudes A_1 and A_2 for the case $k = 0$. Thus for the negative and the positive roots, for $k = 0$, we get

$$\frac{A_1}{A_2} = 1 \qquad \text{acoustical} \tag{15.19}$$

$$\frac{A_1}{A_2} = -\frac{m}{M} \qquad \text{optical} \tag{15.20}$$

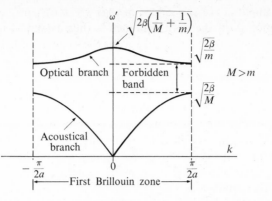

FIG. 15.12. *Dispersion relations for longitudinal waves in a linear diatomic lattice showing the optical branch, the acoustical branch, and the forbidden frequency band between* $\sqrt{2\beta/M}$ *and* $\sqrt{2\beta/m}$.

Equation (15.19) states that in the acoustical branch the ratio of the amplitudes in the two masses is independent of the masses and is always equal to unity, i.e., $A_1 = A_2$. This is shown in Fig. 15.13(a). The two masses have the same direction and phase. Thus the acoustical branch can be stimulated by any force that will cause the atoms to move in the same direction as happens in the case of sound waves or compressional waves, hence the name acoustical branch.

Let us consider Eq. (15.20). In this case masses move opposite to each

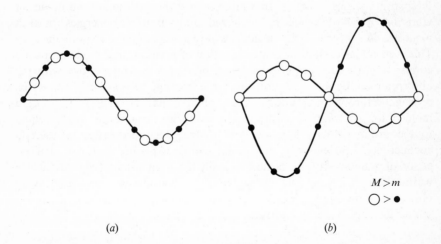

$M > m$

$\bigcirc > \bullet$

(a)   (b)

FIG. 15.13. *Wave motions illustrating* (a) *acoustical waves in which the two masses move in phase with equal amplitude, and* (b) *optical waves in which the two masses move in opposite phases with amplitudes inversely proportional to their masses.*

other. The amplitude of the lighter mass is greater than that of the heavier mass. The motion of the optical branch is thus as shown in Fig. 15.13(b). Even if $M = m$, the ratio $A_1/A_2 = -1$ for the optical branch. Because of the opposite phases of the two masses, the optical branch can be excited by only those excitations that produce the opposite effect on the two adjacent atoms. In a typical case, say in an ionic crystal, the optical branch is excited by means of an electromagnetic radiation, and hence the name optical branch. (Thus in the optical branch neighboring atoms go in opposite directions, while in the acoustical branch they go in the same direction.) The optical frequencies fall in the infrared region of the spectrum, and hence ionic crystals display a strong response to infrared electromagnetic radiation (show strong absorption of the infrared radiation).

The significance of this theory is the indication of the existence of bonding in periodic crystal structure, i.e., there are discrete bands of frequencies that can propagate through crystals. For example, in diatomic crystals, we have shown that there are two branches (optical and acoustical) that can propagate. If there are N kinds of atoms there will be N branches, i.e., the allowed frequencies will split into N bands.

The theory tells us that standing waves at $k = \pi/a$ correspond to incident and reflected rays of x-ray diffraction, thus we can explain how Bragg's law arises from dynamic theory.

The theory makes possible the determination of whether a given crystal is ionic or not by finding out if the optical branch may be excited by means of electromagnetic radiation.

In addition, this model of a vibrating lattice is useful in calculating the thermal properties of solids. In a more refined theory, the normal modes of vibration of a lattice must be quantized, and vibrational energies for each mode are $n\hbar\omega$, where n is an integer (we have neglected the zero point energy). This means that excitation or de-excitation of a vibrational mode of a solid corresponds to absorption or emission of energy $\hbar\omega$. In analogy with the absorption of photons, we introduce the concept of *phonons*[10,11], which propagate through the lattice. Each phonon has an energy $E = \hbar\omega$, a momentum $p = hk$, and its propagation velocity through the solid is equal to the group velocity $v_g = dE/dp = d\omega/dk$. Such properties as thermal conductivity, heat capacity, and others can be explained in terms of interaction of phonons with the lattice. Actually the attenuation of high-frequency waves through a solid can be explained by considering the scattering of phonons by the atoms of the lattice in a manner similar to the Compton scattering of photons by electrons.

4. FREE ELECTRON THEORY OF METALS

The electrical and the magnetic properties of the solids are due to the intrinsic charges and the magnetic moments of the electrons surrounding each atom.

Considering the distribution of electrons leads to the division of solids into insulators and metals. In *insulators*, all the electrons are bound to the atoms, while in *metals* there are always some electrons that behave as if they are free and can easily move about throughout the crystal. Our interest in this section is to explain some of the properties of metals which we discuss under the following two headings:

A. Classical Free-Electron Theory
B. Quantum Mechanical Free-Electron Model (The Sommerfeld Model)

A. Classical Free-Electron Theory

According to Drude, in 1900, metals consist of positive ions that are fixed, while the valence electrons are not attached to any particular ion but are free to move anywhere within the boundaries of the crystal. These electrons form a free-electron gas just like any other ideal gas of kinetic theory. The only difference is that in the electron gas the particles are charged. The motion of these valence electrons is random, but when an electric field is applied, the electrons move in the positive field direction, resulting in an electric current. In order to avoid the acceleration of electrons indefinitely, it is assumed that these electrons collide elastically with the positive ions. Once a steady state is reached, the current is proportional to the applied voltage (Ohm's law). These free electrons are *conduction electrons*, while the electrons in the closed shells are *ion-core electrons*.

Later, in 1909, H. A. Lorentz[12] suggested some modifications. The *classical free-electron theory* of Drude and Lorentz assumes that (i) the repulsion between the electrons is negligible, (ii) the positive ions produce a constant potential field, and (iii) classical statistics (Maxwell-Boltzmann statistics) is applicable. This theory was able to predict qualitatively many properties of metals such as electric and thermal conductivities. In addition to its inability to predict correct temperature dependences, it fails to predict the magnitudes of electronic specific heat, mean free path, diamagnetic susceptibility, and paramagnetic susceptibility, as we shall briefly outline below.

(i) *Electrical and Thermal Conductivities.* All metals obey Ohm's law, i.e., $j = \sigma E$, where σ is the electrical conductivity, j is the current density and E is the electric field. σ is independent of j and E. Using the transport phenomena of classical theory, one can easily obtain an expression for Ohm's law, but for σ the following expression results

$$\sigma \left(\propto \frac{1}{\rho} \propto R \right) \simeq 10^6 / \sqrt{T} \quad \text{(Ohm-cm)}^{-1} \quad (15.21)$$

where R is the resistance, ρ is the resistivity, and T is the absolute temperature. As is obvious from Fig. 15.14, there is a disagreement between the theoretical dependence of σ on T and the experimental values.

On the other hand, the ratio of electrical conductivity, σ, to thermal conductivity, K, is almost the same for all metals, i.e.,

$$\frac{1}{T}\frac{\sigma}{K} = \text{constant } (\simeq 2.5) \tag{15.22}$$

where σ/K is called the *Wiedenmann-Franz ratio*, and is predicted by the classical free-electron theory.

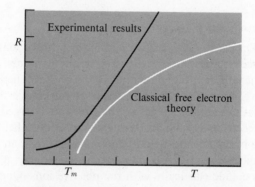

FIG. 15.14. *Plot of resistance R versus temperature T. The theoretical curve is due to the classical theory. In the experimental curve note that above a certain temperature T_m, $R \propto T$.*

(ii) *Opacity and Luster.* Metals have characteristic properties of complete opacity and high luster. These properties are easily accounted for by classical electron theory. When an electromagnetic wave falls on a metal surface, free electrons absorb all the energy carried by the wave, and hence the metal surface appears to be opaque. When these excited electrons return to the ground state, photons (light) are given off in all directions, but only those that are directed towards the metal surface can come out. This is what gives the characteristic metallic surface.

(iii) *Specific Heat.* According to the classical free-electron theory, the electron gas of a metal should behave like an ideal gas. According to kinetic theory of gases, the specific heat of an ideal gas is $(3/2)R$, where R is the universal gas constant, while experimental measurements in the case of metals indicate that the specific heat of a free-electron gas is temperature dependent and is given by

$$C_{v\text{ elec}} = 10^{-4}RT \tag{15.23}$$

There are many aspects of magnetic properties of the solids which cannot be explained satisfactorily by the classical free-electron theory.

B. Quantum Mechanical Free-Electron Model (The Sommerfeld Model)[13,14,15]

The failure of the classical free-electron theory to explain many properties of metals led Sommerfeld to suggest the following two modifications. First, the free electrons were treated quantum mechanically, thus leading to the existence of discrete energy levels. The second and the most important contribution by Sommerfeld was the application of Fermi-Dirac Statistics to the large number of free electrons in metals. We shall discuss the Sommerfeld model in the following parts:

(i)   Quantum Mechanics of Free Electrons in Metals,
(ii) Fermi-Dirac Statistics Applied to Electrons in Metals, and
(iii) Applications of the Free-Electron Theory to the Properties of Metals.

(i) *Quantum Mechanics of Free Electrons in Metals.* The electrons in a crystal are assumed to be completely free. It is also assumed that there are very high potential barriers at the boundaries, or surfaces, of the crystal that prevent these electrons from leaving the crystal. According to Sommerfeld, as suggested in 1928, the potential inside the metal is taken to be constant so that there is no net force acting on an electron. As a matter of fact, the metal is replaced by a cubical box of length L containing the free-electron gas. We showed in Chapter VI that the wave function of the electron in such a box is given by

$$\psi(x, y, z) = \left(\frac{2}{L}\right)^{3/2} \sin\left(\frac{n_x \pi}{L} x\right) \sin\left(\frac{n_y \pi}{L} y\right) \sin\frac{n_z \pi}{L} z \qquad (15.24)$$

where

$$n_x = 1, 2, 3, \ldots, \qquad n_y = 1, 2, 3, \ldots, \qquad n_z = 1, 2, 3, \ldots$$

and

$$k^2 = \frac{2mE_n}{h^2} = k_x^2 + k_y^2 + k_z^2 = \left(\frac{\pi}{L}\right)^2 (n_x^2 + n_y^2 + n_z^2) \qquad (15.25)$$

E_n being the energy of the free electron in nth state, and is given by

$$E_n = \frac{h^2}{8mL^2} (n_x^2 + n_y^2 + n_z^2) = \frac{h^2}{8mL^2} n^2 \qquad (15.26)$$

and

$$n^2 = n_x^2 + n_y^2 + n_z^2$$

Let us make a few important observations at this point. First we note that if L is large, the energy levels of electrons in a crystal are very closely spaced. Thus, for example, if $L = 1$ cm, the difference between E_{n+1} and E_n is

$$E_{n+1} - E_n = \frac{h^2}{8mL^2} (n + 1)^2 - n^2 \qquad (15.27)$$

$$\sim 3.8 \times 10^{-15} \text{ eV}$$

i.e., the energy levels are so closely packed that these almost form a continuum, called the *quasi-continuum* levels, as shown in Fig. 15.15. Note the parabolic variation of energy as a function of n.

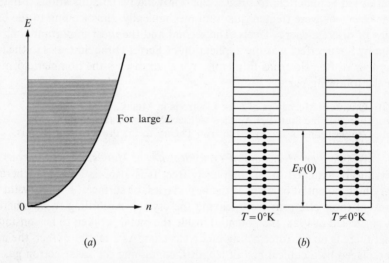

$$(a) \qquad\qquad (b)$$

FIG. 15.15.   (a) *Illustration of quasi-continuum levels for a one dimensional barrier with large L.* (b) *Filling of energy levels by electrons.*

Secondly, from Eq. (15.26) we see that the energy levels are given by the quantum numbers n_x, n_y, n_z. We may add the spin quantum number m_s, resulting in a set of four quantum numbers (n_x, n_y, n_z, m_s) that replace the four quantum numbers n, l, m_l, m_s of an electron in the atom. Thus the energy levels are filled by the electrons according to the Pauli exclusion principle, i.e., one of the quantum numbers n_x, n_y, n_z, or m_s, must be different every time an electron is added to the box. Because $m_s = \pm\frac{1}{2}$, there can be only two electrons for each value of n_x, n_y, or n_z, as shown in Fig. 15.15(b). Note that the ground state energy in this case depends upon n and L; while in the case of an electron in an atom, the ground state energy depends upon Z and the strength of the central Coulomb force.

From Eq. (15.26) it is obvious that various combinations of the integers n_x, n_y, n_z result in the same energy. For example, the levels 211, 121, and 112, all have the same energy but different wave functions. The levels with different wave functions but the same energy are said to be degenerate. The levels 211, 121, 112 are threefold degenerate.

Even though we have been able to calculate the ground state energy in terms of quantum numbers, usually we want to know this in terms of the total number of electrons and the size of the box only, i.e., in terms of the electron density. This leads us to the discussion of momentum space. Since the potential energy of the electron is zero, we may write Eq. (15.26) as

$$E_n = \frac{p^2}{2m} = \frac{h^2}{8mL^2}(n_x^2 + n_y^2 + n_z^2) \tag{15.28}$$

where p is the momentum, and may be expressed as

$$p^2 \left(\frac{2L}{h}\right)^2 = n_x^2 + n_y^2 + n_z^2 = n^2 \tag{15.29}$$

Thus the possible values of the momentum, p, are obtained by various possible combinations of quantum numbers n_x, n_y, n_z. Each possible combination (n_x, n_y, n_z) represents a lattice point in momentum space. As discussed in Chapter IV, the momentum space may be constructed by replacing x, y, z by n_x, n_y, n_z. We define a vector n in the momentum lattice, from the origin to any lattice point, by the relation $n^2 = n_x^2 + n_y^2 + n_z^2$. As n increases, so does the momentum and hence the energy of the state. Since in a typical free-electron model of a metal there are $\sim 10^{23}$ electrons, the lattice points are so closely spaced that the momentum space may be considered as continuous.

Let us consider a cubical box of volume L^3. If the density of the electrons in the box is N per unit volume, the total number of electrons is NL^3. These electrons occupy the lattice points up to a certain maximum value of n, say n_f. The ground state of this system will be determined by the energy of the electron in the state n_f. The maximum energy corresponding to n_f at zero temperature of the system is called the Fermi energy, $E_F(0)$. Thus from Eq. (15.26),

$$E_F(0) = \frac{h^2}{8mL^2} n_f^2 \tag{15.30}$$

The levels corresponding to different values of n smaller than n_f are completely filled with electrons. Taking n_f to be the radius of a sphere, we can calculate the number of electrons in this system. Because of the restriction that n must be positive, we need consider only the positive octant of the sphere in momentum space. Thus the number of integral points in the positive octant of a sphere of radius n_f is $(1/8)(4\pi/3)n_f^3$. Because m_s has two values ($\pm 1/2$), the total number of electrons, NL^3, is given by

$$NL^3 = 2 \left(\frac{1}{8}\right)\left(\frac{4\pi}{3}\right) n_f^3 \tag{15.31}$$

Substituting the value of (n_f/L) from Eq. (15.31) into Eq. (15.30), we get

$$E_F(0) = \frac{h^2}{8\pi^2 m}(3\pi^2 N)^{2/3} = \frac{\hbar^2}{2m}(3\pi^2 N)^{2/3} \tag{15.32}$$

Thus the Fermi energy is a function only of N, the density of electrons, or the number of electrons per unit volume. Fermi energies at zero degree as calculated from Eq. (15.32) for some metals are, Li, 4.72 eV; Na, 3.12 eV; K, 2.14 eV; Cs, 1.53 eV; and Ag, 5.51 eV.

Let us now introduce another quantity, $g(E)$, called the *density of states*, i.e., the number of states per unit energy interval per unit volume, given by the relation

$$\int_0^{E_F(0)} g(E)\, dE = N \tag{15.33}$$

Substituting the value of N from Eq. (15.32) after replacing $E_F(0)$ by E, and evaluating the integral, we have

$$g(E) = \left[\frac{\pi}{2}\frac{8m}{h^2}\right]^{3/2} E^{1/2} \tag{15.34}$$

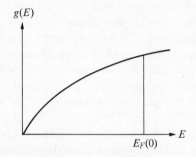

FIG. 15.16. *Plot of g(E), the density states (the number of states per unit energy interval per unit volume) versus E.*

Note that $g(E)$ is independent of the dimensions of the box. Figure 15.16 shows the plot of $g(E)$ versus E according to Eq. (15.34), showing that for a particular crystal at absolute zero temperature all the states below $E_F(0)$ are filled. The average kinetic energy $\bar{E}(0)$ of the electron in the metal at 0°K is given by

$$\bar{E}(0) = \frac{\displaystyle\int_0^{E_F(0)} g(E)E\, dE}{\displaystyle\int_0^{E_F(0)} g(E)\, dE} \tag{15.35}$$

Substituting the value of $g(E)$ from Eq. (15.34), and integrating

$$\bar{E}(0) = \frac{3}{5} E_F(0) \tag{15.36}$$

According to the classical theory $\bar{E}(0)$ should be zero because there is no motion, while according to Eq. (15.36) it is not zero.

The discussion leading to Eq. (15.36) results in the following *zero-point distribution law* for electrons in the box. Any energy state, E, is filled so long as $E < E_F(0)$, while it is completely empty if $E > E_F(0)$. Thus the occupation number, or the probability $f(E)$, that the state is occupied is given by

$$\begin{aligned} f(E) &= 1 \quad \text{for} \quad E < E_F(0) \\ f(E) &= 0 \quad \text{for} \quad E > E_F(0) \end{aligned} \tag{15.37}$$

The plot of this distribution function is shown in Fig. 15.17. The product $g(E)f(E) = N(E)$ is the measure of the number of states corresponding to energy E.

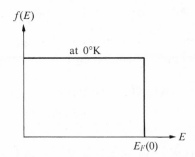

FIG. 15.17.   *The plot of the distribution function $f(E)$ versus E at zero temperature showing that energy state E is filled for $E < E_F(0)$, and is completely empty for $E > E_F(0)$.*

(ii) *Fermi-Dirac Statistics Applied to Electrons in Metals*[16,17].   If the temperature of the system is increased, some electrons are excited into states with energies greater than $E_F(0)$, and thus there is no definite boundary between the occupied and the unoccupied states. Whenever we are dealing with a system containing a large number of particles, we must resort to statistical mechanics. If the particles are assumed distinguishable, we use classical mechanics, known as Maxwell-Boltzmann statistics. On the other hand, if the particles are indistinguishable, use must be made of one of the quantum statistics—either Bose-Einstein statistics or Fermi-Dirac statistics. Indistinguishability in the case of the Bose-Einstein statistics allows a large number of particles to be placed in a lower energy state than would have been possible if the particles were distinguishable. In the case of Fermi-Dirac statistics, in addition to the restriction of indistinguishability, the imposition of the Pauli exclusion principle restricts the particles to one particle per state. This means that when we are dealing with a large number of particles most of the particles are compelled to go to the higher energy states. Hence, even at $T = 0°K$ the average energy is large and as discussed earlier all states up to $E_F(0)$ are occupied. The zero-point distribution function is given by Eq. (15.37).

The distribution of the electrons in a metal at temperature other than $0°K$ is given by the Fermi-Dirac statistics. The distribution function $f(E)$ that gives the probability that a given state is occupied, is the *Fermi-Dirac distribution law*

$$f(E) = \frac{1}{e^{(E-E_F)/kT} + 1} \qquad (15.38)$$

where k is the Boltzmann constant, E_F is the Fermi energy at temperature T, and E is the energy of the state. The expression for the Fermi energy, E_F, at different temperatures in terms of the Fermi energy at $0°K$, $E_F(0)$, is

$$E_F \simeq E_F(0)\left\{1 - \frac{\pi^2}{12}\left[\frac{kT}{E_F(0)}\right]^2\right\} \qquad (15.39)$$

The actual distribution of electrons in different states defined as the number of electrons per unit volume having energies between E and $(E + dE)$ is given by

$$N(E)\, dE = g(E)f(E)\, dE$$

$$= \frac{g(E)\, dE}{e^{(E-E_F)/kT} + 1} \qquad (15.40)$$

The plot of $N(E)$ versus E for metals is shown in Fig. 15.18 for different temperatures. Note that the presence of one in the denominator assures that the density of the electrons, $N(E)$, can never exceed the density of the states, $g(E)$, at a particular energy, E. Let us make some observations from the above discussion.

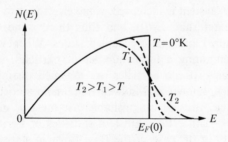

FIG. 15.18. *Plots of $N(E)$, the number of electrons per unit energy, versus E for a metal at different temperatures.*

As expected, at $T = 0°K$, $f(E) = 1$ if $E < E_F$, and $f(E) = 0$ if $E > E_F$. The increase in the temperature above $0°K$ leads to a departure from the step function. Some of the electrons in the levels just below E_F are excited into levels just above. The only region where $f(E)$ differs from zero is in the neighborhood of E_F, extending over the order of energies kT. If the electrons in the lower energy levels absorbed energies of the order of kT($1kT \simeq 0.03$ eV for room temperature), they would have to go to already occupied states, and such transitions are not allowed. Thus the fraction of electrons in a metal that can gain energy from an external source such as thermal, electric, or magnetic is equal to the ratio of the shaded area to the total area, as shown in Fig. 15.19. This is approximately equal to

$$\frac{\text{shaded area}}{\text{total area}} = \frac{kT}{E_F} = \frac{0.03}{3.00} = \frac{1}{100} \qquad \textbf{(15.41)}$$

where E_F is taken to be ~ 3 eV for a typical metal.

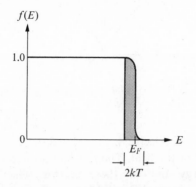

FIG. 15.19. *The fraction of the electrons that undergo transitions when the temperature is raised to T, is equal to the ratio of the shaded area to the total area shown in this figure.*

It is the Pauli principle that forces the electrons in metals to fill the states to high energies of the order of 5 eV. But the importance of quantum statistics lies in the low energy region where $kT \ll E_F$. In such conditions the electron gas is said to be degenerate. A *degeneracy temperature*, T_0, is defined by $kT_0 = E_F(0)$ and is about 10^4 to 10^{5}°K for metals with $E_F(0)$ between 5 eV and 10 eV. Thus the condition for degeneracy is $T \ll T_0$.

(iii) *Application of the Free-Electron Theory to the Properties of Metals.* Many of the properties of metals that could not be explained by classical theory are easily explained by the free-electron quantum theory. We shall discuss the following properties:

(a) Electrical Conductivity
(b) Thermal Conductivity
(c) Electronic Specific Heat

(a) *Electrical Conductivity in Metals.* According to the free electron quantum theory, the valence electrons in a metal occupy definite energy states according to the Fermi-Dirac distribution function. Hence each electron has a definite kinetic energy and a corresponding definite velocity. In the absence of any field, the electrons move randomly in all possible directions. As shown in Fig. 15.20 (the density distribution plot) there are as many electrons moving with a given velocity in the positive X direction as in the negative X direction. Such a random motion of the electrons implies that there is no net current in the metal. Let us see what happens when an external electric field of strength ε is applied, say along the X axis, as shown in Fig.

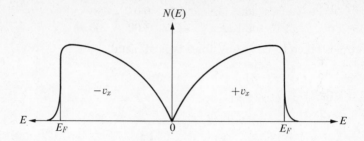

Fig. 15.20.   *The density distribution of electrons moving with velocity* v_x *in the* $+X$ *direction and* $-X$ *direction.*

15.21. The presence of the electric field makes the electrons accelerate toward the positive terminal of the field. The result of acceleration is an increase in the velocity and energy, and only those electrons which are near the Fermi energy, E_F, can gain energy. This leads to a change in the energy density distribution of the electrons, as shown in Fig. 15.21. As is obvious, there are more electrons with velocity components along the $+X$ direction than along the $-X$ direction, and the excess of electrons along the $+X$ direction have shifted to the higher energy states. The net excess of electrons in the $+X$ direction constitutes electrical current, and hence contribution to electrical conductivity.

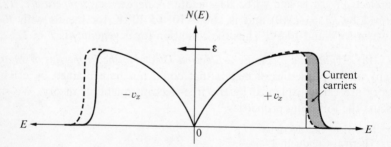

Fig. 15.21.   *The application of an electric field* $\mathcal{E}$ *in the direction shown results in a shift in the density distribution of the electrons. An excess of electrons in the positive x-direction constitutes electrical current.*

This argument may lead us to think that once the external field is applied, the electron will be pushed continuously into higher energy states and that the current will increase continuously. This is contrary, however, to the observed steady-state current in metals. The reason that electrons do not constantly shift to higher energy states is due to the collisions between the electrons and the metallic ions, causing the electrons to lose most of their energy and momentum. The distance the electron travels before colliding with the metallic ion is called the *mean free path*, l. Thus the conductivity, σ, will be directly proportional to l, while resistivity, ρ, will be inversely proportional to l, i.e.,

$$\rho = \frac{1}{\sigma} \propto \frac{1}{l} \tag{15.42}$$

In the classical theory it was assumed that l was equal to the interatomic distance and remains constant with temperature, while the observed change in resistivity with T shown in Fig. 15.14 was due to increase in energy, and hence in velocity of the electrons at higher temperatures. According to quantum statistics, as in Eq. (15.39), the increase in average energy of the conduction electrons with temperature is almost negligible. The variation in ρ with T is due to the variation of l with T as explained below.

The electron is treated as a wave colliding with atoms in a crystal, in a manner similar to the diffraction of x-rays from a periodic array. At absolute zero the atoms are essentially at rest, and hence diffraction of electron waves results in a coherently scattered beam, while the mean free path l is also fixed. As the temperature increases, thermal vibrations result in the displacement of the atoms. This has two consequences. First, the scattered electron beam is incoherent; second, the mean free path is inversely proportional to the square of the atomic-vibration amplitude and hence directly proportional to the temperature, i.e.,

$$l \propto \frac{1}{T} \tag{15.43a}$$

and

$$\rho = \frac{1}{\sigma} \propto T \tag{15.43b}$$

Even though Eq. (15.43b) does not exactly give the ρ versus T plot shown in Fig. 15.14, it does agree very well above a certain temperature. But if one carries out quantitative calculations of the mean free path using quantum mechanics, the results are quite in agreement.

(b) *Thermal Conductivity.* Thermal conductivity can proceed via the atoms as well as the free electrons. In materials other than metals, the conduction is mostly through the atoms. Instead of talking about the vibrations of the atoms, it is convenient to talk in terms of phonons. The number of phonons increases with increasing temperature, but the mean free paths of these phonons (of energy $h\nu$) through the crystal are very small, ~ 10 Å to 100 Å. Thus for nonmetals, the conductivities are very low. On the contrary, for metals even though the phonons mean free paths are small, the mean free paths of the conduction (or free) electrons are very large, resulting in very large thermal conductivities. Because the free electrons in metals are mostly responsible for thermal as well as electrical conductivities, it leads us to suspect that there must be some relation between the two. As a matter of fact the Wiedemann-Franz law discussed earlier is such a relation that predicts that K/σ is the same for all metals. Such a relation has been derived theoretically and the constant is found to be $2.45 \times 10^{-8} (V/°C)^2$, which agrees with experimentally measured values.

(c) *Electronic Specific Heat.*   Once again we consider a metal to be made of two parts—atoms and a free-electron gas. Thus the specific heat of a metal may be written as

$$C_v = C_v(\text{atomic}) + C_v(\text{electronic}) \qquad \textbf{(15.44a)}$$

$C_v(\text{atomic})$ is equal to $3R$, while the electron gas having three degrees of freedom will contribute $3/2\ R$. Thus

$$C_v = 3R + \frac{3}{2}R = \frac{9}{2}R \qquad \textbf{(15.44b)}$$

But it is well known that the specific heat of all solids above the characteristic temperature is the same and is equal to $3R$. Thus how do we get rid of the $(3/2)R$ from the electron gas contribution? According to Fermi-Dirac statistics, in an electron gas at temperature T, only those electrons whose energies are within $E_F \pm kT$ will absorb heat. The fraction of such electrons is $2kT/E_F$. Hence the electronic specific heat is

$$C_v(\text{electronic}) \sim \frac{3}{2}R \times \frac{2kT}{E_F} \sim \frac{3RkT}{E_F} = \gamma T \qquad \textbf{(15.45)}$$

where γ is a constant equal to $3Rk/E_F$. But γT is only one percent of $3R$ (see Eq. (15.41)), and hence there is no appreciable contribution from the free electron gas to the specific heat of a metal.

Further refinements are achieved by calculating the value of γ, using the density of electrons in metals according to the zone theory.

5. QUANTUM THEORY OF SOLIDS

The free-electron theory discussed previously was quite successful in explaining thermal and electrical properties of metals. But this assumption of electrons being free does not apply to the ionic- and covalent-bonded crystals because in these cases the valence electrons are localized near their parent atoms. Actually the theory cannot explain why some solids are insulators, some are conductors and some are semiconductors. The quantum theory of solids, also known as the band theory of solids answers these and many other problems. There are basically two different approaches, but the results are the same.

A.   Schrödinger Equation for a Periodic Potential (Zone Theory)
B.   Band Theory or Tight-Binding Approximation

A. Schrödinger Equation for a Periodic Potential (Zone Theory)

This is actually a refinement over the free-electron model theory. The electron is supposed to be moving in a periodic potential as shown in Fig. 15.22. This periodic potential is due to (i) the periodic charge distribution arising from the ion cores located at the lattice sites, and (ii) the interaction of all other electrons in this crystal with this single electron. The resulting potential and the lattice spacing is quite uniform throughout the crystal except at the surface as shown in Fig. 15.22 for the case of one-dimension. We are interested in solving the Schrödinger wave equation of the electron moving in such a potential and to obtain the energy levels.[18,19]

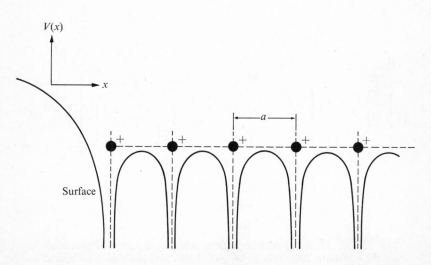

FIG. 15.22. *The periodic potential within a perfectly periodic crystal lattice. The abrupt change in the potential form at the left corresponds to the surface of the crystal.*

The problem is much simplified if the form of the potential shown in Fig. 15.22 is replaced by an infinite periodic one-dimensional square-well potential shown in Fig. 15.23. This is the *Kronig-Penny Model*[20], which we shall now discuss. Let us assume that an electron of mass m is moving in a periodic square-well potential of barrier height, V_0, and width b spaced a distance a apart. The Schrödinger wave equation for a one-dimensional periodic potential $V(x)$ is

$$\frac{d^2\psi(x)}{dx^2} + \frac{2m}{\hbar^2}[E - V(x)]\psi(x) = 0 \qquad (15.46)$$

or

$$\frac{d^2\psi(x)}{dx^2} + k^2\psi(x) = 0 \qquad (15.47)$$

where

$$k^2 = \frac{2m}{\hbar^2}[E - V(x)] \tag{15.48}$$

According to Bloch[21], the wave function $\psi(x)$ for a wave traveling through a lattice of periodicity a with a wave number k must have the same periodicity as the lattice, i.e.,

$$\psi(x) = u(x)e^{ikx} \tag{15.49a}$$

where $u(x)$ is a periodic function such that

$$u(x + a) = u(x) \tag{15.49b}$$

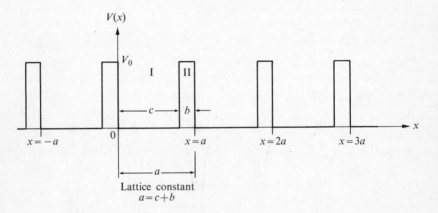

FIG. 15.23. *The ideal periodic infinite series of square well potentials used by Kronig and Penny to investigate the quantum mechanical behavior of electrons in a periodic lattice.*

We could substitute Eq. (15.49a) into Eq. (15.46), solve for $u(x)$ and obtain the allowed energy levels. But we shall follow a simpler procedure given below.

According to Fig. 15.23 there are two types of regions, I and II. For region I, $V(x) = 0$ and hence the S.W.E. is

$$\frac{d^2\psi_\mathrm{I}}{dx^2} + \alpha^2\psi_\mathrm{I} = 0 \qquad \text{for} \qquad (n - 1) < x < na - b \tag{15.50}$$

where n is an integer and

$$\alpha = \sqrt{2mE}/\hbar \tag{15.51}$$

The solution of Eq. (15.50) is

$$\psi_\mathrm{I}(x) = Ae^{i\alpha x} + Be^{-i\alpha x} \tag{15.52}$$

where A and B are arbitrary constants.

For region II, where $V(x) = V_0$, the S.W.E. is

$$\frac{d^2\psi_{II}}{dx^2} + \beta^2\psi_{II} = 0 \quad \text{for} \quad na - b < x < na \quad (15.53)$$

where n is an integer and

$$\beta = \sqrt{2m(V_0 - E)}/\hbar \quad (15.54)$$

and the solution, with C and D as arbitrary constants, is

$$\psi_{II}(x) = Ce^{\beta x} + De^{-\beta x} \quad (15.55)$$

Using the Bloch theorem given by Eq. (15.49) into Eqs. (15.52) and (15.55), we get

$$u_I(x) = Ae^{i(\alpha-k)x} + Be^{-i(\alpha+k)x} \quad (15.56)$$

$$u_{II}(x) = Ce^{(\beta-ik)x} + De^{-(\beta+ik)x} \quad (15.57)$$

We impose the boundary conditions that u_I and u_{II} and their derivative be continuous at $x = 0$ and $x = a$ (or in general at $x = (n - 1)a$ and $x = na - b$ and using the periodicity condition that $u(a) = u(0)$, $\psi(a \pm b) = \psi(\pm b)$, we obtain

$$A + B = C + D$$

$$i(\alpha - k)A - i(\alpha + k)B = (\beta - ik)C - (\beta + ik)D$$

$$Ae^{i(\alpha-k)(a-b)} + Be^{-i(\alpha+k)(a-b)} = Ce^{-(\beta-ik)b} + De^{(\beta+ik)b}$$

$$i(\alpha - k)Ae^{i(\alpha-k)(a-b)} - i(\alpha + k)Be^{i(\alpha+k)(a-b)} = (\beta - ik)Ce^{-(\beta-ik)b}$$
$$- (\beta + ik)De^{(\beta+ik)b} \quad (15.58)$$

The non-trivial solution is obtained by equating the determinant of the coefficient of A, B, C, D equal to zero. This, on simplification, yields

$$\cos ka = \frac{\beta^2 - \alpha^2}{2\alpha\beta} \sinh \beta b \sin \alpha(a - b) + \cosh \beta b \cos \alpha(a - b) \quad (15.59)$$

It is easy to solve this equation for the energy levels of an electron if we assume that b becomes very small and V_0 becomes very large so long as the product $\beta^2 b$ remains constant. This reduces Eq. (15.59) to

$$\cos ka = P \frac{\sin \alpha a}{\alpha a} + \cos \alpha a \quad (15.60)$$

where

$$P = \lim_{\substack{b\to 0 \\ \beta\to\infty}} \left(\frac{1}{2}\beta^2 ab\right) = \frac{ma}{\hbar^2} V_0 b \quad (15.61)$$

The meaning and interpretation of Eq. (15.60) will become clear from the following graphical representations:

(i) *The Right Side of the Equation.* The right side is a function of energy and in Fig. 15.24, the plot of $P[(\sin \alpha a)/\alpha a] + \cos \alpha a$ versus αa is shown by the solid oscillatory curve. The left side of Eq. (15.60), i.e., $\cos ka$ sets a limit on the function given by the right side. The two extreme values of cos ka are $+1$ and -1 and are shown by the horizontal broken lines. For real values of k, the physically meaningful solutions of Eq. (15.60) lie within these two limits. Thus the values of α or E allowed by Eq. (15.60) are shown by the horizontal heavy lines along the αa axis. These energies, called the *allowed zones, allowed regions,* or *allowed bands,* are the only energies that an electron can possess when moving in a periodically varying potential. In between the allowed regions are the *forbidden regions, forbidden bands,* or *forbidden zones* of energy that the electron may not take while moving through the periodic potential. The allowed zones are shown shaded in Fig. 15.24.

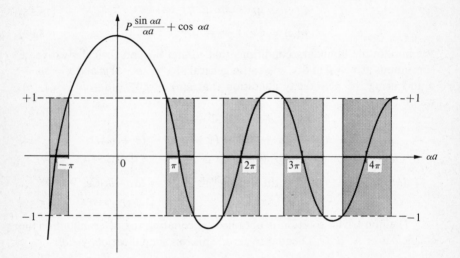

FIG. 15.24. *The graphical solution obtained by the Kronig-Penny Model. The plot of* $[P \sin (\alpha a)/\alpha a] + \cos \alpha a$ *versus* $k\alpha$ *is shown by the solid oscillating curve, while the physically meaningful solutions are obtained by imposing the limitation* $\cos k\alpha = \pm 1$. *Heavy curves are the resulting allowed values.*

The size of the allowed or the forbidden region depends upon the value of the barrier $V_0 b$. If $V_0 b$ increases, so does P and this leads to the narrowing of the allowed energy bands. This is the situation with the inner electrons in an atom that are tightly bound to the nucleus, i.e., these electrons are in between two high potential barriers.

On the other hand if $V_0 b$ decreases, the allowed energy zones become broader, and in the limit $V_0 = 0$ the allowed zones overlap while the forbidden regions disappear. This is the situation with the valence electrons in atoms. Actually, $V_0 = 0$ corresponds to the case of the free-electron theory, i.e., the electron is free to move in the whole lattice.

(ii) *The Left Side of the Equation.* According to the left hand side of Eq. (15.60), cos ka can take only specific values for each allowed value of E. Thus for each value of E there is a corresponding value of k. Figure 15.25(a) shows

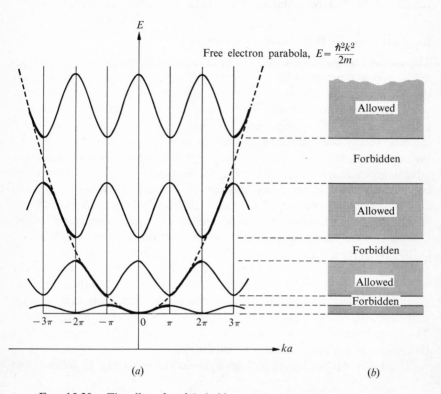

(a)   (b)

FIG. 15.25. *The allowed and forbidden energy regions of an electron in a periodic potential: (a) the Plot of E versus k according to Eq. (15.60). The allowed energies are shown by heavy lines. The broken-line parabolic curve is that for the free electron case, and (b) the resulting allowed and forbidden bands.*

the plot of E versus ka. The allowed values of E of an electron in a periodic potential are indicated by heavy lines. The broken-line parabola shown corresponds to the case of a free electron. Note that the heavy lines depart slightly from the broken-line parabola only in the neighborhood of $\pm n\pi$, n being an integer. This means that the electron in a periodic potential behaves like a free electron for most values of k except those near $\pm n\pi$. That the discontinuities happen at $ka = \pm n\pi$ or $(2\pi/\lambda)a = \pm n\pi$, i.e., $n\lambda = 2a$ which is the Bragg condition for the case of $\theta = 90°$ in the equation $n\lambda = 2a \sin \theta$. Thus discontinuities represent locations at which the electron waves are reflected backward. For large values of k, the electron takes the same energy as that of a free electron, $E = \hbar^2 k^2 / 2m$.

The energy gaps between the allowed energy values correspond to the imaginary values of k and are the forbidden-energy values. If the allowed and the forbidden regions are extended to the right, as shown in Fig. 15.25(b), we get the schematic representation of the allowed and the forbidden bands.

B.   Band Theory or Tight-Binding Approximation[22, 23]

This theory follows just the opposite approach to the one used in zone theory or the periodic potential for an electron. The band theory assumes that all the electrons are tightly bound to their nuclei and investigates what happens when the atoms are brought close enough for the neighboring nuclei to interact with the valence electrons. For metals, it is more convenient to use the zone theory because the valence electrons in a metal may be assumed to be almost free, but in the case of insulators and semiconductors, it is more advantageous to use the band theory. We may point out that it is electrical conductivity that distinguishes between conductors, insulators and semi-conductors. Insulators are those materials that are poor conductors of electricity, such as diamond, quartz, and most covalent and ionic solids. Conductors are those materials that are very good conductors of electricity ($\sim 10^{20}$ times greater than insulators) such as silver, copper, and other metals. In between insulators and conductors are semiconductors. The conductivity of semiconductors is much less than that of the conductors, but their electrical conductivity increases with increasing temperature—a characteristic contrary to the metallic conductors where the conductivity decreases with temperature. The band theory, as we shall see below, can explain the formation of these three types of materials and their conductivities.

Consider a typical atom with its levels as shown in Fig. 15.26(a). When

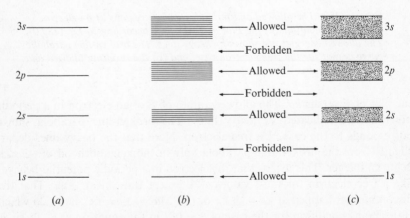

FIG. 15.26.   (a) *The energy levels of an isolated atom.* (b) *The energy bands in a solid containing a small number of atoms.* (c) *Continuous energy levels in energy bands in a solid containing a large number of atoms.*

N such atoms are brought together bands are formed as shown in Fig. 15.26(b). In order to calculate the number of electronic states available in a given energy band of a particular material very involved quantum mechanical calculations are required. But if we assume the tight-binding approximation, the energy band is always formed from the energy levels of isolated atoms; and hence the wave-functions of the band are linear combinations of the wave-functions of the corresponding energy levels of isolated atoms. The degeneracy factor associated with a given energy band will be the same as that in the isolated atom. Thus the $1s$, $2s$, $2p$, $3s$, $3p$, $3d$, . . . bands correspond to $1s$, $2s$, $2p$, $3s$, $3p$, $3d$, . . . energy levels in isolated atoms. If there are N atoms in a solid, each band would have N levels. But if the spin degeneracy is taken into account, there will be $2N$ states in the $1s$ band, $2N$ states in the $2s$ band, $6N$ states in $2p$ band, $2N$ states in $3s$ band, $6N$ states in the $3p$ band, $10N$ states in the $3d$ band and so on. When these bands are formed, there are four different possibilities depending upon the separation between these bands as shown in Fig. 15.27.

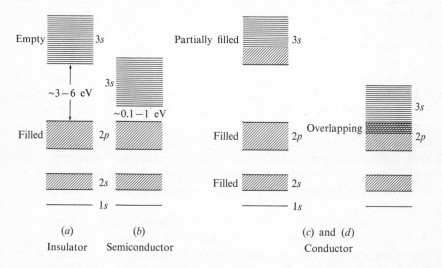

Fig. 15.27.   *Band formation results in four different possibilities: (a) an insulator is formed if the gap between the bands is very large, (b) a semiconductor is formed if the gap is very small, and a conductor is formed, (c) if the upper band is partially filled, or (d) if the filled and empty bands overlap.*

The first possibility is shown in Fig. 15.27(a) where the forbidden region between the highest completely filled band and the lowest empty band is very wide, say ~3–6 eV. It is impossible at the physically achievable temperatures to cause the electrons to move from the filled band to the empty band by means of thermal excitations, or by the application of an electric field. The electrons cannot move about the filled band because of the Pauli exclusion principle. Thus the bands are either full or empty, and no free electron current can be made to flow. Solids with this type of band formation are classified as insulators. The forbidden energy gaps for some insulators are given in Table 15.1. The uppermost filled or partially filled band is referred to as the *valence band*.

TABLE 15.1
FORBIDDEN ENERGY GAPS IN INSULATORS
AND SEMICONDUCTORS

Insulators	Gap in eV	Semiconductors	Gap in eV
Diamond (c)	5.33	Silicon (Si)	1.14
Zinc Oxide (ZnO)	3.2	Germanium (Ge)	0.67
Silver Chloride (AgCl)	3.2	Tellurium (Te)	0.33

The second possibility is shown in Fig. 15.27(b) where the forbidden energy gap is very small, say ~ 0.1 to 1 eV. There is some possibility that the electrons from the highest filled energy band can be thermally excited to the lower portion of the lowest empty band. Those few electrons are thus available for electrical currents in the otherwise empty band. The vacancies, or empty electronic states, that remain near the top of the valence band are called *holes*. These holes behave like "positive electrons" and can contribute to the electron current flow as illustrated in Fig. 15.28. When an electric field is applied the electron below the hole may gain enough energy to jump to and occupy the hole, which is equivalent to saying that the hole has moved to the lower energy state, and such a motion of the hole also contributes to the electric current. Such materials with small forbidden energy bands are *semiconductors*. The forbidden energy gaps for some semiconductors are given in Table 15.1.

The third possibility in band formation is shown in Fig. 15.27(c) where the number of electrons in a crystal is such that it does not completely fill the uppermost energy band. Because the band is partially filled, many of the electrons can behave as free electrons and be used as charge, or current, carriers. Such solids are conductors showing all the characteristics of a metallic conductor. A solid can still be a conductor even if the band is completely filled, provided the empty and the filled bands overlap, shown as a fourth possibility in Fig. 15.27(d).

Let us investigate some specific examples now. Consider an alkali metal such as sodium, Na, ($Z = 11$). Its electronic configuration is $1s^2 2s^2 2p^6 3s^1$. This means in a crystal of N atoms there are $2N$ $1s$ electrons, $2N$ $2s$ electrons, $6N$ $2p$ electrons, and N $3s$ electrons. Hence the $1s$-, $2s$- and $2p$-bands are completely filled while the $3s$ band is only half-full. Thus sodium and all other alkali metals should be metallic conductors, and they are. The situation, however, is more complicated. At an equilibrium distance of $r_0 = 3.67 \times 10^{-8}$ cm for sodium metal, according to tight-binding approximation, the bands $1s$, $2s$, and $2p$ remain undisturbed, but the bands corresponding to $3s$ and $3p$ atomic levels overlap. Thus the N conduction electrons in $3s$ states have $N + 6N = 7N$ empty states available for conduction.

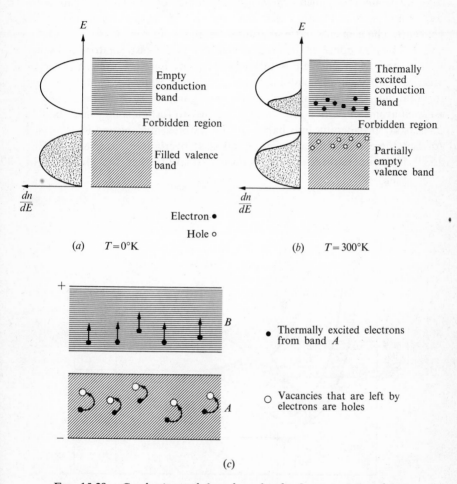

FIG. 15.28. *Conduction and the valence bands of a pure semiconductor at two different temperatures* (a) $T = 0°K$, (b) $T = 300°K$. *The vacancies, or empty electronic states, are called holes and behave like positive electrons. A hole is said to have moved when an electron jumps into it from a neighbor atom as shown in* (c).

Let us consider Mg($Z = 12$) which has an electron configuration of $1s^2 2s^2 2p^6 3s^2$. According to the tight-binding approximation all the bands should be completely filled, and magnesium should be an insulator or semiconductor. But, as in the case of sodium, the $3s$- and $3p$-bands overlap, and hence some of the electrons move over from the $3s$-states to the $3p$-states, leaving the $3s$ state not completely filled. As a matter of fact, there are $2N + 6N = 8N$ states of which only $2N$ states are filled. Thus magnesium and all other solids that have complete shells but whose bands overlap are conductors and are sometimes called *semimetals*. Examples of overlapping bands are $3d$, $4s$ and $4p$ in transition elements, and $4f$, $5d$, $6s$, and $6p$ in rare-earth elements. The elements in these groups are all conductors.

Let us now consider the examples of formations of insulators and semi-conductors. Most covalent solids whose atoms have an even number of valence electrons are insulators. As an example, consider the band formation in diamond (C). Its atomic electronic configuration is $1s^2 2s^2 2p^2$. When N isolated atoms of carbon are brought together to form a solid, the $2s$ and $2p$ levels start broadening into bands. As the interatomic spacing is decreased further, these bands broaden more and start overlapping as shown in Fig. 15.29. If the interatomic distance is decreased still further, the continuum of

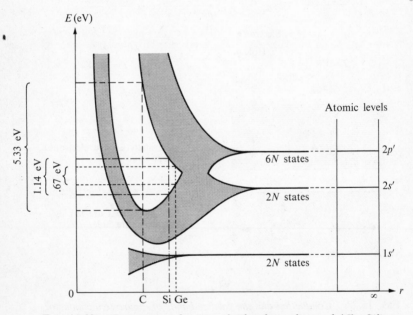

Fig. 15.29. *Energy gaps between the bands in diamond (C), Silicon (Si), and Germanium (Ge) depend upon their respective equilibrium distances as shown.*

$2s$ and $2p$ states that had a total of $2N + 6N = 8N$ states splits into two bands each containing $4N$ quantum states. The four electrons of the carbon atom that were in $2s$- and $2p$-atomic states have now filled the lower band with $4N$ electrons when carbon is in solid state, while the upper band is empty. At the equilibrium distance for diamond, which is $\sim 1.5 \times 10^{-8}$ cm, the lowest valence-band and the upper empty-band separation, as shown in Fig. 15.29 is ~ 5 eV. This is a relatively large forbidden energy gap, and this explains why diamond is a good insulator.

Let us now consider the case of silicon (Si) and germanium (Ge). The same band scheme as for diamond, shown in Fig. 15.29, apply to Si and Ge except that the bands correspond to different atomic-energy levels. But there is one fundamental difference; as shown in Fig. 15.29, the equilibrium separations in Si and Ge are larger than in diamond. This leads to smaller energy gaps in Si and Ge. As compared to the forbidden band of ~ 5 eV in diamond, it is 1.2 eV in silicon, and 0.7 eV in germanium. The small energy gap in Si and Ge imply that electrons from the completely filled valence bands can move to the empty conduction band simply by means of thermal excitation, and hence these electrons in the conduction band serve as current carriers. These materials with small energy gaps are semiconductors.

PROBLEMS

1. Show that the value of the Madelung constant, α, for all face-centered cubic crystals, such as NaCl, is 1.7476; and for a body-centered crystal such as CsCl, the constant is 1.7627.

2. If for N ion-pairs in a crystal

$$U = NE_{p,r_0} = -\frac{N\alpha e^2}{4\pi\epsilon_0 r_0}\left(1 - \frac{1}{n}\right)$$

   Calculate the value of n for NaCl if the lattice energy $E_{p,r_0} = -185.7$ kCal/ion-pair, $\alpha = 1.7476$ and $r_0 = 2.81$ Å.

3. In the case of a KCl crystal, the Madelung constant is 1.7476, and the equilibrium distance between ions of opposite signs is 3.14 Å. If the ionization energy of potassium is 4.34 eV and the electron affinity of chlorine is 3.61 eV, calculate
   (a) the cohesive energy of KCl
   (b) the value of the constant n.
   (c) Explain the difference between the calculated value of the cohesive energy and the measured value of 6.42 eV.

4. For the case of a LiCl crystal the spacing between the ions is 2.57 Å, while the cohesive energy is 6.8 eV per ion-pair:
   (a) What is the value of the Madelung constant?
   (b) Calculate the value of n.

5. If the interatomic distance at equilibrium in cesium chloride is 3.56 Å and n is 11.5, calculate the potential energy of cesium chloride.

6. Show that the Madelung constant for the monatomic linear lattice is 1.38.

7. Calculate the frequencies of the optical and the acoustical branches for (a) $M \rightarrow \infty$ and (b) $m \rightarrow 0$.

8. Assuming sodium to be a linear monatomic lattice, calculate the highest and

lowest possible frequencies of lattice vibrations. Use the known data for sodium.

9. Plot the dispersion relations in the case of a linear diatomic lattice for which $M = 4m$.

10. Consider a monatomic linear lattice in which the interaction takes place between the first two nearest neighbors (instead of just the nearest neighbor). What is the dispersion relation in this case for the longitudinal displacement only?

11. Obtain a dispersion relation for the propagation of transverse waves through a linear monatomic lattice. (It is similar to one obtained for the longitudinal waves except it is decreased in magnitude.)

12. Derive expressions for the wavelength, momentum, and energy of phonons that are created by first-order Brillouin scattering. Let θ be the angle between the incident light and scattered phonon, and k_0 be the incident wave vector.

13. If a state of a system is represented by (n_x, n_y, n_z), calculate the energies corresponding to the following cases:
    (a) E_1 for (2, 2, 2) and E_2 for (3, 2, 2);
    (b) E_3 for (20, 20, 20) and E_4 for (21, 20, 20).
    Also calculate $\Delta E = E_2 - E_1$ and $\Delta E' = E_4 - E_3$. What conclusions do you draw from the comparison of ΔE and $\Delta E'$?

14. What change in the spectrum of the allowed states will result if the electrons were confined to a cylindrical boundary instead of rectangular?

15. Assuming that the kinetic theory is applicable to a Fermi gas, calculate the pressure of a Fermi gas at T = 0°K.

16. What changes will result in the occupation of quantum states if the electrons in the metal were to follow the classical Maxwell-Boltzmann energy distribution instead of Fermi-Dirac?

17. If the average spacing in a solid lattice were increased
    (a) 10-fold
    (b) 100-fold
    what changes will result in the electronic specific heat at room temperature?

18. Derive Eq. (15.36) from Eqs. (15.34) and (15.35).

19. If we define a Fermi temperature $T_0 = E_F(0)/k$, calculate T/T_0 for copper.

20. Calculate the Fermi energy $E_F(0)$ for sodium.

21. Show that if $E_F(0) = 7$ eV and $\overline{E}(0) = \frac{3}{5}E_F(0)$, the classical temperature corresponding to this value of $\overline{E}(0)$ is $\sim 10^4$°K.

22. Show that for copper $E_F(0) \simeq 7.1$ eV (note that $N = 0.83 \times 10^{23}/\text{cm}^3$). From the relation $\overline{E} = \frac{3}{5}E_F(0) = \frac{1}{2}m\overline{v}^2$ calculate $\overline{v}$ at 0°K. How does this value compare with room temperature for which $\overline{E} \simeq 0.025$ eV and $\overline{v} \simeq 10^6$ cm/sec?

23. The Fermi energy in copper is 7.1 eV. Approximately what fraction of the free electrons in copper are in the excited state
    (a) at room temperature
    (b) at 1087°C?

24. What will be the Fermi energy of zinc if its electronic specific heat is $\sim 1.3 \times 10^{-4}T$ kcal/kg °K?

25. If the Fermi energy of aluminum is 11.7 eV, what is its electronic specific heat at 1000°K?

26. Derive Eq. (15.59) from Eq. (15.58).
27. Derive Eq. (15.60).

REFERENCES

1. Mott, N. F., and R. W. Gurney, *Electronic Processes in Ionic Crystals*, 2nd ed. New York: Oxford Univ. Press, 1948.
2. Tosi, M. P., *Solid State Physics*, vol. 16, New York: Academic Press, 1964.
3. Evjen, H. M., *Phys. Rev.*, **39**, 680, (1932).
4. Born, M., *Atomic Physics*, 7th ed., Hafner, 1962.
5. Pauling, L., *The Nature of the Chemical Bond*, Ithaca, N. Y.: Cornell Univ. Press, 1960.
6. Margenau, H., *Revs. Mod. Phys.*, **11**, 1, (1939).
7. Blackman, M., *Proc. Roy. Soc.*, **A148**, 365, (1935), and **A159**, 416, (1937).
8. Born, M., and Th. von Karman, *Phys. Zeit.*, **13**, 297, (1912).
9. Svensson, E. C., B. N. Brockhouse, and J. M. Rowe, *Phys. Rev.*, **155**, 619, (1967).
10. Collins, R. J., and H. Y. Fan, *Phys. Rev.*, **93**, 674, (1954).
11. *International Semiconductor Conferences*, Exter, 1962; Paris, 1964; Kyoto, 1966; Moscow, 1968.
12. Lorentz, H. A., *The Theory of Electrons*, 2nd ed., New York: Dover Publications, Inc., 1952.
13. Sommerfeld, A., *Z. Physik*, **47**, 1, (1928).
14. Sommerfeld, A., *Naturwiss*, **15**, 824, (1927).
15. Sommerfeld, A., and N. H. Frank, *Revs. Mod. Phys.*, **3**, 1, (1931).
16. Fermi, E., *Z. Physik*, **36**, 902, (1926).
17. Dirac, P. A. M., *Proc. Roy. Soc.*, **A112**, 661, (1926).
18. Herman, F., *Proceedings of International Conference*, Paris, 1964.
19. Herman, F., et al., *Proceedings of the Symposium on Energy Bands in Metals and Alloys*, Los Angeles, 1967.
20. Kronig, R. de L., and W. G. Penny, *Proc. Roy. Soc.*, **A130**, 499, (1931).
21. Bloch, F., *Zeit. fur Physik*, **23**, 555, (1928).
22. McKelvey, John P., *Solid State and Semiconductor Physics*, p. 231, New York: Harper & Row Publishing, Inc., 1966.
23. Koster, G. F., *Phys. Rev.*, **98**, 901, (1955).

SUGGESTIONS FOR FURTHER READING

1. Levy, Robert A., *Principles of Solid State Physics*, New York: Academic Press, 1968.
2. Azaroff, Leonid V., and James J. Brophy, *Electronic Processes in Materials*, New York: McGraw-Hill Book Company, 1963.

3. Blakemore, John S., *Solid State Physics*, Philadelphia: W. B. Saunders Company, 1969.

4. Kittel, C., *Introduction to Solid State Physics*, 3rd ed., New York: John Wiley & Sons, Inc., 1966.

5. Seitz, F., *Modern Theory of Solids*, New York: McGraw-Hill Book Company, 1940.

6. Weinreich, G., *Elementary Theory for Advanced Students*, New York: John Wiley & Sons, Inc., 1965.

7. Dekker, A. J., *Solid State Physics*, Englewood Cliffs, N. J.: Prentice-Hall, Inc., 1957.

8. Clark, H., *Solid State Physics*, London: Macmillan and Company Limited; New York: St. Martin's, 1968.

9. McKelvey, John P., *Solid State and Semiconductor Physics*, New York: Harper and Row Publ., Inc., 1966.

10. Ziman, J. M., *Principles of the Theory of Solids*, New York: Cambridge Univ. Press, 1964.

11. Born, M., and K. Huang, *Dynamical Theory of Crystal Lattices*, New York: Oxford Univ. Press, 1956.

12. Slater, J. C., *Quantum Theory of Matter*, 2nd ed., New York: McGraw-Hill Book Company, 1968.

13. Spenk, E., *Electronic Semiconductors*, New York: McGraw-Hill Book Company, 1958.

14. Raimes, S., *The Wave Mechanics of Electrons in Metals*, New York: Interscience Publishers, 1961.

15. Jones, H., *The Theory of Brillouin Zones and Electronic States in Crystals*, Amsterdam: North Holland Publishing Co., 1960.

APPENDIX A

Tables of Constants

DEFINED VALUES AND EQUIVALENTS

Meter (m)	1650763.73 wavelengths of the unperturbed transition $2p_{10} - 5d_5$ in ^{86}Kr
Kilogram (kg)	Mass of the international kilogram
Second (s)	Astronomical 1/31 556925.9747 of the tropical year at 12^hET, 0 January, 1900 (yr = $365^d5^h48^m45^s.9747$)
	Physical 9192631770 cycles of the hyperfine transition (4, 0 → 3, 0) of the ground state of ^{133}Cs unperturbed by external fields
Degree Kelvin (°K)	In the thermodynamic scale, 273.16°K = triple-point of water $T(°C) = T(°K) - 273.15$ (freezing-point of water, 0.0000 ± 0.0002°C)
Unified atomic mass unit (u)	1/12 the mass of an atom of the ^{12}C nuclide
Standard acceleration of free fall (g_n)	9.80665 m s^{-2} 980.665 cm s^{-2}
Normal atmosphere (atm)	101325 N m^{-2} 1013250 dyn cm^{-2}
Thermochemical calorie (cal$_{th}$)	4.184 J 4.184 × 10^7 erg
Int. Steam Table calorie (cal$_{IT}$)	4.1868 J 4.1868 × 10^7 erg
Liter (l)	0.001000028 m^3 (recommended by CIPM 1950) 1000.028 cm^3
Inch (in.)	0.0254 m 2.54 cm
Pound (avdp.) (lb)	0.45359237 kg 453.59237 kg

Taken from E. R. Cohen and J. W. M. DuMond, *Revs. Mod. Phys.*, **37**, 537, (1965). Reprinted with permission.

TABLE A-2
ENERGY CONVERSION FACTORS

1 electron volt	$= 1.60210(2) \times 10^{-19}$ J
	$= 1.60210(2) \times 10^{-12}$ erg
	$= 8065.73(8)$ cm^{-1}
	$= 2.41804(2) \times 10^{14}$ s^{-1}
$V\lambda$	$= 12398.10(13) \times 10^{-8}$ ev cm
1 ev per particle	$= 11604.9(5)°$K
	$= 23061(1)$ cal$_{TH}$ mole^{-1}
	$= 23045(1)$ cal$_{IT}$ mole^{-1}
1 amu	$= 931.478(5)$ Mev
Proton mass	$= 938.256(5)$ Mev
Neutron mass	$= 939.550(5)$ Mev
Electron mass	$= 511006(2)$ ev
Rydberg	$= 2.17971(5) \times 10^{-11}$ erg
	$= 13.60535(13)$ ev
Gas constant, R_0	$= 8.31434 \times 10^7$ erg mole^{-1} deg^{-1}
	$= 0.082053$ liter atm mole^{-1} deg^{-1}
	$= 82.055$ cm^3 atm mole^{-1} deg^{-1}
	$= 1.9872$ cal$_{th}$ mole^{-1} deg^{-1}
	$= 1.9858$ cal$_{IT}$ mole^{-1} deg^{-1}
Standard volume of ideal gas V_0	$= 22413.6$ cm^3 mole^{-1}

Taken from E. R. Cohen and J. W. M. DuMond, *Revs. Mod. Phys.*, **37**, 537, (1965). Reprinted with permission.

TABLE A-3
GENERAL PHYSICAL CONSTANTS

The digits in parentheses following each value represent the standard deviation error in the final digits of the quoted value as computed on the criterion of internal consistency. The unified scale of atomic weights is used throughout ($^{12}C = 12$). C = coulomb; G = gauss; Hz = hertz; J = joule; N = newton; T = tesla; u = unified nuclidic mass unit; W = watt; Wb = weber.

Constant	Symbol	Value	Unit	
			mksA	cgs
Speed of light in vacuum	c	2.997925(1)	$\times 10^8$ m s^{-1}	$\times 10^{10}$ cm s^{-1}
Gravitational constant	G	6.670(5)[a]	10^{-11} N m^2 kg^{-2}	10^{-8} dyn cm^2 g^{-2}
Elementary charge	e	1.60210(2)	10^{-19} C	10^{-20} emu
		4.80298(7)		10^{-10} esu
Avogadro constant	N_A	6.022529(9)	10^{26} kmole^{-1}	10^{23} mole^{-1}
Mass unit	u	1.660043(2)	10^{-27} kg	10^{-24} g
Electron rest-mass	m_e	9.10908(13)	10^{-31} kg	10^{-28} g
		5.48597(3)	10^{-4} u	10^{-4} u
Proton rest-mass	m_p	1.672523(3)	10^{-27} kg	10^{-24} g
		1.00727663(8)	u	u
Neutron rest-mass	m_n	1.67482(3)	10^{-27} kg	10^{-24} g
		1.0086654(4)	u	u
Faraday constant	F	9.64870(5)	10^4 C mole^{-1}	10^3 emu
		2.89261(2)		10^{14} esu
Planck constant	h	6.62559(16)	10^{-34} J s	10^{-27} erg s
	$h/2\pi$	1.054494(25)	10^{-34} J s	10^{-27} erg s
Fine-structure constant $2\pi e^2/hc$	α	7.29720(3)	10^{-3}	10^{-3}
	$1/\alpha$	137.0388(6)		
Charge-to-mass ratio for electron	e/m_e	1.758796(6)	10^{11} C kg^{-1}	10^7 emu
		5.27274(2)		10^{17} esu
Quantum of magnetic flux	hc/e	4.13556(4)		10^{-7} G cm^2
	h/e	1.379474(13)	10^{-11} Wb	10^{17} esu

Constant	Symbol	Value	Unit mksA	Unit cgs
Rydberg constant	R_∞	1.0973731(1)	10^7 m^{-1}	10^5 cm^{-1}
Bohr radius	a_0	5.29167(2)	10^{-11} m	10^{-9} cm
Compton wavelength of electron	h/m_ec	2.42621(2)	10^{-12} m	10^{-10} cm
	$\lambda_C/2\pi$	3.86144(3)	10^{-13} m	10^{-11} cm
Electron radius	$e^2/m_ec^2 = r_e$	2.81777(4)	10^{-15} m	10^{-13} cm
Thomson cross section	$8\pi r_e^2/3$	6.6516(2)	10^{-29} m^2	10^{-25} cm^2
Compton wavelength of proton	$\lambda_{c,p}$	1.321398(13)	10^{-15} cm	10^{-13} cm
	$\lambda_{C,p}/2\pi$	2.10307(2)	10^{-16} m	10^{-14} cm
Gyromagnetic ratio of proton	γ	2.6751927(7)	10^8 rad s^{-1} T^{-1}	10^4 rad s^{-1} G^{-1}
	$\gamma/2\pi$	4.25770(1)	10^7 Hz T^{-1}	10^3 s^{-1} G^{-1}
(Uncorrected for diamagnetism H$_2$O)	γ'	2.675123(7)	10^8 s^{-1} T^{-1}	10^4 rad s^{-1} G^{-1}
	$\gamma'/2\pi$	4.25759(1)	10^7 HzT^{-1}	10^3 s^{-1} G^{-1}
Bohr magneton	μ_B	9.2732(2)	10^{-24} J T^{-1}	10^{-21} erg G^{-1}
Nuclear magneton	μ_N	5.05050(13)	10^{-27} J T^{-1}	10^{-21} s G^{-1}
Proton moment	μ_p	1.41049(4)	10^{-26} J T^{-1}	10^{-23} erg G^{-1}
	μ_p/μ_N	2.79276(2)		
(Uncorrected for diamagnetism in H$_2$O sample)	μ_p/μ_N	2.79268(2)		
Gas constant	R_0	8.31434(35)	J deg^{-1} mole^{-1}	10^7 erg deg^{-1} mole^{-1}
Boltzmann constant	k	1.38054(6)	10^{-23} J deg^{-1}	10^{-16} erg deg^{-1}
First radiation constant ($2\pi hc^2$)	c_1	3.74150(9)	10^{-16} W m^2	10^{-5} erg cm^2 s^{-1}
Second radiation constant (hc/k)	c	1.43879(6)	10^{-2} m deg	cm deg
Stefan–Boltzmann constant	σ	5.6697(10)	10^{-8} W m^{-2} deg^{-4}	10^{-5} erg cm^{-2} s^{-1} deg^{-4}

[a] The universal gravitational constant is not, and cannot in our present state of knowledge, be expressed in terms of other fundamental constants. The value given here is a direct determination by P. R. Heyl and P. Chrzanowski, *J. Res. Natl. Bur. Std.* (U.S.) **29**, 1, (1942).

Index

J

Janicki, L., 497
Jeans, J. H., 106
jj-coupling, 415, 422
    energy level separation, 445
    magnetic quantum numbers in, 448
Jones, E. G., 520
Jordon, P., 126

K

K-series, 472, 473
Kennedy, R. J., 23
Kepler's second law, 280
Kinetic state, 60
King, A. S., 437
Kirchoff's law of radiation, 104
Klein-Gordon equation, 330
Kolloth, R., 69
Kossell, 457
Kroning-Penny model, 621, 624
Kundig, W., 67

L

L-series, 473
Lagrange, J. L., 168
Lagrange undetermined multipliers, 115
Landé *g*-factor, 377, 397, 448
Landé interval rule, 429, 433, 445
    in *hfs*, 505
Landé model, 338
Lanthanides, 488, 493
Larmor's precession (frequency), 379–381,
    508
Larmor's theorem, 380
Lasers, 580
    different types, 580–588
Lattice, crystal, 147, 148
    energy, 596
    linear monatomic, 603
Lattice points, 111
Lattice vibrations, theory of, 603
Lattice waves, 604
Linear combination of atomic orbitals
    (LCAO), 539
Least action principle, 167
Lenard, P., 228
Length:
    contraction, 69, 70
    in momentum units, 61
    in relativity, 35
Light amplification, 580
Light, theories of, 3
Line broadening, 497
Line pattern, 499
Linear absorption coefficient, 484
Linear harmonic oscillator, 212
Linear molecule, 549

Linear monatomic lattice, 603
    dispersion relations, 605
ll-coupling, 416
local frames, 95
Localization, 173, 174
Localized covalent bond, 551
Localized directional bonds, 597
Localized orbital in methane and ethane,
    562
Longitudinal Doppler effect in relativity, 66
Longitudinal mass, 49
Lorentz contraction, 35
Lorentz-Fitzgerald contraction hypothesis,
    23
Lorentz force and relativity, 47
Lorentz, H. A., 23, 28, 609
Lorentz transformations, 24, 28, 31
    for velocity, 32, 33
Lorentz unit, 400, 406
LS-coupling, 415, 416, 420, 429
    magnetic quantum number in, 448
Lummer, O., 105, 108, 497
Luster of metals, 610

M

M-series, 473
Macroscopic systems, 2
Madelung constant, 595
Magnetic dipole moment of current loop,
    375
Magnetic dipole moment, nuclear, 509
Magnetic quantum number, 290, 302, 339
    in *jj*-coupling, 448
    in LS-coupling, 448
    spin, 343
    total, 346
Magnetic moment: 376
    of electron spin, 378
    of orbital motion, 375
    total (of atom), 397
    unit of, 377
Magnetic rigidity, 48
Magnetic spectrograph, Robinson, 485
Marsden, E., 231
Masers, 580
Mass-energy relation, 44, 45
    experimental verification, 71
Mass scales, 244
Mass variation with velocity, 39–41
    experimentals verification, 68, 69
Matrix element, 325, 329
Maupertuis, P. L. M. de, 168
Maximum overlapping, principle of, 558
Maxwell, J. C., 1, 4, 125
Maxwell-Boltzmann statistics, 114, 615
Mean free path, 619
Mean life time, 522
Mendeleyev, D., 228, 486
Menzel, D., 69, 269
Meson decay, 69, 70

Scattering: coherent, 140, 148, 152, 160, 578
  incoherent, 148, 160
  Raman, 578
  Rayleigh, 578
Scattering of x-rays, 139
Scherrer, P., 153
Schrödinger, E., 2, 126, 183, 457
Schrödinger wave equation, 181, 185 (Also see SWE)
  of free particle, 188
  time-dependent, 186
  time-independent, 187
  of two particles, 296
Schüler, H., 520
Schwartzchild, E., 457
Scintillations, 230
Screening constant, 366, 438, 480
Secondary electron emission, 155
Selection rules, 286, 323, 326, 369, 389, 401, 403, 404, 441, 451–455, 517, 570, 571, 573, 577
Selection rules, for absorption, 564
  for f, 504
  for l, 328, 361
  for m, 327
  for n, 329
  for rotational Raman lines, 580
  for x-rays, 474
Self-absorption broadening, 525
Self-consistent field, 362
Semiconductors, 628–631
Semimetals, 630
Sensitive area, 239
Separation of variables, 186, 195, 300
Series, diffused, fundamental, principal and sharp, 361, 369, 439, 440
Series limit, 256
Sharp series, 439
Shells, subshells, 314, 351, 488–490
Shielding electrons, 358
Stilwell, G. R., 67
Shull, C., 161, 162
Siegbahn, K., 478
Simple harmonic oscillator, 277, 568
Simultaneity, 25–28, 38, 78
  geometrical illustration of, 78
Slowing down of Clocks, 37
Slowing down radiation, 133
Snider, J. L., 93
Sodium D lines, 361
Sodium, energy level diagram, 359, 370
Sodium iodide single crystal, 149
Solids, amorphous and crystalline, 593
Solids, band theory of, 620
Sommerfeld, A., 275, 278, 285, 457
Sommerfeld model, 249, 338, 344
Sommerfeld relativity correction, 285
Sommerfeld elliptic orbits, 278
sp^3 hybrid, 597
space invariant, 59

space quantization, 287, 319, 341, 345, 392
  of F, 502
  of I, 500
  of spin, 396, 397
Space-time four vector, 59
Space-time, graphical representation, 72
Space-time invariance, 60
Spatial wave function, 545
Special relativity and electromagnetism, 84
Special relativity postulates, 24
Specific heat, 610, 620
Spectra of alkali metals, 353
Spectra, band, continuous, and discrete, 252
Spectra of calcium, 434
Spectra of first long period elements, 459
Spectra of many valence electron atoms, 415
Spectra of two valence electron atoms, 434, 444
Spectral lines, origin of, 323, 324
  width of, 521
Spectral series, 255
Spectrometers (and spectroscopes), 252
Spectrum of, black-body, 104
  white light, 102
  heated body, 103
Speed of light, principle of constancy, 24
Spherical harmonics, 307
Spherical polar coordinates, 299
  SWE in, 300
Spin angular momentum, 343
Spin degeneracy, 310, 627
Spin flip, 410
Spin g-factor, 378, 397
Spin magnetic quantum number, 343
Spin magnetic moment, 378
Spin matrices, 331
Spin-orbit fine structure, 367, 382
Spin-orbit interaction and splitting, 372, 382, 415, 445
Spin quantum number, 343
Spin resonance, 410
Spin wave function, 545
Spinning electron, 342
$sp\sigma$ bonding, 559
Spontaneous emission, 326, 581–583
ss-coupling, 418
Stark, J., 457
Stark broadening, 525
Stark effect, 457–462
Stationary states, 258
Stationary, vibrations, 111
  waves, 259
Statistics, Bose-Einstein, 615
  Classical, 114
  Fermi-Dirac, 615
  Maxwell-Boltzmann, 114, 615
Statistical distribution, 181
Statistical interpretation of wave function, 182
Statistical weight, 374

Stefan, J., 1, 104
Stefan-Boltzmann law, 104, 106, 120
Stefan constant, 104
Stellar aberration, 12
Sterling approximation, 115
Stern, O., 161, 162, 392
Stern-Gerlach experiment, 392, 395
Stimulated emission, 581, 585
Stokes lines, 580
Stopping potential, 127
Subgroup, sublevel, subshell, 351
Superimposition, principle of, 181
SWE: for H_2^+ molecule, 537
 of a particle in parabolic potential, 568
 in periodic potential, 620
 solution for one-electron atom, 298
 in spherical polar coordinates, 300
Symmetric wave function, 348, 349, 538, 539
 probability density distribution, 539–540

T

Tachyons, 71, 72
Taylor series, 511, 568
Term value, 365, 423, 425, 426
Tetrahedral structure, 597, 600
Thermal conductivity, 609, 619
Thermal excitations, 265
Thermal radiation, 101
Thermodynamic probability, 114, 115
Thomas, L. H., 362, 384
Thomson, J. J., 1, 2, 227, 244
Thomson model, 232
Thorndike, E. M., 23
Threshold frequency, 127, 131
Tight binding approximation, 620, 626, 629
Time-dependent Schrödinger equation, 186
Time-independent Schrödinger equation, 187
Time dilation, 37
 experimental verification, 69, 70
Time invariant, 60
Time in relativity, 35
Tin (grey and white), 602, 603
Total angular momentum, 342, 343
 quantum number, 342
Total electron wave function, 307
Total energy, conservation and invariance, 44
Total magnetic moment, 448
Total magnetic quantum number, 346
Total quantum number, 282, 306
Townsend, J. R., 580
Traid of triplet-multiplets, 443
Transformations, of charge, 84, 86
 current densities, 85
 energy, momentum, mass and force, 57
 Galilean, 6–8
 Lorentz, 28–32
 Newtonian, 7

Transitions (allowed and forbidden), 326, 361, 373
Transition elements, 488, 493
Transition rates, 324
Transition series, 492
Transmission coefficients, 201
Transparency, 204–206
Transuranic elements, 488
Transverse Doppler effect, 66
Transverse mass, 49
Triatomic molecule, 566, 573
Triplet fine structure, 439
Triplet multiplets, 443
Trouton, F. T., 18
Twin paradox, 80
 geometrical illustration, 82
 experimental test, 84
Two-valence electron atom,
 Landé g-factor, 448
 in magnetic field, 447
 total magnetic moment, 448

U

U-state (ungerade) wave function, 551
Uhlenbeck, G. E., 342
Ultraviolet catastrophe, 113
Unbound states, 212
Uncertainty principle, 174–180, 522
Urey, H. C., 269, 342
Unmodified wavelength, 140
 intensity of, 144
Unperturbed Hamiltonian, 325
Unsymmetric charge distribution, 548

V

Valence bonds, 629
Valence bond method, 551, 553
Valence electron, 353, 356
Van der Waals forces, 600
Van Vleck, J. H., 365
Variational method, 366
Variational principle, 167
Vector model, 338
Velocity addition, verification, 71
Velocity, group, phase, propagation, 169–173
Vibrational energy and levels of an oscillator, 569, 571
Vibrational frequency, 567
Vibrational molecular spectra, 566
Vibrational-rotational, absorption spectrum, 573
 levels, 571

W

Wali-Mohammed, 497
Water molecules in ice, 599
Wave amplitude, 181

Wave function:
  antibonding, 539
  antisymmetric, 538, 539, 348
  bonding, 539
  Born interpretation of, 182
  even, 551, 538
  even parity, 329
  g-state, 551
  hybrid, 561
  odd, 538
  odd parity, 329
  normalized, 184
  spatial, 545
  spin, 545
  statistical interpretation of, 182
  symmetric, 538
  unnormalized, 184
Wavelength:
  Compton, 143
  deBroglie, 146
  modified and unmodified, 140
  of particles, 154
Wave number, 188
Wave packets, 169, 173
Wave theory, 3
Wave velocity, 173
Waves and particles, 125
Weighing factor, 173
Weightlessness, 91
Wentzel, G., 444
White dwarfs, 93
Whitelaw, N. G., 365
Wick, G., 160
Width of spectral lines, 521
Width and external effects, 524
Wiedenmann-Franz ratio, 610, 619
Wien, W., 106
Wien's displacement law (formula),
    106–108
Wilson-Sommerfeld quantization rules, 275
Wollan, E., 161, 162
Waller, I., 315
Wilson, H. A., 275
Wood, R. W., 525
Work function, 131, 135
World line, 72

World interval (space like, time like), 79
Wulff, J., 517

X

x-rays:
  absorption, 481
  Avogadro's number, 153
  diffraction, 147, 151
  energy level diagram, 472, 474
    of Uranium, 475
  fine structure, 479
  hard, 478
  notation, 467
  scattering of, 139
  selection rules, 474
  series, 472
  soft, 478
x-ray spectrum:
  characteristic of, 132, 137, 466, 469
    of molybdenum, 136
  production of, 133, 466, 471
  properties of, 466, 471
  of tungsten, 136
x-units, 478

Y

Young's double slit, 181
Young, T., 4, 125

Z

Zeeman effect:
  anomalous, 399–403
  normal, 386–392, 450
  intensity rules, 403
Zeeman effect in hfs, 513–516
Zero point distribution law, 614
Zero-point energy, 216
Zero-point vibrational energy, 569
Zinn, W., 161
Zone theory, 620

RETURN TO: PHYSICS-ASTRONOMY LIBRARY
351 LeConte Hall

LOAN PERIOD 1 **1-MONTH**	2	3
4	5	6

ALL BOOKS MAY BE RECALLED AFTER 7 DAYS
Books may be renewed by calling 510-642-3122

DUE AS STAMPED BELOW

FORM NO. DD 22
2M 7-10

UNIVERSITY OF CALIFORNIA, BERKELEY
Berkeley, California 94720–6000